CONSTRUCTION LAW

AUSTRALIA
LBC Information Services
Sydney

CANADA and USA
Carswell
Toronto

NEW ZEALAND
Brooker's
Auckland

SINGAPORE and MALAYSIA
Thomson Information (S.E. Asia)
Singapore

GREENS CONCISE SCOTS LAW

CONSTRUCTION LAW

By

James P. Connolly, LL.B, Dip.L.P.
Solicitor, Lecturer,
The Robert Gordon University, Aberdeen

EDINBURGH
W. GREEN/Sweet & Maxwell
1999

First published 1999

Published in 1999 by W. Green & Son Ltd
21 Alva Street
Edinburgh EH2 4PS

Typeset by Trinity Typesetting Services
Edinburgh

Printed in England by
MPG Books Ltd, Bodmin, Cornwall

No natural forests were destroyed to make this product; only farmed timber
was used and replanted.

A CIP catalogue record for this book is available from the British Library.

ISBN 0 414 01181 3

This book is dedicated to my parents, James and Anne.

PREFACE

The idea to write this book has grown from a germ in my mind as a practising solicitor on finding myself specialising in an area where I felt a little like a fraud. I had found myself in an international consultancy full of barristers, architects, engineers, quantity surveyors and some qualified in two disciplines, who had hired me as a Scots lawyer to expand their portfolio of services in contractual advice to the construction industry. This was at the end of the 1980s, when the wind of change was blowing through the solicitors' profession, and new business ideas and professional identities were being forged. I took the job and soon discovered that I was one of the least informed of my colleagues in this area. Each day brought new challenges as I was faced with problems for clients that involved research upon research.

I soon became familiar with the encyclopaedic *Emden's Construction Law*; had the colossal twin volumes of *Hudson's Building and Engineering Contracts*, and the three volumes of Walker-Smith, *The Standard Forms of Building Contract* at my side; *Keating on Building Contracts* was my *vademecum*. I constantly found myself searching for answers to what I thought must be simple questions, and found riddles wrapped in mysteries inside enigmas — to paraphrase Churchill's comments on Russia. On top of this, as a Scots lawyer I was sure that there must be an authentic Scottish jurisprudence in the area, although apart from A. I. Connell's *Law Affecting Building Operations and Architects' and Builders' Contracts* (1903) and a short chapter in the *Encyclopaedia of the Law of Scotland* (first published in 1909 and revised in 1927), there was little to help me as I started to put materials together for myself.

After five years of practice in Glasgow, Newcastle and London, and having been accredited as a specialist in construction law by the Law Society of Scotland, I was approached to lecture part-time at The Robert Gordon University, Aberdeen, on what was the first post-graduate LL.M/MSc in Construction Law and Arbitration in Scotland. After some deliberation, I decided instead, almost five years ago, to accept a full-time position here as lecturer and course leader. I took the position mainly to have the opportunity to write what became this text. Whilst I was writing lectures and being inspired by my students, in my first year an excellent piece of scholarship was published in the *Stair Memorial Encyclopaedia* on Building Contracts, written by Arnott and Wolffe. This I will freely admit launched my teaching and research on to a different level. Yet there was no single Scottish textbook available for my students so I continued with my writing. Construction law was soon also being taught at post-graduate level at

Strathclyde University and considerable intellectual effort was being expended on masters' dissertations both in Aberdeen and Glasgow. I felt that there was a place for a text that reflected the taught part of my postgraduate course, and as such I have assumed in the reader some existing familiarity with contract law and delict. I do, however, assume that the reader knows very little about building contracts, but is willing to be challenged and encouraged to think deeply about the special issues they present.

The text begins with introductory comments on building contracts within the framework of contract law generally, and other relevant legal considerations. It then looks at the context of the most used standard forms in the U.K. construction industry in Chapter 2. Chapter 3 is designed to focus on particular problem areas that seem to arise whenever construction contracts are drafted. The third chapter examines a range of problems, and the approach is continued into the fourth chapter with a critical analysis of the current standard JCT 80 form of contract conditions, as adapted for use in Scotland with the Scottish Building Contract. I am grateful to the copyright holders of both forms for allowing them to be reproduced in the appendix. Chapter 4 is likely to be the most use to practitioners seeking an immediate commentary on individual clauses, but the text is not intended to be the last word on these. Often, as in the case of questions relating to assignation of contract or transfer of title in goods, the relevant clauses of JCT 80 serve as a springboard for a deeper analysis of these issues in Scots law, in a way that is not done anywhere else as far as I am aware.

Chapter 5 is headed 'Privity of Contract Issues', which broadly includes a range of issues arising from the complex structure of relationships that exist in a typical construction project. Again the treatment is rather discursive in order to bring together different themes of judicial thought. Chapter 6 is essentially an essay on the confusion that it is suggested exists as to the Scottish position on the question of the delictual liability for defective buildings. This is an important area that I have not seen explored anywhere else. Chapter 7 is an introduction to issues surrounding the architect and other professionals, making use of Scots cases that are not normally referred to in the English texts. It is not a commentary on the current standard form of architect's appointment issued by the RIBA, which has been skilfully done by other writers. Finally, Chapter 8 is also in effect an essay to explain and criticise the governmental initiatives into the legal context of the construction industry as a whole, which resulted in the enactment of the Housing Grants, Construction and Regeneration Act 1996, which came into force on May 1, 1998. It was largely as result of the changes introduced by this Act that the completion of this text was delayed from last summer. I thought it more useful to consider these changes in the text, especially as Amendment 18 of JCT 80 seeks to make JCT 80 comply with the Act. I am grateful to my publishers in accepting this delay in what already had been a long-advertised book.

I would take this opportunity to thank Donna Crichton, Linda Strangward, Lisa King, Sandy Shek and the library staff at RGU for helping me in various ways with aspects of research; also Bryan Porter and Peter MacGillivary who read near final versions of the text and gave advice and encouragement; and my students as the many loose ends and even mistakes in lecture notes were discussed and clarified in seminars. Whilst there is an anxiety in publishing that one's mistakes will be forever recorded, I think that after a wait of almost a century for a Scots law text book, I think it better to make this contribution and hope that it will be of more use than not.

I have considered the law up to April 15, 1999.

A.M.D.G.
James P. Connolly
Aberdeen

CONTENTS

	Page
Preface	vii
Table of Cases	xiii
Table of Statutes	xxxiii
Table of Statutory Instruments	xxxvii
Table of JCT and Other Contract Forms	xxxix

1. What Makes Building or Construction Contracts Distinctive? ... 1
2. Context of Standard Forms of Contract ... 17
3. Particular Difficulties ... 32
4. Critical Analysis of JCT 80 ... 74
5. Privity of Contract Issues ... 244
6. Delictual Liability for Defective Buildings ... 263
7. Architects and the Professional Team ... 279
8. Recent Changes ... 290

Appendix 1 ... 309
Appendix 2 ... 407
Index ... 447

TABLE OF CASES

A/B. *See* under Aktiebolaget
A.M.F. International *v.* Magnet Bowling Ltd [1968] 1 W.L.R. 1028;
    (1968) S.J. 552; [1968] 2 All E.R. 789; 66 L.G.R. 706 .... 4.186, 4.27, 7.24
A.P.D. Installations (Group) *v.* Customs & Excise Commissioners (1987)
    V.A.T.T.R. 36, V.A.T. Tribunal 4.102
Aberdeen Harbour Board *v.* Heating Enterprises (Aberdeen) Ltd, 1988 S.L.T. 762,
    OH; 1989 S.C.L.R. 716; 1990 S.L.T. 416 .... 4.199, 4.201, 5.08
Aberdeen Railway Co. *v.* Blaikie Bros (1854) 1 MacQ. 461; 1852 15 D. 20, HL 4.36
Adam (Scotland) Ltd *v.* Beardsden and Milngavie District Council,
    1996 S.L.T. 21 Sh. Ct 4.43
Aitken & Co. *v.* Pyper (1900) 38 S.L.R. 743 .... 3.38
Aktiebolaget Karlshamns Oljefabriker *v.* Monarch Steamship Co. *See* Monarch
    Steamship Co. *v.* A/B Karlshamns Oljefabriker
Alfred McAlpine Construction Ltd *v.* Panatown Ltd (1998) 58 Con. L.R. 47;
    The Times, February 11, 1998, CA 4.168
Alfred McAlpine Homes North Ltd *v.* Property and Land Contractors Ltd (1995)
    76 Build. L.R. 59 .... 4.25, 4.244
Allison *v.* Davies, Peak's Add. Cas. 82 .... 4.114
Amalgamated Building Contractors Ltd *v.* Waltham Holy Cross U.D.C. [1952]
    W.N. 400; [1952] 2 T.L.R. 269; 96 S.J. 530; [1952] 2 All E.R. 452;
    50 L.G.R. 667, CA; affirming [1952] 1 T.L.R. 1165; 50 L.G.R. 429 .... 4.13, 4.243,
                                                  4.248, 4.252
Amec Building Ltd *v.* Cadmus Investment Co. Ltd (1996) 51 Con. L.R. 105;
    (1997) 13 Const. L.J. 50, QBD 4.28, 4.272, 4.297
American Express Europe Ltd *v.* Adamson [1993] B.C.C. 154 .... 4.332
Anderson *v.* Gibb, 1992 G.W.D. 1–48 .... 4.383
Angus *v.* Bryden, 1992 9 S.C.L.R. 626 .... 4.97
Anisminic *v.* Foreign Compensation Commission [1969] 2 A.C. 147; [1969]
    2 W.L.R. 163; (1968) 113 S.J. 55; 3 W.L.R. 382; 111 S.J. 374;
    [1967] 3 All E.R. 986, CA 4.389, 4.391, 4.392
Anns *v.* Merton London Borough Council; *sub nom.* Anns *v.* London Borough
    of Merton [(1987) 137 New L.J. 794]; [1978] A.C. 728; [1977] 2 W.L.R. 1024;
    (1977) 121 S.J. 377; (1977) 75 L.G.R. 555; [1977] J.P.L. 514; (1977) 243
    E.G. 523, 591; [1977 L.G.C. 498]; (1987) L.S. 319]; [1977] 2 All E.R. 492, HL;
    affirming *sub nom.* Anns *v.* Walcroft Property Co. (1976)
    241 E.G. 311, CA 6.05, 6.06, 6.08, 6.09, 6.12, 6.13, 6.16,
                                                  6.17, 6.18, 6.21, 6.22,
                                                  6.23, 6.24, 6.25, 6.26
Architectural Installation Services *v.* James Gibbon Windows 46 Build. L.R. 91;
    (1990) 16 Con. L.R. 68 .... 4.305
Archivent Sales & Developments *v.* Strathclyde Regional Council (1985) 27
    Build. L.R. 98, Ct of Session, OH 4.120, 4.121, 4.122, 4.124, 4.126
Arenson *v.* Casson, Beckman, Rutley & Co. [1975] 3 W.L.R. 815; 119 S.J. 810;
    [1975] 3 All E.R. 901; [1976] 1 Lloyd's Rep. 179, HL; reversing *sub nom.*
    Arenson *v.* Arenson; *sub nom.* Arenson *v.* Arenson and Casson, Beckman,
    Rutley & Co. [1973 Ch. 346; [1973] 2 W.L.R. 553; 117 S.J. 247; [1973] 2 All E.R. 235;
    [1973] 2 Lloyd's Rep. 104; [123 New L.J. 703], CA 7.16

Armour *v.* Thyssen Edelstahlwerke A.G, 1990 S.L.T. 891; 1991 S.C.L.R. 139;
    reversing 1989 S.L.T. 182 (2nd Div.); 1989 S.C.L.R. 26; [1986 S.L.T. (News)
    265, 277; 1989 S.L.T. (News) 185]; 1986 S.L.T. 94, 452, OH 4.129, 4.130
Asphaltic Limestone Concrete Co. Ltd *v.* Glasgow Corporation,
    1907 S. 463; 14 S.L.T. 706 .... 4.150, 4.319
Astor Chemical Ltd *v.* Synthetic Technology [1990] B.C.C. 97; [1990] B.C.L.C. 1 .... 4.329
Aurdal *v.* Estrella, 1916 S.C. 882 .... 4.156
Ayr Road Trustees *v.* Adams (1883) S.C. XI R. 326 .... 4.61, 4.62, 4.73

B.F.I. GROUP *v.* D.C.B. INTEGRATED SYSTEMS LTD, 1987 C.I.L.L. 348 .... 4.220
Bacal Construction *v.* Down (1975) 8 Build. L.R. 89 .... 5.38
Baese Pty Ltd *v.* R.A. Bracken, 52 Build. L.R. 130 .... 4.227
Balfour Beatty Building Ltd *v.* Chestermount Properties Ltd (1993) 62 Build. L.R. 1;
    32 Con. L.R. 139; (1993) 9 Const. L.J. 117 .... 4.233, 4.248, 4.254, 4.256, 4.271
Balfour Beatty Construction (Scotland) *v.* Scottish Power, 1992 S.L.T. 811;
    1993 S.L.T. 1005; 1994 S.L.T. 807; *The Times,* March 23, 1994, HL 4.213
Balfour Beatty Ltd *v.* Britannia Life Ltd, 1997 S.L.T. 10 .... 3.69, 3.70, 3.73, 4.335,
                                                                          4.343, 4.357
Bank of East Asia Ltd *v.* Scottish Enterprise, 1997 S.L.T. 1213;
    [1996] 5 Bank. L.R. 93; [1996] C.L.C. 351; *The Times,* January 24,
    1996, HL 3.58, 3.60, 3.67, 3.69
Bank of Scotland *v.* The Liquidator of Hutchison Main & Co. Ltd (1914) S.C. 1, HL 3.74
Barclays Bank *v.* Fairclough Building [1995] Q.B. 214; [1994] 3 W.L.R. 1057;
    [1995] 1 All E.R. 289; 38 Con. L.R. 86; 68 Build. L.R. 1; [1995] P.I.Q.R. 152;
    (1995) 11 Const. L.J. 35; (1994) 91(25) L.S. Gaz. 30; (1994) 138 S.J.L.B. 118;
    [1995] E.G.C.S. 10; *The Times,* May 11, 1994, CA; reversing (1994) 10 Const.
    L.J. 48, QBD 4.256
Barking & Dagenham London Borough Council *v.* Stamford Asphalt Co. Ltd,
    82 Build. L.R. 25; 54 Con. L.R. 1; *The Times,* April 10, 1997, CA 4.203
Barnett *v.* Chelsea & Kensington Hospital Management [1969] 1 Q.B. 428;
    [1968] 2 W.L.R. 422; 111 S.J. 912; [1968] 1 All E.R. 1068 .... 4.248
Barratt Scotland Ltd *v.* Keith, 1994 S.L.T. 1337, 1343; 1993 S.C. 142;
    1993 S.C.L.R. 120 .... 2.07
Barry D. Trentham Ltd *v.* Robert McNeil, 1966 S.L.T. 202 OH 3.33
Basildon District Council *v.* Lesser (J.E.) (Properties) [1985] Q.B. 839; [1984]
    3 W.L.R. 812; [1985] 1 All E.R. 20; (1984) 8 Const. L.J. 57; (1987) 8 Con. L.R. 89;
    (1984) 134 New L.J. 330; (1984) 81 L.S. Gaz. 1437 .... 5.32
Baskett *v.* Bendigo Gold Dredging Co. (1902) 21 N.Z.L.R. 166 .... 4.255
Batty and Another *v.* Metropolitan Realisations Ltd [1978] Q.B. 554;
    [1978] 2 W.L.R. 500; (1977) 122 S.J. 63; [1978] 2 All E.R. 445;
    (1977) 245 E.G. 43; (1977) 7 Build. L.R. 1, CA 3.86, 6.12, 6.26
Beattie & Son *v.* Ritchie & Co, 1901 9 S.L.T. 2, OH 4.214, 4.219
Beattie *v.* Gilroy (1882) 10 R. 226 .... 7.02
Beaufort Developments (N.I.) Ltd *v.* Gilbert-Ash (N.I.) Ltd [1998] 2 W.L.R. 860; [1998]
    2 All E.R. 778; 98 N.I. 144; 88 Build. L.R. 1; 59 Con. L.R. 66; [1998] C.L.C. 830;
    (1998) 14 Const. L.J. 280; [1998] E.G.C.S. 85; [1998] N.P.C. 93; [1998] N.P.C. 91;
    (1998) 148 N.L.J. 869; (1998) 95(31) L.S.G. 34; (1998) 95(24) L.S.G. 33; (1998)
    142 S.J.L.B. 172; *The Times,* June 8, 1998, HL; reversing 83 Build. L.R. 1;
    [1997] N.I. 142; (1997) 13 Const. L.J. 321, CA (N.I.) 1.01, 4.01, 4.02, 4.378,
                                                                          8.26, 8.28
Belcher Food Products Ltd *v.* Miller & Black 1999 S.L.T. 142 .... 4.18, 4.59, 4.61, 7.10
Bell (A.) & Son (Paddington) *v.* C.B.F. Residential Care and Housing
    Association [1989] Build. L.R. 102 .... 4.231
Bernhard's Rugby Landscapes Ltd *v.* Stockley Park Consortium Ltd (1997)
    82 Build. L.R. 39 .... 4.304

Beta Computers (Europe) Ltd *v.* Adobe Systems (Europe) Ltd [1996] F.S.R. 367;
   [1996] C.L.C.L. 821; 1996 S.L.T. 604; 1996 S.C.L.R. 587; [1997] Info. T.L.R. 73;
   [1996] Masons Con. L.R. 16, OH 4.142, 5.07
Bickerton & Son *v.* N.W. Metropolitan Regional Hospital Board; *sub nom.* Bickerton
   (T.A.) & Son *v.* N.W. Metropolitan Regional Hospital Board [1969] 1 All E.R. 977;
   (1968) 67 L.G.R. 83; [135 J.P.N. 705], CA 2.17, 4.02, 4.354,
                                                                                    4.369, 4.370, 4.372
Bilton (Percy) *v.* Greater London Council [1982] 1 W.L.R. 794; (1982) 126 S.J. 397;
   [1982] 2 All E.R. 623; [1982] 80 L.G.R. 617; (1982) 20 Build. L.R. 1, HL;
   affirming [1981] 79 L.G.R. 463; (1981) 17 Build. L.R. 1, CA 4.237, 4.371
Black *v.* Cornelius (1879) 6 R. 581 .... 4.26, 7.04
Blackpool and Fylde Aero Club *v.* Blackpool Borough Council [1990] 1 W.L.R. 1195;
   [1990] 3 All E.R. 25; 88 L.G.R. 864; (1991) 155 L.G. reversing. 246;
   (1991) 3 Admin. L.R. 322, CA 3.01
Blue Circle Industries plc *v.* Holland Dredging (U.K.) Ltd (1987) 37 Build. L.R. 40 .... 4.250
Blumer & Sons *v.* Scott & Sons (1874) 1 R. 379 .... 5.07
Bolton *v.* Mahadeva [1972] 1 W.L.R. 1009; [1972] 2 All E.R. 1322, CA 4.11
Bond Worth, Re [1980] Ch. 228; [1979] 3 W.L.R. 629; (1979) 123 S.J. 216;
   [1980] 3 All E.R. 919; [129 New L.J. 651] 4.130
Boot (Henry) Construction *v.* Alstom Combined Cycles Ltd, Technology and
   Construction Ct, January 22, 1999 .... 1.25, 2.15
Boot (Henry) Construction *v.* Central Lancashire New Town Development Corporation
   (1980) 15 Build. L.R. 8 .... 3.26, 4.239 4.250
Borders Regional Council *v.* J. Smart & Co. (Contractors) Ltd,
   1983 S.L.T. 164 .... 4.137, 4.372, 5.04
Borthwick *v.* Scottish Widows Fund [1864] 2 M. 595 .... 3.59
Bottomley *v.* Bannister [1932] 1 K.B. 458 .... 6.10, 6.11
Boulton *v.* Jones (1857) 2 H. & N. 564 .... 4.149
Bovis Construction (Scotland) Ltd *v.* Whatlings Construction [1995] N.P.C. 153;
   (1995) 139 S.J.L.B. 245; *The Times,* October 19, 1995, HL 2.10
Boyd & Forest *v.* Glasgow & South Western Railway, 1902 10 S.L.T. 170;
   1915 S.C. 20, HL 4.84, 4.85, 4.86,
                                                                                    4.92, 4.97
Brabant, The [1967] 1 Q.B. 588; [1966] 2 W.L.R. 909; 110 S.J. 265;
   [1966] 1 All E.R. 961; [1965] 2 Lloyd's Rep. 546 .... 3.24
Bradley (D.R.) (Cable Jointing) *v.* Jefco Mechanical Services (1989) 6
   Construction Law Digest 7–21 .... 8.31
Brakinrig *v.* Menzies (1841) 4 D. 274 .... 4.380
Bramall & Ogden *v.* Sheffield City Council (1983) 29 Build. L.R. 73, DC 4.146
Brand's Trustees *v.* Brand's Trustees (1876) 3 R. 16, HL 4.103
Brickfield Properties *v.* Newton; Rosebell Holdings *v.* Newton [1971] 1 W.L.R. 862;
   115 S.J. 307; [1971] 3 All E.R. 328, CA 7.27
Brightside Kilpatrick Engineering Services *v.* Mitchell Construction (1973);
   (1975) 1 Build. L.R. 62, CA 3.23
Brightside Mechanical & Electrical Services Group *v.* Hyundai Engineering &
   Construction Co. (1988) 41 Build. L.R. 110 .... 5.15
Brinkibon *v.* Stahag Stahal und Stahlwarenhandels GmbH [1983] 2 A.C. 34;
   [1982] 2 W.L.R. 264; (1982) 126 S.J. 116; [1982] 1 All E.R. 293;
   [1982] Con. L.R. 72, HL; affirming [1980] 2 Lloyd's Rep. 556 .... 4.348
British Eagle International Air Lines Ltd *v.* Compagnie Nationale Air France [1975]
   1 W.L.R. 758; 119 S.J. 368; [1975] 2 All E.R. 390; [1975] 2 Lloyd's Rep. 43, HL;
   reversing in part [1974] 1 Lloyd's Rep. 429, CA affirming [1973]
   1 Lloyd's Rep. 414 .... 3.77, 3.78
British Glanzstoff Manufacturing Co. Ltd *v.* General Fire and Life Assurance
   Corporation Ltd, 1912 S.C. 591; affirmed [1913] A.C. 143, HL 4.221

British Steel Corporation v. Cleveland Bridge Engineering Co. Ltd [1984]
1 All E.R. 504; (1983) Build. L.R. 94; [1982] Con. L.R. 54 .... 3.13, 3.17, 4.93
British Telecommunications plc v. James Thomson & Sons (Engineers) Ltd,
1997 S.C. 59; 1997 S.L.T. 767; *The Times,* January 28, 1997, 2 Div.;
affirming 49 Con. L.R. 163, OH; overruled December 10, 1998, HL 4.198
Bryan v. Maloney, 74 Build. L.R. 35; 51 Con. L.R. 29; (1995) 11 Const.
L.J. 274, HC (Aus) 6.02, 6.07
Burden (R.B.) v. Swansea Corporation [1957] 1 W.L.R. 1167; 101 S.J. 882;
[1957] 3 All E.R. 243; 55 L.G.R. 381, HL; affirming (1956) 54 L.G.R. 161;
[1956] C.L.Y. 875, CA 4.80, 4.350

CALA HOMES (SOUTH) LTD V. ALFRED MCALPINE HOMES EAST LTD [1995]
F.S.R. 818, Ch D 3.04
Callaghan (Myles J.) (in receivership) v. City of Glasgow District Council,
1988 S.L.T. 227; 1987 S.C.L.R. 627; 3 B.C.C. 337 .... 4.330
Cammell Laird v. Manganese Bronze & Brass Co. [1934] A.C. 402, HL 5.29
Cape Durasteel Ltd v. Rosser and Russell Building Services (1996)
46 Con. L.R. 75, QBD 8.25
Carr v. J.A. Berryman (J.A.) Pty (1953) 27 A.L.J. 273; (1953) 89 Con. L.R. 327 .... 4.28
Carter Horseley (Engineers) Ltd v. Dawney's, *The Times,* July 5, 1972, CA 3.52, 3.64
Catnic Components Ltd v. Hill & Smith Ltd; *sub nom.* Catnic Components Ltd v.
Hills & Rutter [1981] F.S.R. 60; [1982] R.P.C. 183, HL; reversing
[1979] F.S.R. 619, CA; [1978] F.S.R. 405, Ch D 4.72
Cellulose Acetate Silk Co. Ltd v. Widnes Foundry (1925) [1933] A.C. 20 .... 4.225, 4.227
Cementation Piling and Foundations Ltd v. Aegon Insurance Co. Ltd and Commercial
Union [1995] 1 Lloyd's Rep. 97; 74 Build. L.R. 98, CA; affirming [1993]
1 Lloyd's Rep. 526; (1994) 10 Const. L.J. 301, QBD 4.180, 4.182
Central Provident Fund Board v. Ho Bok Kee (t/a Ho Bok Kee General Contractor)
(1981) 17 Build. L.R. 21, CA Singapore 4.314
Channel Tunnel Group v. Balfour Beatty Construction Ltd; France Manche S.A. v.
Balfour Beatty Construction Ltd [1993] A.C. 334; [1993] 2 W.L.R. 262; [1993]
1 All E.R. 664; [1993] Ill 291; 61 Build. L.R. 1; 32 Con. L.R. 1; [1993] N.P.C. 8;
(1993) 137 S.J.L.B. 36; *The Times,* January 25, 1993, HL; affirming [1992]
Q.B. 656; [1992] 2 W.L.R. 741; [1992] 2 All E.R. 609; [1992] 2 Lloyd's Rep. 7;
56 Build. L.R. 23; (1992) 8 Const. L.J. 150; [1992] N.P.C. 7; (1992) 136 S.J.L.B. 54;
The Times, January 23, 1992; *Financial Times,* January 29, 1992, CA 8.26
Chanthall Investments Ltd v. F.G. Minter Ltd, 1976 S.C. 73 .... 4.222
Chaplin v. Hicks [1911] 2 K.B. 786 .... 3.08
Chapman & Son v. The Edinburgh Prison Board (1844) 6 D. 1132 .... 4.17, 4.61
Chesham Properties Ltd v. Bucknall Austin Management Services Ltd,
82 Build. L.R. 92; 53 Con. L.R. 22, QBD (OR) 7.13, 8.10
Chester Grosvenor Hotel Co. v. Alfred McAlpine Management,
56 Build. L.R. 115 .... 1.03, 4.71
City Axis Ltd v. Daniel P. Jackson [1998] C.I.L.L. 151 .... 4.297
City of Glasgow District Council v. Excess Insurance Co. Ltd, 1986 S.L.T. 585 .... 3.44
City of Glasgow District Council v. Excess Insurance Co. (No. 2) Ltd,
1990 S.L.T. 225 .... 3.44
City of London Corp. v. Bovis Construction (1988) 4 Const. L.J. 203, CA 4.43
Clark Taylor & Co. Ltd v. Quality Site Developments (Edinburgh) Ltd, 1981 S.L.T. 3 .... 3.75
Clayton v. Woodman & Sons (Builders) [1962] 2 Q.B. 53; [1962] 1 W.L.R. 585;
106 S.J. 242; [1962] 2 All E.R. 33; [78 L.Q.R. 319], CA; reversing [1961] 3 W.L.R. 987;
105 S.J. 889; [1961] 3 All E.R. 249; [24 M.L.R. 797; 78 L.Q.R. 107; 111 L.J. 831];
[1961] C.L.Y. 825. Leave to appeal dismissed *sub nom.* Woodman &
Sons (Builders) v. Ware (Charles E.) & Son [1962] 1 W.L.R. 920 .... 4.27
Clement v. Gibbs (t/a/ L.J. Gibbs & Son) 94/1393/B, CA 4.23

Clough Mill Ltd v. Martin [1985] 1 W.L.R. 111; (1984) 128 S.J. 850;
  [1984] 3 All E.R. 982; (1985) 82 L.S. Gaz. 116; [1985] L.M.C.L.Q. 15;
  [82 L.S. Gaz. 1075; 1 Ins. L.P. 621, CA; reversing [1984] 1 W.L.R. 1067;
  (1984) S.J. 564; [1984] 1 All E.R. 721; (1984) L.S. Gaz. 2375 .... 4.130
Clyde Marine Insurance Co. v. Renwick, 1924 S.C. 113; 1924 S.L.T. 41 .... 4.319
Clydebank and District Water Trustees v. Fidelity and Deposit Co. of Maryland,
  The, 1915 S.C. 69, HL 3.46
Clydebank Engineering & Shipbuilding Co. Ltd v. Don Jose Ramos Yzquierdo y Castaneda
  [1905] A.C. 6 .... 4.217, 4.219,
                                                                                        4.220, 4.221
Colbart v. Kumar (H.), 59 Build. L.R. 89; 28 Con. L.R. 58; (1992) 8 Const. L.J. 268;
  [1992] N.P.C. 32 .... 4.15, 4.58
Cole v. Handasyde & Co., 1910 S.C. 68 .... 4.149, 4.150
Commonwealth Smelting v. Guardian Royal Exchange Assurance [1986]
  1 Lloyd's Rep. 121, CA; affirming [1984] 2 Lloyd's Rep. 608;
  (1984) 134 New L.J. 1018 .... 4.194
Computer & Systems Engineering plc v. John Lelliot (Ilford), 54 Build. L.R. 1;
  The Times, February 21, 1991, CA; affirming *The Times,* May 23,1989 .... 4.194
Conoco (U.K.) Ltd and Others v. Phillips Petroleum Co. and Others (1996)
  Bliss 19/08/96 .... 8.27, 8.28
Constable v. Uphall School Board (1918) 35 Sh. Ct Rep. 27 .... 3.03
Cooperative Wholesale Society Ltd (t/a C.W.S. Engineering Group) v. Birse
  Construction Ltd (formerly Peter Birse Ltd); *sub nom.* Birse Construction Ltd
  (formerly Peter Birse Ltd) v. Cooperative Wholesale Society Ltd (t/a C.W.S.
  Engineering Group) [1997] C.L.C. 1290; 84 Build. L.R. 58; 57 Con. L.R. 98;
  (1997) 94(29) L.S. Gaz. 29; *The Times,* August 13, 1997, CA; affirming
  46 Con. L.R. 110, QBD 5.14
Corfield (Alexander) v. Grant (David), 59 Build. L.R. 102; 29 Con. L.R. 58;
  [1992] E.G.C.S. 36 .... 4.60
Cosslett (Contractors) v. Bridgend County Council, 1997 C.I.L.L. 1279 .... 4.214
Cosslett (Contractors) Ltd, Re; *sub nom.* Clark (Administrator of Cosslett
  (Contractors) Ltd) v. Mid Glamorgan C.C. [1998] Ch 495; [1998] 2 W.L.R. 131;
  [1997] 4 All E.R. 115; [1997] B.C.C. 724; 85 Build. L.R. 1, CA; [1997] Ch. 23;
  [1996] 3 W.L.R. 299; [1996] 4 All E.R. 46; [1996] 1 B.C.L.C. 407;
  [1996] B.C.C. 515; 78 Build. L.R. 104; 49 Con. L.R. 56, Ch D 4.115, 4.134
Costain Building & Engineering v. Scottish Rugby Union,1994 S.L.T. 573;
  1993 S.C. 650; 1994 S.C.L.R. 257 .... 4.350, 5.16,
                                                                                        7.18, 8.26, 8.32
Council of the Shire of Sutherland v. Heyman (1985) 157 Con. L.R. 424 .... 6.07
Crestar v. Carr (1987) 131 S.J. 1154; [1987] 2 F.T.L.R. 135; (1987) 37 Build. L.R. 113;
  (1987) 3 Const. L.J. 286; (1987) 84 L.S. Gaz. 1966, CA 4.61
Crosby (J.) & Sons v. Portland Urban District Council (1967) 5 Build. L.R. 121,
  CA 4.300, 4.301
Crossman v. Pritchard (1889) 16 T.L.R. 45 .... 3.01
Croudace v. Lambeth London Borough (1984) 1 Const. L.J. 128;
  [1984] C.I.L.L. 136 .... 4.26, 4.143, 4.286
Crown Estates Commissioners v. John Mowlem & Co., 70 Build. L.R. 1;
  (1994) 10 Const. L.J. 311; *The Independent,* September 5,
  1994 (C.S.), CA 4.15, 4.18, 4.58,
                                                                                        4.59, 4.61, 7.09
Crown House Engineering v. Amec Project Ltd, 48 Build. L.R. 32;
  (1990) 6 Const. L.J. 141, CA 3.14, 4.94
Crux v. Aldred, 1866 14 W.R. 656 .... 4.215
Cullis (F.G.) Construction Ltd v. H.M.V. Fields (Properties) Ltd, 1989 G.W.D. 20–830,
  OH; (1990) G.W.D. 13–637 (Ex. Div) 4.333

Customs & Excise Commissioners v. Jeffs (trading as J. & J. Joinery) [1995] S.T.C. 759;
  The Independent, July 3, 1995 (C.S.), QBD 4.100

D. & F. ESTATES v. CHURCH COMMISSIONERS FOR ENGLAND [1988] 3 W.L.R. 368;
  (1988) 132 S.J. 1092; [1988] 2 All E.R. 992; (1988) 41 Build. L.R. 1 (1988)
  138 New L.J. 210; [1988] L.S. Gaz. September 14, 46, HL; affirming [1978]
  1 F.T.L.R. 405; (1987) Const. L.J. 110; (1987) 36 Build. L.R. 72; (1988)
  11 Con. L.R. 12, CA; affirming in part (1987) 7 Con. L.R. 40 .... 6.15, 6.17,
                                                                                      6.19, 6.20, 6.26
Dakin (H.) & Co. Ltd v. Lee [1916] 1 K.B. 566 .... 4.11
Darlington Borough Council v. Wiltshier Northern [1995] 1 W.L.R. 68; [1995]
  3 All E.R. 895; (1995) 11 Const. L.J. 36; (1994) 91(37) L.S. Gaz. 49; (1994)
  138 S.J.L.B. 161; 89 Build. L.R. 1; _The Times,_ July 4, 1994; _The Independent,_
  June 29, 1994, CA 4.167, 4.169, 4.170
David Wilson Construction Ltd v. Newbattle Properties Ltd,
  1998 G.W.D. 40–2040, OH 2.09
Davis Contractors Ltd v. Fareham Urban District Council [1956] A.C. 696;
  [1956] 3 W.L.R. 37; 100 S.J. 378; [1956] 2 All E.R. 145; 54 L.G.R. 289;
  [72 L.Q.R. 457; 19 M.L.R. 696; 105 S.J. 7], HL; affirming [1955] 1 Q.B. 302;
  [1955] 2 W.L.R. 388; 99 S.J. 109; [1955] 1 All E.R. 275; [71 L.Q.R. 312;
  105 L.J. 212; 106 L.J. 406; 219 L.T. 293], CA; [1955] C.L.Y. 271 .... 4.65, 4.86
Dawber Williamson Roofing v. Humberside County Council (1979) 14 Build. L.R. 70;
  October 22, 1979, DC 4.109, 4.111, 4.121,
                                                                          4.122, 4.133
Dawnays v. Minter (F.G.) and Trollope and Colls; _sub nom._ Dawnays v. Minter (F.G.)
  [1971] 1 W.L.R. 1205; [1971 2 Lloyd's Rep. 192; 115 S.J. 434; [1971] 2 All E.R. 1389;
  [1 New L.J. 1000; 126 New L.J. 141], CA 3.52
Day v. Tait (1900) 8 S.L.T. 40 .... 4.320
De Montfort Insurance Co. plc v. Lafferty, 1998 S.L.T. 535; 1997 S.L.C.R. 622;
  1997 G.W.D. 4–140, OH 3.36
Department of the Environment for Northern Ireland v. Farrans Construction [1981]
  19 Build. L.R. 1 .... 4.234
Department of the Environment v. Thomas Bates [1991] 1 A.C. 499; [1990]
  3 W.L.R. 457; [1990] 2 All E.R. 943; [1990] 46 E.G. 115; (1990) 134 S.J. 1077;
  50 Build. L.R. 61; 21 Con. L.R. 54, HL; affirming [1989] 1 All E.R. 1075;
  [1989] 26 E.G. 121; 13 Con. L.R. 1; 44 Build. L.R. 88; (1989)
  139 New L.J. 39, CA 6.02
Dillingham Construction v. Downs [1972] 2 N.S.W.L.R. 49 .... 5.38
Dingwall v. Burnett, 1912 S.C. 1097; 2 S.L.T. 90 .... 4.223
Dixon Group plc v. Murray-Oboynski, 86 Build. L.R. 16, QBD (OR) 8.28
Dodd v. Churton, 1897 L.R.; 1 Q.B. 562 .... 4.230
Donoghue v. Stevenson; _sub nom._ McAlister (or Donoghue) v. Stevenson; _sub nom._
  Donoghue (or McAlister) v. Stevenson [1932] A.C. 562; 101 L.J.P.C. 119;
  147 L.T. 281; [1932] All E.R. Rep. 1; 1932 S.C. 31;
  1932 S.L.T. 317, HL 6.03, 6.05, 6.06, 6.11, 6.13,
                                                                  6.15, 6.16, 6.19, 6.27
Douglas Milne v. Borders Regional Council, 1990 S.L.T. 558 .... 3.91, 4.383
Dove v. Banham Patent Locks [1983] 1 W.L.R. 1436; (1983) 127 S.J. 748;
  [1983] 2 All E.R. 833; (1983) 133 New L.J. 538 .... 3.86
Drake and Scull Engineering Ltd v. Higgs and Hill Northern Ltd [1995]
  Const. L.J. 214, QBD 3.14, 3.16
Ductform Ventilation (Fife) Ltd v. Andrews-Weatherfoil Ltd,
  1995 S.L.T. 88 .... 4.37, 5.02, 5.03
Dumfries Labour and Social Club and Institute Ltd v. Sutherland Dickie & Copeland,
  1993 G.W.D. 21–1314 .... 3.89

Dunbarton County Council *v.* George Sellars & Sons Ltd, 1973 S.L.T. 67,
Sh. Ct 3.80, 5.05
Duncan's Hotel (Glasgow) Ltd *v.* Ferguson (J. & A), 1972 S.L.T. (Notes) 84;
1974 S.C. 191 .... 1.22, 4.191
Duncanson *v.* Baylis (1869) 7 S.L.R. 139 .... 4.354
Duncanson (T. & R.) *v.* Scottish County Investments, 1915 S.C. 1106 .... 4.209
Dunlop *v.* McGowans, 1980 S.C. 81, HL; 1980 S.L.T. 132 .... 3.87
Dunlop Pneumatic Tyre Co. Ltd *v.* New Garage and Motor Co. Ltd
[1915] A.C. 79 .... 4.216, 4.221
Dutton *v.* Bognor Regis United Building Co. *See* Dutton *v.* Bognor Regis Urban District Council
Dutton *v.* Bognor Regis Urban District Council *sub nom.* Dutton *v.*
Bognor Regis United Building Co. [1972] 1 Q.B. 373; [1972] 2 W.L.R. 299;
(1971) 116 S.J. 16; 70 L.G.R. 57; [1972] 1 All E.R. 463; [1972 1 Lloyd's
Rep. 227, Ca; [35 Conv. 385; [1972] J.P.L. 69; 116 S.J. 264; 136 L.G.R. 362];
affirming [1971] 2 All E.R. 1003 .... 6.02, 6.08, 6.10, 6.12, 6.13, 6.16,
6.17, 6.21, 6.24, 6.25
Dynamco *v.* Holland & Hannan & Cubitts (Scotland); Dynamco *v.* Harrison (James)
& Co. (Builders), 1971 S.C. 257; 1971 S.L.T. 150; 1972 S.L.T. 38, OH 4.293

E.R.D.C. CONSTRUCTION *v.* H.M. LOVE CO., 70 Build. L.R. 67; 1995 S.L.T. 254;
(1995) 11 Const. L.J. 48 .... 4.86, 4.89, 4.91, 4.95
East Ham Borough Council *v.* Sunley (Bernard) & Sons [1966] A.C. 406;
3 W.L.R. 1096; 109 S.J. 874; 3 All E.R. 619; 64 L.G.R. 43; [1965]
2 Lloyd's Rep. 425, HL; reversing [1965] 1 W.L.R. 30; 108 S.J. 918;
[1965] 1 All E.R. 210; [1964] 2 Lloyd's Rep. 491; 63 L.G.R. 119;
[1964] C.L.Y. 362, CA 7.23
East River Steamship Corporation *v.* Transamerica Delaval Inc. (1986)
106 S. Ct 2295 .... 6.18
Eckersley (T.E.) *v.* Binnie (1988) Con. L.R. 1 .... 7.28
Edward Owen Engineering Ltd *v.* Barclays Bank International Ltd. *See* Owen
(Edward) Engineering Ltd *v.* Barclays Bank International Ltd
Egan *v.* State Transport Authority (1982) 31 S.A.S.R. 481 (Australia) 4.122
Ellis-Don *v.* Parking Authority of Toronto [1978] 28 Build. L.R. 98 .... 4.292
Elsley *v.* Collins Insurance Agencies Ltd, 1978 83 D.L.R. (3d) 1 .... 4.225
Emson Eastern Ltd (In Receivership) *v.* E.M.E. Developments Ltd [1991]
55 Build. L.R. 114 .... 4.53
English Industrial Estates Corporation *v.* George Wimpey & Co. (1972) S.J. 945;
(1972) 71 L.G.R. 127; [1973] 1 Lloyd's Rep. 118, CA 3.27, 4.02
Entores *v.* Miles Far East Corporation [1955] 2 Q.B. 327; [1955] 3 W.L.R. 48;
99 S.J. 384; [1955] 2 All E.R. 493; [1955] 1 Lloyd's Rep. 511; 72 L.Q.R. 10;
19 M.L.R. 89; 99 S.J. 446; 220 L.T. 36; [1955] Const. L.J. 148;
3 S.A.L.J. 77, CA 4.348
Equitable Debenture Assets Corporation *v.* Moss (William) (1984) C.I.L.L. 74;
[1984] Con. L.R. 1; 1 Const. L.J. 131 .... 5.43, 5.44
Esal (Commodities) Ltd and Relton *v.* Oriental Credit and Wells Fargo Bank N.A.;
Banque du Caire S.A.E. *v.* Wells Fargo Bank N.A. [1985] 2 Lloyd's Rep. 546;
[1986] FLR 70, CA 3.47
European Commission *v* Italy (1991) 1 C.M.L.R. 115 .... 3.09
Eurotunnel *v.* T.M.L. [1992] C.I.L.L. 754 .... 4.354

FAIRCLOUGH BUILDING LTD *v.* BOROUGH COUNCIL OF PORT TALBOT [1992] 62 Build. L.R. 82;
33 Con. L.R. 24, CA 3.02
Fairclough Building Ltd *v.* Rhuddlan Borough Council [1985] 30 Build. L.R. 26;
(1985) 2 Const. L.J. 55; [1985] C.I.L.L. 208, CA; affirming (1983)
3 Con. L.R. 20 .... 4.370

Fairweather (H.) & Co. *v.* Wandsworth London Borough Council (1987)
   29 Build. L.R. 112; (1988) 39 Build. L.R. 106 .... 4.39, 4.246, 4.249
Fee (J. & J.) *v.* Express Lift Co. (1994) 10 Const. L.J. 151; (1993)
   34 Con. L.R. 147 .... 4.35, 4.37, 5.02
Field & Allen *v.* Gordon (1872) 11 M. 132 .... 3.60, 3.61, 3.62
Finnegan *v.* Sheffield City Council [1988] 43 Build. L.R. 124; (1989)
   5 Const. L.J. 54, OR 4.292
Finnegan (J.F.) Ltd *v.* Community Housing Association Ltd [1993]
   65 Build. L.R. 103 .... 4.231
Finnie *v.* Glasgow & South Western Railway Co. (1857) 3 Macq. 75 .... 5.07
Firholme Builders *v.* McAuley, 1983 S.L.T. 105, S.C. 4.59, 4.61
Flood *v.* Shand Construction, 81 Build. L.R. 31; 54 Con. L.R. 125; [1997] C.L.C. 588;
   [1996] N.P.C. 185; *The Times,* January 8, 1997, CA 4.163
Forbes *v.* Dundee District Council, 1997 S.L.T. 1330; 1997 S.C.L.R. 682;
   1997 Rep. L.R. 48; 1997 G.W.D. 11–450, OH 4.45
Forbes *v.* Underwood (1863) 13 R. 463 .... 4.388
Ford & Co. *v.* Bemrose & Sons Ltd, 1902 9 S.L.T. 170 .... 4.97
Forrest *v.* Scottish County Investment Co., 1916 S.C. 28, HL 4.07, 4.08, 4.24, 7.07
Forrest & Barr *v.* Henderson (1869) 8 M. 187; 42 J. 89; 7 S.L.R. 879 .... 4.214
Fortune *v.* Young, 1918 S.C. 1 .... 3.38
Franks and Collingwood *v.* Gates [1985] 1 Con. L.R. 21 .... 4.101
Franks Howden Ltd *v.* Hamilton Bros Oil & Gas Ltd, 1991
   G.W.D. 32–1890 .... 4.331

G.A. ESTATES *V.* CAVIAPEN TRUSTEES, 1993 S.L.T. 1051 (Ex. Div.); reversing in part
   G.A. Estates *v.* Caviapen Trustees (No. 1) (O.H.), 1993 S.L.T. 1037 and
   G.A. Estates *v.* Caviapen Trustees (No.2) (O.H.), 1993 S.L.T. 1045 .... 3.91, 4.233
G.A. Group *v.* Scottish Metropolitan Property plc, 1992 G.W.D. 16–899 .... 4.231
G.K.N. Foundations *v.* Wandsworth London Borough *sub nom.* G.K.N. Foundations *v.*
   Mayor, Aldermen and Burgesses of the London Borough of Wandsworth (1972)
   70 L.G.R. 276; [1972] 1 Lloyd's Rep. 528, CA 3.52
G.U.S. Property Management *v.* Littlewoods Mail Order, 1982 S.L.T. 533;
   1982 S.C. 157, HL 4.160, 4.162
Gable House Estates Ltd *v.* Halpern Partnership, 48 Con. L.R. 1, QBD (OR) 7.32
Gallagher *v.* McDowell Ltd [1961] N.I. 26; [14 N.I.L.Q. 488] 6.11
General Building and Maintenance plc *v.* Greenwich L.B.C., 92 L.G.R. 21;
   65 Build. L.R. 57; [1993] I.R.L.R. 535; *The Times,* March 9, 1993 .... 3.07
George Fischer Holdings Ltd *v.* Multi Design Consultants Ltd; George Fischer
   Holdings Ltd *v.* Davis Langdon & Everest, 61 Con. L.R. 85; *The Independent,*
   May 4, 1998 (C.S.) QBD (OR) 4.60, 4.143, 4.145
Gilbert-Ash (Northern) *v.* Modern Engineering (Bristol) Ltd [1974] A.C. 689;
   [1973] 3 W.L.R. 421; 117 S.J. 745;[1973] 3 All E.R. 195; 72 L.G.R. 1, HL;
   reversing *sub nom.* Modern Engineering (Bristol) Ltd *v.* Gilbert-Ash (Northern)
   (1973) 71 L.G.R. 162, CA; [126 New L.J. 141] 1.01, 3.52, 3.53,
                                                                                     3.60, 3.63, 3.65, 3.67, 4.02
Gilchrist *v.* White, 1907 S.C. 984 .... 3.04
Glasgow Training Group (Motor Trade) *v.* Lombard Continental 1989 S.L.T. 375;
   1989 S.C. 30 .... 4.194
Gleeson (M.J.) (Contractors) Ltd *v.* London Borough of Hillingdon
   [1970] E.G.D. 495 .... 3.30
Glenlion Construction Ltd *v.* Guinness Trust (1987) 39 Build. L.R. 89 .... 4.41, 4.267
Gloucestershire County Council *v.* Richardson (t/a W.J. Richardson & Son)
   sub nom. Gloucestershire County Council *v.* Richardson [1969] 1 A.C. 480;
   [1968] 3 W.L.R. 645; 112 S.J. 759; [1968] 2 All E.R. 1181; 67 L.G.R. 15;
   [31 M.L.R. 221], HL; affirming [1967] 3 All E.R. 458, CA 4.374, 5.19

Glow Heating v. Eastern Health Board [1992] 8 Const. L.J. 56, High Court of Ireland 3.78
Gold v. Patman & Fotheringham Ltd [1958] 1 W.L.R. 697; 102 S.J. 470; [1958]
    2 All E.R. 497; [1958] 1 Lloyd's Rep. 587; [102 S.J. 733], CA; reversing
    [1957 2 Lloyd's Rep. 319 .... 4.190
Goodwins, Jardine & Co. v. Brand & Son (1905) 13 S.L.T. 329 .... 3.20
Graham (Thomas) & Sons v. Glenrothes Development Corporation
    1968 S.L.T. 2 .... 4.116, 4.120, 4.121, 4.122, 4.126
Grainger v. Raybould, 9 C. & P. 229 .... 4.114
Gray's Trustees v. Behar Coal Co. (1881) 9 R. 225 .... 4.319
Gray (Trustees of The London Hospital) v. T.P. Bennett & Son (a Firm) (1987)
    43 Build. L.R. 63 .... 4.60
Greater Glasgow Health Board v. Baxter Clark & Paul, 1992 S.L.T. 35;
    1990 S.C. 237 .... 3.88
Greater Glasgow Health Board v. Keppie Henderson and Partners and Others,
    1989 S.L.T. 387; 1988 S.C. 109 .... 5.25, 5.27, 5.34
Greater London Council v. Cleveland Bridge & Engineering Co. (1986) 34
    Build. L.R. 50; (1987) 8 Con. L.R. 30, CA; affirming [1984] C.I.L.L. 106;
    (1084) 34 Build. L.R. 50 .... 4.266, 4.269, 4.270
Greater Nottingham Co-operative Society Ltd v. Cementation Piling and
    Foundations Ltd [1988] 3 W.L.R. 396; (1988) 132 S.J. 754; [1988] 2 All E.R. 971;
    (1988) 41 Build. L.R. 43; (1988) 4 Const. L.J. 216; (1988) 138 New L.J. 112, CA;
    reversing [1985] C.I.L.L. 160 .... 1.18, 5.13
Greaves & Co. Contractors v. Baynham Meikle & Partners [1975] 1 W.L.R. 1095;
    119 S.J. 372; 3 All E.R. 99; 2 Lloyd's Rep. 325, CA; affirming [1974] 1 W.L.R. 1261;
    118 S.J. 595; [1974] 3 All E.R. 666; [1975] 1 Lloyd's Rep. 31 .... 5.30
Greig v. Kennedy, 1953 S.L.T. (Sh. Ct) 7 .... 1.13
Grills (R.J.) Ltd v. Dellios [1988] V.R. 136 (Australia) 4.122

Haden Young v. William McCrindle, 1994 S.L.T. 221, OH 4.393
Hadley v. Baxendale (1854) 9 Ex. 341; [27 A.L.J. 666;
    126 New L.J. 420] 4.212, 4.213, 4.278
Hamlyn & Co. v. Talisker Distillery [1894] A.C. 202; (1894) 21 R. 21, HL 4.382
Hampton v. Glamorgan County Council [1917] A.C. 13, HL 3.78
Hancock v. Brazier (B.W.) (Anerley) Ltd [1966] 1 W.L.R. 1317; [1966] 2 All E.R. 901;
    [30 Conv. 395], CA; affirming 110 S.J. 368; 1966 2 All E.R. 1;
    [30 Conv. 318] 5.22, 5.24
Haney v. United States, 230 Ct Cl. 148, 167–168, 676, F 2D 584, 595 (1982) 4.261
Hanson (W.) (Harrow) v. Rapid Civil Engineering and Usborne Developments
    (1987) 38 Build. L.R. 106; (1988) 11 Con. L.R. 119 .... 4.122, 4.123, 4.133
Harbottle (R.D.) (Mercantile) v. National Westminster Bank [1978] Q.B. 146;
    [1977] 3 W.L.R. 752; (1977) 121 S.J. 745; [1977] 2 All E.R. 862 .... 3.50
Harris Simons Construction Ltd, Re [1989] 1 W.L.R. 368; (1989) 133 S.J. 122;
    1989 P.C.C. 229; [1989] 5 B.C.C. 11; [1989] L.S. Gaz. February 22, 43 .... 4.327
Harte (W.J.) Construction v. Scottish Homes, 1992 S.L.T. 948; 1992 S.C. 99 .... 4.153, 4.154
Haskins (Shutters) Ltd v. D. & J. Ogilvie (Builders) Ltd, 1978 S.L.T. 64 .... 3.20, 5.14
Havant Borough Council v. South Coast Shipping Co. Ltd [1996] C.I.L.L. 1146 .... 4.250
Head Wrightson Aluminium Ltd v. Aberdeen Harbour Commissioners,
    1958 S.L.T. 12 .... 4.86
Hedley Byrne & Co. v. Heller & Partners [1964] A.C. 465; [1963] 3 W.L.R. 101;
    107 S.J. 454; [1963] 2 All E.R. 575; [1963] 1 Lloyd's Rep. 485; [234 L.T. 381;
    67 Accountants' Mag. 518; 107 S.J. 582, 622; 113 L.J. 779; 114 L.J. 202, 209;
    74 Accty 877; 149 Acct 520; 60 L.S. Gaz. 740; 80 S.A.L.J. 483; 27 M.L.R. 121;
    [1964] J.B.L. 291; 98 I.L.T. 215; 3 Osgoode Hall L.J. 89; 5 Chart. Sec. 19;
    74 Yale L.J. 286; 153 Acct 163; 73 Accty 829; [1972] J.B.L. 27], HL; affirming
    [1962] 1 Q.B. 396; [1961] 3 W.L.R. 1225; 105 S.J. 910; 3 All E.R. 891;

[25 M.L.R. 246; 105 S.J. 1075; 78 L.Q.R. 107]; [1961] C.L.Y. 518, CA; affirming
    The Times, December 21, 1960; C.L.Y. 186; [45 A.L.J. 20] 4.97, 6.06,
                                                                    6.12, 6.22, 6.27, 6.28, 7.16
Henderson *v.* Merrett Syndicates; Hallam-Eames *v.* Same; Hughes *v.* Same;
    Arbuthnott *v.* Feltrim Underwriting Agencies; Deeny *v.* Gooda Walker
    (In Liquidation) [1995] 2 A.C. 145; [1994] 3 W.L.R. 761; [1994] 3 All E.R. 506;
    [1994] 2 Lloyd's Rep. 468; (1994) 144 New L.J. Rep. 1204; *The Times,* July 26, 1994;
    The Independent, August 3, 1994, HL; affirming *The Times,* December 30, 1993;
    The Independent, December 14, 1993, CA; affirming *The Times,*
    October 20, 1993 .... 5.11, 5.13, 6.28
Highland Engineering Ltd *v.* Anderson, 1979 S.L.T. 122 .... 4.332
Hill *v.* Chief Constable of West Yorkshire [1989] A.C. 53, HL 6.07
Hill (J.M.) & Son *v.* London Borough of Camden (1980)
    18 Build. L.R. 31, CA 4.66, 4.314
Hitchins (Hatfield) Ltd *v.* Prudential Assurance Co. Ltd [1991] 2 Lloyd's Rep. 580;
    60 Build. L.R. 51; *Financial Times,* April 17, 1991, CA 4.184
Hoenig *v.* Isaacs [1952] 1 T.L.R. 1360; [1952] 2 All E.R. 176; [68 L.Q.R. 444], CA 4.11
Holland Dredging (U.K.) Ltd *v.* The Dredging and Construction Co. and
    Imperial Chemical Industries (Third Party) (1987) 37 Build. L.R. 1, CA 4.250
Holland Hannen & Cubitts (Northern) Ltd *v.* Welsh Health Technical Services
    Organisation (1987) 7 Con. L.R. 1; (1987) 35 Build. L.R. 1;
    [1985] C.I.L.L. 217, CA 4.11, 4.33, 5.41, 7.26a
Holme *v.* Guppy (1838) 3 M. & W. 387 .... 4.252
Home Office *v.* Dorset Yacht Co. *sub nom.* Dorset Yacht Co. *v.* Home Office
    [1970] A.C. 1004; [1970] 2 W.L.R. 1140; [1970] 2 All E.R. 294; [1970]
    1 Lloyd's Rep. 453; [33 M.L.R. 691]; 114 S.J. 375, HL; affirming *sub nom.*
    Dorset Yacht Co. *v.* Home Office [1969] 2 Q.B. 412; [1969] 2 W.L.R. 1008;
    113 S.J. 227; [1969] 2 All E.R. 564, CA; affirming 113 S.J. 57;
    [1968] C.L.Y. 2638 .... 6.05, 6.06
Honeywill and Stein Ltd *v.* Larkin Bros Ltd [1934] 1 K.B. 191 .... 4.191
Hopewell Project Management Ltd and Another *v.* Ewebank Preece Ltd [1998]
    1 Lloyd's Rep. 448, QBD 4.194
Hounslow London Borough Council *v.* Twickenham Garden Developments *sub nom.*
    London Borough of Hounslow *v.* Twickenham Garden Developments [1971]
    Ch. 233; [1970] 3 W.L.R. 538; 114 S.J. 603; 69 LGR 109; [1970] 3 All E.R. 326;
    [1970] 7 Build. L.R. 81 .... 4.145, 4.265,
                                                                    4.307, 4.315

I.C.I. *v.* BOVIS CONTRACTORS AND OTHERS (1992) 32 Con. L.R. 90 .... 4.302, 4.303
I.E. Contractors Ltd *v.* Lloyds Bank and Rafidain Bank [1990] 2 Lloyd's Rep. 496;
    51 Build. L.R. 1; *Financial Times,* July 17, 1990, CA; reversing in part
    [1989] 2 Lloyd's Rep. 205 .... 3.50
Ibmac Ltd *v.* Marshall (Homes) (1968) 208 E.G. 851, CA 4.09, 4.12
Independent Broadcasting Authority *v.* E.M.I. Electronics and B.I.C.C. Construction
    (1980) 14 Build. L.R. 1, HL; affirming (1978) 11 Build. L.R. 29, CA 4.374,
                                                                    5.28, 5.31
Invercargill City Council *v.* Hamlin, 72 Build. L.R. 39; (1995)
    11 Const. L.J. 285, CA 6.02
Inverclyde District Council *v.* Hardstock (Scotland) Ltd (1983) 1 Const. L.J. 136;
    1984 S.L.T. 226, Scot First Division 3.30

JACOBSEN SONS & CO. *v.* E. UNDERWOOD & SON (1894) 2 R. 654 .... 4.348
Jamieson *v.* Simon (1899) 1 F. 1211; 1899 36 S.L.R. 883 .... 4.74, 7.30
Jamieson *v.* McInnes (1887) 15 R. 17 .... 4.97
Jarvis Brent Ltd *v.* Robinson Construction Ltd (1990) 6 Const. L.J. 292 .... 4.231

Jarvis (John) *v.* Rockdale Housing Association (1987) 3 Const. L.J. 24;
(1987) 36 Build. L.R. 48; (1986) 10 Con. L.R. 51, CA; affirming (1985)
5 Con. L.R. 118 .... 4.66
Jefco Mechanical Services Ltd *v.* Lambeth London Borough Council (1983)
24 Build. L.R. 1, CA 4.375
Johannesburg Municipal Council *v.* D. Stewart & Co. (1902) Ltd 1909 S.C. 860;
1909 S.C. 53, HL 3.40
John Barker Construction *v.* London Portman Hotel (1996) 83 Build. L.R. 31;
50 Con. L.R. 43; 12 Const. L.J. 277, QBD (OR) 4.260, 7.15
John Cochrane & Co. *v.* Robert McAlpine & Sons Ltd, 1989 G.W.D. 6–262 .... 3.66
John Laing Construction *v.* County & District Properties Ltd (1982)
23 Build. L.R. 1 .... 4.55, 4.375
John Lelliot (Contracts) *v.* Byrne Bros (Formwork) 31 Con. L.R. 89 .... 4.70
John L. Haley Ltd *v.* Dumphries & Galloway Regional Council, unreported,
November 8, 1988 .... 4.235, 4.243
John Mowlem & Co. *v.* Eagle Star Insurance Co., 62 Build. L.R. 126; 33 Con. L.R. 131
Johnston *v.* Robertson (1861) 23 D. 352 .... 3.57, 3.60, 3.61, 4.214
Jones *v.* Sherwood Computer Services [1992] 1 W.L.R. 277; [1992] 2 All E.R. 170;
The Times, December 14, 1989, CA 8.27
Jones *v.* Stroud District Council [1986] 1 W.L.R. 1141; (1986) 130 S.J. 469; [1988]
1 All E.R. 5; (1986) 84 L.G.R. 886; (1986) 279 E.G. 213; (1986) 2 Const. L.J. 185;
(1986) 34 Build. L.R. 27; (1987) 8 Con. L.R. 23; [1986] 2 E.G.L.R. 133, CA 3.86
Junior Books *v.* Veitchi Co., The [1983] 1 A.C. 520; [1982] 3 W.L.R. 477; [1982]
126 S.J. 538; [1982] 3 All E.R. 201; [1982] Con. L.R. 221; (1982) 79 L.S. Gaz.
1413; (1981) 21 Build. L.R. 66, HL 5.13, 6.26, 6.27, 6.28

KAYE (P. & M.) *v.* HOSIER & DICKINSON [1972] 1 W.L.R. 146; (1971) 116 S.J. 75;
[1972] 1 All E.R. 121, HL; affirming [1970] 1 W.L.R. 1611; 114 S.J. 929;
[1971] 1 All E.R. 301, CA 4.58, 4.60, 4.61, 4.142
Kennedy *v.* Glenbelle Ltd,1996 S.C. 95 .... 4.193
Kensington & Chelsea & Westminster Area Health Authority *v.* Wettern Composites
(1985) 31 Build. L.R. 57; [1985] 1 All E.R. 346; (1984) 134 New L.J. 887, DC 4.74
Kerr *v.* Dundee Gas Light Co. (1861) 23 D. 197 .... 4.112, 4.113, 4.115
Ketteman *v.* Hansel Properties [1987] 1 A.C. 189; [1987] 2 W.L.R. 312;
(1987) 131 S.J. 134; [1988] 1 All E.R. 38; [1987] 1 F.T.L.R. 284; (1987)
85 L.G.R. 409; (1987) 36 Build. L.R. 1; [1987] 1 E.G.L.R. 237; (1987)
84 L.S. Gaz. 657; (1987) 137 New L.J. 100; [(1987) 84 L.S. Gaz. 3562], HL
affirming [1984] 1 W.L.R. 1274; (1984) 128 S.J. 800 ; [1985] 1 All E.R. 352;
(1985) P. & C.R. 257; (1985) 27 Build. L.R. 1; [1984] C.I.L.L. 109; (1984)
271 E.G. 1099; (1984) 81 L.S. Gaz. 3018, ... 3.86
Kiely & Sons Ltd *v.* Medcraft (1965) 109 S.J. 829, CA 4.11
Kier Construction *v.* Royal Insurance (U.K.), 30 Con. L.R. 45 .... 4.183
Kitsons Sheet Metal Ltd *v.* Balfour Beatty Building (1989) 47 Build. L.R. 82 .... 3.15
Kruger Tissue (Industrial) Ltd (formerly Industrial Cleaning Papers Ltd) *v.* Frank
Galliers Ltd 57 Con. L.R. 1; (1998) 14 Const. L.J. 437, QBD (OR) 4.194,
4.198, 4.204

LACEY (WILLIAM) (HOUNSLOW) *v.* DAVIS [1957] 1 W.L.R. 932; 101 S.J. 629;
[1957] 2 All E.R. 712; [101 S.J. 755; 107 L.J. 723; 73 L.Q.R. 443; 21 Conv. 396] 3.02
Laing (Liquidator of Inverdale Construction Co.) *v.* Lord Advocate 1973 S.L.T.
(Notes) 81 .... 3.56
Lamb *v.* Camden London Borough Council [1981] Q.B. 625; [1981] 2 W.L.R. 1038;
(1981) 125 S.J. 356; [1981] 2 All E.R. 408, CA 4.244
Lamb (W.) Ltd *v.* Jarvis & Son plc, 1998 C.I.L.L. 1427 .... 4.256
Landless *v.* Wilson (1880) 8 R. 289 .... 3.04

Leith Dock Commissioners *v.* Colonial Life Assurance Co. (1861) 24 D. 64 .... 4.150
Leon Engineering & Construction Co. *v.* Ka Duk Investment Co. (1989)
   5 Const. L.J. 288, High Ct of Hong Kong 7.21
Leyland Shipping *v.* Norwich Union Fire Insurance Society [1918] A.C. 350 .... 4.247
Linden Gardens Trust Ltd *v.* Lenesta Sludge Disposals; St Martins Property Corporation *v.*
   Robert McAlpine & Sons [1994] 1 A.C. 85; [1993] 3 W.L.R. 408; [1993]
   3 All E.R. 417; 63 Build. L.R. 1; 36 Con. L.R. 1; (1993) 137 S.J.L.B. 183;
   [1993] E.G.C.S. 139; (1993) 143 New L.J. 1152; *The Times,* July 23, 1993;
   The Independent, July 30, 1993, HL; reversing in part 57 Build. L.R. 57;
   30 Con. L.R. 1 (1992) 8 Const. L.J. 180; *The Times,* February 27, 1992;
   The Independent, March 6, 1992; *Financial Times,* February 20, 1992, CA;
   reversing 52 Build. L.R. 93; 25 Con. L.R. 28 [1991] E.G.C.S. 11 .... 4.148, 4.161, 4.163,
                                                                    4.165, 4.166, 4.167, 4.169
Lindenberg (Edward) *v.* Canning (Joe) 62 Build. L.R. 147; 29 Con. L.R. 71;
   (1993) 9 Const. L.J. 43 .... 5.44
Lindley Catering Investments Ltd *v.* Hibernian Football Club Ltd 1975 S.L.T.
   (Notes) 56 .... 1.16
Lintest Builders Ltd *v.* Roberts (1980) 13 Build. L.R. 38, CA; affirming (1978)
   10 Build. L.R. 120 .... 4.143
Lodder *v.* Slowey [1904] A.C. 442 .... 4.87
Loke Hong Kee Pte Ltd *v.* United Overseas Land (1992) 23 Build. L.R. 35, PC 4.307
London Congregational Union *v.* Harriss [1988] 1 All E.R. 15; (1986) 280 E.G. 1342;
   (1987) 3 Const. L.J. 371; (1987) 35 Build. L.R. 58; (1987 8 Con. L.R. 52; [1986]
   2 E.G.L.R. 155, CA; reversing in part [1985] 1 All E.R. 335; [1984] C.I.L.L. 85;
   (1984) 1 Const. L.J. 54 .... 3.86
Long *v.* Cummins, 1982 S.L.T. 489 .... 3.62
Lord Advocate *v.* Shipbreaking Industries Ltd, 1991 S.L.T. 838 .... 2.07
Lord Elphinstone *v.* Monkland Iron & Coal Co. (1886) 13 R. 98, HL 4.215
Loudon (William) & Son Ltd *v.* Cunninghame District Council,
   1985 S.L.T. 149 .... 3.44, 4.330
Lovell Construction *v.* Independent Estates (In Liquidation) [1994] 1 B.C.L.C. 31 .... 3.74
Lubenham Fidelities and Investments Co. Ltd *v.* South Pembrokeshire District Council
   and Wigley Fox Partnership (1986) 33 Build. L.R. 39; (1986) 6 Con. L.R. 85;
   (1986) 2 Const. L.J. 111, CA; affirming [1985] C.I.L.L. 214 .... 4.306, 4.350, 4.354, 8.32
Luxor (Eastbourne) Ltd *v.* Cooper [1941] A.C. 108 .... 5.41
Lyle *v.* Falconer (1842) 5 D. 236 .... 8.28

M.T.M. Construction Ltd *v.* William Reed Engineering Ltd
   & Another, 1997 S.C.L.R. 778 .... 1.22, 4.191
McAlpine Humberoak Ltd *v.* McDermott International Inc. (No. 2),
   58 Build. L.R. 1, CA 4.96, 4.258
MacBean *v.* Napier (1870) 8 S.L.R. 250 .... 4.96
McCrone *v.* Boots Farm Sales Ltd 1981 S.L.T. 103 .... 1.03
McElroy & Sons *v.* Tharsis Sulphur and Copper Co. Ltd (1877) 5 R. 161;
   (1878) 5 R. 171, HL 4.228
McIntyre & Co. *v.* Clow, 1985 2 R. 278 .... 1.10
MacJordan Construction Ltd *v.* Brookmount Erostin, 56 Build. L.R. 1;
   [1992] B.C.L.C. 350; *The Times,* October 29, 1991, CA 3.73
MacKay *v.* Parochial Board of Barry (1883) 10 R. 1046 .... 4.96
MacKay (G.) & Son *v.* Police Commissioners of Leven (1893) 20 R. 1093 .... 4.208
MacKay (G.) & Son *v.* Lord Advocate (War Department), 1914 S.L.T. 33 .... 4.83, 4.84
McKnight & Sons *v.* District Committee of the Middle Ward of Lanarkshire and
   Others, 1899 7 S.L.T. 47, OH 7.03
McLeod *v.* Scottish Special Housing Association, 1990 S.L.T. 749 .... 6.26
McPhail *v.* Cunninghame District Council, 1985 S.L.T. 149 .... 3.44, 4.330

McPhail *v.* Lothian District Council, 1981 S.L.T. 173; 1981 S.C. 109 .... 4.330
McWhirter *v.* Longmuir, 1948 S.C. 577; 1948 S.L.T. 493 .... 5.26
Macob Civil Engineering *v.* Morrison Construction Ltd (1999) 89 Build. L.R. 93;
    The Times, March 11, 1999 .... 8.29
Main *v.* City of Glasgow District Licensing Board,1987 S.L.T. 305; [1978] S.L.T.
    (News) 157, 353 .... 4.347
Margrie Holdings Ltd *v.* City of Edinburgh District Council, 1994 S.L.T. 971 .... 4.278
Mark (Frederick) *v.* Schild (1971) 115 S.J. 948; *The Times,* October 21, 1971; [1972]
    1 Lloyd's Rep. 9, CA 3.52
Maxwell (John) & Sons (Builders) *v.* Simpson, 1990 S.C.L.R. 92 .... 4.227
Medway Oil and Storage *v.* Silca Gel Corporation (1928) 33 Com. Cas. 159 .... 5.29
Mendok B.V. *v.* Cumberland Maritime Corporation, 1989 S.L.T. 192 .... 4.383
Merton London Borough Council *v.* Leach (Stanley Hugh) (1985) 32 Build. L.R. 51;
    (1986) 2 Const. L.J. 189 .... 4.34, 4.35, 4.37, 4.38, 4.235,
                                                                     4.237, 4.268, 4.301, 5.03, 5.41
Merton London Borough Council *v.* Lowe (1982) 18 Build. L.R. 130, ... 7.28, 7.30
Methodist Homes Housing Association *v.* Scott & McIntosh, 1997
    G.W.D. 22–1064, OH 4.238, 4.239
Mettoy Pension Trustees Ltd *v.* Evans [1990] 1 W.L.R. 1587; [1991] 2 All E.R. 513;
    Financial Times, February 9, 1990 .... 4.318
Milne *v.* Kidd (1869) 8 M. 250 .... 3.38
Minter F.G. Ltd *v.* Welsh Health Technical Services Organisation (1980)
    13 Build. L.R. 1 .... 4.278, 4.283, 4.284, 4.290
Mona Oil Equipment & Supply Co. Ltd *v.* Rhodesian Railways [1950] W.N. 10;
    [1949] 2 All E.R. 1014; 83 Lloyd's L. Rep. 178 .... 5.41
Monarch Steamship Co. *v.* A/B Karlshamns Oljefabriker *sub nom.* A/B Karlshamns
    Oljefabriker *v.* Monarch Steamship Co. [1949] A.C. 196; [1949] L.J.R. 772;
    65 T.L.R. 217; 93 S.J. 117; [1949] 1 All E.R. 1 [95 S.J. 38; 65 L.Q.R. 137;
    12 M.L.R. 372]; 80 Lloyd's L. Rep. 151; 1949 S.C. 179; 11947 S.L.T. 140 .... 4.245
Moody *v.* Ellis (t/a Warwick & Ellis) (1984) 26 Build. L.R. 39, CA 3.28
Moore *v.* Gleddon (1869) 7 M. 1016 ....4.43, 4.107, 4.109, 4.113, 4.115, 4.145
Moresk Cleaners Ltd *v.* Hicks [1966] 2 Lloyd's Rep. 538; 116 New L.J. 1546 ...... 4.53, 7.30
Morrison *v.* Harkness (1890) 9 M. 35 .... 3.38
Morrison-Knudsen Co. Inc. *v.* British Columbia Hydro and Power Authority
    (1972) 31 D.L.R. (3d) 633, British Columbia Supreme Court 4.89, 5.38
Morrison's Associated Companies *v.* James Rome & Sons, 1964 S.C. 160 .... 4.19
Morton (William) & Co. *v.* Muir Bros & Co. Ltd, 1907 S.C. 1224 .... 5.26
Mottram Consultants *v.* Sunley (Bernard) & Sons (1974) S.J. 808; [1975]
    2 Lloyd's Rep. 197, HL; affirming *sub nom.* Sunley (Bernard) & Sons *v.*
    Mottram Consultants (1973) 228 E.G. 723, CA [126 New L.J. 141] 3.64
Muldoon *v.* Pringle (1882) 9 R. 916 .... 4.15, 4.58, 4.64
Mullen (B.) & Sons (Contractors) Ltd *v.* Ross (1996) 54 Con. L.R. 163, CA (N.I.) 3.78
Murphy *v.* Brentwood Borough Council [1991] 1 A.C. 398; [1990] 3 W.L.R. 414;
    [1990] 2 All E.R. 908; (1990) 22 H.L.R. 502; (1990) 134 S.J. 1076; 21 Con. L.R. 1;
    89 L.G.R. 24; (1990) 6 Const. L.J. 304; (1990) 154 L.G.R. 1010; [1990] L.S. Gaz.
    August 29, 15; (1990) 134 S.J. 1058; (1990) 134 S.J. 1974; [1990] L.G.C.
    September 14, 14; 50 Build. L.R. 1; (1991) 3 Admin. L.R. 37; (1990) 6 P.N. 158;
    (1990) 6 P.N. 150; [1990 134 S.J. 125, HL: reversing [1990] 2 W.L.R. 944; [1990]
    2 All E.R. 269; 88 L.G.R. 333; (1990) 134 S.J. 458; [1990] L.S. Gaz. February 7,
    42, CA; affirming 13 Con. L.R. 96 .... 4.189 3.81, 6.02, 6.05, 6.08, 6.09,
                                                                     6.14, 6.15, 6.18, 6.20, 6.21, 6.22, 6.24, 6.26
Murphy (J.) & Sons *v.* Southwark London Borough Council (1983) 127 S.J. 119;
    (1983) 81 L.G.R. 383; (1983) 22 Build. L.R. 41, CA; (1982) 18 Build. L.R. 1 ....4.376
Murray *v.* Legal & General Assurance Society [1970] 2 Q.B. 495; [1970] 2 W.L.R. 465;
    113 S.J. 720; [1969] 3 All E.R. 794; [1969] 2 Lloyd's Rep. 405 .... 4.320

NATIONAL TRUST FOR PLACES OF HISTORIC INTEREST *v.* HADEN YOUNG LTD (1994) 72 Build. L.R. 1;
The Times, August 11, 1994; *The Independent,* August 31, 1994, CA 4.203
Needox Ltd *v.* The Mayor Aldermen and Burgesses of the Borough of Swinton and
Pendlebury (1958) 5 Build. L.R. 34 .... 4.35, 4.267
Nelson (W.M.) Cladding Ltd *v.* Murray Williamson (Builders) Ltd,
1995 S.L.T. 86, Sh. Ct 4.279
Nene Housing Society *v.* National Westminster Bank (1980) 16 Build. L.R. 22 .... 3.45
Nevill (H.W.) (Sunblest) *v.* William Press (1982) 20 Build. L.R. 78 .. 4.61, 4.137, 4.141, 4.143
Newham London Borough *v.* Taylor Woodrow-Anglian (1982)
19 Build. L.R. 99, CA 5.41
Newton *v.* Forster, 12 M. & W. 772 .... 4.114
Nicol Homeworld Contracts *v.* Charles Gray Builders Ltd, 1986 S.L.T. 317 .... 5.14
Nikko Hotels *v.* M.E.P.C. [1991] 2 E.G.L.R. 103; [1991] 28 E.G. 86 .... 8.28
Nordhoek-Energie Diving & R.O.V. Services B.V. *v.* Subsea Offshore Ltd, unreported,
March 29, 1996, OH 3.18
Norta Wallpapers (Ireland) *v.* Sisk & Sons (Dublin) [1978] I.R. 114; (1978)
14 Build. L.R. 49 .... 5.31
North West Metropolitan Regional Hospital Board *v.* Bickerton (T.A.) & Son Ltd
[1970] 1 W.L.R. 60 .... 3.30
Northern Regional Health Authority *v.* Crouch (Derek) Construction Co. [1984]
Q.B. 644; 2 W.L.R. 676; (1984) 128 S.J. 279; [1984] 2 All E.R. 175; (1984)
26 Build. L.R. 1; [[1986] C.I.L.L. 244], CA; affirming [1983]
24 Build. L.R. 60, DC 4.240, 4.378, 8.26, 8.28
Norwest Holst Construction Ltd *v.* Renfrewshire Council, 1996 G.W.D. 40–2261 .... 7.27
Norwich City Council *v.* Harvey (Paul Clarke) (1988) 39 B.C.R. 75; (1988)
4 Const. L.J. 217 .... 4.200, 4.201
Norwich Union Life Insurance Society *v.* Covell Matthews Partnership,
1987 S.L.T. 452 .... 6.08
Nova Scotia *v.* Hellenic Mutual War Risks Association (Bermuda) Ltd [1990]
1 Q.B. 818 .... 4.256
Nye Saunders (a firm) *v.* Bristow (A.E.) (1987) 37 Build. L.R. 92 .... 7.32

OGILVIE BUILDERS LTD *v.* CITY OF GLASGOW DISTRICT COUNCIL, 1995 S.L.T. 15;
1994 S.C.L.R. 546 .... 4.278, 4.279
O'Neil *v.* Scottish Joint Negotiating Committee for Teaching Staff, 1987 S.L.T. 648;
1987 S.C. 90; 1987 S.C.L.R. 275 .... 4.389
O'Reilly *v.* Mackman [1983] 2 A.C. 237 .... 4.391
Otto *v.* Bolton & Norris [1936] 2 K.B. 46; [1936] 1 All E.R. 960 .... 6.10, 6.11
Owen (Edward) Engineering *v.* Barclays Bank International [1977] 3 W.L.R. 764; (1977) 121
S.J. 617; [1978] 1 All E.R. Rep. 976; [1978] 1 Lloyd's Rep. 166; (1977) 6 Build. L.R. 1, CA

P.C. HARRINGTON CONTRACTORS LTD *v.* CO-PARTNERSHIP DEVELOPMENTS LTD (1988)
88 Build. L.R. 44 .... 3.41
Pacific Associates *v.* Baxter [1989] 2 All E.R. 159 .... 7.20, 7.21
Parkhead Housing Association *v.* Phoenix Preservation Ltd, 1990 S.L.T. 812 .... 6.26
Parkinson (Sir Lindsay) & Co. *v.* Commissioners of His Majesty's Works and Public
Buildings [1949] 2 K.B. 632; [1950] 1 All E.R. 208; [210 L.T. 25; 100 L.J. 677],
CA; affirming [1948] W.N. 446; 93 S.J. 27 .... 4.96
Parklea Ltd *v.* W. & J.R. Watson, 1988 S.L.T. 605 .... 3.22, 5.14
Patman & Fotheringham Ltd *v.* Pilditch, *Hudson on Building Contracts* (1904), Vol. 2,
p. 368 .... 5.39
Paterson (Robert) & Sons Ltd *v.* Household Supplies Co. Ltd, 1975 S.L.T. 98 .... 4.61
Peak Construction (Liverpool) *v.* McKinney Foundations (1971)
69 L.G.R. 1, CA 4.233, 4.239, 4.252, 4.253
Pearce and High Ltd *v.* Baxter, *The Times,* March 24, 1999, CA 4.144

Peddie *v.* Henderson (1869) S.L.R. 608 .... 4.63
Perar B.V. *v.* General Surety & Guarantee Co. (1994) 43 Con. L.R. 110, CA 3.45
Petrofina (U.K.) *v.* Magnaload [1984] Q.B. 127; [1983] 3 W.L.R. 805; (1983)
    127 S.J. 729; [1983] 3 All E.R. 35; [1983] 2 Lloyd's Rep. 91; (1984)
    25 Build. L.R. 37; (1983) 80 L.S. Gaz. 2677 .... 4.195
Philips (Hong Kong) *v.* Attorney General of Hong Kong 1993 61 Build. L.R. 41;
    (1993) 9 Const. L.J. 202; *The Times,* February 15, 1993, PC; affirming
    58 Build. L.R. 113; (1991) 7 Const. L.J. 340, CA of Hong Kong; reversing
    50 Build. L.R. 125, High Ct of Hong Kong 4.216, 4.218,
                                                                                                           4.219, 4.220
Piggot Foundations Ltd *v.* Shepherd Construction Ltd (1994) C.I.L.L. 947 .... 5.18
Pillar P.G. *v.* Higgins (D.J.) Construction (1986) 10 Con. L.R. 46; (1986)
    2 Const. L.J. 223; 34 Build. L.R. 43, CA 4.288
Pirelli General Cable Works *v.* Faber (Oscar) & Partners [1983] 2 A.C. 1;
    [1983] 2 W.L.R. 6; (1983) 127 S.J. 16; [1983] 1 All E.R. 65; (1983) 265 E.G. 979;
    (1983) 133 New L.J. 63, HL; reversing (1982) 263 E.G. 879, CA 3.85, 3.86, 3.87
Pratt *v.* George J. Hill (1987) 38 Build. L.R. 25 .... 7.29
Property and Land Contractors Ltd *v.* Alfred McAlpine Homes (North) Ltd (1995)
    76 Build. L.R. 59, QBD 4.290, 4.296
Pullar *v.* Window Clean Ltd, 1956 S.C. 13 .... 4.189

QUEENSLAND GOVERNMENT, RAILWAYS AND ELECTRIC POWER TRANSMISSION PTY *V.*
    MANUFACTURERS MUTUAL INSURANCE LTD [1969] 1 Lloyd's Rep. 214 .... 4.184

R. *V.* PORTSMOUTH CITY COUNCIL EX P. COLES; R. *V.* Portsmouth City Council ex p.
    George Austin (Builders) Ltd 81 Build. L.R. 1; [1997] C.L.C. 407; (1997)
    16 Tr. L.R. 83; (1997) 9 Admin. L.R. 535; (1997) 161 J.P. Rep. 312; *The Times,*
    November 13, 1996, CA 3.07
R.H.M. Bakeries (Scotland) Ltd *v.* Strathclyde Regional Council 1985 S.L.T. 214 ...... 4.193
Ramsay *v.* Brand (1898) 25 R. 1212 .... 4.04, 4.08, 4.53, 4.138,
                                                                                                           4.141, 7.10, 7.12
Rapid Building Group *v.* Ealing Family Housing Association (1984)
    24 Build. L.R. 5, CA 4.239, 4.253
Rattray *v.* Yuille (1878) 2 Guthrie Sh. Ct Rep. 27 .... 3.03
Redpath Dorman Long *v.* Cummins Engine Co., 1982 S.L.T. 489 .... 3.60, 3.67, 8.32
Redpath Dorman Long *v.* Redpath Construction, 1982 S.C. 14 .... 3.55
Redrow Homes Ltd *v.* Bett Brothers plc *sub nom.* Redrow Homes Ltd *v.*
    Betts Brothers plc, 1997 S.C. 143; 1997 S.L.T. 1125; [1997] F.S.R. 828;
    1997 S.C.L.R. 469; *The Times,* May 2, 1997, 2 Div; reversing 1996
    S.L.T. 1254, OH 3.04
Rees Hough *v.* Redland Reinforced Plastics Ltd (1985) 27 Build. L.R. 136;
    [1984] C.I.L.L. 84; (1984) Const. L.J. 67; (1984) 134 New L.J. 706 .... 4.107
Rees and Kirby *v.* Swansea City Council (1985) Build. L.R. 1; (1985) 129 S.J. 622;
    [1985] C.I.L.L. 188; (1985) 1 Const. L.J. 378; (1985) 82 L.S. Gaz. 2905, CA;
    reversing in part (1984) 128 S.J. 46; (1984) 35 Build. L.R. 129 .... 4.278, 4.282, 4.286
Reid *v.* MacBeth & Gray (1904) 6 F. 25, HL 4.109, 4.120, 4.122
Renfrew Golf Club *v.* Ravenstone Securities Ltd, 1984 S.L.T. 170 .... 3.87
Richard Roberts Holdings Ltd *v.* Douglas Smith Stimson Partnership (No. 2),
    46 Build. L.R. 50 ; 22 Con. L.R. 69 .... 7.26
Robert McAlpine *v.* Lanarkshire & Ayrshire Railway Co. (1899) 17 R. 113 .... 4.36, 5.03
Robert McAlpine (Sir) *v.* The Royal Scottish Academy of Music and Drama,
    1989 G.W.D. 34–1582 .... 3.54
Roberts *v.* Bury Improvement Commissioners (1870) L.R. 5 C.P. 310 .... 5.41
Robertson *v.* Driver's Trustees (1881) 8 R. 555 .... 4.215, 4.230, 5.40
Robertson *v.* Jarvie,1908 15 S.L.T. 703 .... 4.27, 7.08, 7.09, 7.10

Rotary Services Ltd *v.* Honeywell Control Systems, 1993 S.L.T. 781, OH 4.294
Rotherham Metropolitan Borough Council *v.* Frank Haslam Milan & Co. Ltd
    (1996) 78 Build. L.R. 1, CA 4.70
Royal Bank of Scotland *v.* Dinwoodie, 1987 S.L.T. 82 .... 3.43
Rutherford Ltd *v.* Allied Breweries Ltd, 1990 S.L.T. 249; 1990 S.C.L.R. 186 .... 2.10
Rutherglen Magistrates *v.* Cullen (1773) 2 Pat. 305, HL 5.36
Ruxley Electronics & Construction Ltd *v.* Forsyth; Laddingford Enclosures Ltd *v.*
    Forsyth [1995] 3 W.L.R. 118; [1995] 3 All E.R. 268; 73 Build. L.R. 1;
    45 Con. L.R. 61; (1995) 14 Tr. L.R. 541; [1995] E.G.C.S. 11; (1995)
    11 Const. L.J. 381; (1995) 145 N.L.J. Rep. 996; (1995) 139 S.J.L.B. 163;
    The Times, July 3, 1995; *The Independent,* July 12, 1995, HL; reversing [1994]
    1 W.L.R. 650; [1994] 3 All E.R. 801; 66 Build. L.R. 23; 36 Con. L.R. 103;
    (1994) 91(7) L.S. Gaz. 31; (1994) 138 S.J.L.B. 31; *The Times,* January 7,
    1994, CA 4.53
Rylands *v.* Fletcher (1868) L.R. 3 H.L. 330; [203 L.T. 82; 204 L.T. 237;
    [1956] Const. L.J. 13; 23 Sol. 191; 72 L.Q.R. 184; 73 L.Q.R. 311; 19 M.L.R. 419;
    100 S.J. 659; 11 Conv. 259; 11 I.C.L.Q. 937; 3 *Legal Executive* 3;
    121 New L.J. 183] 4.193

S.M.K. CABINETS *V.* HILL MODERN ELECTRICS PTY [1984] V.R. 391;
    (1984) 1 Const. L.J. 159, Supreme Court of Victoria 4.255
St Martins Property Corporation *v.* Robert McAlpine & Sons.
    See Linden Gardens Trust Ltd *v.* Lenesta Sludge Disposals
St Mowden Developments Ltd *v.* Bowmer and Kirkland Ltd (1996) C.I.L.L. 1203 .... 4.297
St Paul Fire & Marine Insurance Co. (U.K.) Ltd *v.* McConnell Dowell Constructors Ltd
    [1955] 2 Lloyd's Rep. 116; 74 Build. L.R. 112; 45 Con. L.R. 89; Lloyd's List,
    June 8, 1995 (I.D.), CA. [1993] 2 Lloyd's Rep. 503; 67 Build. L.R. 72;
    37 Con. L.R. 96 .... 4.185
Salliss (Michael) *v.* E.C.A. Calil (1988) 4 Const. L.J. 125 .... 7.16, 7.17, 7.20
Samuels *v.* Davis (1943) 1 K.B. 526 .... 5.28
Sanders (Arthur), Re (1981) 17 Build. L.R. 125 .... 3.70, 3.73
Sanderson (A.) & Son *v.* Armour & Co. Ltd 1921 S.C. 18; affirmed 1922
    S.C. 117, HL 1.15, 4.382
Saphena Computing *v.* Allied Collection Agencies Ltd [1995] F.S.R. 648, CA;
    affirming [1995] F.S.R. 616, QBD 4.142
Sauter Automation *v.* Goodman (H.C.) (Mechanical Services) (In Liquidation)
    (1986) 34 Build. L.R. 81 .... 3.21, 4.123
Schindler Lifts (Hong Kong) *v.* Shui On Construction Co. (1984) 29 Build. L.R. 95,
    C.A. of Hong Kong 5.15
Schroeder (A.) Music Publishing Co. *v.* Macaulay (formerly Instone) [1974]
    1 W.L.R. 1300; 118 S.J. 734; [1974] 3 All E.R. 616, HL; affirming *sub nom.*
    Instone *v.* Schroeder (A.) Music Publishing Co. [1974]
    1 All E.R. 171, CA 1.16
Scott *v.* Gerard, 1916 S.C. 793; 1916 2 S.L.T. 42 .... 1.15
Scott & Morris *v.* Hatton (1827) 6 S. 413 .... 5.39
Scott Lithgow Ltd *v.* G.E.C. Electrical Projects Ltd, 1992 S.L.T. 244;
    1989 S.C. 412 .... 4.170, 5.07, 5.12
Scottish Power plc *v.* Kvaerner Construction (Regions) Ltd, March 6,
    1988, OH 4.37, 4.39
Scottish Discount Co. Ltd *v.* Blin, 1985 S.C. 216; 1986 S.L.T. 123 .... 4.103
Scottish Homes *v.* Inverclyde District Council,
    1997 S.L.T. 829, OH 4.148, 4.150, 4.154, 4.163
Scottish Special Housing Association *v.* Wimpey Construction U.K. [1986]
    1 W.L.R. 995; (1986) 130 S.J. 592; [1986] 2 All E.R. 957; (1986) 34 Build. L.R. 1;
    (1986) 2 Const. L.J. 149; (1987) 9 Con. L.R.; (1986) 136 New L.J. 753;

(1986) 83 L.S. Gaz. 2652, HL; reversing (1985) 31 Build. L.R. 17,
Ct of Session 4.196, 4.197, 4.198,
4.199, 4.203
Seath & Co. *v.* Moore (1886) 13 R. 57, HL 1.12, 4.108, 4.109,
4.120, 4.121, 4.122
Shanks & McEwan (Contractors) *v.* Mifflin Construction (O.H.),
1993 S.L.T. 1124 .... 4.390
Shanks & McEwan (Contractors) *v.* Strathclyde Regional Council
1995 S.L.T. 172 .... 7.10
Sharpe *v.* Sweeting (E.T.) & Son Ltd [1963] 1 W.L.R. 665; 107 S.J. 666;
[1963] 2 All E.R. 455 .... 6.11
Sharpe *v.* San Paulo Railway Co. 1872 L.R. 8 Ch. 597 .... 5.37
Shetland Islands Council *v.* B.P. Petroleum Development Ltd, 1990 S.L.T. 82;
1989 S.C.L.R. 48 .... 4.103
Shui On Construction Co. Ltd *v.* Shui Kay Co. Ltd (1985) 4 Const. L.J. 305,
H.K. Supreme Ct 7.20
Sika Contractors *v.* Gill (1978) 9 Build. L.R. 11 .... 7.06
Simaan General Contractors Co. *v.* Pilkington Glass Ltd (No. 2) [1988] Q.B. 758;
[1988] 2 W.L.R. 761; (1988) 132 S.J. 463; [1988] 1 All E.R. 791; [1988]
F.T.L.R. 469; (1988) 40 Build. L.R. 28; (1988) 138 New L.J. 53; (1988)
L.S. Gaz. March 16, 44, CA 6.28
Simpson *v.* Jack, 1948 S.L.T. (Notes) 45 .... 3.38
Simpson *v.* Ross & Morton 1992 S.L.T. (Sh. Ct) 33, ... 7.05
Sims (C.J.) Ltd *v.* Shaftesbury plc (1991) 25 Con. L.R. 72 .... 3.16
Sinclair *v.* Logan, 1961 S.L.T. (Sh. Ct) 10; 76 Sh. Ct Rep. 161 .... 3.03
Sinclair *v.* MacDougall Estates Ltd, 1994 S.L.T. 76 .... 3.87
Siporex Trade S.A. *v.* Bank Indosuez [1986] 2 Lloyd's Rep. 146 .... 3.50
Site Preparations Ltd *v.* Secretary of State for Scotland, 1975 S.L.T. (Notes) 41 .... 3.04
Skipscredittforeningen *v.* Emperor Navigation [1977] 2 All E.R. 257;
[1977] 2 B.C.L.C. 398 .... 1.03
Smail *v.* Potts (1847) 9 D. 1043 .... 4.85
Smallman Construction Ltd *v.* Redpath Dorman Long Ltd, 47 Build. L.R. 15;
25 Con. L.R. 105; (1989) 5 Const. L.J. 62, CA 4.331
Smith *v.* South Wales Switchgear [1978] 1 W.L.R. 165; (1977) 122 S.J. 61;
[1978] 1 All E.R. 18 (1977) 8 Build. L.R. 5, HL 3.22
Smith and Montgomery *v.* Johnson Bros & Co. Ltd (1954) 1 D.L.R. 392 .... 5.06
Sparham-Souter *v.* Town and Country Developments (Essex) [1976] Q.B. 858;
[1976] 2 W.L.R. 493; 120 S.J. 216; [1976] 2 All E.R. 65; 74 L.G.R. 355, CA;
[[1976] L.G.C. 247] 6.12
Speirs Ltd *v.* Peterson, 1924 S.C. 428 .... 4.06
Stanley Miller *v.* Ladhope, 1988 S.L.T. 514, OH 4.227
Steel Aviation Services Ltd *v.* H. Allan & Son Ltd, 1996 S.C. 427, 2 Div. 4.169
Steel *v.* Bell (1890) 3 F. 319; 8 S.L.T. 381 .... 4.229, 4.230,
4.235, 4.254
Steel (William) *v.* R.L. Young [1907] S.C. 360 .... 4.06, 4.08, 7.07
Sterling County Council *v.* Official Liquidator of John Frame Ltd,
1951 S.L.T. 37 .... 4.114
Stevenson *v.* Maule & Son, 1920 S.C. 335 .... 4.154
Stevenson's Trust *v.* Campbell & Sons (1896) 23 R. 711 .... 3.38
Stewart Gill Ltd *v.* Horatio Meyer & Co. Ltd [1992] Q.B. 600; [1992] 2 W.L.R. 721;
[1992] 2 All E.R. 257; (1991) 11 Tr. L.R. 86; 31 Con. L.R.; (1992)
142 New L.J. 241, CA 1.03, 3.65
Stewart Roofing Co. Ltd *v.* Shanlin, 1958 S.L.T. 53 .... 4.07, 4.08
Strachan & Henshaw Ltd *v.* Stein Industrie (U.K.) Ltd (No. 2), 87 Build. L.R. 52;
(1998) 14 Const. L.J. 370, CA 4.273

Strathclyde Regional Council *v.* Border Engineering Contractors Ltd,
  1997 S.C.L.R. 100, OH 4.12
Strathclyde Regional Council *v.* W.A. Fairhurst & Partners, 1997 S.L.T. 658, OH 3.91
Strathford East Kilbride *v.* H.L.M. Design Ltd, 1997 S.C.L.R. 877; 1997 Rep. L.R. 112;
  1997 G.W.D. 31–1554; *The Times,* December 1, 1997, OH 4.170, 5.09, 7.05
Stroud Architectural Systems *v.* John Laing Construction [1994] B.C.C. 18;
  [1994] 2 B.C.L.C. 276; 35 Con. L.R. 135; (1993) 9 Const. L.J. 337, QBD 4.130
Sumpter *v.* Hedges [1898] 1 Q.B. 673 .... 4.08, 4.09
Sunley *v.* Cunard White Star [1940] 1 K.B. 740 .... 4.290
Surrey Heath Borough Council *v.* Lovell Construction and Hasden Young
  48 Build. L.R. 108; 24 Con. L.R. 1; (1990) 6 Const. L.J. 179, CA affirming
  15 Con. L.R. 68; 42 Build. L.R. 25; (1988) 4 Const. L.J. 226 .... 4.143, 4.196
Surzur Overseas Ltd *v.* Ocean Reliance Shipping Co. Ltd (unreported) Q.B.D.
  (Com. Ct) Transcript 1977 F–No. 83 .... 1.03
Sutcliffe *v.* Thackrah [1974] A.C. 727; [1974] 2 W.L.R. 295; 118 S.J. 148; [1974]
  1 All E.R. 859; [1974] 1 Lloyd's Rep. 318, HL; reversing [1973] 1 W.L.R. 888;
  117 S.J. 509; [1973] 2 All E.R. 1047; [1973] 2 Lloyd's Rep. 115, CA 7.11, 7.12, 7.16
Sutherland *v.* Maton (C.R.) & Son [1976] J.P.L. 753; (1976) 240 E.G. 135;
  (1976) 3 Build. L.R. 87 .... 6.12
Sworn Securities *v.* Chilcott, 1977 S.L.T. 86 .... 4.135

Tatung (U.K.) *v.* Galex Telesure [1989] 5 B.C.C. 325 .... 4.130
Tay Valley Joinery *v.* C.F.C. Fire Services, 1987 S.L.T. 207 .... 3.75
Tay/Forth Premium Unit Consortium *v.* Secretary of Scotland, October 20, 1995, OH 3.07
Taylor *v.* Renn,79 Illinois 181 .... 4.209
Taylor Petitioner, 1982 S.L.T. 172 .... 4.330
Taylors *v.* Maclellans (1891) 19 R. 10 .... 4.239
Taymech *v.* Trafalgar House Construction (Regions) (O.H.), 1995 S.L.T. 202;
  1995 S.L.T. 1003; 1994 G.W.D. 7–42 .... 5.16
Temloc *v.* Erril Properties (1988) 39 Build. L.R. 30; (1988)
  4 Const. L.J. 63, CA 4.225, 4.226, 4.227, 4.242
Tennant Radiant Heat Ltd *v.* Warrington Development Corporation (1988) 11 E.G. 71;
  (1988) 4 Const. L.J. 321, CA 4.256
Tern Construction Group Ltd *v.* R.B.S. Garages Ltd (1992) 34 Con. L.R. 137 .... 4.10
Terson's Ltd *v.* Stevenage Development Corporation [1965] 1 Q.B. 37; [1964]
  2 W.L.R. 225; 107 S.J. 852; [1963] 3 All E.R. 863; [1963] 2 Lloyd's Rep. 333;
  [1963] R.A. 393, CA 4.233
Tesco Stores *v.* Norman Hitchcox Partnership Ltd; Clark Care Group Ltd *v.* Norman
  Hitchcox Partnership Ltd; Maidstone Grove Ltd *v.* Norman Hitchcox
  Partnership Ltd, 56 Con. L.R. 42, QBD (OR) 4.60
Tharsis Sulphur and Copper Co. Ltd *v.* McElroy & Sons (1878) 5 R. 171; (1878)
  3 App. Cas. 1040, HL 4.29, 4.30, 4.356, 5.37
Themehelp Ltd *v.* West [1996] Q.B. 84; [1995] 3 W.L.R. 751; [1995] 4 All E.R. 215;
  The Times, May 2, 1995; *The Independent,* June 26, 1995 (C.S.), CA 3.42
Thompson (John) Horsely Bridge Ltd *v.* Wellingborough Steel and Construction Co. Ltd,
  The Times, February 23, 1972, CA 3.52
Thompson (N.E.I.) *v.* Wimpey Construction (1987) 39 Build. L.R. 65, CA 3.67
Thorn *v.* London Corporation (1876) 1 A.C. 120 .... 4.83, 5.37, 5.39
Tiffney *v.* Bachurzewski, 1985 S.L.T. 165; 1984 S.C. 108 .... 4.278
Tinghamgrange Ltd (t/a Gryphonn Concrete Products) *v.* Dew Group Ltd and
  North West Water Ltd, 47 Con. L.R. 105, CA 4.274
Token Construction Co. Ltd *v.* Naviewland Properties Ltd, unreported May 11, 1972 ...... 3.52
Tony Cox (Dismantlers) Ltd *v.* Jim 5 Ltd (1997) 13 Const. L.J. 209, QBD (OR) 4.101
Tout & Finch Ltd, Re [1954] 1 W.L.R. 178; 98 S.J. 62; [1954] 1 All E.R. 127; 52 L.G.R. 70
  [18 Conv. (N.S.) 78] 3.77, 3.79

Townsend (Builders) Ltd v. Cinema News and Property Management Ltd; *sub nom.*
    Townsends (Builders) Ltd v. Cinema News and Property Management Ltd
    (David A. Wilkie & Partners Third Party) [1959] 1 W.L.R. 119; 123 J.P. 115;
    103 S.J. 74; 57 L.G.R. 174; [1959] 1 All E.R. 7; [1959] P.L. 109;
    103 S.J. 360, CA 4.46
Trafalgar House Construction (Regions) Ltd v. General Surety and Guarantee Co. Ltd
    [1995] 3 W.L.R. 204; [1995] 3 All E.R. 737; 73 Build. L.R. 32; 44 Con. L.R. 104;
    (1995) 139 S.J.L.B. 177; (1995) 92(28) L.S. Gaz.; (1995) 145 New L.J. Rep. 1221;
    The Times, July 4, 1995, HL; reversing 66 Build. L.R. 42; 38 Con. L.R. 53;
    (1994) 10 Const. L.J. 240, CA 3.34, 3.47,
                                                                                                                      3.48, 3.49, 4.320
Trentham (G. Percy) Ltd v. Beattie Williamson & Partners Ltd,
    1987 S.L.T. 449, OH 4.98, 7.18
Trollope and Colls and Holland & Hannen and Cubitts (t/a Nuclear Civil Constructors)
    (A Firm) v. Atomic Power Constructions [1963] 1 W.L.R. 833; 107 S.J. 254;
    [1962] 3 All E.R. 1035 .... 3.13
Turkiye IS Bankasi AS v. Bank of China [1993] 1 Lloyd's Rep. 132;
    [1994] 3 Bank. L.R. 34, QBD 3.42
Turnbull v. Liquidator of Scottish County Investment Co., 1939 S.C. 5;
    1938 S.L.T. 584 .... 4.319
Turner & Sons Ltd v. Mathind (1986) 5 Const. L.J. 273 .... 4.224
Turriff Construction v. Regalia Knitting Mills (1971) 22 E.G. 169 .... 3.13

UNIROYAL LTD v. MILER, 1985 S.L.T. 101 .... 3.17
University of Glasgow v. W. Whitfield and John Laing Const Ltd (1988)
    42 Build. L.R. 66 .... 5.44

VEITCHI CO. v. CROWLEY RUSSELL & CO., 1972 S.C. 225 .... 3.79
Vickers Oceanic Ltd v. Ross (Liquidator of Speedcranes Ltd), 1985 J.L.S. 85 .... 4.320
Victoria University of Manchester v. Hugh Wilson and Lewis Womersley and
    Pochin (Contractors) Ltd (1984) C.I.L.L. 206; [1985] Con. L.R. 43 .... 5.43, 5.44
Viking Grain Storage v. T.H. White (T.H.) Installations (1985) 33 Build. L.R. 103;
    [1985] C.I.L.L. 206; (1985) 3 Con. L.R. 52 .... 5.27
Virgin Interactive Entertainment (Europe) Ltd v. Bluewall Ltd [1998] Masons
    C. L.R. Rep. 83, Ch D 4.142
Visionhire v. Britel Fund Trustees Ltd, 1991 S.L.T. 883; 1992 S.C.L.R. 236 (1st Div.);
    affirming 1991 S.L.T. 347; 1991 S.C.L.R. 92 (OH) 4.209, 4.314

WADE v. WALTON, 1909 S.C. 571 .... 1.15, 4.88
Wagner Associates v. Joseph Dunn (Bottlers), 1986 S.L.T. 267 .... 4.24, 7.25
Walford v. Miles [1992] 2 W.L.R. 174 .... 3.13, 3.16, 3.18
Walter Lawrence & Son v. Commercial Union Properties (U.K.) Ltd [1984]
    4 Con. L.R. 37 .... 4.247
Wates Construction (South) v. Bredero Fleet, 63 Build. L.R. 133; 37 Con. L.R. 1 .... 4.78
Watson (W. & J.R.) Ltd v. Lothian Health Board, 1986 S.L.T. 292 .... 3.53
Watt v. Lord Advocate, 1979 S.L.T. 137 .... 4.389
Webster v. Lord Advocate, 1985 S.L.T. 361; 1985 S.C. 173; varying 1984 S.L.T. 13 ..... 4.43
Weldtech Equipment, Re [1991] B.C.C. 16; [1991] B.C.L.C. 393; *The Times,*
    December 7, 1990 .... 4.130
Wells v. Army & Navy Co-operative Society, 1902 86 L.T. 764 .... 4.230, 4.252
Wessex Regional Health Authority v. H.L.M. Design Ltd, 71 Build. L.R. 32;
    (1994) 10 Const. L.J. 165, QBD 4.55, 7.19
West v. Secretary of State for Scotland, 1992 S.L.T. 636; 1992 S.C. 385;
    1992 S.C.L.R. 504; [1992 S.L.T. (News) 257; 1993 S.L.T. (News) 51] (1st Div.);
    affirming 1991 S.C.L.R. 795 (OH) 4.388, 4.390

West Faulkner Associates *v.* Newham London Borough Council, 71 Build. L.R. 1;
    (1995) 11 Const. L.J. 157; [1994] E.G.C.S. 179; [1994] N.P.C. 142; *The Times,*
    November 16, 1994; *The Independent,* December 19, 1994 (C.S.), CA;
    affirming 61 Build. L.R. 81; (1993) Const. L.J. 232; [1992]
    E.G.C.S. 139, QBD 4.250, 4.308, 7.14
Westminster Corporation *v.* Jarvis (J.) & Sons *sub nom.* Westminster City Council *v.*
    Jarvis (J.) & Sons [1970] 1 W.L.R. 637; 68 L.G.R. 470; [1970] 1 All E.R. 943, HL;
    reversing *sub nom.* Jarvis (J.) & Sons *v.* Westminster City Council [1969] 1 W.L.R.
    1448; 113 S.J. 755; [1969] 3 All E.R. 1025, CA; reversing (1968) 118 New L.J. 590;
    The Times, June 18, 1968 .... 4.135, 4.136, 4.137
Westminster City Council *v.* Rema Construction (No. 2) (1990) 24 Con. L.R. 26 .... 4.332
Wharf Properties *v.* Eric Cumine Associates (No. 2) (1991) 7 Const. L.J. 251, PC 4.302
Whiteley *v.* Hilt [1918] 2 K.B. 808, CA 4.156
Whittal Builders *v.* Chester-le-Street District Council, 40 Build. L.R. 82;
    11 Con. L.R. 40, DC 4.292, 4.298
Wilkie *v.* Hamilton Lodging-House Co. (1902) 4 F. 951 .... 4.97
William Press Ltd (V) (1983) 20 B.L.R. 78 .... 4.137, 4.143
Tomkinson (William) *v.* Parochial Board Council of St Michael, 6 Const. L.J. 319 .... 4.53
Wilson *v.* Wallace and Connell (1859) 21 D. 306 .... 5.37
Wimpey Construction (U.K.) Ltd *v.* Martin Black & Co. (Wire Ropes) Ltd,
    1982 S.L.T. 239 .... 4.288, 4.293
Winnipeg Condominium Corporation No. 36 *v.* Bird Construction Co. Ltd and Smith
    Carter Partners, 74 Build. L.R. 1; 50 Con. L.R. 124; (1995) Const. L.J. 306,
    Sup. Ct (CAN) 6.02
Winterbottom *v.* Wright (1842) 10 M. & W. 109 .... 6.10
Wolf and Wolf *v.* Forfar Potato Co. 1984 S.L.T. 100 .... 2.10
Wraight Ltd *v.* P.H. & T. (Holdings) Ltd (1968) 13 Build. L.R. 27 .... 4.338

YORKSHIRE WATER AUTHORITY *V.* SIR ALFRED MCALPINE (NORTHERN) (1985)
    32 Build. L.R. 114 .... 4.250
Young & Martin Ltd *v.* McManus Childs Ltd [1969] 1 A.C. 454; [1968] 3 W.L.R. 630;
    112 S.J. 744; [1968] 2 All E.R. 169; 67 L.G.R. 1, HL; affirming *sub nom.* Prior *v.*
    McManus Childs [1967] C.L.Y. 354 .... 4.107, 4.374, 5.19, 5.20,
                                                                                5.24, 5.26, 5.28
Yuen Kun Yeu *v.* Attorney-General of Hong Kong [1988] A.C. 175 .... 6.07

TABLE OF STATUTES

1592 Compensation Act 3.56, 3.57, 3.58
1856 Mercantile Law Amendment Act
    (Scotland) (19 & 20 Vict., c. 60)—
    s. 8 .... 3.39
1889 Public Bodies Corrupt Practices Act
    (52 & 53 Vict., c. 69) 4.334
    Factors Act (52 & 53 Vict.,
    c. 45) 4.117, 4.118
    s. 2(1) 4.116, 4.118
    s. 5 .... 4.116, 4.118
1890 Factors (Scotland) Act (53 & 54
    Vict., c. 40 .... 4.117, 4.118
    s. 1(2) 4.116
1893 Sale of Goods Act (56 & 57 Vict.,
    c. 71) 4.104, 4.109,
                                4.114, 4.116,
                                4.121
    s. 25 .... 4.116, 4.121, 4.122
    (2) 4.117, 4.119
    (3) 4.117
    s. 61(4) 4.109
1906 Prevention of Corruption Act
    (6 Edw. 7, c. 34) 4.334
1907 Limited Partnership Act (7 Edw. 7,
    c. 24) 4.316
1916 Prevention of Corruption Act
    (6 & 7 Geo. 5, c. 64) 4.334
1930 Third Parties (Rights against
    Insurers) Act (20 & 21
    Geo. 5, c. 25) 4.318
1936 Public Health Act (26 Geo. 5 &
    1 Edw. 8, c. 49) 6.19
1948 Companies Act (11 & 12 Geo. 6, c. 38)—
    s. 302 .... 3.77
1959 Building (Scotland) Act (7 & 8
    Eliz. 2 c. 24) 4.44, 4.45, 5.42
    s. 10(i) 4.45
    s. 19A 4.45
1968 Sewerage (Scotland) Act (c. 47) 4.48
1972 Defective Premises Act
    (c. 35) 6.09, 6.17,
                                6.24, 6.25
    s. 1(1) **6.09**
    s. 3(1) **6.25**
    (2)(a) 6.25
    Administration of Justice
    (Scotland) Act (c. 59)—
    s. 3 .... 4.382

1973 Prescription and Limitation
    (Scotland) Act (c. 52) 2.07,
                                3.81, 3.82, 3.88
    s. 6 .... 3.82, 3.88
    (1) 3.82
    (a) 3.82
    s. 7 .... 3.90
    (1) 3.82
    (2) 3.82
    s. 10 .... 3.88
    s. 11(1) 3.82
    (2) 3.82
    (3) **3.82**
    (4) 3.90
1974 Health and Safety at Work,
    etc. Act (c. 37) 4.187
    ss. 2–8 .... 4.187
    s. 47 .... 4.187
    Control of Pollution Act
    (c. 40) 4.43
    s. 60 .... 4.43
    s. 61 .... 4.43
1975 Finance (No. 2) Act
    (c. 45) 2.03, 4.361
1977 Patents Act (c. 37)—
    s. 60 .... 4.72
    s. 61 .... 4.72
    Unfair Contract Terms Act
    (c. 50) 1.03, 1.24,
                                4.69
    s. 15(2)(a) 1.03
    (c) 1.03
    s. 17 .... 1.03
    s. 20 .... 4.107
    s. 21 .... 4.107
    s. 25(2) 1.03
    Sched. 2 .... 1.03
1979 Sale of Goods Act
    (c.54) 1.10, 4.107, 4.126,
                                4.127, 4.354, 5.22
    s. 14(2) 5.20
    s. 16 .... 4.104, 4.105
    s. 17 .... 4.104
    (1) **4.104**
    s. 18 .... 4.104, 4.106
    s. 19 .... 4.104, 4.121,
                                4.127
    s. 25 .... 4.123, 4.126

1980 Water (Scotland) Act (c. 45) . 4.48
　　Limitation Act (c. 58) 3.84
　　s. 14A 3.85
　　s. 14B(1) 3.84
1982 Supply of Goods and Services
　　Act (c. 29) 1.02, 1.10, 3.65,
　　　　　　　4.67, 4.107, 4.127, 5.23
　　Pt 1A 1.02, 4.107
　　s. 9(4)–(6) 4.70
　　s. 11A(3) 4.107
　　s. 11B 1.02, **4.127**
　　　　(2)(b) 4.129
　　s. 11D 1.02, 5.23
　　　　(5) 5.23
　　　　(6) 5.23
1983 Value Added Tax Act (c. 55) ... 4.100
1984 Roads (Scotland) Act (c. 54) 4.48
1985 Law Reform (Miscellaneous
　　Provisions) (Scotland)
　　Act (c. 73)—
　　s. 8 .... 1.08, 4.97
　　s. 9 .... 4.97
　　s. 10 .... 4.97
　　Companies Act (c. 6)—
　　s. 36B 2.08
　　s. 395 .... 4.130
　　s. 425 .... 4.326
　　Insolvency Act (c. 65)—
　　Pt II, Chap. III 4.324
1986 Latent Damage Act (c. 37)—
　　s. 1 .... 3.85
　　Gas Act (c. 44) 4.48
　　Insolvency Act (c. 45) 4.131,
　　　　　　　　　　　4.317, 4.331
　　Pt I 4.326
　　Pt II 4.324
　　s. 8(1)(a) 4.326
　　　　(3) **4.326**
　　　　(4) 4.326
　　s. 9(3)(a) 4.324
　　s. 11 .... 4.324, 4.332
　　s. 14(1)(a) 4.329
　　s. 29(2) 4.325
　　s. 51 .... 4.324, 4.325
　　s. 130(4) 4.318
　　s. 144 .... 4.318
　　s. 251 .... 4.324, 4.325
　　Bankruptcy (Scotland) Act
　　　(c. 66) 4.317
1987 Consumer Protection Act
　　(c. 43)—
　　Sched. 1 .... 3.84
1988 Income and Corporation Taxes
　　Act (c. 1)—
　　s. 567 .... 1.05

1989 Electricity Act (c. 29) 4.48
1990 Law Reform (Miscellaneous
　　Provisions) Act (e. 40)—
　　s. 66 .... 4.380
　　s. 72 .... 2.08
　　Sched. 7 .... 4.383
　　Environmental Protection
　　Act (c. 43) 4.43
　　s. 34 .... 4.43
　　s. 82 .... 4.43
1994 Value Added Tax Act (c. 23) 4.99
　　s. 30(2A) 4.100
　　Sched. 8 .... 4.100
　　Group 6 .... 4.100
　　Sale and Supply of Goods
　　Act (c. 35) 4.67, 4.107
　　s. 6 .... 1.02
　　s. 11A(3) 4.67
　　s. 11D 4.67, 4.69
　　　　(1) 4.68
　　　　(2) 4.67
　　　　(3) 4.67
　　　　(4) 4.69
　　　　(5) 4.69
　　　　(6) 4.69
　　　　(7) 4.69
　　　　(8) 4.69
　　　　(9) 4.69
　　s. 11E 4.67, 4.69
　　s. 11L 4.69
　　s. 72 .... 4.69
　　Sched. 1 .... 1.02
　　Local Government, etc. (Scotland)
　　Act (c. 39) 4.44, 4.334
1995 Requirements in Writing
　　(Scotland) Act (c. 7) 2.08
　　s. 1 .... 2.06
　　　　(3) 2.06
　　　　(4) 2.06
　　　　(5) 2.06
　　　　(7) 2.06
　　s. 2 .... 2.06
　　　　　(a)(iii) 2.07
　　　　(2) 2.09
　　　　(3) 2.06
　　s. 3(1) 2.08
　　s. 7(1) 2.06
　　　　(3) 2.06
　　s. 8(1) 2.06
　　　　(2) 2.06
　　　　(5) 2.06
　　Environment Act
　　　(c. 25) 4.43
　　Sale of Goods (Amendment) Act
　　　(c. 28) 4.105

1996 Arbitration Act (c. 23) 4.382
  s. 1(a) 8.25
  s. 42 .... 8.32
  Housing Grants, Construction
  and Regeneration Act
  (c. 53) 1.04, 1.09, 2.04,
      2.29, 3.51, 3.67, 3.69,
      3.81, 4.12, 4.14, 4.64, 4.76,
      4.173, 4.176, 4.341, 4.344,
      4.349, 4.350, 4.354,
      4.358, 7.03, 8.01, 8.15, 8.16,
      8.17, 8.18, 8.21, 8.23,
      8.24, 8.30, 8.32
  Pt II 1.04, 8.18
  s. 104 .... 4.374, 8.18
    (1) **1.04**
    (2) **1.04**, 8.18
    (4) 8.18
    (5) 8.18
      (a) 1.04
    (7) 1.04
  s. 105 .... 1.05, 8.18, 8.19
    (1) **1.05**
    (2) **1.05**
      (d) 8.18, 8.19
  s. 106 .... 1.05, 8.20
  s. 107 .... 1.05, 2.07, 8.21
    (2) 2.07
    (6) 2.07, 8.21
  s. 108 .... 4.27, 7.03, 8.22, 8.23, 8.26
    (1) 8.25
      (e) 8.24
      (f) 8.24
    (2) 8.25
    (2)(c) 8.23
    (3) 4.359, 8.23, 8.25
    (4) 8.25
    (5) 8.25

1996 Housing Grants, Construction and
  Regeneration Act — *cont.*
  s. 109 .... 1.04, 1.09, 2.04, 2.29,
     3.52, 4.12, 4.344, 7.03, 8.22, 8.31
    (2) 4.344, 8.30
    (3) 4.344, 8.30
  s. 110 .... 4.342, 4.344, 7.03,
      8.22, 8.32
    (1) 3.67, 4.349
    (2) 4.346, 4.349, 4.350
      (b) 8.32
      (b) 3.56, 8.32
  s. 111 .... 4.344, 4.347, 4.349,
      8.22, 8.32
    (1) **3.67**, 4.232
  s. 112 .... 3.68, 4.354,
      7.03, 8.22, 8.33
    (2) 4.35, 8.33
    (3) 8.33
    (4) 8.33
  s. 113 .... 5.15, 5.17, 8.22, 8.34
    (1) **8.34**
  s. 114 .... 7.03
  s. 115(4) 4.348
  s. 116 .... 4.347
  s. 150 .... 1.04
1997 Contract (Scotland) Act
  (c. 34) 1.07, 2.10
  s. 1 .... 2.10
    (1) 1.07
    (2) 1.07, 2.10
    (3) 1.07, 2.10
1998 Late Payment of Commercial
  Debts (Interest) Act
  (c. 20) 4.284, 4.342
  s. 8(1) 4.342
    (2) 4.342
  s. 11 .... 4.342

TABLE OF STATUTORY INSTRUMENTS

1961 Construction (Lifting Operations)
(S.I. 1961
No. 1581) 4.188
1975 Building Operations (Scotland)
Regulations (S.I. 1975
No. 549) 4.45
1984 Control of Noise (Codes of Practice
for Construction and Open
Sites) Order (S.I. 1984
No. 1992) 4.43
1985 Value Added Tax
(General) Regulations (S.I. 1985
No. 886) 4.99
1988 Construction Contracts (Scotland)
Exclusion Order (S.I. 1988
No. 686) 8.18
art. 3 .... 8.18
art. 4 .... 8.18
art. 5 .... 8.18
art. 6 .... 8.18
1989 Construction (Head Protection)
Regulations (S.I. 1989
No. 2209) 4.188
1990 Building (Scotland) Regulations
(S.I. 1990 No. 2179) 4.44,
5.42
Pts A–H 4.44
Pts J–K 4.44
Pts M–N 4.44
Pts P–T 4.44
reg. 10 .... 5.42
reg. 11 .... 5.42
1991 Building Forms (Scotland)
Regulations (S.I. 1991
No. 160) 5.42
Public Works Contracts Regulations
(S.I. 1991 No. 2680) 3.05,
3.08, 4.149
reg. 2.1 .... 3.09
reg. 10(2)(c) 3.12
Sched. 1 .... 3.09
1992 Health and Safety at Work
Regulations (S.I. 1992
No. 2051) 4.187
1993 Amendment to Building (Scotland)
Regulations (S.I. 1993
No. 1457) 4.44

1993 Chemicals (Hazard Information
and Packaging) Regulations
(S.I. 1993 No. 1746)—
reg. 7 .... 1.06
1994 Unfair Terms in Consumer Contracts
Regulations (S.I. 1994
No. 3159) 1.03
reg. 2(1) 1.03
reg. 4(1) 1.03
reg. 6 .... 1.03
Sched. 2 .... 1.03
(d) 1.03
Sched. 3 .... 1.03
para. 1(b) 1.03
para. 5 .... 1.03
Amendment to Building (Scotland)
Regulations (S.I. 1994
No. 1266) 4.44
Construction (Design and
Management) Regulations
(S.I. 1994 No. 3140) 1.06, 2.03,
4.20, 4.49, 4.50, 4.52, 4.145,
4.187, 4.188, 4.311, 8.19
reg. 2 .... 1.06
reg. 5 .... 4.49
reg. 10 .... 4.49, 4.187
reg. 15(4) **4.50**
(5) 4.50
reg. 16(1)(c) 4.49, 4.187
reg. 21 .... 4.49, 4.187
1995 Value Added Tax (Construction
of Buildings) Order (S.I. 1995
No. 280)—
art. 2 .... 4.100
Value Added Tax Regulations
(S.I. 1995 No. 2518) 4.99
reg. 89 .... 4.99
reg. 93 .... **4.99**
1996 Construction (Health, Safety
and Welfare) Regulations
(S.I. 1996 No. 1592) 4.188
Amendment to Building (Scotland)
Regulations (S.I. 1996
No. 2251) 4.44
1997 Amendment to Building (Scotland)
Regulations (S.I. 1997
No. 2157) 4.44

1998 Scheme for Construction Contracts
(Scotland) Regulations
(S.I. 1998 No. 687) 4.341,
4.344, 8.23
    reg. 2(1) 4.345
    reg. 4 .... 4.345
    reg. 8 .... 4.345
    reg. 9 .... 4.346
    reg. 10 .... 4.347
    reg. 12 .... 4.345

1998 Late Payment of Commercial
Debts (Interest) Act
(Commencement No. 1)
Order 1998 (S.I. 1998 No. 2479)—
    art. 2(2) 4.342
    Sched. 2 .... 4.342
    Late Payment of Commercial
Debts (Rate of Interest) (No. 2)
Order (S.I. 1998 No. 2765)—
    art. 4 .... 4.342

TABLE OF JCT AND OTHER CONTRACT FORMS

ICE 5th Contract 8.26
  cl. 66(2) 8.26
JCT 63 .... 2.02, 3.24, 3.26, 3.28, 3.33,
  3.53, 4.02, 4.18, 4.38, 4.60, 4.73,
  4.86, 4.122, 4.136, 4.165, 4.167,
  4.196, 4.199, 4.234, 4.235, 4.243,
  4.248, 4.249, 4.266, 4.267, 4.283,
  4.285, 4.286, 4.350, 4.354, 4.369,
  4.370, 4.372, 4.375, 4.376, 5.43,
            5.44, 7.17, 8.03
  cl. 11 .... 4.76, 4.88
    (6) 4.282, 4.283
  cl. 12 .... 3.28, 3.29
  cl. 12(1) 3.24, 3.26, 3.30, 3.33
  cl. 14 (July 1977) 4.121
    (1) 4.110
  cl. 15 .... 4.136, 4.137, 4.143
  cl. 15(1) 4.137
  cl. 16 .... 4.146
    (e) 4.146
  cl. 17 .... 4.162, 4.164
  cl. 23 .... 4.235, 4.268
  cl. 24 .... 4.268
  cl. 24(1) 4.237, 4.283
  cl. 25 .... 4.38, 4.308, 4.316
    (2) 4.332
    (4)(d) 3.44
  cl. 27 .... 4.372
    (c) 3.77
JCT 80 (with Quantities) 1.14, 1.23,
  2.02, 2.04, 2.17, 2.22, 2.29, 2.34, 3.24,
  3.25, 3.27, 3.33, 3.72, 3.74, 4.08, 4.10,
  4.13, 4.14, 4.37, 4.40, 4.48, 4.49, 4.53,
  4.54, 4.55, 4.62, 4.66, 4.82, 4.102,
  4.124, 4.132, 4.139, 4.176, 4.179,
  4.181, 4.188, 4.201, 4.203, 4.205,
  4.232, 4.233, 4.235, 4.240, 4.246,
  4.250, 4.258, 4.261, 4.271, 4.279,
  4.284, 4.285, 4.316, 4.333, 4.344,
  4.349, 4.349, 4.354, 4.358, 4.364,
  4.369, 4.370, 4.375, 4.394, 7.14, 8.05
  Pt 3 .... 4.375
  Pt 5 .... 1.11
  cl. 1 .... 4.13, 4.19
  cl. 1.1 .... 4.102
  cl. 1.2 .... 3.33
  cl. 1.2.2 .... 4.102

JCT 80 — cont.
  cl. 1.3 .... 4.287
  cl. 1.4 ..... 4.15, 4.56, 4.59, 4.102, 4.102
  cl. 1A 4.102
  cl. 1A.3 .... 4.102
  cl. 2 ... 4.19, 4.56, 4.57, 4.102, 4.207
  cl. 2.1 .... 4.57, 4.58, 4.59, 4.177
  cl. 2.2.1 .... **3.24**, 3.25, 3.33
  cl. 2.2.2 .... 4.66
  cl. 2.2.2.1 .... 2.13
  cl. 2.2.2.2 .... 4.97
  cl. 2.3 .... 4.24, 4.26, 4.45
  cl. 2.6.1 .... 5.33
  cl. 3 .... 4.25, 4.102
  cl. 4 .... 4.29, 4.56, 4.75
  cl. 4.1.1 .... 4.26, 4.77
  cl. 4.1.1.1 .... 4.76
  cl. 4.1.2 .... 4.27, 4.309
  cl. 4.2 .... 4.27
  cl. 4.2.5 .... 4.367
  cl. 4.3.1 .... 4.29
  cl. 5 .... 4.31, 4.102
  cl. 5.3.1.1 .... 4.277
  cl. 5.3.2. .... 3.28, 4.22, 4.31, 4.277
  cl. 5.4 .... 4.31
  cl. 5.4.1 .... 4.237
  cl. 5.4.2 .... 4.237
  cl. 5.5 .... 4.31
  cl. 5.6 .... 4.31
  cl. 5.7 .... 4.31
  cl. 6 .... 4.43
  cl. 6.1.1 .... 4.45
  cl. 6.1.3 .... 4.26
  cl. 6.1.5 .... 4.45
  cl. 6.1.6 .... 4.47
  cl. 6.1.7 .... 4.47
  cl. 6.3 .... 4.48
  cl. 6A 4.49, 4.188
  cl. 6A.1 .... 4.52
  cl. 6A.2 .... 4.50, 4.52
  cl. 6A.3 .... 4.52
  cl. 7 .... 4.26, 4.53, 4.102
  cl. 8 .... 4.21, 4.54, 4.56, 4.59,
         4.66, 4.75, 4.102, 4.207
  cl. 8.1.1 .... 4.57, 4.59, 4.65
  cl. 8.1.2 .... 4.59, 4.65
  cl. 8.2.2 .... 4.57, 4.59

JCT 80 — *cont.*
cl. 8.1.3 .... 4.20, 4.43, 4.57, 4.59
cl. 8.3 .... 4.26, 4.59
cl. 8.4 .... 4.26, 4.59
cl. 8.5 .... 4.59
cl. 8.4.1 .... 4.58
cl. 8.5 .... 4.26
cl. 9 .... 4.72
cl. 9.2 .... 4.72
cl. 10 .... 4.72, 4.73
cl. 11 .... 4.75
cl. 12 .... 4.26, 4.72, 4.73
cl. 13 .... 4.24, 4.75, 4.76, 4.88
cl. 13.1 .... 4.76, 4.82
cl. 13.1.1 .... 4.77, 4.78
cl. 13.1.2 .... 4.77
cl. 13.1.2.1 .... 4.76
cl. 13.1.2.2 .... 4.76
cl. 13.1.2.3 .... 4.76
cl. 13.1.2.4 .... 4.76
cl. 13.1.3 .... 4.77
cl. 13.2 .... 4.26
cl. 13.2.1 .... 4.82
cl. 13.2.2 .... 4.77
cl. 13.2.5 .... 4.82
cl. 13.3 .... 4.26
cl. 13.3.1.2 .... 4.78
cl. 13.4.1 .... 4.76
cl. 13.4.1.1 .... 4.25
cl. 13.4.1.2 .... 4.76
cl. 13.5 .... 4.81
cl. 13.5.1 .... 4.76, 4.78, 4.274
cl. 13.5.1.3 .... 4.78, 4.82
cl. 13.5.2 .... 4.76
cl. 13.5.3 .... 4.76
cl. 13.5.4 .... 4.76, 4.79, 4.82
cl. 13.5.5 .... 4.76
cl. 13.5.6 .... 4.76
cl. 13.5.7 .... 4.76, 4.274
cl. 13.7 .... 4.25
cl. 13A 2.03, 4.76, 4.76, 4.82, 4.271
cl. 14 .... 4.23, 4.97, 4.114
cl. 14.1 .... 3.25
cl. 14.2 .... 4.97
cl. 15 .... 4.99
cl. 15.2 .... 4.101
cl. 16 .... 4.103, 4.110, 4.124,
        4.132, 4.134, 4.354, 4.374, 8.31
cl. 16.1 ... 4.103, 4.124, 4.133, 4.134
cl. 16.2 .... 4.103, 4.114, 4.134
cl. 17 .... 4.135
cl. 17.2 .... 4.26, 4.53
cl. 17.3 .... 4.26
cl. 18 .... 4.210
cl. 18.1 .... 4.146

JCT 80 — *cont.*
cl. 18.1.4 .... 4.146, 4.146
cl. 19 .... 4.164, 4.174
cl. 19.1.1 .... 4.164, 4.310
cl. 19.1.2 .... 4.164
cl. 19.2 .... 4.155
cl. 19.2.1 .... 4.171
cl. 19.2.2 .... 4.171, 4.174, 4.310
cl. 19.3 .... 4.172, 4.340
cl. 19.4 ...... 4.132, 4.133, 4.172, 4.234
cl. 19.4.3 .... 4.172, 4.175
cl. 19.4.2 .... 4.110, 4.172
cl. 19.5.1 .... 4.174
cl. 19.5.2 .... 4.174
cl. 19A 4.173
cl. 20 .... 4.176, 4.196
cl. 20.1 .... 4.339
cl. 20.2 .... 4.194
cl. 20.3 .... 4.197
cl. 20.3.1 .... 4.196
cl. 21 .... 4.176, 4.179
cl. 21.2.1 .... 4.190
cl. 22 .... 4.176
cl. 22.2 .... 4.180, 4.197
cl. 22.2.2 .... 4.181, 4.184
cl. 22.3 .... 4.205
cl. 22.3.2 .... 4.202
cl. 22A 4.180, 4.184, 4.194
cl. 22A.1 .... 4.177
cl. 22B 4.134, 4.180, 4.184,
                        4.194, 4.197
cl. 22B.1 .... 4.177
cl. 22C 4.134, 4.180, 4.194, 4.197
cl. 22C.1 .... 4.177, 4.190, 4.196,
                  4.197, 4.198, 4.202
cl. 22C.2 .... 4.184, 4.197
cl. 22C.3 .... 4.194
cl. 22C.4.3.1 .... 4.194
cl. 22D 4.204
cl. 22FC 4.206
cl. 23 .... 4.207, 4.296
cl. 23.1 .... 4.210
cl. 23.1.1 .... 4.207
cl. 23.1.2 .... 4.207, 4.208, 4.276, 4.280
cl. 23.2 .... 4.26, 4.208
cl. 23.2.1 .... 4.288
cl. 23.3 .... 4.210
cl. 24 4.13, 4.102, 4.146, 4.211, 4.231
cl. 24.1 .... 4.231
cl. 24.2.1 .... 4.231, 4.232, 4.360
cl. 24.2.2 .... 4.234
cl. 24.2.3 .... 4.231
cl. 25 ..... 4.38, 4.48, 4.52, 4.139, 4.211,
        4.235, 4.237, 4.238, 4.239, 4.242,
                  4.270, 4.275, 4.288, 7.14

JCT 80 — cont.

cl. 25.1	4.242
cl. 25.2.1.1	4.237, 4.241, 4.242
cl. 25.2.2	4.13
cl. 25.2.2.2	4.242
cl. 25.3	4.13
cl. 25.3.1	4.242
cl. 25.3.2	4.271
cl. 25.3.3	4.242, 4.271
cl. 25.3.4.1	4.235, 4.240, 4.270, 4.275, 4.277
cl. 25.3.4.2	4.275
cl. 25.4	4.237, 4.237
cl. 25.4.5.1	4.24, 4.82
cl. 25.4.6	4.31
cl. 25.4.7	4.239, 4.373
cl. 25.4.11	4.48
cl. 25.4.13	4.207
cl. 25.4.16	4.246
cl. 25.4.18	4.354
cl. 26	4.336, 4.339
cl. 26.1	4.194
cl. 26.1.1	4.280
cl. 26.1.2	4.285
cl. 26.2	4.237, 4.276, 4.277, 4.280, 4.281
cl. 26.2.3	4.24
cl. 26.2.7	4.82
cl. 26.2.10	4.354
cl. 26.3	4.239
cl. 26.4.1	4.207
cl. 26.5	4.239
cl. 26.6	4.237, 4.273
cl. 27	1.16, 4.59, 4.66, 4.194, 4.305, 4.316, 4.338
cl. 27.2	4.305
cl. 27.2.1	4.306, 4.307, 4.312, 4.354
cl. 27.2.1.1	4.277, 4.306
cl. 27.2.1.2	4.306, 4.354
cl. 27.2.1.3	4.309
cl. 27.2.2	4.309, **4.312**, 4.313
cl. 27.2.3	4.309, **4.313**, 4.315
cl. 27.2.4	4.309
cl. 27.3.1	4.322
cl. 27.3.2	4.322
cl. 27.4	4.10, 4.102
cl. 27.4.2.2	3.76, 3.77, 3.78
cl. 27.5	4.125, 4.335
cl. 27.5.1	4.125, 4.335
cl. 27.5.2.1	4.335
cl. 27.5.2.2	4.335
cl. 27.5.4	4.335
cl. 27.5.5	4.336
cl. 27.5.6	4.336
cl. 27.6	4.305

JCT 80 — cont.

cl. 27.7	4.305
cl. 28	1.16, 3.52, 4.194, 4.337, 4.338
cl. 28.2.1.2	4.338, 4.350
cl. 28.2.1.3	4.338
cl. 28.3.1	4.338
cl. 28.3.3	4.338
cl. 28.4	4.338
cl. 28.5	4.337
cl. 28A	4.194, 4.337, 4.339
cl. 28A.5.5	4.339
cl. 29	4.340
cl. 30	4.194, 4.336, 4.341, 4.360, 7.09
cl. 30.1	4.175
cl. 30.1.1	3.52, 4.342
cl. 30.1.1.1	4.172, 4.234, 4.349
cl. 30.1.1.2	4.343
cl. 30.1.1.3	4.344, 4.349
cl. 30.1.1.4	4.232, 4.344
cl. 30 1.1.5	4.344, 4.349
cl. 30.1.1.6	4.351, 4.355
cl. 30.1.2.1	4.352
cl. 30.1.2.2	4.352
cl. 30.1.3	4.349, 4.353
cl. 30.1.4	4.237, 4.287, 4.306, 4.337, 4.354
cl. 30.2	4.352, 4.355
cl. 30.2.1	4.356
cl. 30.2.1.1	4.356
cl. 30.4	8.17
cl. 30.5	8.17
cl. 30.6.1	4.285
cl. 30.7	4.353
cl. 30.8	4.353
cl. 30.8.3	4.232
cl. 30.9	4.398
cl. 30.9.1	4.359
cl. 30.9.3	4.359
cl. 30.9.4	4.359
cl. 30.10.1	4.56
cl. 30.11	4.360
cl. 30.12.1	4.360
cl. 30.12.2	4.360
cl. 30.12.3	4.360
cl. 30.12.4	4.360
cl. 30.12.5	4.360
cl. 30.3	4.114, 4.132, 4.134
cl. 30.4	2.07, 4.357
cl. 30.5	2.07, 4.357
cl. 30.7	4.358
cl. 30.8	4.279, 4.358
cl. 30.9.1.1	4.15, 4.59
cl. 31	4.361
cl. 31.1.4	3.52

JCT 80 — *cont.*
cl. 32 .... 4.362
cl. 33 .... 4.362
cl. 34 .... 4.363
cl. 34.2 .... 4.26
cl. 35 .... 4.26, 4.340, 4.364, 4.368
cl. 35.2 .... 4.174
cl. 35.4 .... 4.364
cl. 35.13.5 .... 3.76
cl. 35.13.5.3 .... 3.78
cl. 35.15 .... 4.373
cl. 35.20 .... 4.368
cl. 35.21 .... 4.367
cl. 35.21.1 .... **4.367**
cl. 35.21.2 .... **4.367**
cl. 35.21.3 .... **4.367**
cl. 35.21.4 .... **4.367**
cl. 35.24 .... 4.369, 4.370
cl. 35.24.10 .... 4.371
cl. 36 .... 4.26, 4.374, 5.21
cl. 36.4 .... 4.374, 5.21
cl. 36.5 .... 5.21
cl. 37 .... 4.375
cl. 38 .... 4.375, 4.377
cl. 38.2 .... 4.375
cl. 38.2.3 .... 4.375
cl. 38.2.3.3 .... 4.375
cl. 38.4.7 .... 4.242
cl. 39 .... 4.375, 4.376, 4.377
cl. 39.3 .... 4.376
cl. 39.5.7 .... 4.242, 4.376
cl. 39.7.2 .... 4.376
cl. 40 .... 4.375, 4.377
cl. 40.7 .... 4.242
cl. 41.3.3 .... 4.82
cl. 41A 3.52, 4.378, 4.379
cl. 41B 3.52, 4.378, 4.380
cl. 41B.2 .... 4.383
cl. 41B.6 .... 4.383
cl. 41B.6.1 .... 4.383
cl. 41C 3.52, 4.378
cl. 42 .... 2.03, 4.21, 4.47,
                                4.394, 4.398
cl. 42.5 .... 4.398
cl. 42.6 .... 4.398
cl. 42.17 .... 4.396
cl. 42.17.1 .... 1.11, 4.21
cl. 42.17.1.1 .... 4.21
cl. 42 17.1.2 .... 4.21
cl. 42.17.2 .... 4.396
JCT 81 with Contractor's Design 3.14,
                                3.45, 4.196, 5.33
cl. 2.5.1 .... 5.33
cl. 27.4.3.2 .... 3.78
JCT Conditions 4.03

JCT Intermediate Form of Contract
  (1984) 2.34
JCT Minor Works Form 4.203
JCT Standard Form of Management
  Contract (1987 Ed.) 2.26, 3.69
JCT Standard Form of Prime Cost
  Contract (1992 Ed.) 2.27
JCT Standard Form of Tender
  (1992) 4.374
  Sched. 1 .... 4.374
  Sched. 2 .... 4.374
  Sched. 3 .... 4.374
SBC Contractor's Designed Portion   2.21
SBC Model Supplementary
  Agreement (1994) 2.02
SBC (September 1997)—
  cl. 41.3.2 .... 4.27
SBC with Quantities (August 1998)
  (SBC) 2.17, 4.01, 4.03,
                        4.14, 4.15,
                                4.41
  cl. 1 .... 4.15
  cl. 2.1 .... 4.15
  cl. 5.4 .... 4.41
  cl. 54.1 .... 4.41
  cl. 5.4.2 .... 4.41
  cl. 25.4.6.1 .... 4.41
  cl. 25.4.6.2 .... 4.41
  cl. 26.2.1.1 .... 4.41
  cl. 26.2.1.2 .... 4.41
  cl. 27 .... 4.331
  cl. 27.3.1 .... 4.321
  cl. 27.3.2 .... 4.321, 4.331
  cl. 27.3.3 .... 4.331
  cl. 27.3.4 .... 4.331
  cl. 27.4 .... 4.334
  cl. 30.9.3 .... 3.84
  cl. 41A 4.27
  cl. 41A.5.2 .... 4.348
  cl. 41B 4.27, 4.383
  cl. 41C 4.27
  App I (Scottish Supp.) 4.03
  App II (Abstract of
    Conditions) 4.03, 4.13
SBC without Quantities 2.18
SBC with approximate Quantities .. 2.19
SBC with Contractor's Design 2.22
SBC Sectional Completion
  Edition 2.20
Scottish Building Agreement—
  cl. 41A.8.4 .... 2.08
Scottish Building Contract —
  Prime Cost Contract 2.27
Scottish Management Contract
  Phased Completion Edition 2.26

Scottish Measured Term Contract
  for Maintenance and Minor
  Works (April 1998) 2.25
Scottish Minor Works Contract
  (1986 Ed.) 2.29
Standard Method of Measurement of
  Building Works (7th Ed.)
  (SMM 7).............. 2.13, 2.15, 2.16
  cl. 1.1 .... **2.13**
  cl. 1.2 .... 2.14
  r. 10.1 .... 2.14, 4.13

Standard Method of Measurement — *cont.*
  r. 10.2 .... 2.14, 4.13
  r. 10.3 .... 2.14, 4.13
  r. 10.4 .... 4.13
  r. 10.5 .... 2.14, 4.13
  r. 10.6 .... 4.13
  cl. 13 .... 2.16
  cl. 13.5.1–13.5.7 .... 2.16
Standard Method of Measurement
  of Building Works
  (August 1998) 2.17, 2.19

CHAPTER 1

WHAT MAKES BUILDING OR CONSTRUCTION CONTRACTS DISTINCTIVE?

INTRODUCTION

Academic and judicial comments

A building or construction contract, like any other contract, may be   1.01
considered in the light of a suitable definition of what a contract is. There is
scope for academic debate as to what a suitable definition of a contract
should be, but Professor A. D. Gibb's definition that:

> "a contract is an agreement between parties having the capacity to make it,
> in the form demanded by the law, to perform, on one side or both, acts which
> are not trifling, indeterminate, impossible or illegal, creating an obligation
> enforceable in a court of law",[1]

is as relevant to a construction contract as to any other. This definition,
however, does not take into account obligations created by the promise of
one party (which are also known as unilateral gratuitous obligations) and
which may be enforced against the promiser in Scotland, without the need
for consideration, as would be required in England.[2]

Similarly, as regards the appropriate legal rules for judicial construction
and interpretation of a building contract, Lord Morris of Borth-y-Gest stated
in *Gilbert Ash (Northern) Ltd v. Modern Engineering (Bristol) Ltd*[3]:

> "When parties enter into a detailed building contract there are no overriding
> rules beyond those which generally apply to the construction of contracts."

Recently, Lord Lloyd stated in the Lords[4]:

---

[1] Quoted in Burns and Quaar, *Commercial Law of Scotland* (3rd ed., Wm. Hodge), p. 1.
[2] Since August 1995 in terms of the Requirements of Writing (Scotland) Act 1995, s.
 1(2)(a)(ii), unless a promise is made in the course of business, writing is required for the
 constitution of a promise. To be formally valid, subscription by the promiser will be
 sufficient: s. 2(1).
[3] [1974] A.C. 689 at 699, [1973] 3 All E.R. 195, HL.
[4] *Beaufort Developments (N.I.) Ltd v. Gilbert-Ash N.I. Ltd*, reported on May 20, 1998 on the
 House of Lords website: http://www.parliament.the-stationery-office.co.uk/pa/ld199798/
 ldjudgmt/jd980520/beau01.htm.Hard copy [1998] 2 All E.R. 778.

"Standard forms of building contract have often been criticised by the courts for being unnecessarily obscure and verbose. But in fairness one should add that it is sometimes the courts themselves who have added to the difficulty by treating building contracts as if they were subject to special rules of their own."

RELEVANT STATUTORY CONSIDERATIONS

Supply of Goods and Services Act 1982

1.02 In Scotland a construction contract may be a "contract for the transfer of goods" in terms of the Supply of Goods and Services Act 1982, Part 1A, whether or not services are also provided,[5] if one party transfers or agrees to transfer property in goods to another. The effect of this is that there are now terms that will be implied into a construction contract by statute about title,[6] and quality or fitness for any particular purpose of goods supplied.[7]

Unfair Contract Terms Act 1977 and Unfair Terms in Consumer Contracts Regulations 1994

1.03 A construction contract may also be one which "relates to the transfer of ownership or possession of goods from one person to another (with or without work having been done on them)",[8] or "relates to services of whatever kind",[9] or a "consumer contract" in terms of the Unfair Contract Terms Act 1977[10] and the Unfair Terms in Consumer Contracts Regulations 1994,[11] or a "standard

---

[5] Part 1A, Supply of Goods as Respects Scotland, introduced by the Sale and Supply of Goods Act 1994, s. 6 and Sched. 1.

[6] *ibid*. s. 11B.

[7] *ibid*. s. 11D

[8] Unfair Contract Terms Act 1977, s. 15(2)(a).

[9] *ibid*. s. 15(2)(c).

[10] *ibid*. s. 25(2); provided the contract is not a contract of sale by competitive tender.

[11] S.I. 1994 No. 3159. Note that in terms of reg. 2(1) a consumer must be a natural person, which will restrict the applicability of the Regulations in a construction context. The Regulations are in other respects more far-reaching than the Act as an "unfair term" means any term which is "contrary to the requirement of good faith (and) causes a significant imbalance in the parties' rights and obligations under the contract to the detriment of the consumer" *per* reg. 4(1). Schedule 2 to the Regulations provides that regard shall be had to particular matters in the assessment of good faith including "the extent to which the seller or supplier has dealt fairly and equitably with the consumer" *per* Sched. 2(d). Regulation 6 provides that: "A seller or supplier shall ensure that any written term of a contract is expressed in plain and intelligible language, and if there is doubt about the meaning of a written term, the interpretation most favourable to the consumer shall prevail." Also, Sched. 3 provides an illustrative and indicative list of terms which may be regarded as unfair (and therefore not binding under para. 5) which are wider than those set out in Sched. 2 to the Act concerning reasonableness, and includes set-off by the seller (Sched. 3, para. 1(b)). Certain exclusions

form contract"[12] in terms of that Act. If a construction contract is a "consumer contract" or a "standard form contract"[13] under the 1977 Act then it will be subject to section 17. Section 17 applies the "fair and reasonable" test to exclusions or restrictions of liability for breach of contract to the prejudice of the consumer or customer. The same section also applies the same test to a contractual obligation to render no performance, or to render a performance substantially different from that which the consumer or customer reasonably expected from the contract.

Housing Grants, Construction and Regeneration Act 1996

Recently there has been a highly significant piece of legislation enacted concerning the construction industry, and which regulates certain terms in construction contracts. In terms of Part II of the Housing Grants, Construction and Regeneration Act 1996 (HGCRA),[14] a construction contract is defined as follows: 1.04

> "104.—(1) In this Part a 'construction contract' means an agreement with a person for any of the following —
> (a) the carrying out of construction operations;
> (b) arranging for the carrying out of construction operations by others, whether under sub-contract to him or otherwise;
> (c) providing for his own labour, or the labour of others, for the carrying out of construction operations.
> (2) References in this Part to a construction contract include an agreement —
> (a) to do architectural, design or surveying work, or
> (b) to provide advice on building, engineering, interior or exterior decoration or on the laying-out of landscape,
> in relation to construction operations."

This definition applies to England, Wales and Scotland,[15] and to construction contracts which are entered into after the commencement date of May 1, 1998.

Section 105 of HGCRA gives a detailed definition of "construction operations" and what are not "construction operations", with the definition largely drawn from section 567 of the Income and Corporation Taxes Act 1988 as follows: 1.05

---

of set-off terms had been held to be unreasonable under the Act in the construction context in *Stewart Gill Ltd v. Horatio Myer & Co. Ltd* [1992] 2 All E.R. 257, but not followed in other types of contract: see *Skipskredittforeningen v. Emperor Navigation* [1977] 2 B.C.L.C. 398 and *Surzur Overseas Ltd v. Ocean Reliance Shipping Co. Ltd* (unreported) (QBD (Comm. Ct) Transcript 1977 F-No. 83.
12   Not defined in the Act, but see *McCrone v. Boots Farm Sales Ltd*, 1981 S.L.T. (O.H.) 103.
13   In *Chester Grosvenor Hotel Co. Ltd v. Alfred McAlpine Management Ltd and Ors* (1991) 56 B.L.R. 115 the plaintiffs were held not to be a consumer under the Act on the basis that they had entered into the contracts as part of their business. However the contracts (non-JCT forms) were held to be standard forms of contract, and a clause which excluded liability beyond sums recovered from the construction contractors was not unreasonable.
14   c. 53.
15   ss. 104(5)(a) and (7) and s. 150.

"105.—(1) In this part 'construction operations' means, subject as follows, operations of any of the following descriptions —

(a) construction, alteration, repair, maintenance, extension, demolition or dismantling of buildings, or structures forming, or to form, part of the land (whether permanent or not);

(b) construction, alteration, repair, maintenance, extension, demolition or dismantling of any works forming or to form, part of the land, including (without prejudice to the foregoing) walls, roadworks, power-lines, telecommunication apparatus, aircraft runways, docks and harbours, railways, inland waterways, pipe-lines, reservoirs, water-mains, wells, sewers, industrial plant and installations for purposes of land drainage, coast protection or defence;

(c) installation in any building or structure of fittings forming part of the land, including (without prejudice to the foregoing) systems of heating, lighting, air-conditioning, ventilation, power supply, drainage, sanitation, water supply or fire protection, or security or communications systems;

(d) external or internal cleaning of buildings and structures, so far as carried out in the course of their construction, alteration, repair, extension or restoration;

(e) operations which form an integral part of, or are preparatory to, or are for rendering complete, such operations as are previously described in this subsection, including site clearance, earthmoving, excavation, tunnelling and boring, laying of foundations, erection, maintenance or dismantling of scaffolding, site restoration, landscaping and the provision of roadways and other access works;

(f) painting or decorating the internal or external surfaces of any building or structure.

(2) The following operations are not construction within the meaning of this Part —

(a) drilling for, or extraction of, oil or natural gas;

(b) extraction (whether by underground or surface working) of minerals; tunnelling or boring, or construction of underground works, for this purpose;

(c) assembly, installation or demolition of plant or machinery, or erection or demolition of steelwork for the purposes of supporting or providing access to plant or machinery, on a site where the primary activity is —
  (i) nuclear processing, power generation, or water or effluent treatment, or
  (ii) the production, transmission, processing or bulk storage (other than warehousing) of chemicals, pharmaceuticals, oil, gas, steel or food and drink;

(d) manufacture or delivery to site of —
  (i) building or engineering components or equipment,
  (ii) materials, plant or machinery, or
  (iii) components for systems of heating, lighting, air-conditioning, ventilation, power supply, drainage, sanitation, water supply or fire protection, or for security or communications systems, except under a contract which also provides for their installation;

    (e)   the making, installation and repair of artistic works, being sculptures, murals and other works which are wholly artistic in nature."

The provisions of the Act do not apply to a construction contract with a residential occupier,[16] and only where the construction contract is in writing.[17] The effect of this legislation is discussed further in the text.[18]

Construction (Design and Management) Regulations 1994

Specific safety legislation affects the construction industry. In terms of the Construction (Design and Management) Regulations 1994,[19] a different definition of "construction work" is given.[20-21]   1.06

Contract (Scotland) Act 1997[22]

This short Act is also relevant for construction contracts in relation to admissibility of oral or documentary evidence for the proof of additional express terms of a contract or a unilateral voluntary obligation,[23] but also any term to the effect that all the express terms are documented — a so-called "entire agreement" clause — is made conclusive by section 1(3).   1.07

---

[16] s. 106.
[17] s. 107.
[18] See Chaps 4 and 8 *passim.*
[19] S.I. 1994 No. 3140.
[20-21] The Construction (Design and Management) Regulations 1994, reg. 2: "construction work" means the carrying out of any building, civil engineering or engineering construction work and includes any of the following — (a) the construction, alteration, conversion, fitting out, commissioning, renovation, repair, upkeep, redecoration or other maintenance (including cleaning which involves the use of water or an abrasive at high pressure or the use of substances classified as corrosive or toxic for the purposes of regulation 7 of the Chemicals (Hazard Information and Packaging) Regulations 1993), de-commissioning, demolition or dismantling of a structure, (b) the preparation for an intended structure, including site clearance, exploration, investigation (but not site survey) and excavation, and laying or installing the foundations of a structure, (c) the assembly of prefabricated elements to form a structure or the disassembly of prefabricated elements which, immediately before such disassembly, formed a structure, (d) the removal of a structure or part of a structure or of any product or waste resulting from demolition or dismantling of a structure or from disassembly of prefabricated elements which, immediately before such disassembly, formed a structure, and (e) the installation, commissioning, maintenance, repair or removal of mechanical, electrical, gas, compressed air, hydraulic telecommunications, computer or similar services which are normally fixed within or to a structure, but does not include the exploration or extraction of mineral resources or activities preparatory thereto carried out at a place where such exploration or extraction is carried out."
[22] c. 34.
[23] ss. 1(1) and (2).

Law Reform (Miscellaneous Provisions) (Scotland) Act 1985, s. 8

1.08   This Act gives the Court of Session or the Sheriff statutory power to rectify a document in any manner the court may specify to give effect to a document which fails to accurately express the common intentions of the parties.

COMMON LAW CONSIDERATIONS

General

1.09   As well as these statutory aspects, there are a range of special difficulties at common law that arise from the very nature of building contracts. These difficulties might be identified by separating out typical problem areas. A building contract can typically involve:

(1) the carrying out by an independent contractor of works which may or may not have been designed to any extent by him;

(2) and over which he may or may not have to exercise to any extent an element of choice in carrying out the works to effect the design;

(3) with the provision of materials which may or may not be manufactured, supplied or designed to any extent by him; and which require to conform to a statutory standard, or a higher contractual standard;

(4) and which materials over the course of time are to become incorporated into heritable property, and where defects in workmanship, materials, or design, may not become apparent until long after the works are carried out.

(5) Part of these works might be assigned or sub-let by the contractor, or he may have to accept their assignation or sub-letting to others; and part of the works may fall within the exclusive jurisdiction of certain statutory bodies.

(6) There may or may not be complex provisions as to valuation of, payment for and completion of the works, or any part of them (and since the HGCRA such provisions have to conform to a statutory position);

(7) which may be subject to the approval of a third party to the contract;

(8) and provisions as to when these works might be taken over by the employer, and the effect of taking over the works;

(9) and for payment, delivery, possession and title to materials;

(10) which may be subject to the security rights of third parties;

(11) or the intellectual property rights of third parties.

(12) There may be a number of parties joined in contractual relationships; or having an interest or role in the contractual relationships of others;

(13) or in such close proximity that duties of care at common law arise in delict independently of contract.

(14) Obligations may arise expressly or impliedly under contract, or under delict, or concurrently in both; and correspondingly, obligations can extinguish.

(15) The contract may be affected by E.U. law, U.K. law, and secondary legislation such as building regulations;

(16) and obligations may exist under the law of restitution.

(17) There are also likely to be provisions for variation of the works;
(18) provisions within the contract specifying occurrences that might otherwise be breaches of contract so as to allow for more time to be given, or money to be paid, to the contractor where progress is hindered;
(19) provisions that enable the employer to claim liquidate and ascertained damages from the contractor in the event of delay;
(20) provisions to safeguard the employer in the event of the contractor's failure to complete at all;
(21) a dispute resolution mechanism to avoid court proceedings.

Given that these are indicative of areas where problem issues might arise, and bearing in mind that the construction industry operates on a worldwide scale, and in the U.K. straddles two distinct legal systems which have much in common, but in the final analysis a separate jurisprudence, it is not surprising that the Scottish legal perspective will produce differences in important respects from the English position, and an important source of comparative law with other jurisdictions.

Roman law classifications: contracts of location

A classical Scottish analysis of what type of contract a building contract is would involve an analysis of the writings of Institutional Writers who systematically expounded on Scots law, drawing on the law of ancient Rome, to establish principles from which Scots common law is derived. The Roman Jurists distinguished between contracts of sale and contracts of hire. However, there is no detailed analysis among the ancients of the difficulties that exist under building contracts.[24] There were three types of contract of hire. The first was the hire or letting of property, heritable or moveable, for the use of and enjoyment of another (*locatio conductio rei*). The second was the hiring out of one's labour or services (*locatio conductio operarum*). The third would be the letting of one's property for work to be done to it or on it (*locatio conductio operis*). The different types of contract had different effects relating to the risks which might arise, *e.g.* destruction of the subjects.[25] However, the ancients did not fully analyse the effects for building contracts, which could fall into the second or third categories, and be further complicated by the question of who provides the materials that get fixed to land — the employer or the contractor. Indeed there was also a question of whether the services hired out were subject to supervision, or provided as professional services by a member of the upper classes. One of the crucial differences between sale and contracts of hire related to the passing of property in goods. Many of these analytical distinctions have become less

1.10

---

[24] Nichols, *Introduction to Roman Law* (Clarendon Press), p. 183.
[25] For example, in the case of the destruction of a partially constructed brick wall by a gale the risk was with the employer, *McIntyre & Co. v. Clow* (1875) 2 R. 278, following Roman law (Dig. 1. 19, tit. 2, lex 59).

important with the recent application of the Supply of Goods and Services Act 1982 (introduced in Scotland in 1994)[26] which introduces implied terms as to the quality, fitness for purpose, right to transfer title, and quiet possession of goods transferred under a building contract, similar to the long-established implied terms for the sale of goods. However, difficulties remain as to when title to property passes along a chain of contracts and sub-contracts and suppliers' contracts, some of which will be covered by the Sale of Goods Act 1979, some by the Supply of Goods and Services Act 1982, and there might be common law considerations.[27]

Contracts for hire of labour

1.11   Bell in his *Principles*[28] distinguishes between the hiring of ordinary labour,[29] the hiring of skilled labour[30] and the hiring of artisans who are hired for labour to be performed in a factory along with other workmen.[31] With respect to the hiring of ordinary labour he writes[32]:

> "This strictly is an engagement to do certain work on materials furnished to the workman, the material being 'bailed' or delivered to the temporary possession of the workman, to have labour bestowed on it. Where the thing is to be prepared for materials to be furnished by the workman (as in the general case of manufactures), the contract partakes of sale. It is the executory sale of the English law.'

Bell distinguishes between ordinary and skilled labour. With respect to the latter he writes: "the engagement is to bestow attention, art and skill on the act to be performed; skill being presumed in all professional persons".[33] However, he appears to view contractors as ordinary labour, but it is submitted that perhaps much would depend on the degree of skill employed by a contractor, whether there is a design element provided by the contractor, or works have to perform to a certain specified level.[34]

Title to materials at Scots common law

1.12   One of the main issues that arise at common law with building contracts concerns whether ownership of materials passes to the employer under a

---

[26] See p. 2, n. 5.
[27] See discussion of cl. 16 of JCT 80 at paras 4.103 *et seq.*
[28] Bell, *Principles of the Law of Scotland* (10th ed., 1899), Book 1, Chap. III.
[29] *ibid.* paras. 146 *et seq.*
[30] *ibid.* paras. 153 *et seq.*
[31] *ibid.* para. 190.
[32] Bell's *Principles, op. cit.*, para. 147.
[33] *ibid.*, para. 153.
[34] For example, under Part 5 of JCT 80 for Performance Specified Work. Clause 42.17.1 requires the Contractor to exercise reasonable skill and care in the provision of Performance Specified Work.

building contract or any sub-contract if materials are delivered to site but not yet used in the building operations. The answer seems to be that property does not pass on delivery alone till the work is done.[35] In Bell's *Commentaries*[36] however he seems to indicate that it may be a question of judgment:

> "Where the contract of sale is complicated with *locatio operarum*, it does not seem to be settled whether mere delivery of the materials be sufficient to transfer. If, intending to build a house, I purchase the materials, and employ a mason and a carpenter to construct and fashion to my wish, the materials, the stone, the lime, and the wood, when brought upon my premises, are actually delivered to me, independently of the operations of the builder and carpenter. There are here two contracts distinct — a contract of sale, and a contract of *locatio operarum* — which may be completed independently of each other. But if I contract with a builder, and he procure the materials, are those materials, when laid down on my ground or deposited in my sheds, actually delivered, although the final act, which was to close the workman's undertaking, and to complete the transfer of the particular materials, is unperformed? In the more complex machines, it is necessary not only to have the wheels, etc., properly prepared and nicely fitted, but to have a person of skill to erect them in the place where the engine is to be used. Watt and Boulton, for example, when they receive an order for a steam engine, not only send the various parts of the engine, but send persons along with it properly qualified to place the work. In the same way, where a machine is to be improved, or, having received injury, any of the wheels are to be taken off and others substituted, the engineer does not hold his order as completed merely by sending the necessary wheels, but he sends a workman to put them up. On the other hand, it often happens that, in large manufactories, engineers are kept by the manufacturer for the purpose of attending to the machinery; in which case, the person who furnishes the wheels, etc., is not required to send a person to place them. In cases of this kind, the determination may often be difficult; but probably a distinction would be made between vendition simple, and when complicated with the contract of *locatio operarum*. Wherever the contract is fairly resolvable into simple vendition, the possession of the thing ordered, the delivery of it upon the premises of the vendee, seems to be sufficient as an absolute and perfect transference. Where again it is resolvable into a contract for performance of a particular act or piece of labour, of which the articles sent are merely the materials, the act of delivery seems not to complete till the work be performed."

---

[35] *Seath v. Moore* (1886) 13 R. (H.L.).
[36] Part III, Chap. II at p. 193.

An executory sale

1.13   In *Greig v. Kennedy*[37] there was a pre-SBCC/JCT form of building
contract where a builder undertook to modernise an employer's bathroom
and supply a new bath selected by the employer. The bath proved defective
as enamel deteriorated and the manufacturer supplied a new bath free of
charge. The builder refused to fit it free of charge. The sheriff decided the
case as a straightforward breach of a contract to instal a good bath, and
not two separable contracts merely because the employer had selected
the bath:

> "I have had some doubt, as I have said, as to whether the item of the bath can
> be separated from the rest of the contract and treated as a 'Sale of Goods'. As
> I indicated at the debate, I tended to regard the transaction as a whole, like a
> building contract, in which the contractor supplied the labour and the materials
> — what I think Professor Bell (*Principles*, 10th edition, p. 147) would have
> called an executory sale."

Bell was not, of course, speaking of building contracts particularly, as his
example was to "manufactures", *e.g.* the construction of a train, "where the
thing [author's emphasis] is to be prepared of materials furnished by the
workman". The problem with building contracts is that they involve the
construction on land, which is possibly a different matter from the
construction of a thing. It is submitted that Bell's notion of an executory
sale is one which involves work on the materials themselves, and it is a
different matter when materials such as stone or wood or slates are to be
incorporated into a building. On the subject of risk Bell writes:

> "In proper *locatio operis*, where the subject on which the work is to be
> bestowed belongs to the employer, the risk is with the employer — *res
> perit domino*. The hire is not forfeited, or repayment demandable, if the
> thing should, without fault of the workman, perish with the work on it.[38]
> Such is the case of ... building work performed on the ground of the
> employer[39] .... But if the workman be hired to accomplish some particular
> operation which he undertakes to do for a specific sum, and the whole
> perishes before he has completed his undertaking, *i.e.* in the phraseology
> of the English law, if the contract be *entire*,[39-40] the loss of his work would
> seem to fall on him; yet in those cases of executory contracts where the
> price is paid periodically, and the subject appropriated to the employer at
> the several payments, the whole would perish to the employer. If the
> workman is to make an article of manufacture of materials to be found by
> himself, the risk is with the workman, and the unfinished work perishes to

---

[37] 1953 S.L.T. (Sh. Ct.) 7 at 9.
[38] Pothier, *Traite du Contrat de Louage* (M. Bugnet, ed., 1864).
[39-40] *McIntyre & Co. v. Clow & Co.* (1875) 2 R. 278; *Richardson v. Dumfries Rd. Trs.* (1890) 17
R. 805; 1 Bell's *Commentaries* 456.

him. It is an incomplete executory sale, and he cannot claim the price of his labour."[41]

What may be said is that the sheriff in *Greig v. Kennedy*[42] decided the case as an entire contract, rather than, as he indicated, an executory sale. It is a difficulty that continues to this day; exactly what type of contract a building contract is appears to have evaded formulation from the bases of first principles.

In order to deal with the common law and statutory problems of transfer   1.14
of title of building materials and their delivery, and of the quality of materials, the current standard form of building contract JCT 80 (Private with Quantities — incorporating amendments 1–18) makes detailed provisions which are discussed in Chapter 4.

What are the material terms of a building contract?

The materiality of terms in a contract was explained in *Wade v. Waldon*[43]   1.15
as follows:

> "... in any contract which contains multifarious stipulations there are some which go to the root of the contract that a breach of those stipulations entitles the party pleading the breach to declare that the contract is at an end. There are others which do not go to the root of the contract, but which are part of the contract and which would give rise if broken, to an action of damages."

There is perhaps a flaw in this classic Scottish definition in that the reference to being at an end is not strictly accurate: other provisions will continue to subsist, *e.g.* an arbitration clause.[44]

Under English law a distinction is drawn between a condition, a breach of   1.16
which will give rise to repudiation; and a warranty, a breach of which will give rise to a right of damages only. There is also a tendency among English lawyers to categorise clauses of contracts into dependent covenants, fundamental terms, conditions precedent and the like with consequent uncertainty. In any case there appears to be a principle in Scots law that if a material breach is remediable the innocent party is not entitled to treat the contract as rescinded without giving the other party an opportunity to remedy the breach.[45]

---

[41] *Principles, op. cit.,* para. 152.
[42] *op. cit.*
[43] 1909 S.C. 571 at 576.
[44] *Scott v. Gerrard,* 1916 S.C. 793, 1916 2 S.L.T. 42; *Sanderson & Son v. Armour & Co. Ltd,* 1921 S.C. 18, affd 1922 S.C. (H.L.) 117.
[45] *Lindley Catering Investments Ltd v. Hibernian Football Club Ltd,* 1975 S.L.T. (Notes) 56. Also, *Strathclyde Regional Council v. Border Engineering Contractors Ltd,* 1988 S.L.T. 175 in relation to an ICE 4th ed. contract it was held that if a pipe was wrongly laid and there was a contractual obligation to remedy defects, the contractor was bound and entitled to remedy the defects. A right to sue for damages for breach of contract did not arise until the contractor was "functus", which Lady Cosgrove appeared to equate with practical completion (approving *Keating on Building Contracts* at p. 268 and *Hudson on Building Contracts* at p. 672). Her Ladyship held that for the purposes of calculating prescriptive periods it would be "totally unacceptable" that there could be a different prescriptive period for every component of a composite whole.

In the standard forms of contract published by the Joint Contracts Tribunal (JCT) or the Scottish Building Contract Committee (SBCC) none of the English lawyers' distinctions are actually used; and, in any case, in the standard forms there are contractual mechanisms for making claims[46] and operating determination of contract clauses[47] through the contract rather than as a result of breach of contract. In taking the Scots lawyer's approach, it is appropriate to ask at the outset what the material terms in standard forms of building contracts are.

There are immediate problems with so-called standard forms of construction contract because there are many different types of them; they are complex and often have practice notes to accompany them; most have been subject to many amendments; and some may have been expressly or impliedly adapted for use in Scotland. So-called standard forms are not standard in the sense that a standard security would be to a conveyancer (*i.e.* only one type), or standard in the sense of prescribed by legislation. There is in fact a great diversity in such contracts, so much so that it is difficult to say whether one of Lord Diplock's classifications of standard forms of contract in other commercial areas would apply[48]:

> "Standard forms of contract are of two kinds. The first of very ancient origin, are those which set out the terms on which mercantile transactions of common occurrence are carried out. Examples are bills of lading, charterparties, policies of insurance, contracts of sale in the commodities markets. The standard clauses in these contracts have been settled over the years by negotiation by representatives of the commercial interests involved and have been widely adopted because experience has shown that they facilitate the conduct of trade .... If fairness or reasonableness were relevant to their enforceability the fact that they are widely used by parties whose bargaining power is fairly matched would raise a strong presumption that their terms are fair and reasonable."

Types of contract

1.17   In the construction industry, the main contractual division is between civil engineering contracts and building contracts. There is very often no easy practical distinction as to which form of contract would be more appropriate, as some building contracts, and sub-contracts, can involve substantial civil engineering works, *e.g.* excavation and related works (normally referred to as earthworks). Building contracts in the U.K. are dominated by JCT contracts and civil engineering by ICE (Institution of Civil Engineers) contracts. Rather confusingly, integral parts of a construction process might be carried out on standard forms issued by

---

[46] JCT 80, cl. 26.
[47] JCT 80, cll. 27 and 28.
[48] *Shroeder Music Publishing Co. Ltd v. Macaulay* [1974] 1 W.L.R. 1300.

different bodies. Mechanical and electrical engineering sub-contracts, demolition works, process engineering, and water treatment contracts might all be carried out on contracts that are not designed to be compatible with other forms of contract used elsewhere in the same project. This is to say nothing of standard forms of engagement that might be used between the employer, his architect, or project manager.

Parties

Not all parties who are intended to have contractual obligations and   1.18
important roles to play in the construction process will be parties to a standard form of contract. All interested parties might be the employer, architect, engineer, quantity surveyor, project manager, clerk of works, contractor, sub-contractors (domestic and nominated), suppliers (domestic or nominated), plant hire companies, insurers and guarantors under a performance bond. A funder may have a central interest, as may a key tenant in a new development. Planning and building control authorities will also have a role to play. Yet under the JCT forms of contract the contracting parties are simply the employer and the main contractor. Certainly, other parties may be referred to, notably the architect, quantity surveyor, clerk of works, sub-contractors and suppliers, but crucially the main contract is only an agreement between the employer and the main contractor. It had been thought until recently that general duties of care in delict would exist anyway and that these could fill in any contractual gaps in appropriate cases, but this is something that the courts have started to show a reluctance to do where parties could have made contractual arrangements and did not.[49] The contractual gaps are being increasingly filled in practice by so-called collateral warranties[50] between relevant parties who are not parties to the main contract.

In analysing who will do what, the employer is perhaps the only non-   1.19
variable, *i.e.* there should always be a readily identifiable employer or client, but even then, the client may not own the site or building on which works are to be carried out, and rights may be created for third parties, *e.g.* on death or insolvency, novation or assignation. It is also possible that the employer and the contractor may become one and the same, thus extinguishing contractual obligations by confusion. How construction works will be carried out for the client can vary greatly. In its simplest arrangement the builder will do the work and the employer (or more likely his architect) will supply a completed design to build to. Often the reality is that a partially

---

[49] *Greater Nottingham Co-operative Society Ltd v. Cementation Piling and Foundations Ltd* [1988] 2 All E.R. 971.
[50] The SBCC versions of the Standard Forms of Agreement for Collateral Warranties for Main Contractors to Purchasers and Tenants and Funders were published in January 1994. In August 1998 the SBCC published a Standard Form of Employer/Sub-Contractor Warranty Agreement.

completed design is given to the contractor, and some items of work are described as provisional. The builder then builds and the employer accepts the work, and pays for it. The builder does not therefore design, in the normal sense of the word, although there may be a blurring of boundaries where the builder selects materials, or is relied on to select materials; or suggests design changes; or builds to a design he should have known was defective.

1.20 Alternatively, the entire design responsibility may be taken on by the contractor. In this case the builder would normally employ his own "in-house" architect and design to meet the employer's requirements. He would then build to his own design: thus a design-and-build contract.

1.21 Another common system involves the contractor taking a managerial role and packaging out the works to various works contractors as in management contracting. In all cases the use of sub-contractors, who may or may not be specialists, is commonplace.

1.22 The employer has certain obligations and duties both express and implied under standard form contracts. He may also under the law of agency be liable as principal for the acts of his agents, including the architect and quantity surveyor, and perhaps of the contractor also in respect of risks to third parties.[51]

1.23 The contractor also has certain obligations, express and implied, and some that are largely procedural and concerned with the administration of the contract. But his central obligation, *i.e.* to build, is surprisingly difficult to identify on a strict legal analysis. Under JCT 80 the contractor's obligation to carry out "the works" may only involve a short description of the works, *e.g.* "erect 10 houses". Detailed items might be identified in a bill of quantities, which is to be interpreted with reference to another document — a standard method of measurement — and there may also be a specification describing how the works are to be carried out, or a performance specification describing what the works are to achieve. Architects' drawings containing a greater or lesser amount of detail will also describe the works and it is normally from these drawings that the necessary quantities are taken, either formally by a quantity surveyor who is employed for that purpose by the employer and then priced by the contractor, or taken off by the contractor himself.

Consensus ad idem

1.24 In classic theory a meeting of minds between the parties to a contract (*consensus ad idem*) is required. There is clearly plenty of scope for gaps as to a precise consensus for the ultimate extent of works. Much depends on the clarity of understanding that exists between the employer and his

---

[51] See *Duncan's Hotel (Glasgow) Ltd v. J. & A. Ferguson Ltd*, 1974 S.C. 191; *MTM Construction Ltd v. William Reid Engineering Ltd*, 1997 S.C.L.R. 778.

architect as to design and cost; the quality and completeness of the drawings at the outset; whether there is a bill of quantities; the accuracy of the quantities that are taken off; the interpretation of these in relation to a standard method of measurement; and the efficiency and profit motive of the contractor as to how he plans to carry out the works. Added to this in all standard form contracts it is reserved to the employer to vary the works for whatever reason or none, be these aesthetic or matters of cost. This in itself poses conceptual difficulties of consensus where one party retains a unilateral power to alter the object of the contract. It is perhaps even possible that such a clause which enables one party to render no performance or a substantially different performance from that contracted for might prima facie be unreasonable under the Unfair Contract Terms Act 1977. This does not appear to have been tested in the courts, and perhaps would never succeed because of the nature of JCT contracts which are issued only with the consensus of its members, and the widespread practice in the construction industry which accepts the practice of variations. Nevertheless it may be argued that variations may so substantially alter the scope of a contract as to create a new collateral contract with different terms. Bell's *Principles*, para. 151 appears to accept that what is to be done in a building contract is not an absolute and variations are part and parcel of such a contract. He states:

> "In a contract for work to be done according to plans and specifications, there is no implied warranty by the employer that the work can be done in the way described. Extra work contemplated by the contract is to be paid at the rates provided in the contract; but if additional work or varied work, so different as not to be within the contract at all, becomes necessary, it appears that the contractor may refuse to go on with the contract, or go on and claim quantum meruit; but in the latter case, he ought to give notice of the footing on which he is to proceed."

Price and contract value

Perhaps it is not surprising that if what is to be done is not always clear in the details then the actual contract value is not always clear-cut either. Contracts can be priced on a lump sum plus or minus variations basis under standard forms of contract. What is to be done may not have been decided upon in any detail at the tender stage and so-called "provisional sums" are inserted in a bill of quantities with special rules applying to the expenditure of these sums.

One of the difficulties with this is that it can be difficult to identify or work out how the lump sum was arrived at when attempting to identify the appropriate rates to use for valuing variations. In practice what many contractors do is use a pricing rule of thumb based on labour costs, plant costs, and material costs with a percentage add-on for profit. That lump sum is then spread across the bill of quantities in as shrewd a way as the contractor possibly can to anticipate items that are likely to be varied.[52]

1.25

---

[52] A practice judicially approved of in the context of an ICE 6th ed. contract recently in *Henry Boot Construction Ltd v. Alstom Combined Cycles Ltd*, Technology and Construction Court, January 22, 1999 at http://www.courtservice.gov.uk/or_tccmenu.htm.

1.26   Remeasurement is where the parties have agreed a contract sum, but nevertheless, once the works have been completed, revalue the works on the basis of what was actually done. This is particularly common in ICE and engineering contracts.

Schedule of rates

1.27   Some contracts may have a schedule of rates. This can occur when the nature of the possible works can be priced, for example, in routine maintenance contracts, but the extent of these works is not known.

CHAPTER 2

CONTEXT OF STANDARD FORMS OF CONTRACT

As already noted the Joint Contracts Tribunal (JCT) issues the construction industry's standard building contract. The adoption by the JCT of the principles in Sir Michael Latham's report *Constructing the Team*, published in July 1994, led to changes in its structure and constitution. The Joint Contracts Tribunal Limited came into being in April 1998 and its members are:

Royal Institute of British Architects	(RIBA)
Construction Confederation	(C.C.)
Royal Institution of Chartered Surveyors	(RICS)
Scottish Building Contracts Committee	(SBCC)
Local Government Association	(LGA)
National Specialists Contractors' Council	(NSCC)
Association of Consulting Engineers	(ACE)
British Property Federation	(BPF)

Each constitent body is a member of the new company, and the new JCT Council discharges the functions of the previous body. The recent history of JCT contracts centres on the JCT 63 contract which is now almost obsolete and its successor JCT 80. This latter contract has now been amended 18 times since it was issued in 1980. The amendments are issued separately, and occasionally JCT 80 is reprinted to incorporate the amendments, and to make small corrections.[1] For some reason an amendment relating to terrorism cover issued in April 1994 is not numbered, merely called Amendment TC/94, and is to be cut out and inserted when required.[2] Keeping track of the amendments is not easy on the face of the documents themselves. The last page of the current published edition of the JCT 80 conditions gives a sort of history and index of the changes, but does not

2.01

2.02

---

[1] The most recent printing of JCT 80 was in December 1998, incorporating amendments 1-18 and various corrections, with some footnote lettering revised.

[2] The Scottish Building Contract Committee issue the SBC Model Supplementary Agreement (July 1994 ed.) for incorporating TC/94 into the standard forms of contract. This amendment introduces new provisions for damage by fire or explosion caused by terrorism where such "terrorism cover" is excluded from policies but covered by standard premiums graded according to risk and administered by the re-insurer established by the Government, who act as the re-insurer of last resort (Pool Re-Insurance Company Ltd — "Pool Re").

demonstrate what was redrafted or changed on each occasion. In order to carry out that exercise it is best to refer to Emden's *Construction Law* which records superseded documents and illustrates the changes, or *Walker-Smith on The Standard Forms of Building Contract*.[3] Each are excellent works, but regrettably they do not pay any attention to Scottish changes. At the time of writing no such work exists. The only practicable means which the author is aware of for keeping up with the Scottish changes is to subscribe to the Forms of Contract Update Service (FOCUS) through the Royal Incorporation of Architects in Scotland Practice Services.[4]

Practice Notes

2.03   In addition to the Amendments there are a plethora of Practice Notes:

Practice Note 1	Sectional completion supplement (For reference only in Scotland)
Practice Notes 2–5 (1981)	2. Insurance provisions 3. Insurance — liability etc. of employer — provisional sum 4. Drawings — additional copies 5. Payment for off-site materials and goods (Practice notes 2 and 3 officially withdrawn by and incorporated into Practice Note 22)
Practice Notes 4 and 5 (Oct. 1987)	As above
Practice Note 6 (July 1980)	VAT Now withdrawn
Practice Note 7 (July 1980)	Standard Forms of Building Contract for use with Bills of Approximate Quantities
Practice Note 8 (August 1980)	Finance (No.2) Act, 1975 — Statutory Tax Deduction Scheme

[3]   Knights Loose Leaf Library.
[4]   RIAS Practice Services, 15 Rutland Square, Edinburgh, EH1 2BE.

Practice Notes 9–13 (Oct. 1982)	9. Domestic sub-contractors 10. Nomination of a sub-contractor 11. Employer/nominated sub-contractor agreement 12. Direct payment and final payment to nominated sub-contractors 13. Proposed nomination as a sub-contractor not effected & re-nomination
Practice Notes 14–19 (1982)	14. Variations and provisional sum work 15. Nominated suppliers 16. Extension of time and liquidated damages 17. Fluctuations 18. Payment & retention 19. Applicability of Practice Notes 9–18 to contracts in Scotland
Practice Note 20 (Revised August 1993)	Deciding on the appropriate form of JCT Main Contract
Practice Note 21 (1982)	The employer's position under the 1980 Edition of the Standard Form of Building Contract compared to the 1963 Edition
Practice Note 22 (1987)	Guide to the amendments to the insurance and related liability provisions: 1986
Practice Note 23 (1987)	A contract sum analysis
Practice Note 24 (1992)	Insolvency of the main contractor
Practice Note 25 (August 1993)	Performance specified work: treatment in clause 42

Practice Note 26 (January 1994)	Guidance on the alternative valuation and certification procedures under optional clause 13A, introduced by JCT amendment 13
Practice Note 27 (March 1995)	Guidance on the application of the Construction (Design and Management) Regulations 1994 to contracts on the JCT Standard Forms of Contract
Practice Note 28 (August 1995)	Mediation on a building contract or sub-contract dispute. SBCC Practice Note 1/95 adapts Practice Note 28 for use in Scotland
Notes CD/1A, CD/1B (August 1995)	Standard Form of Building Contract with Contractor's Design 1981
CD/2 (Revised April 1996)	Contractor's Designed Portion Supplement 1981 Ed. For reference only in Scotland.
Practice Note MC/1	Management contracts under the JCT documentation
Practice Note MC/2	Commentaries on Management Contract 1987
Practice Note MTC/1	Measured Term Contract
Practice Note PCC/1 and Guide	Summary and outline of the Standard Form of Prime Cost Contract For reference only in Scotland

These Practice Notes are of questionable status in construing the various conditions, and there is no clause that specifically refers to them as an aid to construction of the terms of the contracts.

Copyright and Domestic Sub-Contracts

Whilst copyright in JCT 80 belongs to RIBA publications, copyright in the appropriate form of domestic sub-contract for use with JCT 80 (DOM/1) belongs to the Building Employers' Confederation (now the Construction Confederation). This form has also been published incorporating many amendments, and is issued with Practice Note DOM/1/GN. There is at the time of writing considerable confusion about which standard form of sub-contract is appropriate for the puposes of the provisions of HGCRA 1996, as the SBCC published its own sub-contract documentation in September 1997 (and revised in August 1998),[5] as did the former Building Employers' Confederation, quite separately. It is understood that JCT are currently working to standardise the position. Suffice to say that great care has to be taken in interpreting what revision of a JCT contract has been used, the appropriate amendments that apply, and the appropriate sub-contract documents.

2.04

SBCC and SBC

In Scotland the Scottish Building Contract Committee (SBCC) is now, since April 1998, a sole "relevant college" in respect of JCT forms modified for use in Scotland to reflect Scots law and practice, and has two seats on the JCT Council and one director on the Board. The SBCC issues its own contract (the Scottish Building Contract — SBC) and amends the conditions of JCT 80 for the purposes of meeting Scots law requirements. The contracts issued by the SBCC are distinct contractual documents, but largely incorporate by reference the relevant JCT conditions. They re-define terms and introduce some uniquely Scottish aspects, some of which like the governing law being Scottish, and a clause to take account of the separate framework of arbitration law in Scotland are not surprising. Many others, such as the different rights of an employer to terminate on the contractor's insolvency, are not immediately reconcilable with the stated aims of the SBCC to harmonise contractual conditions north and south of the border.

2.05

Execution of the contract: interest in land

The Requirements of Writing (Scotland) Act 1995 provides in section 1 that "writing shall not be required for the constitution of a contract, unilateral obligation or trust" and then goes on to list exceptions where writing is

2.06

---

[5]   Scottish Building Sub-Contract, Dom/A/Scot; Standard Form of Sub-Contract Tender for use in Scotland, Dom/T/Scot Parts 1 & 2; Domestic Sub-Contract Conditions, Dom/C/Scot. None of these are yet suitable if the sub-contractor has a design responsibility (the pre-Latham appropriate form was DOM/2/ Scot).

required. The relevance of these exceptions for construction contracts is debatable, as one of these exceptions is for contracts for the creation of an "interest in land". This phrase is defined in section 1(7) as including "any right to occupy" for more than one year. If a construction contract were to be considered to create an "interest in land" by occupation of a site for more than a year, then there are special rules as to how such a contract, and any annexations such as drawings, are to be executed. The contract would require to be subscribed (s. 2) which means signing at the end of the last page (s. 7(1) and (3)). Section 8(1) makes provision for incorporation of schedules and other annexations into a written document, and these simply have to be referred to in the document and identified on their face as being the annexations incorporated into the document. Section 8(2) relates to annexations which "show" all or any part of the land and which may be drawings, photographs or other representation. These need to be signed on each page; or signed on the last page where it is an inventory, appendix, schedule or other writing. In both cases the annexation also has to be referred to in the document and identified on its face. Section 8(5) allows an annexation to be signed at any time before it is founded on in legal process or registered for preservation. The effect of all this is that if a construction contract where a site is occupied for more than a year is considered to be a contract relating to an interest in land, then all these signing formalities would have to be followed, or it would not be "valid". This lack of formal validity need not be fatal as section 1(3), (4) and (5) provides a statutory replacement of the former rules of personal bar, known as *rei interventus* and homologation, which, simply put, prevents one party from relying on the deficiencies in validity if that turns out to suit him. The defective document may still be used in evidence to prove that consensus had been achieved.[6] There are also special rules for the authentication of alterations, such as deletions in section 5 . The important point is whether the alteration was made before or after subscription; and if after subscription it will be invalid unless signed afresh.

Retention

2.07   As well as the exception requiring writing to constitute a contract for an interest in land, there is another exception requiring writing for a trust formed by a person who declares himself to be the sole trustee of his own property (s. 2 (a)(iii)). In construction contracts that is what may be intended to happen in relation to funds that are retained by an employer from interim payments made to the contractor[7] — the employer becomes the trustee over his own property.[8] On this point alone a construction contract would

---

[6]   s. 2 (3).
[7]   See for example clauses 30.4 and 30.5 of JCT 80.
[8]   But see discussion at Chap. 3, paras 3.69–3.75.

require to be in writing and subscribed, irrespective of the debate over the "interest in land" question.[9] It is worth noting at this point that section 107 of the Housing Grants, Construction and Regeneration Act 1996 proceeds on the basis that the Act would only apply to construction contracts in writing. At section 107 (2) an agreement in writing may be as the result of an exchange of correspondence, the agreement may be unsigned, or may be evidenced in writing: writing is to be interpreted as recorded by any means (s. 107(6)).

"Self Proving"

The SBCC recommend that a single "self proving" contract be signed by both parties. The self proving status means that the contract, and more especially the arbitration clause, can be registered in the Books of Council and Session for preservation and execution of any decree arbitral that may subsequently be issued. The Scottish Building Contract provides for both parties to consent to the registration of the contract, and means that an arbitral award under it can be enforced without the need to ask the court for a decree conform to the award. It has even been suggested that registration of a self proving contract means that diligence can be carried out on interim certificates, but this has not been tested in the courts.[10] To be "self proving", and hence presumed to have been subscribed by the granter, on the date stated and the place stated, the contract would also have to be attested — normally by one witness at the same time, having capacity, giving his name and address, and signing anywhere on the document. For companies subscription is governed by section 36B of the Companies Act 1985,[11] which simply stated requires (a) subscription of two directors, or (b) a director and the secretary, or (c) two persons authorised to sign on behalf of the company. This would also make it self proving (s. 3(1A))[12] without the need for any further witness — although one may also sign.[13] The Scottish

2.08

[9]   The different phrase "obligation relating to land" used in the Prescription and Limitation (Scotland) Act 1973 was considered in *Lord Advocate v. Shipbreaking Industries Ltd*, 1991 S.L.T. 838 *per* Lord Coulsfield at 840 J-K ; and again in *Barratt Scotland Ltd v. Keith*, 1994 S.L.T. 1343. In the latter, Lord Justice-Clerk Ross opined that building works were contracts for services in which land "was merely the environment within which the services are to be performed... not to be regarded as obligations relating to land".
[10]   Note in this context that the new clause 41A.8.4 of the Scottish Building Contract relating to the decision of an adjudicator provides a contractual mechanism for the subscription and witnessing of an award within seven days of a request to do so. This clause would tend to suggest that the drafters of the SBC do not believe an interim certificate itself could be registered for diligence purposes, at least without the same formalities as for an adjudicator's decision.
[11]   Inserted by the Law Reform (Miscellaneous Provisions)(Scotland) Act 1990, s. 72.
[12]   Requirements of Writing (Scotland) Act 1995.
[13]   *ibid*, s. 3(1).

Building Contract Committee has introduced its revised "Note to Users: Attestation" (August 1995) which advises subscription by one director and a witness in each case for a company employer or contractor.[14]

Exchange of letters

2.09   The author's perception of life in the Scottish construction world is that few formal SBC contracts are actually signed.[15] Very often contracts are completed by exchange of correspondence which purport to incorporate standard conditions, or variations on these. Section 2 (2) of the Requirements in Writing Act 1995 provides that a contract may be constituted by a subscribed offer and acceptance. Whether an exchange of letters produces *consensus ad idem* or not can be a difficult matter of interpretation.

2.10   If the Scottish contract is used it is normally concluded by a process whereby the contractor receives an invitation to tender, then tenders, and there normally follows correspondence with regard to savings. These are then formally incorporated into the Scottish Building Contract. This avoids the common law difficulties of an offer which is not accepted outright falling,[16] and the evidential problems of the parole evidence rule, which prevented the admissibility of evidence, written or oral, to prove that a contract had terms which were not embodied in the document. This rule admitted of many confusing exceptions in any case,[17] and has been replaced by the Contract (Scotland) Act 1997. Section 1 of the 1997 Act creates a rebuttable presumption that a document which appears to contain all the express terms of agreement does so, but now allows extrinsic oral or documentary evidence to be led (s. 1(2)). The Act does seem to permit finality by the recognition of the use of an "entire contract" clause (s. 1(3)), but it remains to be seen how this might be interpreted.[18]

---

[14]   At the time of writing the Government is considering a Secure Electronic Commerce Bill which it is expected will address issues relating to execution of documents in the electronic age. Proposals in these respects can be found in the UNCITRAL Model Law on Electronic Commerce 16/DEC/1996 http://www.un.or.at/uncitral/english/texts/electcom/ml-ec.htm. The JCT in Spring 1998 published *A Code of Practice: Use of Electronic Data Interchange in the Construction Industry.*

[15]   For an interesting, and slightly amusing, example of the problems that can arise in pre-contract negotiations, leading ultimately to a decision that no contract at all had been formed, see *David Wilson Construction Ltd v. Newbattle Properties Ltd*, November 17, 1998, *per* Lord Macfadyen. Reported at Court of Session Opinions at http://www.scotcourts.gov.uk/

[16]   *Wolf and Wolf v. Forfar Potato Co.*, 1984 S.L.T. 100; *Rutherford Ltd v. Allied Breweries Ltd*, 1990 S.L.T. 249. There are particular difficulties in relation to the formation of contract when there are protracted negotiations and the *locus poenitentiae* (literally, place of repentance) exists, so as to allow a party to withdraw because of a lack of formal agreement. The orthodox Scottish position has been criticised by Professor Forte, " The Qualified Acceptance: A Revisionist View of the Fundamentals of Commercial Contract Formation in Scots Law" in *Contemporary Issues in Law*, Vol. 1, Issue II, p. 43.

[17]   *Bovis v. Whatlings*, 1994 S.L.T. 865.

[18]   See Campbell, Kenneth, "Three Bad Rules of Contract Rectified?", 1997 S.L.T. 225.

THE JCT "FAMILY" OF CONTRACTS

The JCT have produced a wide range of contractual documentation for 2.11
different types of project. The SBCC then, normally, produce what are
sometimes referred to by the industry as "kilted" versions for Scotland.
Simply put, the main distinctions in the types of main contract depend upon
whether a bill of quantities is used in the documentation or not; whether
there is to be any element of design carried out by the contractor; whether
the contract works are to be completed in discrete sections; whether the
works are essentially for maintenance and repair; whether the works are to
be paid for on a fixed fee or on the basis of actual cost plus a percentage for
profit; and whether the contractor's role is mainly to manage other
contractors. Contracts combining these variables are produced, as are
versions where the employer is a local authority.

Broadly speaking, there are three main categories of possible building 2.12
contracts where prices are tendered in competition. One type of contract
may use a schedule of rates. The contract will not be for a lump sum, and
the contractor prices for specific tasks and these tasks are later identified
by the architect or engineer and the contractor is instructed to carry them
out. A schedule of rates can be used where the works are not sufficiently
pre-planned or capable of estimation in advance, *e.g.* in a term maintenance
contract. Secondly, the contractor may have considered the construction
processes and tendered a lump sum but with an accompanying bill of
quantities (or even schedule of rates) which has significance if variations
to the contract have to be valued, and sometimes also for interim payments.
In such a case the bill of quantities may or may not form part of the contract.
Lastly, and most typically, the employer provides a blank bill of quantities
at tender stage which the contractor prices and adds up to produce a total
contract sum. The bill of quantities is incorporated into the contract (a "with
quantities" contract), and is used for valuing variations, interim payments,
and for recalculating a final measurement of the contract sum.

In both civil engineering and building contracts with quantities, "Standard 2.13
Methods of Measurement" are incorporated for use with such contracts.
Clause 2.2.2.1 of JCT 80 incorporates "the Standard Method of
Measurement of Building Works, 7th ed." (SMM 7). In the introduction to
its general rules at clause 1.1 SMM 7 provides:

> "This Standard Method of Measurement provides a uniform basis for
> measuring building works and embodies the essentials of good practice. Bills
> of Quantities shall fully describe and accurately represent the quantity and
> quality of the works to be carried out. More detailed information than is
> required by these rules shall be given where necessary in order to define the
> precise nature and extent of the required work."

Clause 1.2 of SMM7 provides that the rules apply to proposed work and 2.14
executed work, and rule 10.1 provides that where work can be described
but the quantity cannot be accurately determined, an approximate quantity

be given. Rule 10.2 further provides that where the work cannot be described, a Provisional Sum shall be given, and if this is because the work is not completely designed then, by rule 10.3, information about the nature and construction of the work, how, where and what the work is to be fixed to, quantities which indicate the scope and extent of the work, and any specific limitations shall be provided. If this information cannot be given then, by rule 10.5, a Provisional Sum for undefined work is given for which the Contractor will be deemed to have made no allowance in programming, planning and pricing Preliminaries. Where the Provisional Sum is for defined work he will be deemed to have made these allowances.

2.15   SMM 7 describes an encyclopaedic range of building activities and how they are to be classed; measured; defined; what coverage of incidental work is included; and any supplementary information, all in tabular form. However, there is nothing which specifically shows where the profit mark-up for each rate is in relation to the contractor's overheads. In the Preliminaries section of the Bills the contractor's "general cost items" for management and staff; site accommodation; services and facilities such as power, telephone, security; mechanical plant charges; and "dayworks" for labour, plant and materials have to be priced, but again no specific profit centre need be shown. The contractor therefore has scope to gamble by keeping his Preliminaries low and boosting certain prices per rate, in the shrewd expectation that the employer's quantity surveyor has underestimated certain quantities, which the contractor will argue ultimately should be valued at the contractor's favourable rates.[19] He may also choose to boost the Preliminaries, on the basis that many of these will be paid first, and that if there is likely to be extensions of time granted in the contractor's favour, many of these Preliminaries will be claimed for by simply applying a multiplier corresponding to the number of weeks' extension. This is sometimes referred to as "front end loading".

2.16   The bills come into their own when a variation under clause 13 is issued. Clauses 13.5.1 to 13.5.7 contain detailed valuation rules under clause 13, Alternative B, notably that where additional or substituted work is of similar character to, is executed under similar conditions as, and does not significantly change the quantity of, work set out in the Contract Bills, then the rates and prices in the Contract Bills shall determine the valuation . If the conditions under which the work is to be executed change, or the quantity significantly alters, the rates and prices in the Bills shall be the basis of determining the valuation with a fair allowance for such differences. The problem with all this is that in reality the contractor will normally have estimated his price on the basis of the cost of labour, plant and materials to him, and added a percentage for his overheads, recovery and profit. However,

---

[19]   A practice judicially approved of in the context of an I.C.E. 6th Contract recently in *Henry Boot Construction Ltd v. Alstom Combined Cycles Ltd* Technology and Construction Court 22 January 1999 at http://www.courtservice.gov.uk/or_tccmenu.htm

since Amendment 18 and the introduction of Alternative A, the Contractor will now have the option to submit a price statement for a Variation, which if not agreed can be referred under the new Adjudication provisions of clause 41A to an Adjudicator.

The following is a brief description of current standard forms of building contract for use in Scotland.

Scottish Building Contract with Quantities

This is the most common form of contract, suitable for large, complex projects where the designer designs and the Contractor builds; but design may be carried out by a Nominated Sub-Contractor and a Prime Cost Sum inserted in the Bills for this.[20] These are lump sum contracts, plus or minus variations. A Bill of Quantities is "taken off" the drawings by the Employer's Quantity Surveyor and used as the basis of tendering by the Contractor. The current Standard Method of Measurement is compulsory. The Bills are used to value variations where appropriate. This contract is based on JCT 80 with Quantities (which it incorporates, including the Amendments to it), and the current Scottish version is the August 1998 revision, which is the 11th Scottish revision since 1980. The history of these revisions is given on the last four pages of the current revision.

2.17

Scottish Building Contract without Quantities

Here no Bills are prepared for the Employer, these are replaced by the Specification and/or Schedule of Work. The Contractor prices on the basis of a bill of rates, which he prepares. These rates are then used as the basis for valuing variations. In other respects the contract is similar to the above, is for a lump sum, and might be used for large but less complex projects which are fully designed pre-contract.

2.18

Scottish Building Contract with Approximate Quantities

This can be used where the full extent of works is not known or prepared in time and a complete remeasurement of the works takes place at the end. The complexity of the project should not be substantial. The remeasurement will be carried out on the basis of the appropriate Standard Method of Measurement.

2.19

Scottish Building Contract Sectional Completion Edition

These are used where identifiable sections of the works are agreed and should reach completion prior to the overall completion date. However the contractual consequences of reaching or failing to reach completion for

2.20

---

[20] In *Bickerton v. N.W. Metropolitan Regional Hospital Board* [1970] 1 WLR 607, Lord Reid said at p. 623 that the ordinary meaning of Prime Cost Sums was 'sums entered or provided in bills of quantities for work to be executed by nominated subcontractors'.

each section apply irrespective of the overall Completion Date. The works are fully designed and tend to be for durations of more than 12 months. This is distinct from Phased Completion, where particular phases might be identifiable but it is only the ultimate Completion Date which is material for the purposes of calculating damages for late completion, insurance, etc.

Scottish Building Contract Contractor's Designed Portion

2.21   This confers upon the Contractor certain design responsibilities, *e.g.* for specialist work such as pre-stressed concrete or timber roof trusses. The architect may nevertheless still provide loadings and dimensions which could give rise to difficult questions of liability if there is an error.

Scottish Building Contract — With Contractor's Design

2.22   This is currently in its August 1998 revision. This is quite different from the JCT 80 contractual position because the Contractor not only builds but is solely responsible for the design as well. The conditions which are incorporated are largely the JCT WCD 1981 Conditions. These contracts are becoming more common but are not discussed in any detail in this text. The contract documents are quite different from JCT 80 as the "Employer's Requirements" are met by the "Contractor's Proposals", attatched to which is a "Contract Sum Analysis".

Private or Local Authority Contracts

2.23   JCT issue distinct sets of conditions depending on who the employer is. These contracts are substantially similar but for the premise behind the local authority contracts that a local authority is a safe employer and will not go bust. This premise is reflected in the determination clauses, the retention clauses where there needs to be no separate identification of retention sums withheld from the contractor, and different insurance provisions. The appropriate Scottish Building Contract can incorporate either set of conditions by deletion as required.

Fluctuations and Formula rules

2.24   These are optional clauses which are particularly relevant where the contract period extends over a considerable time and it is expected that there will be price rises due to inflation or taxation changes, which affect the Contractor's risk. An appropriate formula is agreed for calculating fluctuations based on price indices. They are published separately by JCT.

Scottish Measured Term Contract for Maintenance and Minor Works

2.25   This, currently in its April 1998 revision, is used when, for example, a local authority may require regular maintenance and repair of its housing stock and let out a contract for a number of years. Often the Employer produces a schedule of rates and the Contractor tenders on the basis of an addition or subtraction to these rates. No designer is involved, and there are no provisions for a form of sub-contract. Appendix No. II includes the maximum and minimum values of any one order, and an approximate anticipated value of work. The contract period is for the minimum of one year.

Scottish Management Contract; Scottish Management Contract Phased Completion Edition

These are currently in March 1998 revision, and largely incorporate the JCT Standard Form of Management Contract 1987 ed. These forms are for use on "fast track" contracts where the works are not fully designed at the outset. The Management Contractor is employed directly by the Employer to employ Works Contractors and manage them so that they complete on time. The Management Contractor is not responsible for the budget and therefore such contract is regarded as low risk for a Management Contractor, but also low return. It is fraught with cost problems for an employer and is, of course, not a lump sum contract. Normally the Quantity Surveyor prepares a Contract Cost Plan and most of the obligations for carrying out the works are sub-contracted to the Works Contractors. The SBCC publish Works Contract/1/Scot (March 1998) and Notes for Guidance (revised January 1994) for use between the Management Contractor and the Works Contractor. The Employer in Scotland may also enter into a direct Contract of Purchase of Materials with a Works Contractor: Works Contract/3/Scot (March 1998), and Notes for Guidance are published (1991). Management Contracting is distinct from Construction Management for which at present there is no standard form issued by the SBCC. Neither form of procuring construction works is discussed in this text.

2.26

Scottish Building Contract: Prime Cost Contract

This is currently in its July 1997 edition. It largely incorporates the JCT Standard Form of Prime Cost Contract 1992 edition. The Contractor is paid a fixed fee or a percentage fee on the Prime Cost of the Works. This type of contract might be used for works involving alterations or repair where actual costs are unknown. Eight schedules are prepared setting out the scope; Prime Cost; the Fee; the components of the Prime Cost; provision for Domestic and Nominated Sub-Contracts; Nominated Suppliers; and matters reserved for execution by the Employer. This form of contract is not discussed in the text.

2.27

Nominated Sub-Contractors

The SBCC publish (July 1997 ed. – August 1998 revision) invitation to tender and tender documents in two parts; particular conditions; a nomination instruction; a sub-contract; warranty agreements and largely incorporate the Nominated Sub-Contract Conditions published by JCT: NSC/C (March 1991 ed.). Great care has to be taken with this documentation as the NSC/C form has been amended seven times since March 1991.

2.28

Distinct Scottish documents

As well as the contracts that for the most part incorporate JCT conditions, the SBC also issue some of their own contracts that do not incorporate conditions by reference to JCT documents.

The Scottish Minor Works Contract 1986 Edition (August 1998 revision):

2.29   The SBCC proposed that this contract be used where, at 1987 prices, works not exceeding £70,000 were involved. However, complexity of the works is the best basis for considering whether to use the Scottish Minor Works contract, normally lasting less than six months and with no fluctuations. The Minor Works contract may be with or without quantities, and in the former case the Standard Method of Measurement is mandatory. It is a lump sum contract and an architect is appointed. Sub-contracting may take place using the Scottish Minor Works Sub-Contract 1986 ed. (although this has not at the time of writing been made compliant with HGCRA). But there is no provision for the use of nominated sub-contractors, or anyone other than the architect having design responsibility. Care has to be taken by the Contractor with respect to the insurance provisions which are different from JCT 80.

Domestic Sub-Contracts

2.30   In 1977 the SBCC issued its own domestic sub-contract forms, and these have since been revised again in August 1998. The JCT position is currently undergoing review.

Nominated Suppliers

2.31   The SBCC publish a standard form of tender for use in Scotland by a Nominated Supplier (January 1992 revision) and Schedule 3: warranty agreement for use in Scotland by a Nominated Supplier (January 1992 revision).

Contracts of Purchase

2.32   The SBCC publish separate contracts for the purchase from the Contractor, Sub-Contractor or Works Contractor of materials which are their property (July 1991 revision).

Miscellaneous Documents

2.33   There are occasional documents that are prepared by the JCT and SBCC. Included among these are the SBCC Insolvency Practice Guide (June 1991); the SBCC Standard Forms of Agreement for a Collateral Warranty by a Main Contractor to a Purchaser, Funder or Tenant (1994 ed., August 1998 revision); the SBCC Guidance Notes upon Dispute Resolution in Scotland

(April 1998) which contains a model form of Adjudication Agreement; and SBCC Practice Note 1/95 on Mediation on a Building Contract or Sub-Contract Dispute, which adopts JCT Practice Note 28 for use in Scotland.

JCT Intermediate Form of Contract 1984

There is also a fairly commonly used contract in England issued by the JCT known as the Intermediate Form of Contract (IFC84) for use where neither JCT 80 nor the Minor Works Contract is appropriate for administrative reasons. There is also appropriate sub-contract documentation for so-called "named sub-contractors". IFC has never been adapted for use in Scotland by the SBCC.

2.34

CHAPTER 3

PARTICULAR DIFFICULTIES

Formation of contract; non-supersession clauses; performance bonds; compensation and set-off; retention funds; direct payment provisions; latent defects.

FORMATION OF CONTRACT

Tenders

3.01   Contractors normally employ persons as estimators[1] to deal with tender opportunities. Normally a contractor wants a tender to be accepted, but in reality sometimes they do not — perhaps due to pressure on resources with other projects — but still want to be seen to be competing. Nevertheless, there are always costs involved in preparing tenders. The difficult question can arise as to whether the employer has to pay the contractor the costs of preparing the tender. In *Blackpool and Fylde Aero Club Ltd v. Blackpool Borough Council*,[2] because of a mistake in logging the time of receipt of tenders, the plaintiff's tender was disregarded and the tenderer sued for damages on a contractual basis and in tort. The contractual argument was the only one dealt with. It was held that there was an implied contractual obligation on the invitors to consider the tender in the circumstances of this case. The tenders were solicited from parties known to the invitor, there was a procedure common to all tenderers, and an absolute deadline. In the Court of Appeal Bingham L.J. held that the council's invitation to tender was to a limited extent an offer and the plaintiff's submission of a timely and conforming tender was an acceptance. Although the tenderer was exposed to a number of risks, such as that the project might not proceed, or that the invitor is not committed to accepting the lowest tender or any tender (or to justify his reasons), there was at least an implied contractual right to be duly considered. "Had the club, before tendering, inquired of the council whether it could rely on any timely and conforming tender being considered along with others, I feel quite sure that the answer would have been 'of course'. The law would, I think, be defective if it did not give effect to that."

---

[1]   The word estimate is not a term of art and there may be a distinction between an estimate and an offer which is capable of acceptance. See *Crossman v. Pritchard* (1889) 16 T.L.R. 45.

[2]   [1990] 1 W.L.R. 1195.

In *William Lacey (Hounslow) v. Davis*[3] it was held on the basis of quasi-contract that additional estimates over and above those which had been made in the expectation of winning a contract, and which had been requested by the building owner's quantity surveyor, had to be paid for *quantum meruit* when the work did not proceed due to the building owner selling the building. But, in *Fairclough Building Ltd v. Borough Council of Port Talbot*,[4] Fairclough were held to have been legally removed from the council's tender list as the wife of the managing director of Fairclough had become the principal architect for the council. It was held that there was no absolute right to keep a tenderer on a list indefinitely, and provided some consideration is given to a tender, even if only to say there is a conflict of interest, that would be sufficient for there not to be a breach of contract.[5]   3.02

In Scotland, unlike England, the common law recognises unilateral promises as enforceable, and perhaps would be more likely to view such cases in that light. However, in Scotland there have been cases where it has been held that there were implied contracts for preliminary work and therefore entitlement to be paid *quantum meruit*. For example, in *Sinclair v. Logan*[6] drawings prepared by a joiner for a proposed alteration to premises had to be paid for; in *Constable v. Uphall School Board*[7] an architect had to be paid for plans he prepared where building works were postponed by war; and in *Rattray v. Yuille*[8] a sheriff found that there was a custom that a surveyor was entitled to be paid when he had prepared schedules but could not carry out the measurement part because the building was never built. The custom was that he was due one-half of $1\frac{1}{2}$ per cent of the estimated value of the works, where the contract had been for $1\frac{1}{2}$ per cent of the "finished cost".   3.03

Claims for damages cases which do not rely on implied contract but on recompense have not fared well in the Scottish courts. In *Site Preparations Ltd v. Secretary of State for Scotland*[9] plans were prepared by the pursuers for the development of Peterhead Harbour in the hope of winning a contract. In fact the defenders proceeded with the contract themselves, but were alleged to have taken advantage and made use of the plans, and to that extent were *lucratus* (enriched). The pursuer's claim failed on the basis that recompense as a remedy is excluded where expenditure is incurred in the expectation of benefit to the spender. In this case there was no argument that what had happened was a breach of copyright, which might have   3.04

---

3   [1957] 1 W.L.R. 932.
4   [1992] 62 B.L.R. 82; 33 Con. L.R. 24, CA.
5   For further discussion on these points see Arrowsmith, "Protecting the interests of Bidders of Public Contracts: the Role of the Common Law" (1994) 53 C.L.J. 104, pp. 126–132.
6   1961 S.L.T. (Sh. Ct.) 10.
7   (1918) 35 Sh.Ct. Rep. 27.
8   (1878) 2 Guthrie Sh. Ct. Rep. 27.
9   1975 S.L.T. (Notes) 41.

succeeded.[10] An earlier case of *Landless v. Wilson*[11] was distinguished. In *Landless* building works did not proceed after a competition amongst architects, but the plans were used to effect an advantageous bargain when the ground was sold. As a matter of fact it was held that the owner had failed to establish that the employment of the architect was gratuitous, and payment was due *quantum meruit*. In *Gilchrist v. Whyte*[12] Lord Ardwall held that the courts would not as a rule investigate: "nice and difficult questions as to which of the parties had behaved reasonably or unreasonably in order to determine the question of who was to blame for the contract not being proceeded with." Professor McBryde summarises the difficulties in recovering loss from abortive negotiation under the head of recompense as:

(1) the pursuer must show loss;
(2) the pursuer must not have had the intention of donation;
(3) the defender must have gained;
(4) the expense must not have been incurred for the pursuer's benefit;
(5) according to some authorities but not all, there must be an error of fact; and
(6) reimbursement must in all the circumstances be equitable.[13]

Public Procurement[14]

3.05   With the passing of the European Communities Act 1972 European Community law became part of U.K. law. The 1957 Treaty of Rome lays down certain fundamental principles that have a bearing on the issue of procurement. Article 7 prohibits discrimination on the grounds of nationality that hinders the basic freedoms which are relevant: such as freedom of movement of goods and the prohibition on quantitative restrictions on imports and exports and measures which have equivalent effect (Arts 30–37); the freedom of establishment — the right to set up business in another state (Arts 52–58); and the freedom to provide services (Arts 59–66). Specifically since 1971 there has been Council Directive 71/305[15] which interpreted the freedom to provide services as it relates to the public works and the construction industry. This directive was amended by the Directive 89/440[16] and latterly consolidated by Directive 93/37.[17] The relevant U.K. law is to

---

[10] See *Cala Homes (South) Ltd v. Alfred McAlpine Homes East Ltd* [1995] F.S.R. 818; but it has been held that under the Copyright, Designs and Patents Act 1988, ss. 96(2) and 97(2) there is no right to exemplary damages as well as an accounting of profits: see *Redrow Homes Ltd v. Bett Brothers plc*, 1997 S.C. 143; 1997 S.L.T. 1125; recently affirmed by the House of Lords on January 22, 1998, and declaring that *Cala Homes* was wrongly decided: http://www.parliament.the-stationery-office.co.uk/pa/ld199798/ldjudgmt/jd980122/redrow.htm

[11] (1880) 8 R. 289.

[12] 1907 S.C. 984.

[13] McBryde, *The Law of Contract in Scotland* (W. Green & Son Ltd, 1987) at 3–37.

[14] For a full exploration of this topic the author can do no better than recommend Arrowsmith, *The Law of Public and Utilities Procurement* (Sweet & Maxwell, 1996).

[15] [1971] O.J. L185/1.

[16] [1989] O.J. L210/1.

[17] [1993] O.J. L199/54.

be found in the Public Works Contracts Regulations 1991 (S.I. 1991 No. 2680) which came into effect on December 21, 1991.

There has been surprisingly little activity in the courts as to the 3.06 interpretation of these Directives and Regulations, despite their complexity and far-reaching effect. Indeed, in a Green Paper entitled "Public Procurement in the European Union: Exploring the way forward",[18] the Commission noted that of the 110,000 contracting authorities and utilities to which the provisions apply, about 85 per cent, especially local authorities, do not follow the advertising and award procedures correctly; and that only three Member States had correctly implemented all the existing rules. On March 11, 1998 priorities for public procurement policy were outlined by a communication of the Commission. The Commission intends to propose amendments to the existing Directives later in 1998 so as to consolidate the Directives on public supplies (93/36), works (93/37) and services (92/50) into a single Directive. Other proposals will be to simplify and make flexible the existing legal framework; encourage Member States to set up or designate independent authorities to act as contact points for the resolution of problems; and encourage electronic procurement over the internet.

Many infringement notices have been issued (as at September 1997 the 3.07 figure was 39); *e.g. Commission of the European Communities v. Germany* where the European Court of Justice found that Germany had failed to implement Directive 89/440 (and 88/295).[19] It is strange that lawyers have largely ignored this area (perhaps because of its complexity)[20] as there are remedies that can be explored. National courts may make interim orders (for example, the suspension of the award procedure); set aside technical specifications that amount to covert discrimination; and award damages to aggrieved suppliers or contractors. The question of damages is an interesting one as this is the only remedy if the contract in question has been entered into. To date there have only been three cases in the U.K. where a contractor has based an action on an infringement of the procurement rules. In *General Building and Maintenance plc v. Greenwich* LBC[21] the court refused to grant an injunction requiring Greenwich to invite the plaintiffs to tender where a request from the plaintiffs to be invited to tender had been rejected on the basis of the plaintiff's safety record. In *R. v. Portsmouth City Council*[22] private building contractors appealed against the decision to dismiss their applications for judicial review of Portsmouth's decision to award the majority of its contracts for maintenance and improvement of housing to its own Direct Labour Organisation. It was held that the Council had not

---

[18] Cm. (96) 83.
[19] Case C–433/95, August 11, 1995, ECJ.
[20] See for example Whish, "The enforcement of EC Competition Law in the Domestic Courts of Member States", 1994 E.C.L.R. 2, 60–67.
[21] (1993) 65 B.L.R. 57; *The Times,* March 9, 1993.
[22] [1997] 81 B.L.R. 1 (CA).

disclosed the criteria for awarding contracts, which was contrary to the 1991 Regulations. Conversely in Scotland in the unreported case of *Tay/Forth Premium Unit Consortium v. Secretary of Scotland*[23] Lord Cameron held in the Outer House that the Secretary of State had adequately stated the criteria for his award decision. It had been argued that a criteria of the lowest price rather than the stated criteria of "most economically advantageous" (MEAT) had been used.

3.08   Quantification of damages raises interesting points. In 1993 the European Court of Justice found Denmark had committed serious breaches of procurement rules by imposing on tenderers the requirement to make the greatest use of Danish materials, labour and equipment in the construction of the Storebaelt Bridge. The Danish courts have since made awards of damages amounting to around £10 million. The remedial measures that are taken by the Commission are carried out under Directive 89/665 — for procurement throughout the public sector — which gives the Commission power to intervene when it learns of breaches, and to seek explanations and demand that the breaches be rectified. The Commission may then take the matter to the European Court of Justice. In the U.K. the Compliance Directive 89/665 was adopted in the 1991 Regulations. However, the U.K. has accepted the derogation from the Compliance Directive by which an individual may not have an award of a public contract set aside once it has been granted. An action of damages is the only remedy, but the difficult question is how this is to be quantified if direct damage cannot be shown. Loss of opportunity is a controversial area, but the court might be influenced by *Chaplin v. Hicks*[24] and award damages based on the likely percentage chance of winning the contract and apply that percentage to any relevant damages for loss of profit. No guidance is given in the Regulations as to how damages might be calculated.

Scope of procurement

Public works

3.09   There are separate Directives concerning Public Works (93/37), Public Supplies (93/36), Public Services (92/50), and Utilities in the WETT sector (*i.e.* Water, Energy, Transport and Telecommunications) (92/50). However, a contract may not fit easily into one or other category. The general rule is that if a contract involves more than 50 per cent of any type of operation, then the directive relating to that operation will apply. But there are exceptions, as where, for construction or civil engineering works, the value of the services exceeds the value of the goods supplied, then the contract will still fall under the Public Works Directive. In *European Commission v. Italy*[25] the Italians

---

[23] October 20, 1995, O.H. Discussed in Cobb and Mathieson, " The Public Procurement Regulations reach the Scottish Courts" (1997) J.L.S.S., Vol. 42, No. 5, p.187.

[24] [1911] 2 K.B. 786.

[25] (1991) 1 C.M.L.R. 115.

unsuccessfully argued that a contract for the supply of computer hardware did not fall within the Supply Directive as there were elements of installation and maintenance. Activities constituting "works" are classified and sub-classified in Schedule 1 to the 1991 Regulations and conform to the general industrial classification of economic activities within the Communities (reg. 2(1)) and range from paper hanging to demolition.

Public bodies

Directives are addressed to Member States, but that includes specific   3.10
bodies which are listed in Annex 1 to the Directive, such as universities, the HSE, Docklands Light Railway, the National Rivers Authority, and fire, police and health service authorities. This list is given to be as "exhaustive as possible". A public body is defined as one that is:

(1)   a body established for the specific purpose of meeting needs in the general interest, not being of a commercial or industrial nature;
(2)   a body which has a legal personality;
(3)   a body which is financed for the most part by the state, regional authority or other bodies governed by public law, or which is subject to the management supervision by those bodies; or which has an administrative, managerial or supervisory board, more than half of whose members are appointed by the state, regional or local authorities or other bodies governed by public laws.

Threshold

The current thresholds applicable to public authorities are: 3.11

(i)   £4,016,744 (5,150,548 ECU) for works contracts;
(ii)   £160,670 (206,022 ECU) for supplies contracts;
(iii) £160,670 (206,022 ECU)for services contracts.

Particular difficulties relate to the "aggregation" of contractual thresholds which involves adding contract values together to prevent the avoidance of the thresholds in the Directives.

Tendering procedure

The tendering procedure relates to the selection of contractors and the   3.12
formal notices that must be prepared. There are three basic types of tendering procedure: open, restricted and negotiated; all with a view to allowing a level playing field for tenderers. Particular difficulties arise in the case of the Private Finance Initiative which is concerned with the procurement of what would traditionally be capital intensive projects, such as hospitals, as revenue expenses for the supply of services in hospitals over a substantial period such as 25 years. The problem is that the restricted procedure which is preferred for PFI does not permit post-tender negotiation, and reliance has been placed on regulation 10(2)(c) for using the negotiated procedure:

"exceptionally, when the nature of the work or works to be carried out under the contract as such, or the risks attaching thereto are such, as not to permit prior overall pricing".

HOW IS CONSENSUS ACHIEVED?

3.13   It is a disturbing fact of life in the construction industry that often important practical steps are taken, even to bringing a building to practical completion, without a formal contract being executed. The problem of whether there was a contract at all applies particularly when so-called "letters of intent" are issued,[26] and work progresses on that basis. It may be that the contractor will start ordering materials that have a long delivery time, such as steel, at a very early stage. Each case will turn on its own circumstances in determining whether a letter of intent leaves open contractual negotiations and the *locus poenitentiae*; or does not affect the reality of *consensus ad idem* reached by the parties; or creates a condition precedent or suspensive condition. Interpretation of the correspondence will be to determine (i) whether a letter of intent discloses an intention to create a contractual relationship; (ii) whether all essential terms to make the contract workable as a matter of commercial common sense are agreed, either expressly or impliedly; and (iii) whether there is a sufficiently clear manifestation of acceptance of the offer as then made.[27] However, an agreement to negotiate is not enforceable.[28]

3.14   *Drake and Scull Engineering Ltd v. Higgs and Hill Northern Ltd*[29] concerned the supply and fix of mechanical and electrical installations by the plaintiffs as sub-contractors to the defendants under a JCT 81 design and build main contract with a hospital employer. The plaintiffs sought a declaration that the sub-contract works were done in the absence of a contract, or alternatively under a "bare" contract with an agreement that they would be indemnified for all expenditure including overheads and profit for all work undertaken. The appropriate standard form DOM/2 was not used; instead there was exchange of correspondence. As a result of the exchange of correspondence all terms save one for a binding contract were found to have been agreed: dayworks rates had not been agreed. Fox-Andrews J. in the Official Referee's Court found that lacuna could be cured by the implication of a term that a reasonable sum would be paid for dayworks. But even so, the parties had expressly stated in correspondence that the sub-contract was "subject to the execution of a sub-contract

---

[26] See particularly *British Steel Corporation v. Cleveland Bridge Engineering Co. Ltd* [1981] 24 B.L.R. 94 and *Turriff Construction Ltd v. Regalia Mills Ltd* (1971) 9 B.L.R. 20. For a useful text see Furmiston and others, *Contract Formation and Letters of Intent* (1998).
[27] *Trollope and Colls Ltd v. Atomic Power Construction* [1963] 1 W.L.R. 333.
[28] See *Walford v. Myles* [1992] 2 W.L.R. 174.
[29] 1995 Const. L.J. 214.

contractor". The judge found that these words were not qualified. The defendant had written on March 25, 1992: "we confirm that it is our intention to enter into a sub-contract with you for design, supply and installation.... The formal sub-contract document will be completed and forwarded to you in due course and will comprise the following..." The plaintiffs replied on April 1, 1992 denying design responsibility (later agreed) and seeking an indemnity "in respect of all expenditure which we may incur, in the event that for any reason outside our control, the order is not placed with us". Work commenced on April 6, 1992 without clarification. In response to a reminder the defendant wrote some five weeks later on May 11: "We would conclude by confirming that we will indemnify you in respect of all reasonable expenditure which [you] may incur [in] the event that for any reason outside of your control the order is not placed with you. The formal sub-contract documents are currently being compiled and will be forwarded in due course...." The works proceeded to practical completion in July 1993, but it was not until May 18, 1993 that the plaintiffs were sent a copy of their tender to be formally executed. After a review of authorities Fox-Andrews J. considered this case to be an exception to the authorities that suggest that the courts will not normally stand on a lack of formality when much of the works are done. He reached his view not so much on the basis of the wording of the letter of intent but because of the indemnity agreement, which was a distinct agreement. Also, he stated: "If both parties, five weeks after works have commenced so clearly state that a sub-contract will not come into being until it has been formalised, it is not for the court to interfere and impose its own inclination." The judge was however unable to reach a conclusion as to what was meant by "all reasonable expenditure" until consideration was given to the quantification of the sub-contractor's claim; in much the same way as Bingham J. had been unable to do so in *Crown House Engineering v. Amec Projects Ltd.*[30]

The status of letters of intent and the problems of the lack of a formal contract have exercised the courts a great deal in recent years. In *Kitsons Sheet Metal Ltd v. Balfour Beatty Building*[31] a letter of intent left unanswered how Kitsons were to be paid. The defendants were main contractors and the plaintiffs submitted a tender for sub-contract work in October 1987. In March 1988 the defendants sent a letter of intent saying it should be accepted as authority to proceed with design. Later, in August 1988 Balfour Beatty sent a contract to Kitsons. Kitsons said this was not what they tendered for, nor did it cover the variations since they tendered, and did not sign it. It was held that there was no formal contract reached, particularly as regards payment or a payment schedule, but there was a right to be paid on an equitable basis.

3.15

---

[30] (1989) 48 B.L.R. 32.
[31] (1989) 47 B.L.R. 42.

3.16   In *C.J. Sims Ltd v. Shaftesbury plc Ltd*[32] works commenced on the basis of a letter of intent which stated that:

> "In the unlikely event of the contract not proceeding [Sims] will be reimbursed their reasonable costs which have been and will be incurred and costs for which they are liable including those of their sub-contractors and suppliers, such costs to include loss of profit and contributions to overheads, all of which must be substantiated in full to the reasonable satisfaction of [Shaftesbury's] quantity surveyor."

The works progressed to practical completion and in the Official Referee's Court it was conceded that the letter of intent followed by the commencement of work gave rise to a contract. The substantive matter in this case was whether substantiation to the quantity surveyor was a condition precedent to payment, which it was held to be. Interestingly, this case does not appear to have been cited to the court in *Drake and Scull* (*supra*).

3.17   In Scotland, in *Uniroyal Ltd v. Miller*[33] Lord Allanbridge agreed with the observations of Goff J. in *British Steel Corporation v. Cleveland Bridge & Engineering Co.*[34] that "there is no hard and fast answer to the question whether the letter of intent will give rise to a binding agreement: everything must depend on the circumstances of the particular case". In *Uniroyal* Lord Allanbridge came to the view that the phrase "letter of intent follows", did not indicate that the parties were still in negotiation, as there were no terms left to negotiate.

3.18   Scots law recognises that contracts can be formed in all material respects but that their operation is suspended pending a future event, *e.g.* that a future event occurs (the Millenium). In such a case "the grantor... has no right to resile".[35] Again, the wording of a letter of intent would require to be examined to consider whether it creates such a suspensive condition.[36] Recently, for example, in *Noordhoek-Energie Diving & ROV Services BV v. Subsea Offshore Ltd*[37] Lord Penrose held that a clause relative to the "securement" of a licence for diving operations in the North Sea was suspensive of obligation. It has even been suggested by the authors of the *Stair Memorial Encyclopaedia*[38] that a letter of intent might be framed in such a way as to amount to an enforceable "lock-out" agreement so as to preclude negotiation with others; although an agreement to negotiate is not normally enforceable.[39]

---

[32]   (1991) 25 Con. L.R. 72.
[33]   1985 S.L.T. 101 at 107.
[34]   [1984] 1 All E.R. 504.
[35]   Erskine, *Prin.*, III. i. 3.
[36]   See W.W. McBryde, *The Law of Contract in Scotland* (1987), pp. 42–44.
[37]   Lord Penrose, O.H., Mar. 29, 1996, unreported.
[38]   Butterworths, *Building Contracts* Vol. 3, para. 22.
[39]   *Walford v. Myles* [1992] 2 W.L.R. 174.

Contractual step-down provisions

Often there is difficulty with the terms of sub-contracts where the main   3.19
contractor purports to incorporate the terms of the main contract into the
sub-contract by referring to the main contract conditions; or by changing
the main contract provisions to fit the sub-contract in all respects, apart
from consequential minor changes, by using the phrase *"mutatis mutandis"*.

In *Haskins (Shutters) Ltd v D. & J. Ogilvie (Builders) Ltd*[40] the main   3.20
contract provided that the sub-contract "shall be in the same terms and
conditions applicable to the main contract". In the main contract there was
an arbitration clause which provided that disputes between the employer
and the main contractor were to be referred to arbitration. It was held by the
sheriff — following the decision of the First Division in *Goodwins, Jardine
& Co. v. Brand & Son*[41] — that if the result of the arbitration between the
employer and the main contractor had a bearing on the sub-contract then it
was binding on the sub-contractor. But, the arbitration clause did not apply
to disputes between the main contractor and the sub-contractor: "if this had
been intended then it would and should have been made a matter of express
provision."

In *Sauter Automation v. Goodman (H.C.) (Mechanical Services) Ltd (in*   3.21
liquidation)[42] a supplier of materials quoted to the main contractor on
conditions of sale which retained title in the goods until payment was made
in full. The main contractor placed an order on slightly different terms on
price and provided: "Terms and Conditions in accordance with main contract
CC/Wks/1." The main contract required that the main contractor enter into
sub-contracts providing for materials brought onto site to vest in the
employer. It was held that the main contractor's order represented a counter-
offer accepted by supply and that what was offered was a sub-contract where
the relationship between the main contractor and the supplier was such as
to be consistent with the main contract, so that there should be no conflict
between them. The retention of title clause accordingly did not prevail over
the main contract terms.

Further, in *Smith v. South Wales Switchgear*[43] an offer was placed "subject   3.22
to our General Conditions of Contract obtainable on request" and the
conditions were not requested, but it turned out that there were three styles
of these conditions. It was held that the offer referred to the conditions
current at the time of the offer.

Lord Jauncey in *Parklea Ltd v. W. & J.R. Watson Ltd*[44] looked at "a number   3.23
of unsuccessful attempts … made to incorporate all the provisions of a
principal contract into a sub-contract by shorthand methods". After looking

---

[40] 1978 S.L.T. 64.
[41] (1905) 13 S.L.T. 329.
[42] (1986) 34 B.L.R. 81.
[43] (1977) 8 B.L.R. 5, (HL).
[44] 1988 S.L.T. 605.

at the Scots and English authorities he found "no principles can be derived therefrom".[45] He did however note that in *Brightside Kilpatrick Engineering Services v. Mitchell Construction*[46] the Court of Appeal held that the words "the Conditions applicable to the Sub-Contract with you shall be those embodied in the R.I.B.A. as above agreement" did not in the particular circumstances import all the R.I.B.A. conditions into the sub-contract, but rather created a sub-contractual relationship wherein there would be no conflict between the principal contract and the sub-contract. Lord Jauncey followed that line even where there were repetitions and some contradictions, so that the sub-contract must be capable of performance within, but not necessarily upon, the terms of the main contract.

Regulation of the relationship between different contract documents

3.24   There is a peculiarity in JCT forms regarding formation. Clause 2.2.1 of
           JCT 80 provides:

> "nothing contained in the Contract Bills shall override or modify the application or interpretation of that which is contained in the Articles of Agreement [defined in the Scottish Building Contract as the foregoing Building Contract], the Conditions or the Appendix [which in the Scottish Building Contract is Appendix II]."

The normal rule of interpretation is that written words (*i.e.* the Bills) prevail over printed words[47] (*i.e.* the Conditions). Hudson's *Building and Engineering Contracts* (11th ed.) is scathing in its criticism of such a clause (para. 1–226). In practice what often happens is that the Contract Bills are drafted purporting to incorporate differing conditions which are set out in the Bills. The justification of such a "non-supersession" clause seems to be standardisation of tendering procedures. JCT 80's predecessor JCT 63 was examined by the courts on this question on a number of occasions and produced inconsistent decisions. JCT 63 is slightly different from JCT 80 in this respect. Clause 12(1) of JCT 63 provides that:

> "the quality and quantity of the work included in the Contract Sum shall be deemed to be that which is set out in the Contract Bills… but save as aforesaid nothing contained in the Contract Bills shall override, modify or *affect in any way whatsoever*… these Conditions" [author's emphasis]

3.25   The emphasised words have been altered in JCT 80, and reference to "quality and quantity of the work" now appears separately at clause 14.1. *Keating on Building Contracts* (6th ed.) at page 546 suggests that it is not clear whether matters of quantity and quality are unaffected by clause 2.2.1 of JCT 80, but that in most cases quality and quantity will not be matters featuring in the Articles (the Scottish Building Contract), the Conditions, or the Appendix (Appendix II of the Scottish Building Contract).

---

[45] *op. cit.* at p. 608D.
[46] [1975] 2 Lloyd's Rep. 493.
[47] See *The Brabant* [1967] 1 Q.B. 588.

In *Henry Boot v. Central Lancashire New Town Development* 3.26
Corporation[48] the main contractor under JCT 63 priced Contract Bills which
contained provisional sums for work to be executed by certain statutory
undertakers, but which also stated that such sums were to be expended
under the direct order of the employer. Various services were constructed
by statutory undertakers engaged directly by the employer. The court held
that in clause 12(1) of JCT 63 the phrase "quality and quantity of the work
included in the Contract Sum" was wide enough to allow it to look at the
Contract Bills to interpret the scope of works priced by the contractor; and
found the works carried out by the statutory undertakers were not properly
part of the contract works priced for by the main contractor.

The words now omitted (affect in any way whatsoever) were considered 3.27
in *English Industrial Estates v. Wimpey*[49] where it was held that in so far as
the Bills dealt with matters covered by the Conditions they had no effect on
the printed Conditions. Keating suggests that under JCT 80 the court is
entitled to look at the Bills and to give effect to them to the extent that the
Bills supplement the Conditions. In so far as the Bills purport to override or
modify the Articles of Agreement (the Scottish Building Contract), the
Conditions or the Appendix (Appendix II of the Scottish Building Contract),
they continue to have no effect.

In *Moody v. Ellis*,[50] a professional negligence action against an architect 3.28
was brought by the employer. The employer claimed that the architect was
liable for payments found due by the employer to the contractor for delays
after an arbitration involving a JCT 63 form. The Court of Appeal made
obiter remarks concerning clause 12 of JCT 63. The court said that a
provision in the Bills by which the Contractor was to carry out the works in
conformity with a programme agreed with the architect, was sustainable
and did not contravene the printed conditions. This outcome would probably
come as a surprise to contractors familiar with JCT contracts who typically
interpret a programme as indicative of likely progress, and not a matter that
imposes obligations to keep to it; for example, see clause 5.3.2 of JCT 80.

The courts have been difficult to follow in principle in their interpretation of 3.29
clause 12 of JCT 63, and perhaps for this reason, it is common practice in the
industry to attempt to delete clause 2.2.1 in the Scottish Building Contract (Articles
in England), or the Conditions, or when inviting tenders. There is however always
likely to be a danger in attempting to delete clause 2.2.1 in the Bills themselves.

In relation to the predecessor of clause 2.2.1, *viz.* clause 12(1) of JCT 63, 3.30
the First Division of the Inner House in *Inverclyde District Council v. Hardstock
(Scotland) Ltd*[51] followed the decisions in *M.J. Gleeson (Contractors) Ltd v.
London Borough of Hillingdon*[52] and *North West Metropolitan Regional*

---

[48] (1980) 15 B.L.R. 1.
[49] [1973] 1 Lloyd's Rep. 118 (C.A.).
[50] (1983) 26 B.L.R. 39 (C.A.).
[51] 1984 S.L.T. 226.
[52] [1970] E.G.D. 495.

Hospital Board v. T.A. Bickerton & Son Ltd.[53] *Inverclyde* was a case where the contract particulars provided that: "Execution of the Building Contract shall be deemed to have taken place when a tender and a letter of acceptance have been exchanged between the parties...." It also provided that:

> "the Works shall be completed in accordance with, and the rights and duties of the Employer and the Contractor shall be regulated by (A) the Schedule of Conditions of The Standard Form of Building Contract Local Authorities/ Private Edition with/without Quantities (1963 Edition) (July 1973 Revision) issued by the Joint Contracts Tribunal which is held to be incorporated in and forms part of this Contract, as modified by the provisions contained in the Scottish Supplement forming Appendix No. I hereto, (B) the Abstract of the said Schedule of Conditions forming Appendix No. II hereto..."

No comment in the case related to the failure to delete to show which edition was to be used, or whether it was to be with or without Quantities. The Abstract of the schedule of conditions which formed Appendix II stated:

Clause no.

Date for Possession	21	To be agreed
Date for Completion	21	130 weeks
Liquidate and Ascertained Damages	22	at the rate of £5 per house per week.

3.31   In paragraph 4(c) of Bill No. 1 headed "Description of the Works" it stated:

> "The Contractor, on acceptance of his offer will proceed immediately with the preparation of a programme which will set out the sequence of all operations and the time limits within which the Contractor proposes that each operation will be commenced and completed. Within the period allocated to each operation, the number of house units to be completed within each week will be identified.... The house hand over operations sequence on the programme will identify the date of each block hand over and will be so programmed to give 19 houses handed over by the end of the first 54 week period and a regular hand over of houses thereafter.... Liquidate and ascertained damages as specified in Appendix II of these conditions will apply to any shortfall on the total number of houses due to have been handed over by the end of any assessment period and will be deducted from the sum due in the subsequent valuations."

3.32   An arbiter had held that the attempt to levy liquidate and ascertained damages by the district council at any time prior to the date for completion, which was 130 weeks after the date for possession, or as ascertained, was inconsistent with clause 12(1). On appeal by the district council, the Lord President (Lord Emslie) giving the opinion of the court:

---

[53] [1970] 1 W.L.R. 60.

"had no hesitation in holding that the appeal fails.... In our opinion condition 12 is fatal to the District Council's attempt to justify their deductions by invoking the terms of para. 4(c) of bill no.1... 'special arrangements' would, in the circumstances of this case, necessarily have required modification of cond. 22 or at least cond. 12(1) to permit reliance upon para. 4(c) of bill no.1 notwithstanding that it might be thought to override, modify, or affect the provisions of cond. 22... para. 4(c) ... purports to modify or affect cond. 22 in a drastic way."

What seems to have been particularly significant in this case was that the court thought that anything but this interpretation could render the contractor: "liable for failure to meet sectional completion dates in circumstances in which the date for completion has, for good and relevant reasons, been substantially postponed by extensions of time".

Recently, however, in *Barry D. Trentham Ltd v. Robert McNeil,*[54] Lord Penrose   3.33
in the Commercial Court seems, on similar facts, to have drawn a distinction between clause 12(1) of JCT 63 and clause 2.2.1 of JCT 80 and the Scottish Supplement. He noted that the 1980 provisions require the Building Contract, the Conditions and the Appendix to be read as a whole (clause 1.2). As the Appendix was partly typewritten, it had priority over the printed conditions on ordinary principles of construction of contracts.[55] Therefore, an Appendix that provided for liquidated damages for failure to meet phases, details of which were expanded upon in the bills, was not subordinated by clause 2.2.1; as the relevant documents had to be read as a whole and had to be construed together. Lord Penrose held that reading all the documents as a whole, it was impossible to avoid the conclusion that there were inconsistencies that made it impossible to give effect to all sets of words. In construing the documents together, the Appendix should have priority over the conditions on ordinary principles. It seems, therefore, in Scotland at least, that the courts will take a different view in interpreting these so-called "priority clauses" depending on whether JCT 63 or JCT 80 is used. *Inverclyde* was distinguished, on the basis that it was decided on the wording of a quite different contract.

Performance and payment

Performance bonds have been the subject of much criticism and, indeed,   3.34
confusion in recent years. In *Trafalgar House Construction v. General Surety*[56] it was said "it is difficult to see why commercial men persist with the outmoded language [of performance bonds]". Also in the Latham Report *Constructing the Team*[57] criticisms of the language of bonds, and alternatives to their use, were made.

---

[54] 1996 S.L.T. 202 (OH).
[55] "It is a general rule that if the record of the contract consists of a printed form with alterations or additions in writing, the written portion is to rule in the event of any discrepancy", *Gloag on Contract*, p. 339.
[56] [1994] 66 B.L.R. 42 at 49, 52 and 54.
[57] See Chapter 8, *post.*

3.35   Performance Bonds have been described as "a third party contract
          between the employer, the contractor and the surety guaranteeing
          performance by providing the employer with a stated maximum financial
          benefit (normally 10% of the contract value) in the event of non-
          performance".[58] The NJCC guidance notes comment on the subject of
          performance bonds as follows:

> (i)   The correct operation of selective tendering procedures means that the
>   contractors should not default and should not go into liquidation;
> (ii) these add to the building costs and are an unnecessary cost; and
> (iii) obtaining the bond may actually limit the contractor's financial resources
>   to the extent where he is more likely to be in default on the contract.

          The notion then is that performance bonds are a type of financial "long
          stop", but there grew from the 1960s, particularly in international
          construction projects, the requirement of letters from a bank which were to
          be paid "on demand" as a source of compensation should the contractor
          fail to perform. Confusion has continued as to the meaning of such bonds.
3.36   The drafting of these bonds often differs with each project and for
          Scotland and England. In Scotland styles are to be found in J. M. Halliday,
          Conveyancing Law and Practice.[59] The style of bond given there is the
          Institution of Civil Engineers' form, which is remarkable in having an
          arbitration clause if there is any dispute or difference between employer
          and contractor concerning the relevant date under a maintenance certificate
          or the withholding of a maintenance certificate. Clearly, as there is no such
          thing as a maintenance certificate under JCT forms, great care should be
          taken with an unquestioning use of this style. Also, Halliday gives a style
          of an indemnity to the guarantor that would normally be given by the
          contractor. However, the style of the indemnity is payable on demand whilst
          the performance bond is clearly conditional. A contractor might be exposed
          to a greater risk with this form of indemnity than the performance bond
          itself. For example, in *De Montford Insurance Co. plc v. Lafferty*[60] it was
          held that there could be circumstances where payment could be demanded
          of the grantor of a personal bond to an insurer which were wider than the
          circumstances requiring payment by the insurer under a bond.[61]
3.37   One of the main difficulties with bonds is in anticipating what the courts
          will make of them, as there appears to be two opposing schools of thought
          at work. The first of these is that a performance bond is like a letter of
          credit and designed to release "no quibble" cash to the bearer in the event
          of the bond being called; presumably to tide the bondholder over in the

---

[58]   National Joint Consultative Committee for Building, Guidance Note "Performance Bonds"
       (1986).
[59]   (1985) Vol. 1, pp. 405–407.
[60]   1998 S.L.T. 535.
[61]   *ibid.* at 540 J–L.

event of having to get the works completed by someone else. This is the so-called "on demand" bond. The second school is that bonds are to be construed according to the established law of suretyship or, in Scotland, caution.

A cautionary obligation is "an accessory obligation or engagement, as 3.38 surety for another, that the principal obligant shall pay the debt or perform the act for which he was engaged, otherwise the cautioner shall pay the debt or fulfil the obligation".[62] It has to be distinguished from an independent obligation,[63] delegation, a representation as to credit,[64] an indemnity[65] and insurance. An indemnity is an obligation to relieve the other contracting party of any loss incurred by him by entering into a certain transaction; it is bilateral, while cautionry is trilateral. Insurance is an obligation to pay a sum on the occurrence of an event.

There is in Scotland a distinction between proper and improper caution. 3.39 Cautionry is proper when the fact that the parties are principal debtor and cautioner appears on the face of the deed; it is improper where they are bound as co-obligants although in fact they are principal debtor and cautioner.[66] The significance of the distinction is that in proper caution the creditor has certain duties to the cautioner; in improper caution he can treat the cautioner as a co-obligant although the rules of cautionry apply between the cautioner and the principal debtor. The crucial question is whether the creditor has to constitute his claim against the principal debtor before turning to the cautioner. This was the position at common law for proper cautionry and it is questionable whether that may still apply in so far as cautionry is in respect of the performance of obligations *ad factum praestandum* other than the payment of money debts.[67]

In *Johannesburg Municipal Council v. D. Stewart & Co. (1902) Ltd*[68] 3.40 there was an action for damages against the suppliers of engineering plant and against the guarantors in a performance bond, and it was held by the Lord President that there was no action against the guarantors until there was a failure to recover from the contractor on proof of breach of contract. On appeal to the Lords it was held that the matter was governed by English law but the comments of the Lord President were not disapproved.

The typical position under a performance bond in the Halliday style is that improper caution is created. However, even if the principal debtor and cautioner are co-obligants *ex facie* the deed, if the creditor knows at the

---

[62] Bell, *Principles*, s. 245.
[63] *Morrison v. Harkness* (1870) 9 M. 35; *Stevenson's Tr. v. Campbell & Sons* (1896) 23 R. 711; *Aitken & Co. v. Pyper* (1900) 38 S.L.R. 74.
[64] *Fortune v. Young*, 1918 S.C. 1.
[65] *Milne v. Kidd* (1869) 8 M. 250; *Simpson v. Jack*, 1948 S.L.T. (Notes) 45.
[66] Bell, *Principles*, s. 247.
[67] See Gloag and Irvine, *Law of Rights in Security* (1897), p. 788; see Mercantile Law Amendment (Scotland) Act 1856, s.8.
[68] 1909 S.C. 860, *per* Lord President Dunedin; on appeal 1909 S.C. (H.L.) 53.

time of entry to the obligation that they are in fact principal debtor and cautioner he must treat them as such.[69] It is necessary that the debtor be in default, and whether there is default is a question of fact.[70]

3.41   In England "on demand" bonds are regarded as similar to letters of credit. In *Edward Owen Engineering Ltd v. Barclay's Bank International Ltd*[71] a bond provided that the sum stated therein was "payable on demand without proof or conditions". Lord Denning said:

> "All this leads to the conclusion that the performance guarantee stands on a similar footing to a letter of credit. A bank which gives a performance guarantee must honour that guarantee according to its terms. It is not concerned in the least with the relations between the supplier and the customer; nor with the question whether the supplier has performed his contracted obligation or not; nor with the question whether the supplier is in default or not. The bank must pay according to its guarantee, on demand, if so stipulated, without proof or conditions. The only exception is when there is a clear fraud of which the bank has notice."

What was remarkable about this case was that the employers themselves were in clear breach of contract at the time in that they had failed in their obligation to open an irrevocable letter of credit, but the Appeal Court did not hold that this constituted fraud.

3.42   Recently in *Turkiye IS Bankasi AS v. Bank of China*[72] the *Edward Owen* authority was followed and it was held that the party seeking to challenge a demand made on a performance bond had to show that the only realistic inference which a bank could draw was that the demand was fraudulent and not simply make allegations expecting the bank to check whether the demand was well founded. Similarly, in *Themehelp v. West*[73] where a judge had been satisfied that there was an arguable case of fraud, an injunction could be obtained against bondholders from calling on the bond.

3.43   However, in the Scottish case of *The Royal Bank of Scotland Ltd v. Dinwoodie*[74] the defender contractor had issued a performance bond in a style similar to the Halliday style. It read:

> "Now the condition of the above written bond is such that if the contractor shall duly perform and observe all the terms, provisions, conditions and stipulations of the said contract on the contractor's part to be performed and observed according to the true purport, intent and meaning thereof or if on default by the contractor the surety shall satisfy and discharge the damages sustained by the employer thereby up to the amount of the above written bond then this obligation shall be null and void but otherwise shall be and remain in full force and effect."

---

[69]   Gloag & Irvine, p. 674; *Mackenzie v. Macartney* (1831) 5 W. & S. 504.
[70]   Gloag & Irvine, p. 789.
[71]   [1978] 1 All E.R. 976 (AC).
[72]   *The Times*, March 8, 1996.
[73]   [1995] 3 W.L.R. 751 (AC).
[74]   1987 S.L.T. 82.

In this case it was held that the pursuers who paid out as if it were an on demand bond and who then sought to call the counter-indemnity that the contractor had given the bank, had not acted correctly. There was a certificate from the engineer that the contractor had failed to proceed with the work with due diligence, but there was no more than an estimate of damages likely to be incurred. The court held "that the pursuers would require to be satisfied at the very least that damages had been sustained by the employer, and as to the quantification of these damages". The English cases were distinguished on the basis that different wording had been used in the bonds in those cases, and specifically that in *Dinwoodie* there was no such phrase as "payable on demand".[75] Indeed, Lord Sutherland noted that from the terminology used in the bond "it would appear that if there is a default by the contractor, but the employer sustains no damages as a result, the obligation is nullified without any payment".[76]

In relation to a performance bond given in a style similar to the Halliday style, it has been held that this constitutes a cautionary obligation and not an indemnity or contract of insurance, *per* Lord Ross in *City of Glasgow District Council v. Excess Insurance Co. Ltd.*[77] This case concerned whether a claim under a bond had prescribed. There is a five-year prescriptive period in respect of cautionry obligations and a 20-year period in respect of an indemnity or a contract of insurance. A contractor had gone into receivership on July 8, 1976 and the summons had been signeted on June 7, 1983. The loss was not quantified until August 24, 1981. It seemed to have been accepted by both sides that going into receivership constituted default. Lord Ross held that the date of receivership was the relevant date for five-year prescription to run even though only an estimate of loss could be given and might be met by the defence that the defenders had made good the loss. However, Lord Mayfield dealt with exactly the same circumstances and parties in *City of Glasgow District Council v. Excess Insurance Co. Ltd (No.2)*.[78] Here the pursuers argued that it had been erroneously conceded in the first case that the date of receivership constituted the relevant date, and that the contractor was not in default until he failed to pay on an architect's certificate direct loss and/or damage caused to the employer on determination under JCT 63, clause 25(4)(d). The certificate was issued in February 1986. Lord Mayfield assumed that the architect's certificate clause had not been pled in the first case. He then found, following the decision in *McPhail v. Cunninghame District Council; William Loudon & Son Ltd v. Cunninghame District Council*[79] that the contractor's obligation to make payment to the employer under the relevant determination clause arose when that amount was quantified, and an architect's certificate issued; and not therefore on

3.44

---

75 *op. cit.* at 84E.
76 *op.cit.* at 84F.
77 1986 S.L.T. 585.
78 1990 S.L.T. 225.
79 1985 S.L.T. 149.

the appointment of the receiver. The claim on the bond had not prescribed and decree *de plano* was granted. He also found that when the bond stated that it expired on practical completion, that meant when practical completion was achieved by the obligant under the bond, and not a replacement contractor. The second case did not affect the question of whether the bond was a cautionary obligation.

3.45 In *Perar BV v. General Surety & Guarantee Co.*[80] there was a JCT Design and Build Standard Form of Contract 1981 for £13 million and a performance bond for 10 per cent. The surety was to be notified of any breach or default on the part of the contractor, of any variation, and be given permission to perform where the contractor had failed. Clauses 27.2 and 27.4 provided for the respective rights and duties of the employer and the contractor in the event *inter alia* of the appointment of an administrative receiver to the contractor. It provided that in this event the employment of the contractor shall be forthwith automatically determined but that said employment may be reinstated if agreed. Clause 27.4.5 provided that the contractor should allow or pay to the employer the amount of any direct loss and/or damage caused to the employer by the determination. It was held that the contractor going into administrative receivership did not amount to an anticipatory breach of contract. The relevant clauses provided an exclusive code and the employer had no option but to continue the contract and for an accounting. The contractor was not in default, as such, and therefore the bond could not be called. What this effectively meant was that if a contractor had his employment terminated for abandoning the works then the bond could be called, but if his employment was determined because of insolvency, it could not, as automatic determination was a contractual term, even if it resulted in abandonment of the works as a subsequent fact. That this was effectively a loophole was pointed out and made the subject of academic criticism.[81] The position would be different where there are pre-existing breaches of contract before the intervention of insolvency.[82]

3.46 Cautionary obligations are normally construed strictly as was seen in *Clydebank and District Water Trustees v. Fidelity and Deposit Company of Maryland.*[83] Contractors were employed to lay water pipes, and, as required by their employers, they obtained from an insurance company a policy insuring the employers against loss arising out of failure duly to complete the work. The policy contained a clause declaring that it was executed "upon the following express conditions, which shall be conditions precedent to the right of the employer to recover hereunder". The first of the conditions was: "The surety shall be notified in writing of any non performance or

---

[80] (1994) 43 Con.L.R. 110 (AC).
[81] I. Duncan Wallace, "Strict canons in the Court of Appeal, Not "Business Commonsense", 1996 C.L.J. 178.
[82] *Nene Housing Society v. National Westminster Bank* (1980) 16 B.L.R. 22.
[83] 1915 S.C. (H.L.) 69.

non observance on the part of the contractors of any of the stipulations or provisions contained in the said contract, and on their part to be performed and observed, which may involve a loss for which the surety is responsible hereunder."

The contractors did not commence laying the pipes till long after the commencement date, and about half way through the contract went into liquidation. The Lord Chancellor stated:

"... a delay in commencing the work so serious in extent must have involved the possibility of the contractors being unable to complete it within the proper time, with the resultant claim for damages, from which claim the engineer could not have fairly exonerated the contractor by his certificate. That the delay was a breach of the conditions of the contract is of course beyond dispute. It was a breach which, in my opinion, might have involved loss for which the surety would have been responsible. It might have involved such loss, even if the frost and bad weather were really the causes of the delay; and in those circumstances it was essential, in order to satisfy the condition precedent in the bond, that due notice should be given to the insurance company that such breach had occurred. In fact the delay was never overtaken".

In this case no details are given as to any counter bond that might have been given by the contractor to the insurance company, and it is difficult to see just where the insurers were prejudiced, except that the surety might have better organised its cashflow, or perhaps there never was any counter bond. It was noted that the employers could have caused delay themselves which would prevent their claim on the surety. It was also noted in this case that there was a delay in obtaining access to the site but that could be disregarded on a view of the whole progress which was not notified to the insurers.

In comparing English and Scottish cases it seemed recently that the English 3.47 courts might take a different view from the Scottish position. In *Trafalgar House Construction (Regions) Ltd v. General Surety and Guarantee Co. Ltd* [84] a bond similar to the Halliday style was considered difficult to construe, and would not make sense if the contractors were guaranteeing their own performance. It is submitted that the bond is not unusual in the context of improper caution. In this case it was held that for a bond as between a subcontractor and guarantor to a main contractor, the purpose of it was to provide ready cash to the main contractor in the event of the sub-contractor's insolvency. A call on the bond in good faith was all that was required without detailed quantification of a net amount. Where there is a claim on a conditional bond, the claimant has to assert that a particular event has occurred and that loss has suffered as a result. The claimant does not have to have a court or arbitration award to support these contentions, he must merely have to assert these things (see *ESAL (Commodities) Ltd and Relton Ltd v. Oriental Credit and Wills Fargo Bank NA*[85]).

---

[84] 1994 C.L.J. 240 (CA).
[85] [1985] 2 Lloyd's Rep. 546 (AC).

3.48   Until *Trafalgar House* was appealed to the Lords we had seemed to have moved away from the position as set out in Gloag and Irvine, *Rights in Security*, p. 624:

> "Cautionary, in Scotland, corresponds to suretyship in England; and the principles that regulate the contract are practically identical in both countries."

However, on June 29, 1995, the Lords reversed the decision of the Court of Appeal[86] in a judgment of the court given by Lord Jauncey (who is, of course, Scottish). The bond was construed as a conditional bond and proof of damage, not the mere assertion in good faith, was necessary. Lord Jauncey continued the criticism of the bond, whilst noting that similar bonds had been in existence for some 150 years. He said:

> "I find great difficulty in understanding the desire of commercial men to embody so simple an obligation in a document which is quite unnecessarily lengthy, which obfuscates its true purpose, and which gives rise to unnecessary argument and litigation as to its meaning."

3.49   In fact, the bond in the *Trafalgar House* case was almost identical to the *Perar* bond (ignoring the notice provisions) with the relevant changes made as between main contractor and sub-contractor.

3.50   There has been some suggestion that well-drawn bonds would make the intervention of a third party necessary, for example, an arbiter (under the ICE style) or a judge, but it is not easy to get a concession like this from an employer. On-demand bonds seem to be interpreted in England in the way Scots law would consider an indemnity, as where a bank pledges its own credit; for example, see *Harbottle (R.D.) v. National Westminster Bank*.[87] In this case, both parties should have granted bonds to each other. The buyer did not, but the court held that this did not prevent him from calling up the supplier's bond, *i.e.* there was not mutuality about these matters.

3.51   Recently, the Association of British Insurers have published a form of bond, and also the Institution of Civil Engineers have produced a new style of bond. It remains to be seen whether these can solve the difficulties associated with this topic. Clause 10.3 of the FIDIC (3rd ed.) Conditions of Contract for Electrical and Mechanical Works provides that the employer is not entitled to make a claim under the performance bond unless: a breach has been notified to the contractor and it has not been remedied within a specific period; or the employer and the contractor have agreed in writing the amount due; or the employer has obtained an award under an arbitration.

---

[86] [1995] 3 W.L.R. 204 (HL).
[87] [1978] 2.B. Lloyd's Rep. 146.
[88] [1986] 2.B. Lloyd's Rep. 146.

There is also the interesting question whether a bond in a construction   3.51
contract setting would be a "construction contract" for the purposes of the
Housing Grants, Construction and Regeneration Act 1996, and therefore
subject to the adjudication provisions.[89]

Set-off and payment certificates

Building contracts normally involve interim payments[90] and a   3.52
certification process in this regard. JCT 80 at clause 30.1.1 deals with interim
certificates. The contractor is to be paid within 14 days of the certificate
being issued by the architect/contract administrator to the employer. Clause
41B is the arbitration clause in the Scottish Building Contract and this
provides that one matter which may be taken to arbitration is whether a
certificate has been improperly withheld by the architect/contract
administrator or is not in accordance with the conditions. Under previous
editions of the Scottish Building Contract arbitration was not barred until
after practical completion for such matters.Under the current August 1998
revision such disputes can be the subject of adjudication under clause 41A,
and thereafter arbitration under clause 41B (where this clause applies rather
than clause 41C in relation to court proceedings), apparently at any time
until 60 days after the issue of a final certificate.This means that the
certificates are not conclusive in themselves. Very frequently what happens
is that the employer does not pay the contractor and the contractor does not
pay the sub-contractors, even though there are appropriate certificates. Non-
payment can activate the determination by contractor provisions in JCT
80, which are in clause 28; and the new suspension provisions that are
introduced by amendment 18 in clause 30.1.4. Normally what is argued for
withholding payment is that a party has a right of set-off, for example where
there is defective workmanship, or the sub-contractor has involved the main
contractor in incurring loss and expense, or the employer argues that the
architect has over-certified — negligently, in breach of contract, fraudulently,
or otherwise. The high watermark of certificate cases came with Lord
Denning's judgment in *Dawnays Ltd v. F G Minter.*[91] In this case, Lord
Denning said: "There must be cash flow in the building trade. It is the very
lifeblood of the enterprise.... An interim certificate is to be regarded virtually
as cash, like a bill of exchange."

Contractors were, of course, delighted with this judgment and several
cases followed this line. One which was subsequently taken to the House
of Lords was *Gilbert Ash (Northern) Ltd v. Modern Engineering Ltd*[92] in

---

[89] [1990] 2 Lloyd's Rep. 496 (AC).
[90] See Chapter 8, para. 8.18.
[91] The position since May 1, 1998 is statutory under the Housing Grants, Construction and
Regeneration Act 1996, s. 109; see Chapter 8, para. 8.32.
[92] [1971] 1 W.L.R. 1205.

which Viscount Dilhorne stated that there was "no scintilla of authority" for Lord Denning's view, despite the fact that it had been followed in five subsequent cases.[93]

3.53   What is the Scottish position? The *Gilbert Ash* decision was followed in *W. & J. R. Watson Ltd v Lothian Health Board*.[94] This was a JCT 63 case. The employer refused to pay the sum certified by the architect. Lord Davidson held that *Gilbert Ash* was rightly considered and allowed set-off. But in this case, the contractor conceded that Lord Denning was wrong, *i.e.* Lord Davidson did not have to decide this point. What was argued for the contractor was that the employer was entitled to withhold payment on a certificate only if it was not in accordance with the contract; for example, where the architect did not have power to issue a certificate. The contractor unsuccessfully argued that the employer was not entitled to refuse to pay if he disputed the amount of a valuation.

3.54   In the case of *Sir Robert McAlpine v. The Royal Scottish Academy of Music and Drama*[95] an application was made for summary judgment under rule 89B of the Court of Session Rules. The contractor wanted to be paid under a certificate and the employer refused. Rule 89B provides a short form of procedure. The contractor argued that where there is no bona fide defence, the contractor is entitled to be paid in terms of the certificate. Lord McCluskey held that if there appears to be a bona fide dispute and there is an arbitration clause, summary judgment was inappropriate and the matter must go to an arbitration prima facie, *i.e.* Lord McCluskey did not share Lord Denning's view either.

3.55   However, there must be an arbitral dispute. In *Redpath Dorman Long v. Tarmac Construction*[96] there were conditions of sub-contract which allowed the contractor to "set-off... the amount of any claim for loss and/or expense which has actually been incurred by the contractor..." and there was also an arbitration clause for any "dispute or difference". The main contractor sought to set off amounts under many heads of loss and/or expense, but all except two referred to costs that would be incurred in the future, and post-certification. Lord Ross granted decree *de plano* to the pursuers on the basis that there was no relevant defence of set-off pled for non-payment of the certificate, with the exception of the two heads of claim arising before

---

[93]   [1974] A.C. 689.
[94]   *Frederick Mark Ltd v. Schild* [1972] 1 Lloyds Rep. 9; *GKN Foundations Ltd v. Wandsworth London Borough Council* [1972] 1 Lloyd's Rep. 528; *John Thomson Horsely Bridge Ltd v. Wellingborough Steel and Construction Co. Ltd* (1972) *The Times*, February 23; *Token Construction Co. Ltd v. Naviewland Properties Ltd* (May 11, 1972), unreported ; and *Carter Horseley (Engineers) Ltd v. Dawney's Ltd* (July 3, 1972), unreported.
[95]   1986 S.L.T. 292.
[96]   1989 G.W.D. 34–1582.

certification. Decree for £210,000 was granted and the remaining amount in dispute (£76,976) was sisted for arbitration.

Terminology

The Scots lawyer must first recognise that the term "set-off" is not a term of art in Scots law. It is merely a convenient neutral term.[97] In Gloag, *The Law of Contract* (2nd ed.) it states "the term set-off is sometimes used as a synonym for compensation though it is properly applicable to the law of England".[98] The phrase has recently surfaced as part of Scots law in section 110(2)(b) of the Housing Grants, Construction and Regeneration Act 1996, where it appears to have been used in a sense which Scots lawyers would associate with compensation. The Scots lawyer has to distinguish between compensation under the Compensation Act 1592; retention which operates out of the principle of mutuality of contract (*i.e.* that one party can only insist on the other carrying out his obligations if he will too); retention as a contractually stipulated sum retained from interim payments to reduce the risk of loss in the event of the contractor's insolvency; retention of plant and machinery by the employer as a security; and retention by the contractor of the employer's materials which are lawfully in the possession of the contractor.

3.56

Compensation

As regards the 1592 Compensation Act it provides:

"that any debt de liquido in liquidum [of a liquid sum against a liquid sum], instantly verified by writ, or oath of party, before the giving of decree, be admitted by all judges within this realm by way of exception, but not after the giving thereof in the suspension, or in the reduction of the same decree".

In *Johnston v. Robertson*[99] the Second Division held that in an action for payment by a contractor of the alleged balance due under a certificate of the contract price and for extra work, which was met by a claim for "a penalty of £5 sterling for every week during which the whole of said works remain unfinished", this would not be a matter of compensation under the Act.[1] The pursuer had to prove that he had done the work and the defender had to prove that it had been delayed: "When that is proved, the provision of the contract, that the damage is to be estimated at £5 per week, liquidates it at once."[2] The issues were truly that of retention under the principle of mutuality of contract, *i.e.*:

3.57

---

[97] 1982 S.C. 14.

[98] *Laing v. Lord Advocate*, 1973 S.L.T. (Notes) 81.

[99] At p. 644.

[1] *Johnston v. Robertson* 1861 XXIII Dunlop 352.

[2] *ibid.* at 357, *per* Lord Benholme: "I do not think the Act of 1592 applies to this case at all, because this is not a defence by which it is sought to meet one liquid by another liquid claim, which is the case contemplated by the Act."

"one party to a mutual contract, in which there are mutual stipulations, cannot insist on having his claim under the contract satisfied, unless he is prepared to satisfy the corresponding and contemporaneous claims of the other party to the contract. I think the rule of law, that an illiquid claim cannot be set off against a liquid claim, does not apply to such a case; and that at all events, if the one claim be liquid, and the other partly illiquid, yet contemporaneous, the rule would suffer some qualification or relaxation if the claims arose under one contract. The counter claims must be contemporaneous, for, if not, the rule would apply."[3]

3.58   The Compensation Act will not apply where liquidate damages are claimed by the employer and the contractor is seeking payment. That would be a question of mutuality of contract. The practical difference appears to be that compensation extinguishes a claim, but cannot exceed it, if liquid, and arises from any source. It is a defence by way of exception (*ope exceptionis*). Recently, Lord Jauncey, in the House of Lords, in *Bank of East Asia Ltd v. Scottish Enterprise*[4] stated that the ratio of the principle of compensation is:

"to avoid unnecessary litigation the mutual debts do not require to arise out of the same contract or even out of the same course of dealing; it is sufficient that they are both for amounts which are ascertained or immediately ascertainable when the plea is taken. That is the time when present exigibility is tested. An exception to the strict rule that both debts must be liquid arises in cases of bankruptcy or insolvency where a debt due to a bankrupt may be compensated by a future or contingent one or by one that is disputed as to its existence or amount. Once again the plea must be taken and it is at that time that the bankrupt's obligations must be looked at...."

A further exception to the rule arises

"where the illiquid or unascertained claim arises out of the same contract as the debt which is sued for, and where the enforcement of immediate payment would result in enabling the pursuer to obtain satisfaction of his claim under the contract when he has not implemented the obligation of which that claim is counterpart (*Gloag on Contract* (2nd ed.), p. 627)"

3.59   This exception of retention, however, has a more limited effect than compensation as appears from the following dictum of Lord Justice-Clerk Inglis in *Borthwick v. Scottish Widows Fund*[5];

---

2   *ibid. per* Lord Justice-Clerk at 361.
3   *ibid. per* Lord Benholme at 357.
4   1997 S.L.T. 1213 at 1215E–G.
5   [1864] 2 M. 595 at 607.

"Retention is a right to resist a demand for payment or performance till some counter obligation be paid or performed; and it has not the effect of extinguishing obligations as compensation has, but barely of suspending them, till the counter obligation be fulfilled (3 Ersk., 4, 20) This right never can emerge or be available as a security until a demand for payment or performance be made upon the person who is to plead retention. It is, according to its true etymological meaning, a right to retain, and nothing else. It seems to follow as a necessary consequence, that this mere passive resistance can never be operative or available to a debtor in an obligation, of which the term of payment has not come, and above all can never, in such circumstances, be reared up into an active and presently valuable security over the estate of a bankrupt, to the effect of securing a preference over the general body of the creditors."

In the House of Lords (five-judge) decision in *Bank of East Asia Ltd v. Scottish Enterprise*, Lord Benholme's judgment in *Johnston v. Robertson*[6] was considered, but, as in *Redpath Dorman Long v. Cummins Engine Co.*[7] in the Second Division, his later *obiter* remarks in *Field & Allen v. Gordon*[8] were not — on the question of whether retention against certificates under a building contract was not possible. The *Bank of East Asia* case concerned the differences in Scots law between compensation and retention in circumstances where there were stipulated instalment payment stages (albeit at lengthy intervals) that required the contractor to reach their own interim funding arrangements with the Bank of East Asia by assigning the full benefit of all sums due and payable by the employer to the bank. The contractor had accepted that they had carried out defective work that gave rise to losses agreed at £168,512.40 prior to the first instalment payment becoming due on May 15, 1990. On May 29 the contractor ceased work on site following insolvency and the appointment of an administrative receiver. The payment stage on May 15 was for the sum of £416,916.72. The question was whether the employer was entitled to withhold payment of the balance pending quantification of liquidate damages for non-completion under condition 24, and also in respect of sums to be quantified as damages for failure to complete, as well as the agreed £168,512.40. The established differences between compensation (a liquid sum against another liquid sum), and retention (may be an illiquid sum against a liquid sum if arising from the same contract and "con-temporaneous" — *per* Lord Benholm in *Johnston v. Robertson*[9]) were considered in the House. The precise meaning of "contemporaneous" where there were different stages of completion under the same contract was the issue. Could sums due at one stage for works duly completed to that stage be withheld in respect of losses not yet

3.60

---

[6]   1861 XXIII Dunlop 352.
[7]   1982 S.L.T. 489.
[8]   (1872) 11 M. 132. The relevant part of the judgment is discussed at para. 3.61, *post*.
[9]   *op.cit.*

quantified? The House held that they could not be retained, as the basis of retention in mutuality of contract did not go as far as to provide that any material breach disentitled that person from enforcing any and every obligation due to the other party. The terms of the contract had to be looked at, and contemporaneous obligations meant counter obligations "exigible or prestable at the same time". It was held that in this case where the contract was to be performed by both sides in stages, the counter obligation and consideration for payment of stage one was the completion of the work for that stage conform to contract. Therefore the employers were not entitled to retain the sums they claimed. The decision of the Inner House in *Redpath Dorman Long Ltd v. Cummins Engine Co. Ltd*[10] was approved. In that case employers were required to pay sums certified as due to the contractors within 21 days. Five interim certificates were issued and none were paid. The employers claimed a right of retention in respect of defective and delayed performance of the contract works and disruption to other contractors. Clause 43 of the contract provided expressly:

> "Whenever under the contract any sum of money shall be recoverable from or payable by the contractor such sum shall be deducted from or reduced by the amount of any sum or sums then due or which at any time thereafter may become due to the contractor under or in respect of the contract."

The sheriff had held that this clause ousted the common law right of retention. On appeal the Second Division held that it did not, unless, looking at the contract as a whole, it was excluded by necessary implication. In this respect *Gilbert-Ash (Northern) Ltd v. Modern Engineering (Bristol) Ltd*[11] was followed (despite that in the *Gilbert-Ash* case the particular set-off clause was found to have ousted the common law position by allowing "bona fide contra accounts"). Before the Second Division clause 43 was held not to oust the common law right, but that right had to be contemporaneous, which in this case meant that the breaches alleged had to have arisen when payment was due at the expiry of each of the 21-day periods. The Second Division did not say why they did not consider that clause 43 did not oust the common law right, simply that in their opinion it did not.

Retention and certificates as the "life blood"

3.61   Gloag[12] wrote: "it has been suggested that the general rule regarding retention may not apply to a building contract with the provision for payment by instalments."

---

[10] 1982 S.L.T. 489.
[11] [1974] A.C. 689.
[12] *The Law of Contract* (2nd ed.), p. 627.

This last question of whether the employer has any right to withhold payment of an instalment by virtue of an unliquidated claim against the builder was not fully developed in *Field & Allan v. Gordon*[13] where the Second Division made *obiter* and not necessarily reconcilable *dicta*. The Lord Justice-Clerk thought instalments could be retained by the employer in the event of a contractor's insolvency; Lord Neaves found it unnecessary in that case to define the circumstances in which a plea of retention could be sustained; but Lord Benholme went much wider in his comments.

The case concerned an action of furthcoming by a supplier against an employer. A number of issues arose but the crucial point seemed to be an inconsistent position taken by the employer. On the one hand he argued that he had a right of retention in respect of having to get someone else to finish the works; and on the other hand, that he had paid the amount of an interim certificate direct to his architect, and there was nothing to make furthcoming, even though the architect had then returned the cheque to the employer's solicitors. All three judges were of the view that one could not claim retention when payment had already been made. Therefore the question of principle of whether retention is possible against instalments under a building contract was *obiter*. Lord Benholme's remarks in this respect are of interest to the modern question. At page 136 of the case report he states:

> "There is a large class of contracts entered into between proprietors and tradesmen the basis of which is payment by instalments. They are often considerable in amount, and embrace a tract of time. In such cases it is of the last importance to the tradesman that they should be supplied from time to time with the means of enabling them to go on with their part of the undertaking. There can be no doubt that as the work progresses that the landlord gets something added to his estate. It was so in this case with Colonel Gordon, and as he got value added to his estate he became bound to make payment of certain instalments. It appears to me that whenever the architect had given his certificate that so much work was done, Colonel Gordon, on the one hand had his estate increased by so much, and on the other was under the distinct obligation to pay over to the contractor the sum certified to enable him to go on with the work. If he withheld the money he might thereby embarrass his contractor, and be himself the cause of the ultimate bankruptcy during the progress of the contract undertaken. That is the principle which distinguishes all such contracts when there are no such stipulations as to instalments. A mutual is an indivisible contract — a unum quid — not divisible into parts. That is the general principle which underlies the judgement in the case of *Johnston*[14] quoted to us… it will not do to say that in consequence of the contractor's subsequent difficulties the contract could not be gone on with, and that therefore damages are due to the defender. That has nothing to

---

[13] (1872) 11 M. 132.
[14] *Johnston v. Robertson* 1861 XXIII Dunlop 352.

do with the performance of their obligation by the parties up to the date of the arrestments. If Colonel Gordon had paid in virtue of the architect's certificate, then Field & Allan would in all probability have supplied just what was wanted to complete the work, namely, more material."

3.62　　On one view this supports Lord Denning's pronouncement in *Dawnays*, so that there might be 'a scintilla of authority' for Denning's view after all. The matter was also not developed in *Redpath Dorman Long v. Cummins*[15] as again it was conceded by counsel for the pursuers that building contracts were not an exception. *Field & Allen* was probably cited in this case as the judgment noted that there had been a submission by counsel for the defenders on the exception point, but it was unnecessary to dispose of the point as it was conceded. It is perhaps regrettable that the matter was never addressed.

3.63　　In the *Gilbert-Ash*[16] case there was a nominated sub-contractor working on Gilbert Ash's standard conditions. These said, *inter alia*, at clause 14(4):

"the main contractor reserves the right to deduct from any payments certificate as due to the sub-contractor and/or otherwise to recover the amount of any bona fide contra account and/or other claims which the main contractor may have against the sub-contractor in connection with this or any other contract".

3.64　　What was set off here was a claim for loss for delay and loss for alleged defective works. The House of Lords said that if there was, as there appeared to be, a bona fide particularised claim then that could be contractually set off against a certificate. Clause 14(4) did not provide that a liquid sum only could be set off. Also, generally, the common law set-off position could only be excluded by clear unequivocal words.

In *Mottram Consultants v. Bernard Sunley*,[17] Lord Morris said "the so called principle of *Dawnays* no longer exists." There were very unique circumstances in *Mottram* which involved the building of a supermarket in Zaire for developers who were being funded by a Zaire government organisation. There were all manner of allegations of fraudulent overpayments made to suppliers and sub-contractors. The employer stopped paying on the existing basis of weekly imprest accounts presented by Sunley and uncertified by the architect, followed by monthly certificates. There were various attempts to make business sense of the operation and ultimately Sunley determined. The House of Lords, with Lords Morris and Salmon dissenting, construed an express term of the contract that the only sums that could be deducted from the amounts certified were retention money (a contractual percentage agreed as withheld) and any sum previously paid, as excluding the common law position.

3.65　　Whilst *Gilbert-Ash*[18] allows the parties to write their own set-off clause, a clause in a contract governed by the Supply of Goods and Services Act 1982

---

[15]　1982 S.L.T. 489.
[16]　[1974] A.C. 689.
[17]　[1975] 2 Lloyd's Rep. 197.
[18]　*op.cit.*

(such as a building contract), which seeks to exclude set-off can be held to be unfair as unreasonable under the Unfair Contract Terms Act 1977. The Court of Appeal so held in *Stewart Gill Ltd v. Horatio Myer & Co. Ltd.*[19] On the way to *Bank of East Asia*,[20] in 1988 Lord Sutherland in the Outer House considered *John Cochrane & Co. Ltd v. Robert McAlpine & Sons Ltd*[21] in connection with a claim for summary decree under rule 89B of the Court of Session Rules by a joinery sub-contractor at the new Glasgow sheriff court. The sub-contractor claimed:

3.66

(i) retention monies due to be released at practical completion and at the end of the maintenance period;
(ii) sums certified after practical completion; and
(iii) a repayment of the main contractor's discount which was only due if there had been prompt payment.

The contractors claimed set-off of a portion attributable to the sub-contractors of liquidated and ascertained damages which had been assessed on them by the employers for late completion. The form of sub-contract was in a non-standard form and Lord Sutherland held that there was an arguable defence against summary decree by way of set-off, when the contractual provisions for notices and adequate quantification could be argued to have been properly given. He found however that did not apply to half of the retention which should have been released at practical completion, or in respect of the lack of prompt payment thereof.

In England the *Gilbert-Ash* case is the definitive leading case[22] and in Scotland it appears to be *Redpath Dorman Long v. Cummins Engine Co. Ltd*[23] and now *Bank of East Asia.*[24] It is questionable just how far the new provisions of the Housing Grants, Construction and Regeneration Act 1996, which were designed to prevent abuse of set-off (so-called "subbie bashing"), actually change much, if indeed set-off, properly understood as retention, was a rule that was open to abuse in Scotland. Section 110(1) of the Act provides that every construction contract shall provide an adequate mechanism for determining what payments become due under the contract, and when, and provide for a final date for payment in relation to any sum which becomes due. Section 111(1) provides that:

3.67

"A party to a construction contract may not withhold payment after the final date for payment of a sum due under the contract unless he has given an effective notice to withhold payment."

---

[19] [1992] Q.B. 600 (CA).
[20] *op.cit.*
[21] 1989 G.W.D. 6–262
[22] See *NEI Thompson v. Wimpey Construction* (1987) 39 B.L.R. 65 (CA).
[23] 1982 S.L.T. 489.
[24] *op.cit.*

3.68   On one reading of this section, the only protection that is given, such as it is, refers to the *final date for payment*. This would not appear to advance the question of interim payments. Similarly, section 112, which deals with the right to suspend performance for non-payment, only relates to sums due "that have not been paid by the final date for payment". The parties remain free to define when the final date for payment should be, but in the absence of agreement the Scheme for Construction Contracts will apply.[25] If the Scheme applies, the final date for payment applies to each interim payment — see para. 4.345 *post.*

Contractual Retention Clauses

3.69   It is regrettable that the word retention is found and used in most standard and non-standard forms in a quite different way to that understood in Scots law as explained above in relation to *Bank of East Asia.*[26] Retention is normally used in standard forms in a way that is distinguishable from set-off. So-called retention sums are in effect amounts contractually agreed to be withheld from interim payments. Some in the industry view the purpose of retention funds as to provide some sort of safeguard to the employer, in that he can withhold sums against the risk of practical completion and the remedying of defects not being achieved for insolvency or some other reason. Others note the language of standard form retention clauses and see that retention sums are supposed to be held in trust for the contractor or sub-contractor. Therein lies the problem, because the courts north and south of the border appear to have reached entirely different views as to how retention clauses should be interpreted. At the heart of the problem is the question of who bears the risks of any of the other parties becoming insolvent during the course of the works in a way that is compatible with existing insolvency law. The Latham Report[27] recommended that "mandatory trust funds for payment" be set up as standard and that employers pay into them at the beginning of each payment period. The trust funds could then be used to pay sub-contractors direct if the main contractor became insolvent, or could be used if the client failed.[28] This recommendation did not reach the Housing Grants, Construction and Regeneration Act 1996.

Two recent cases show the divergent interpretations that can be placed on the same retention clauses in relation to the JCT Management Contract (1987 ed.) in Scotland in *Balfour Beatty Ltd v. Britannia Life Ltd,*[29] and in the Appeal Court in England in *P.C. Harrington Contractors Ltd v. Co Partnership Developments Ltd.*[30]

---

[25]   See discussions on these new issues at chap. 4 in relation to cll. 30.1.1.1 to 30.1.1.5.
[26]   *op.cit.*
[27]   Recommendation 27 of the Latham Report, where Sir Michael reported: "Separate provisions will be required for Scots Law, but I am told it is possible to devise them to obtain the same results [*i.e.* secure trust funds]." For the Latham Report generally, see Chap. 8.
[28]   For an interesting discussion on these points, albeit from a purely English law point of view see Odams and Davis, *Security for Payment — Contemporary Issues in Construction Law* (1996), Vol. 1.
[29]   1997 S.L.T. 10.
[30]   (1998) 88 B.L.R. 44.

Balfour Beatty were works contractors when a receiver was appointed   3.70
in January 1993 to the management contractors (MDW), thereby
determining the management and works contracts. The works contractors
had completed the works but the defects liability periods had not expired.
In *Balfour Beatty*'s case £36,600 by way of retention monies was in dispute.
The employers had not set the retention sums aside despite a request to do
so. Clause 4.8 of the management contract stated:

> "The Retention including that held in respect of all Works Contracts shall be
> subject to the following rules:—
> .1 The Employer's interest in the Retention is fiduciary as trustee for the
> Management Contractor and for any Works Contractor (but without
> obligation to invest);
> .2 at the date of each Interim Certificate the Architect ... shall prepare a
> statement setting out the amount of Retention held at that date in respect
> of the Management Contractor and the total amount held in respect of
> each Works Contractor; and such statement shall be issued to the
> Management Contractor and by the Management Contractor to each Works
> Contractor named in that statement;
> .3 ... the Employer shall, if the Management Contractor or, through the
> Management Contractor, any Works Contractor so requests, at the date of
> payment of each Interim Certificate place the Retention held thereby in a
> separate bank account (so designated as to identify the amount of Retention
> held by the Employer on trust as provided in clause 4.8.1) and certify to
> the Architect/the Contract Administrator with a copy to the Management
> Contractor that such amount has been so placed. The Management
> Contractor shall similarly inform each Works Contractor in respect of
> whom the Employer is holding retention. The Employer shall be entitled
> to the full beneficial interest in the separate banking account and shall be
> under no duty to account for any such interest to the Management
> Contractor or to any Works Contractor."

The works contract provided, in clause 4.24, that:

> "The Retention is subject to the rules set out in clause 4.8 of the Management
> Contract Conditions. Where the Works Contractor requests ... that retention
> shall be held in a separate banking account by the Employer, the Management
> Contractor shall immediately pass on such request and inform the Works
> Contractor that the provisions of Clause 4.8.3 of the Management Contract
> Conditions have been complied with by the Employer."

Clause 4.29.1 provided:

> "The Management Contractor's interest in the Works Contractors Retention ...
> is fiduciary as trustee for the Works Contractor (but without obligation to invest)."

Lord Penrose in a lengthy judgment gave little support to the works
contractor, who may have felt that he had right on his side as the innocent
party. The decision is worrying from the Scottish point of view because it
effectively means that all existing retention clauses in JCT contracts in
Scotland will not protect the contractor's claim to retention funds. It is also

worrying in that the full range of English authorities were apparently not brought to the court's attention.[31] The essence of Lord Penrose's decision was that the draftsmanship "was wholly ineffective to achieve what may have been the intended purpose of the draftsman" (18–G). His opinion was that the language of clauses 4.8.1 and 4.8.2 which speaks of sums being "held" is not actually what happens, in the sense of being appropriated to a trust. Instead, sums are withheld as a quantified future liability, conditional on due performance. Further, if as here there was a contractual right for the employer to make deductions from the retained sums then there could not also be a trust. Also, where, as here, there was a contractual determination provision that stopped all further payments to the management contractor in the event of the management contractor's insolvency until after practical completion and a final accounting, that superseded any argument that a secure trust had been set up. In particular, Lord Penrose concluded that clause 4.3.2 of the contract allowed the employer to apply set-off against all sums held, including those which related only to the works contractors involvement. It is on this last point that the Court of Appeal in England in *P.C. Harrington Contractors*[32] have since taken the opposite view.

3.71   Again in *P.C. Harrington* the management contractor became insolvent but there was a difference in that all retention sums had actually been set aside in a separate bank account. The Court of Appeal did not address Lord Penrose's difficulties concerning the effect of the determination provisions, and the set-off provisions being inconsistent with the creation of a trust. Instead they decided that the management contract provisions and the works contract provisions existed in parallel and that there was no right of set-off against the sums deducted and retained in relation to the works contractor as these did not become due to the management contractor. The works contractor's retained sums were held in trust for him alone. Only sums due to the management contractor could be set off. This is exactly contrary to Lord Penrose's conclusion and leaves one in doubt as to what the position might be in future were similar circumstances to be appealed.

3.72   In England, there have been several other cases involving retention clauses in standard form contracts. For example, in *Wates Construction (London) Ltd v. Franthom Property Ltd*,[33] the employer argued that he did not need to set retention monies aside when requested to do so under JCT 80, particularly as the relevant clause had been deleted; he could simply use the retention as working capital. The employer was unsuccessful with this argument as it was considered that not separating the funds would amount to a breach of trust. *Wates* was not argued before Lord Penrose who presumably would have taken a different view from the Court of Appeal.

---

[31] For example *Re Arthur Sanders* 17 B.L.R. 125, which bears a striking resemblance to the circumstances in *Balfour Beatty*.

[32] *op.cit.*

[33] [1991] 53 B.L.R. 23.

In *MacJordan Construction Ltd v. Brookmount-Erostin Ltd*,[34] the 3.73
employer under a JCT 81 contract had not put the funds into a separate
account. A floating charge crystallised over the employer's assets at a time
when no action had been taken to set up the fund. The receiver's claim
prevailed over the contractor's. The court was of the view that any action to
set up the separate fund would be voidable as a preference under the
insolvency legislation. The difference between this case and *Re Arthur
Sanders*[35] was that there was a solvent employer and insolvent contractor.
Considerations of equity should prevent the solvent employer from
benefiting from his failure to set aside a fund. In other respects the decision
in *MacJordan* bears similarities to the conclusion of Lord Penrose in *Balfour
Beatty*. It was said in the Court of Appeal that the plaintiff's argument's:

> "fundamental flaw lies, in my opinion, in attempting to treat an unsatisfied
> and unsecured contractual right to payment of money as something more ....
> [The Employer's] implied obligation under clause 30.4.2.1 is, on analysis,
> no more than an obligation to pay money, the payee being [the employer]
> itself as trustee."[36]

In Scotland, liquidators, receivers or administrators simply cannot ignore 3.74
a trust. In *Bank of Scotland v. Liquidator of Hutchison, Main & Co. Ltd*,[37]
there is clear authority that funds in trust cannot be taken for the general
body of creditors. The problem plainly is setting up a valid trust. Interestingly
the New Engineering Contract (NEC) has at Appendix 7 a sample trust
deed that seems to cover most issues, and particularly a separation between
the employer and the trustees.[38]

In Scotland one can be a trustee of one's own property, but there are 3.75
tests which have to be satisfied. In *Clark Taylor & Co. Ltd v. Quality Site
Developments (Edinburgh) Ltd*,[39] it was held that the following tests had to
be satisfied for an asset that was purportedly put in trust:

(i) there must be an amount;
(ii) there must be dedication;
(iii) there must be a beneficiary with a right; and
(iv) there must be delivery and divestiture.

---

[34] [1991] 56 B.L.R. 1 (CA).
[35] *op.cit.*
[36] *MacJordan (supra)* at p. 15.
[37] (1914) S.C. 1 (HL).
[38] An arrangement where in England a supplemental agreement to JCT 80 created an escrow
account that was impressed with a trust and operated by the parties' solicitors was
successfully upheld against liquidators in the unreported case of *Lovell Construction Ltd v.
Independent Estates Ltd*, Official Referee's Business 25/6/92. See Odams and Davies,
Security for Payment — Contemporary Issues in Construction Law, Vol. 1 (1996).
[39] 1981 S.L.T. 3.

In this case, manufacturers of bricks sold bricks to a contractor on their standard terms. These included that if the contractor sold any of the bricks whilst the retention of title clause was operable, "it will hold in trust for the seller all his rights under such contract of resale". The contractor used the bricks and went into liquidation without having paid for them. Monies received for them were put into their usual bank accounts. The First Division held that no valid trust had been created as the condition only created a contractual obligation and did not give the manufacturers any beneficial rights in the sub-sales. Also, a valid trust required the delivery of an asset and this was not satisfied by a mere obligation. However, the reasoning in this case has been criticised[40] and does not sit squarely with *Tay Valley Joinery v. CFC Fire Services.*[41] In the *Tay Valley* case book debts were factored. Any money that came in was to be held in trust for the factors. Was this a trust? What seemed to be decisive was that such debts had a stamp placed on them by the company which was enough to constitute a trust. Also, the contract was governed by English Law.

Direct payment provisions

3.76   These are provided for in clause 35.13.5 of JCT 80 in relation to nominated sub-contractors. They provide for payments directly to the sub-contractor by the employer. The architect can demand proof of payment by the main contractor to the sub-contractor, and if this is not forthcoming he issues a certificate to that effect and the employer can deduct such sums from the main contractor. Clause 27.4.2.2 is a discretionary means of direct payment to a supplier or sub-contractor in addition to clause 35.13.5.

However, there is a difficulty. If the employer decided to make a payment direct to a sub-contractor rather than to the main contractor, what happens if the main contractor becomes insolvent? Can the employer still pay direct to the sub-contractor? Does this contravene the principle of *pari passu*? Is this a preference in favour of the sub-contractor as against the rights of the general body of creditors of the main contractor?

3.77   The English case of *Re Tout and Finch Ltd*[42] dealt with clause 27(c) of JCT 63 which was in similar terms to clause 27.4.2.2 of JCT 80. It was held quite legal to make payments to the sub-contractor after the insolvency of the main contractor and practical completion, but before the issue of a final certificate. Compare this, however, with the House of Lords decision in *British Eagle International Airlines Ltd v. CIE Nationale Air France.*[43] Here airlines that carried passengers on behalf of other airlines operated a clearing-house scheme and balances due were regularly calculated. It was held that

---

[40] Professor Wilson, 1982 S.L.T. (News) 129.
[41] 1987 S.L.T. 207.
[42] [1954] 1 W.L.R. 178.
[43] [1975] 2 All E.R. 390.

this scheme could not operate after the insolvency of one of the airlines as it would give an unfair preference over ordinary creditors, contrary to section 302 of the Companies Act 1948. Some have thought that this might have a bearing on direct payment provision on a contractor's insolvency, and the wording of clause 27.4.2.2 now excludes the employer's discretion to pay direct on the contractor's bankruptcy or liquidation, which is said by Keating[44] to reflect the view that the decision in *Tout & Finch* has not survived *British Eagle.*

    In a case in the High Court of Ireland — *Glow Heating v. Eastern Health Board*[45] — *British Eagle* was distinguished. There was a direct payment provision from the employer to a nominated sub-contractor, and in the sub-contract it provided that monies received by the main contractor in respect of the sub-contract works should be held in trust for the nominated sub-contractor. The sub-contract further provided that in the event of default by the main contractor in paying the sums certified in respect of the nominated sub-contractor, the nominated sub-contractor could apply to the employer direct for payment. The main contractor went into liquidation having failed to pass on payments to the nominated sub-contractor, and had spent them. An action was raised against the employer to pay the sums not passed on by the main contractor, and to deduct the same from monies retained in respect of the main contract work. It was held that the provisions for direct payment were not void as contrary to public policy, because the liquidator took the property of the main contractor subject to the liabilities which affected it and the money was not, in all the circumstances, the main contractor's property. However, this case was not followed and was distinguished in *B. Mullan & Sons (Contractors) Ltd v. Ross*[46] where the Court of Appeal for Northern Ireland held that, on liquidation, the direct payment provisions could not apply. The distinction drawn between the *Glow Heating* case was that in *Glow Heating* there was a mandatory provision in the contract that if all nominated sub-contractors' accounts had not been duly discharged by the main contractor, the employer "shall himself pay" the amounts certified by the architect as falling due to sub-contractors and deduct the amount of any such payment from any sums otherwise payable to the main contractor. The employers in *Mullan* were entitled but not obliged to make direct payment to the sub-contractors under clause 27.4.3.2 of JCT 81 which was regarded as a point of distinction. It should be noted that the language of clause 27.4.3.2 of JCT 81 and of clause 27.4.2.2 of JCT 80 are permissive and not mandatory in relation to sub-contractors and suppliers, but clause 35.13.5.3 of JCT 80 is mandatory in relation to nominated sub-contractors. It would be an interesting point in Scots law if mandatory language would create a *jus quaesitum tertio* in favour of a sub-contractor[47] in the absence of privity of contract.[48]

3.78

---

[44]   May, *Keating on Building Contracts* (6th ed., 1995), p.663.
[45]   [1992] 8 Const. L. J. 56.
[46]   (1996) 54 Con. L.R. 163 (CA (N.I.)).
[47]   See Chap. 5, paras 5.07–5.09.
[48]   See *Hampton v. Glamorgan County Council* [1917] A.C. 13 (HL).

3.79   In the case of *Veitchi Co. v. Crowley Russell & Co.*[49] the provisions of clause 30 of the General Conditions of Contract for Building Works in Scotland dated September 1, 1954 read:

> "The architect shall state in each certificate issued by him the amounts included in respect of the work of the various subcontractors, and the principal contractor shall (unless on cause shown to the satisfaction of the architect) within three days after receiving payment of the instalment due to him on the said certificate by the architect, pay over to each subcontractor the sum due to each subcontractor in respect of work carried out by him and covered by the certificate. The principal contractor shall not be entitled to obtain another certificate from the architect for another instalment unless and until he satisfies the architect, by the production of vouchers or other sufficient evidence, that he has settled with his subcontractor or subcontractors for the sum or sums due to each subcontractor or subcontractors in respect of work carried out by him or them and covered by the previous certificate granted by the architect or that the failure to settle was not due to fault or default on his part."

A certificate was granted on January 5, 1962 and the principal contractor went into liquidation on February 16, 1962, without paying the pursuer. A declarator was granted that the principal contractor was not entitled to another certificate until the condition was satisfied and an interdict was granted against the principal contractor or his liquidator from seeking further certificates until the condition was satisfied. The judge distinguished the right to a certificate from an entitlement to payment as a preference against the ordinary creditors. This could result in no further certificates being granted at all, or the liquidator could make an offer to the sub-contractor to make a payment to free up future certificates. The judge apparently did not think that would create a preference and in this respect followed *Re Tout & Finch*.[50] However he did not hold that the sub-contractors were entitled to payment as this clause was an administrative one and not one that had the effect of creating a secure trust fund, unlike the position in *Tout & Finch*.

3.80   Clause 30 of the Scottish 1954 conditions has been held not to create privity of contract between the employer and the sub-contractor, nor did it create a relationship of agency between the principal contractor and the employer.[51]

Latent Defects, Damage, & Prescription and Limitation

3.81   There may be all manner of disputes that can arise in relation to construction works, and a crucial question relates to when any such disputes must be brought to a court or arbiter in terms of the Prescription and Limitation (Scotland) Act 1973, or be lost forever. The operation of this Act in the

[49] 1972 S.C. 225.
[50] *op.cit.*
[51] *Dunbarton County Council v. Sellars & Sons Ltd*, 1973 S.L.T. (Sh.Ct) 67.

construction sector has been criticised for the effect it seems to have in attenuating the period in which actions for breach of contract may be raised. There have been three recent reports on this matter: *Report on Prescription and Limitation of Actions (Latent Damage And Other Related Issues)*, Scottish Law Commission No. 122, 1989 pre (*Murphy*[52]); *Professional Liability: Report of the Construction Professionals Study Team* (October 1989), Department of Trade and Industry, the "Bishop Report"; and since then there has also been the Latham Report, *Constructing the Team* (1994),[53] whose recommendations as regards a 10-year liability period, backed by mandatory single-project insurance failed to reach the Housing Grants, Construction and Regeneration Act 1996. Those recommendations have been referred to the Law Commission.

The Prescription and Limitation (Scotland) Act 1973 provides *inter alia*: 3.82

> "6.— (1) If, after the appropriate date, an obligation to which this section applies has subsisted for a continuous period of five years —
>   (a) without any relevant claim having been made in relation to the obligation, and
>   (b) without the subsistence of the obligation having been relevantly acknowledged,
>   then as from the expiry of that period the obligation shall be extinguished....
>
> 7.— (1) If, after the date when any obligation to which this section applies has become enforceable, the obligation has subsisted for a continuous period of twenty years—
>   (a) without any relevant claim having been made in relation to the obligation, and
>   (b) without the subsistence of the obligation having been relevantly acknowledged,
>   then as from the expiration of that period the obligation shall be extinguished....
> (2) This section applies to an obligation of any kind (including an obligation to which section 6 of this Act applies)....
>
> 11.— (1) Subject to subsections (2) and (3) below, any obligation (whether arising from any enactment, or from any rule of law or from, or by reason of any breach of, a contract or promise) to make reparation for loss, injury or damage caused by an act, neglect or default shall be regarded for the purposes of section 6 of this Act as having become enforceable on the date when the loss, injury or damage occurred....
>
> (3) In relation to a case where on the date referred to in subsection (1) above (or, as the case may be, that subsection as modified by subsection (2) above) the creditor was not aware, and could not with reasonable diligence have been aware, that loss, injury or damage caused as aforesaid had occurred, the said subsection (1) shall have effect as if for the reference therein to that date there were substituted a reference to the date when the creditor first became, or could with reasonable diligence have become so aware."

---

[52] *Murphy v. Brentwood District Council* [1991] 1 A.C. 398; discussed in detail in relation to liability for defective buildings in delict in Chap. 6.
[53] For a commentary see Chap. 8.

3.83   The two main areas of difficulty with these statutory provisions relate to
        the phrases "having become enforceable on the date that the loss, injury or
        damage occurred", and "could not with reasonable diligence have been aware".
        There is a distinction built-in between the date of any breach of duty, loss or
        damage occurring, and what might be called "discoverability" of the loss or
        damage. The issue is particularly problematic in relation to latent defects, *i.e.*
        defects which were not patent when the works were carried out.

3.84   The law in Scotland and England proceeds from different statutes and,
        prior to 1986, different concepts. In the English Limitation Act 1980 breach
        of duty[54] was the starting point for the running of their long limitation period,
        rather than when the loss, injury or damage occurred.[55]

3.85   In *Pirelli General Cable Works v. Oscar Faber & Partners*[56] the
        defendants were a firm of consulting engineers who advised the plaintiffs
        on the design and erection of a boiler flue chimney some 160ft high. The
        chimney was allegedly negligently designed, and in due course cracks
        occurred in the internal lining of the chimney. The chimney was built in
        June and July 1969. The plaintiffs issued their writ in October 1978. The
        trial judge found that the cracks occurred not later than April 1970, that the
        plaintiffs did not discover the cracks till November 1977 and that it was not
        proved that the plaintiffs could with reasonable care have discovered the
        defects before October 1972. The House held that the time began to run
        when the defect became physically apparent in cracks, even though the
        owner could not have known that he had suffered loss at that time. Under
        the Limitation Act 1970, as it then stood, the action had prescribed by one
        year. However, their Lordships did express dissatisfaction with the result.
        Lord Fraser thought it "unsatisfactory, unreasonable and contrary to
        principle"; while Lord Scarman said that it was "unjustifiable in principle
        that a cause of action should be held to accrue before it is possible to discover
        any injury (or damage). A law which produces such a result... is harsh and
        absurd". They called for legislative changes to build discoverability into
        the English system, now to be found in section 14A of the Limitation Act,
        as added by the Latent Damage Act 1986, s. 1.

3.86   The *Pirelli* decision has most continuing relevance in relation to latent
        defects in providing that a physical manifestation of damage is necessary,
        as distinct from the breach of obligation that causes the damage. To put this
        in Scots law terms there must be concurrence of *damnum* (loss) and *injuria*
        (wrongful conduct). Therefore the knowledge that some conduct amounted
        to a breach of obligation should be distinguished from whether that breach

---

[54] s. 14B(1).
[55] But note that in the field of product liability in Scotland and England under the Consumer
     Protection Act 1987, Sched.1, the start date for the running of time periods is the date of
     first supply by the manufacturer.
[56] [1983] 2 A.C. 1.

actually caused loss, injury or damage, and when this was "discoverable".[57] A danger that comes to light as a result of a survey, or a comparison with other buildings that have failed, will not create an enforceable obligation until physical damage is manifest. The "doomed from the start" cases which have as their starting point *Batty v. Metropolitan Realisations* have produced unsuccessful defences in respect of limitation (see *Dove v. Banham Patent Locks*,[58] *Ketteman v. Hansel Properties*,[59] *Jones v. Stroud District Council*,[60] *London Congregational Union v. Harriss & Harris*[61]).

The Scottish courts have followed the *Pirelli* decision as regards the manifestation of damage principle. In *Renfrew Golf Club v. Ravenstone Securities Ltd*[62] Lord Allanbridge in the Outer House held that, when greens on a golf course flooded in 1976, even though in May 1973 some remedial work had been carried out but where there was no damage to the playing surface, the five-year prescriptive period would not have expired until 1981. Also, in *Sinclair v. MacDougall Estates Ltd*[63] Lord Maclean followed *Renfrew* and *Pirelli* in finding that:

3.87

> "the existence of defects will not by itself constitute damnum [loss, injury and/or damage]: there must be a physical manifestation of the damage.... The right to raise an action, then, accrues when injuria [breach of legal duty or obligation] concurs with damnum. As Lord Keith pointed out in *Dunlop v. McGowans* 1980 S.C. (H.L.) at 81 and 1980 S.L.T. at 132, some interval of time may elapse between the two, and if that is the case, time runs from the date when the damnum results, not from the earlier date of the injuria."

In this case it was held that the act, neglect or fault founded upon was not a breach of the general duty under a Scottish House-Purchasers' Agreement that a flatted dwellinghouse "be designed and constructed in an efficient and workmanlike manner and of proper materials", but was constituted by certain *specified* failures, *i.e.* defects in design of the lintels, and construction of building ties, mortar and movement joints which gave rise to damage that occurred about 18 years after its construction (a bulging in the external leaf of the building and a stepping in the brickwork forming the lintels of the building). A clear distinction was drawn between "snagging" and, as Lord Maclean put it:

---

[57] The problem is compounded in construction contracts in relation to the legal status of a final certificate, particularly if there is a related clause which prevents the taking of a dispute to arbitration within a stated contractual period — for example, 60 days, *per* clause 30.9.3 of the Scottish Building Contract With Quantities (August 1998 rev.).

[58] [1983] 1 W.L.R. 1436.

[59] [1987] A.C. 187.

[60] [1988] 1 All E.R. 5.

[61] [1988] 1 All E.R. 15.

[62] 1984 S.L.T. 170.

[63] 1994 S.L.T. 76.

> "It seems to me that it would work considerable injustice for pursuers if a minor failure to design and construct on the part of the defenders, which had come to light earlier, were held to be sufficient to constitute injuria in relation to a major and different failure to design and construct which was discovered much later."[64]

3.88   However, under the Prescription and Limitation (Scotland) Act 1973, there may be a trap for the unwary employer. In *Greater Glasgow Health Board v. Baxter Clark & Paul*[65] architects were appointed in 1966 for reconstruction works which were carried out between 1969 and 1971 by a separately contracted builder. The Health Board knew that certain windows and areas of mosaic were defective in 1972, but they did not know who was in breach, *i.e.* the architects or the builders. In 1978 the architects signed a formal deed which was expressly purported to be a "relevant acknowledgement" under sections 6 and 10 of the Act acknowledging that the obligation still subsists. An action against the architects was raised in 1982. It was held that the action had prescribed before the purported "relevant acknowledgement". The deed itself read as follows:

> "As yet it has not been practicable to ascertain the full extent and nature of those defects and faults or the causes thereof or the amount of loss and damage suffered by the Board... or to have determined... whether such defects... had been caused wholly or in part through our fault or negligence... Therefore we agree that these presents shall constitute a relevant acknowledgement within the meaning of s. 10 of the 1973 Act."

Lord Clyde was of the view that this deed fell short of a "relevant acknowledgement", even though it purported to be so, as it did not relate to an obligation subsisting in 1978. This was because the deed specifically stated that neither party was then aware whether that obligation existed (p. 42–G). Also, the pursuers were held not to have relevantly pled why it was not possible to be aware of the loss, injury or damage, and that no plea of personal bar against the architects taking this position was properly pled, as the Health Board had not pled that they had acted on the faith of a representation of a fact to their prejudice.

3.89   In *Dumfries Labour and Social Club and Institute Ltd v. Sutherland Dickie & Copeland*[66] architects and builders were sued in negligence and breach of contract in respect of design and construction work. Phase 3 of the work to the premises was added in 1975. In 1979 cracking appeared and the architect advised that settlement had occurred but that no further movement was expected. In 1980 more cracking was discovered and monitoring was advised. The cracks were infilled and no systematic process of monitoring was followed. More cracking was discovered in June 1983

---

[64]   *supra* at 82–K.
[65]   1992 S.L.T. 35.
[66]   1993 G.W.D. 21–1314.

after phase 4 was completed. In June 1984 boreholes were dug and it was discovered that there was a previously unknown public sewer close to the building and that back-filling might have weakened lateral support. A separate architect's report recommended demolition, but underpinning work was carried out in 1985. An action was raised in March 1988. It was held that the five-year prescriptive period had begun to run in 1980 and the action had accordingly prescribed.

In Scotland under sections 7 and 11(4) of the 1973 Act there is a so-called "long stop" which has been criticised as being illogical and irrelevant.[67] This is the long negative prescription period of 20 years after which no action can be raised. The illogicality is that the 20-year long stop also depends on the manifestation of physical damage. In other words the five-year period and the 20-year period may both run from the same date, rather than the position in England where the long stop runs from the breach of the duty and ignores any question of discoverability. Clearly some sort of balance is necessary between an almost unlimited possible obligation, and the possibility of a party losing any right to sue without even being aware that he has suffered any loss. The Scottish Law Commission still appear to cling to the discoverability ethos, despite the absence in the market place of adequate insurance possibilities. The Bishop Report recommended that the date of completion of a building contract should be the date from which a 10-year long stop should run.

3.90

Particular care needs to be taken as regards the issue of a notice of arbitration under the ICE Conditions of Contract (5th ed.), as in *Douglas Milne v. Borders Regional Council*[68] where it was held by the Second Division that where there was a contractual obligation to refer a matter under that contract for a decision of the engineer before a reference to arbitration could be taken, the five-year prescriptive period started from the rejection by the engineer of the final claims evaluation, and in the circumstances an arbiter could not competently consider the question.

3.91

It is also a moot point whether prescription can continue to run where a claim under one heading has commenced in court, but a claim under another related heading has not.[69] However, it should be noted that the party alleging that an obligation has prescribed bears the onus of proof.[70]

---

[67] See MacQueen, "Latent Defects, Collateral Warranties and Time Bar", 1991 S.L.T. (News) 91.
[68] 1990 S.L.T. 558.
[69] *G.A. Estates Ltd v. Caviapen Trustees Ltd*, 1993 S.L.T. 1051 (Extra Div).
[70] *Strathclyde Regional Council v. W.A. Fairhurst & Partners*, 1997 S.L.T. 658 (OH).

CHAPTER 4

CRITICAL ANALYSIS OF JCT 80

4.01   Even for a lawyer coming new to the current Scottish Building Contract
With Quantities (August 1998 revision) (abbreviated to SBC in the text) it
can appear to be a rather perplexing document.[1] Copyright in the form is
with the Scottish Building Contract Committee (abbreviated to SBCC in
the text) whose constituent bodies are:

> Royal Incorporation of Architects in Scotland;
> Scottish Building Employers' Federation;
> Royal Institution of Chartered Surveyors in Scotland;
> Scottish CASEC;
> Convention of Scottish Local Authorities;
> National Specialists Contractors' Council;
> Association of Consulting Engineers (Scottish Group);
> Confederation of British Industry;
> Association of Scottish Chambers of Commerce.

4.02   The SBCC's current constituting members reflected the membership of
the JCT (Joint Contracts Tribunal) before its reorganisation in 1998, and
indeed it was on the recommendation of the McEwan-Younger Report in
1964 that this should be the case, so as to provide continuity of contract
north and south of the border.[2] The English equivalent was the "Placing
and Management of Contracts for Building and Civil Engineering" — the
Banwell Report 1964. This rather mixed bag of interested parties does not
have an immediately obvious *raison d'être*. The Latham Report, *Constructing
The Team*,[3] published in 1994, made firm recommendations for the
restructuring of JCT to reflect the need for greater input from clients. It
recommended a Construction Clients Forum, representing public and private

---

[1]   In *Beaufort Developments (N.I.) Ltd v. Gilbert-Ash N.I. Ltd* [1998] 2 W.L.R. 860 Lord
Hoffman said: "I have no wish to add to the anthology of adverse comments on the drafting
of the JCT Standard Form Contract. In the case of a contract which has been periodically
re-negotiated, amended and added to over many years, it is unreasonable to expect that
there will be no redundancies or loose ends." See also the House of Lords web-site http://
www.parliament.the-stationery-office.co.uk/pa/ld199798/ldjudgmt/jd980520/beau01.htm.
[2]   *Organisation and Practices for Building and Civil Engineering* — The McEwan-Younger
Report (1964).
[3]   See particularly Chap. 8.

private sectors; a Construction Industry Council, representing main contractors and suppliers; and a Contractors Liaison Group, representing specialist and sub-contractors. The Scottish Building Contract Committee were recommended to have observer status.

There is no specific body providing a legal input, although the Secretary and Legal Adviser [4] of the SBCC is a partner in a firm of solicitors based in Edinburgh; neither are the Chartered Institute of Arbiters involved — despite the contract having an extensive arbitration clause.[5] The JCT form is the result of a unanimous consensus among its members, which may explain why it has "often been criticised by the courts for being unnecessarily obscure and verbose"[6]; or "deviously drafted" and "unnecessarily amorphous and tortuous"[7]; "a farrago of obscurities"[8]; "notorious for its obscurities".[9]

Part of the difficulty, apart from draftsmanship, is that the SBC cannot be understood on its own: it must be read with the relevant JCT conditions. The JCT conditions have been amended 18 times since their publication in 1980. The current edition of the conditions is published incorporating up to amendment 18, but at different times in the past has been significantly behind the amendments, entailing a careful search to find the relevant conditions. Also, the SBCC issues its own amendments to incorporate — or not, as the case may be — current JCT amendments. Therefore, the SBC can only be made sense of by reading the SBC and its two Appendices ("The Scottish Supplement", forming Appendix I, and the "Abstract of Conditions", forming Appendix II), any relevant amendments, and the relevant JCT conditions and amendments as published from time to time. If this were not difficult enough, there are also separate editions of the SBC as discussed in Chapter 2.

4.03

ENTIRE CONTRACTS

Before venturing deeper into the conditions, it is useful to consider at this stage whether a building contract is at common law an "entire contract". An entire contract is one in which the entire performance by one party is a precondition to the liability of the other party. The leading case in Scotland on the matter is *Ramsay v. Brand*.[10] The opinion of the court was given by the Lord President as follows:

4.04

---

4   Mr J.M. Arnott, MacRoberts, Solicitors, 27 Melville Street, Edinburgh, EH3 7JF.
5   cl. 41B.
6   *Beaufort Developments, ibid., per* Lord Lloyd.
7   *T. A. Bickerton & Sons Ltd v. North West Metropolitan Regional Hospital Board* [1969] 1 All E.R. 977 at 979, *per* Sachs L.J.
8   *English Industrial Estates Corporation v. George Wimpey & Co. Ltd* [1973] 1 Lloyd's Rep. 118 at 126 *per* Edmund-Davies L.J.
9   *Gilbert Ash (Northern) Ltd v. Modern Engineering (Bristol) Ltd* [1974] A.C. 689 at 697, [1973] 3 All E.R. 195 at 198 (H.L), *per* Lord Reid. However, at p. 726, the JCT 63 form was said to work well enough in practice.
10 (1898) 25 R. 1212.

"No man can claim the sum stipulated to be paid on the completion of certain specified work unless he has performed that work *modo et forma*, and this applies to building contracts just as much as to other contracts. The parties may if they please, and very often do, agree to vary the contract, but we have nothing of the kind here. The builder has no right either to disregard the specification altogether or to modify it as by supplying one material in place of another; and neither in the case of total departure nor in the case of partial deviation from the specification will it avail to prove that what has been done is as good as what was promised. Accordingly the rule is, that if the builder chooses to depart from the contract he loses his right to sue for the contract price. But further, losing his right to sue for the contract price he does not acquire right to sue for *quantum meruit*, the other party never having agreed to pay according to its value for work which *ex hypothesi* he never ordered.

In the application of this rule it suffers a modification which in no way invades the principle. A building contract by specification necessarily includes minute particulars, and the law is not so pedantic as to deny action for the contract price on account of any and every omission or deviation. It gives effect to the principle by deducting from the contract price whatever sum is required to complete the work in exact compliance with the contract.

4.05   The question whether, in any given case, the deviations are of such materiality as to fall within the general rule, or are of such detail as to fall within the modification of this rule, is necessarily one of degree and circumstance. If the deviations are material and substantial, then the mere fact that the house is built would not prevent the proprietor of the ground from rejecting it and calling on the contractor to remove it, and he might do so if he were not barred by conduct from insisting in his right. If this right were so insisted in, then the contractor would of course have right to the materials, but he would have no right to payment. If, on the other hand, the proprietor made the best of it and let the house stay, the only claim the contractor could have would be a claim for recompense; and this, be it observed, would be not for *quantum meruit* the builder, but for *quantum lucratus est* the proprietor. Accordingly, when contractors do not stick to their contracts they do not only unmoor themselves from their contract rights, but they drift into much less certain and much less definite claims. Now the architect to whose satisfaction the work is to be done according to specification cannot approve of work done disconform to specification, for without special permission he has no authority to dispense with performance of the express terms of the contract. His approval only applies to the mode of fulfilling the express provisions of the contract. Of course in many cases departures from the contract are agreed upon by the parties as the work proceeds, and very often the architect represents the employer in such arrangements. But this is a totally different matter, and does not affect the principle now stated."

4.06   Whilst this dictum would seem to be well and good, there have been a number of authorities that would appear to set confusing precedents. In

William Steel v. R.L.Young[11] there was a contract for the execution of mason and brick work as alterations to a villa. The contractor used milled lime instead of the contractually stipulated cement mortar. The deviation could only be cured by taking down and rebuilding substantially the whole work, but the value of the buildings as erected was only about £5 less than if the cement had been used. The action was for the balance of the contract sum of which about half had been paid. The walls were roughcast in any case, so concealing the defect. It was held that the contractor could not sue for payment under the contract, but could only recover by way of a restitutionary remedy for a sum to reflect how much the defender was *lucratus* (enriched).

However in *Speirs Ltd v. Peterson*[12] a mansion house was built on the island for the owner of the island of Eigg with materials called "Spiersesque Plasmentic" in which timber, steel and cement took the place of stone and lime. No reference in the specification was made to a damp-proof course, and no proprietary brand was used. The defender refused to pay the balance of the price as the pursuer had "failed to take the usual and necessary precautions to protect the house from damp". Some steps had been taken as regards damp, including putting rubble under the foundations, and it was held that the breach was not so material as to prevent the pursuers from suing under the contract, and recovering the balance of the price under deduction of the cost to the defender of bringing the building into conformity with the contract. The Lord Justice-Clerk drew a distinction as to the remedy for breach of contract:

> "according as the contract is one for a lump sum or a measure and value contract. The former type of contract falls to be performed in its entirety. In the latter the various parts of the contract are separable, with a different value attaching to each, and it would be inequitable, merely because some small slip has been made, to deny the contractor the right to sue upon the contract."

Quite what sort of contract Lord Justice-Clerk Alness had in mind for a measure and value contract is unclear, but it may mean a lump sum plus or minus variations contract where there is a bill of quantities, and provision for interim payments (see Lord Parmoor in *Forrest*[13] below). Indeed the sheriff in *Stewart Roofing Co. Ltd v. Shanlin*[14] was of the view that the dictum may be too widely stated if it were to mean that if separate quotations were given for foundations, shell and roof, the employer would still have to pay for the roof if erected on a two-storey house instead of a three-storey one. With respect to the sheriff, that would hardly be "one small slip".   4.07

The *Stewart Roofing* case involved a garage being rebuilt in place of one that had been blown down in a storm. Whilst the contractor did not   4.08

---

[11] 1907 S.C. 360.
[12] 1924 S.C. 428.
[13] *Forrest v. Scottish County Investment Co.*, 1916 S.C. (H.L.) 28 at 36.
[14] 1958 S.L.T. 53 at 56.

follow his own suggestion that the walls have supporting butts of given dimensions, nevertheless there was expert evidence that the walls were sound and could be made reasonably conform to contract. The sheriff allowed the action for payment in contract subject to a deduction of the reasonable cost of rectification. The sheriff doubted whether the *Steel* case had been properly decided and followed Lord Parmoor in *Forrest v. Scottish County Investment Co.*[15] and other dicta in the House of Lords in the *Forrest* case. In *Forrest* the contractor built a number of houses in Garrioch Crescent in Glasgow but, it was argued, departed from the specification detailing the dimensions and placement of rybats of the windows. It was held that the specification was a matter of construction practicality which was within the architect's authority to approve and measure. This was not the same as substituting a wholly different material for another, and on that basis the Lord Chancellor distinguished *Steel v. Young.* Lord Parmoor seems to have decided this case on a different basis though. Lord Parmoor's view was that a contract such as the one in *Forrest,* where there were plans (but which were not very detailed); a schedule of works that was made up by measurers from the plans (which seems similar to modern bills of quantities); where the work was to be carried out to the "entire satisfaction of the proprietors and the architect"; and was to be measured and charged at rates contained in the schedule "in proportion thereto and in proportion to slump sum in letter of offer"; and where there was a simple offer to "execute… the works… according to plans thereof… as described in and in conformity with the foregoing estimate, and at the rates affixed thereto, for the sum of £…"; that this was a measure and value contract.[16]

Lord Parmoor went on:

> "A similar case to *Ramsay v. Brand*[17] is that of *Sumpter v. Hedges*[18] — 'Where there is a contract to do work for a lump sum, until the work is completed the price of it can not be recovered.' These cases and dicta are not applicable to the contract entered into between the appellants and the respondents in the present case. In such a contract the covenants for work are independent of each other in this sense that a builder, who has completed a number of items conform to the contract, and has handed over the works to the building owner, and has obtained the final certificates of the architect and measurers, is not disentitled to recover in respect of these items on the ground that on other items he has failed to conform to the contractual conditions."

And further at page 38:

> "I think it is shown on the face of the contract that the main purpose of the priced schedule in the contract is to fix a price applicable to the contract work, and that, if the description in the schedule is not applicable, a deduced price may be certified by the measurers."

---

[15] *op.cit.*
[16] *op. cit.* at 35.
[17] *op.cit.*
[18] [1898] 1 Q.B. 673.

Lord Parmoor seems to be talking about a contract like JCT 80 with quantities, being a lump sum plus or minus variations contract, with provision for interim payment.

Interestingly, none of the Scottish cases are cited in *Hudson*[19] or *Emden*.[20] The learned author of *Hudson* is of the view at paragraph 4.009 at page 477: "Thus nearly all measured or schedule contracts, with or without Bills of Quantities, will be entire contracts." He cites in support *Ibmac Ltd v. Marshall Ltd.*[21] In it, roadworks contractors tendered for a job and provided a full bill of quantities, and also stated that the works were remeasurable on completion. The contractors abandoned the works one third of the way through because of surface water and sued for what they had done. The employer had the works completed by another contractor. Lord Denning in the Court of Appeal held that *Sumpter v. Hedges*[22] applied and that as this was an entire contract the contractor was entitled to nothing on abandonment.

4.09

More recently in *Tern Construction Group Ltd v. RBS Garages Ltd*[23] it was held by the Official Referee that having regard to the elaborate and detailed provisions of JCT 80, especially its provisions for partial possession by the employer, determination of the contractor's employment without determination of the contract itself, and payment by instalments, that it was not an entire contract. In this case the particular provisions of clause 27.4 enabled the employer to have other contractors complete the works, and not be bound to make further payments to the insolvent contractor. It did not provide for what should happen if the employers chose not to have the works completed as here. It was held that there must be implied a term to the effect that when the employers expressly stated, or by their conduct showed, that they did not intend to complete the works, or when after a reasonable time failed to re-start them, the bar on their liability to make payments to the contractor must be lifted. However the employer's common law remedies remained.

4.10

In non-JCT contracts the English law on what is an entire contract is neatly summarised in *Holland Hannen & Cubitts (Northern) Ltd v. Welsh Health Technical Services Organisation*,[24] in a way that is rather more subtle than stated above in *Hudson*:

4.11

> "(2) Whether a contract is an entire one is a matter of construction; it depends upon what the parties agreed. A lump sum contract is not necessarily an entire contract. A contract providing for interim payments, for example as work proceeds, but for retention money to be held until completion is usually entire as to the retention moneys, but not necessarily the interim payments: Denning L.J. in *Hoenig v. Isaacs* [1952] 2 All E.R. 176, C.A.

---

[19] I. Duncan Wallace, *Hudson's Building and Engineering Contracts* (11th ed.).
[20] *Emden's Construction Law.*
[21] (1968) 208 E.G. 851.
[22] *op.cit.*
[23] (1992) 34 Con.L.R. 137.
[24] (1981) 18 B.L.R. 89.

(3) The test of complete performance for the purposes of an entire contract is in fact 'substantial performance': *H. Dakin & Co. Ltd. v. Lee* and *Hoenig v. Isaacs.*

(4) What is substantial is not to be determined on a comparison of cost of work done and work omitted or done badly: *Kiely & Sons Ltd v. Medcraft* (1965) and *Bolton v. Mahadeva* (1972)."

4.12 The Housing Grants, Construction and Regeneration Act 1996 now provides for an entitlement to stage payments at section 109 which would appear to remove the possibility of all but construction contracts for periods of less than 45 days being entire contracts. The problem of what would happen if the circumstances of abandonment in *Ibmac v. Marshall* arose again have not been addressed in the Act.

Although there may be an entitlement to interim payments, this will not mean that the contract is fulfilled bit by bit, with for example different prescriptive periods running from the date each brick is laid. Lady Cosgrove has recently held in the Outer House that for an ICE contract "it would be artificial and unrealistic" to say that a breach giving rise to a claim for damages occurred when each individual piece of pipeline was laid. Her Ladyship held the occurrence of such *injuria* was the date of "substantial completion".[25]

The JCT 80 Conditions

Clause 1

4.13 Clause 1 deals with interpretation and definitions. In *Amalgamated Building Contractors Ltd v. Waltham Holy Cross UDC*[26] the pre-JCT 63 form (the RIBA form) was likened by Denning L.J. to a legislative code. However, the JCT are not a delegated legislative body. The drafting of such contracts shows a marked difference from what one might expect from a parliamentary draftsman. They are not comprehensive, unambiguous or consistently drafted. There have been simple errors of capitalisation and use of quotation marks and use of undefined words over the history of JCT 80, some of which are tidied up in subsequent amendments or revisions. It might be argued that this is mere legal pedantry, but often matters are confusing. For example, the SBC have introduced a definition of "Contract Works" as well as "Works". The Date for Completion, defined as the date fixed and stated in Appendix II of the SBC, and the Completion Date in

---

[25] *Strathclyde Regional Council v. Border Engineering Contractors Ltd and Babtie Shaw & Morton*, 1997 S.C.L.R. 100. Although Lady Cosgrove also appears to consider the contractor as *functus* at practical completion which is surprising as there remains the defects liability period.

[26] [1952] 2 All E.R. 452 at 453 (CA).

clause 25.2.2 and 25.3 can be one and the same. Also, perhaps pedantically, Appendix II of SBC actually makes provision for Liquidate and Ascertained Damages (*i.e.* capitalised, and without the "d", when compared with clause 24 of JCT 80). The definitions of "Approximate Quantity" and "provisional sum" (in small case) were not actually added till Amendment 7 in July 1988, and these definitions make reference to an extrinsic document, *i.e.* the Standard Method of Measurement (7th ed.) (General rules 10.1 to 10.6), although, in fairness, the relevant general rules are set out in a footnote.

With the issue of Amendment 18 there is a further layer of complexity, as some of these amendments are in order to make JCT 80 comply with HGCRA 1996; whilst others are derived from the Latham Report, but not made compulsory by legislation. Careful attention has accordingly to be paid to achieve what is actually wanted in the contract by incorporation or deletion. Annexed to the SBC With Quantities (August 1998 revision) is a so-called correction sheet which renumbers clauses in a way that the author cannot make sense of, particularly with respect to the applicable law clause. Also on this sheet are some rather obvious matters and an important alteration to the labour and material cost and tax fluctuations clause 39, introducing a clause *Re* landfill tax. Unquestionably, the whole structure is far from user-friendly. It is understood that efforts are in hand to put this documentation on to CD-ROM. It is hoped that this will make for ease of navigation around the contract.

4.14

The Scottish Building Contract has an interpretation section which changes some of the definitions for Scottish use. Clause 1 of the SBC provides what the contract documents are; and clause 2.1 states the Contractor's obligation to carry out and complete the Works in compliance with the Contract Documents. Clause 1.4 of JCT 80 was introduced by Amendment 5 dated January 1988 and states that the contractor "shall remain wholly responsible for carrying out and completing the Works". There was a guidance note published with this which states that the Architect is not, under the standard form, made responsible for the supervision of the works which the Contractor is to carry out and complete. We shall see that the role of the architect in certifying work and his responsibility for its quality — particularly as regards the effect of the issue of a Final Certificate — was the subject of recent case law in England,[27] and led to Amendment 15 in July 1995, which amended clause 1.4 and redrafted clause 30.9.1.1. The difficulty has been in interpreting the Contractor's obligations in clause 2.1 with the proviso in clause 2.1: " that where and to the extent the approval of the quality of materials or of the standards of workmanship is a matter for the opinion of the Architect, such quality and standards shall be to the reasonable satisfaction of the Architect."

4.15

---

[27] *Crown Estates Commissioners v. John Mowlem & Co. Ltd* (1994) 10 Const. L.J. 311 (CA), approving *Colbart v. Kumar* [1992] 59 B.L.R. 89.

In the light of recent difficulties in interpreting the architect's role in certifying workmanship, it is perhaps useful at this stage to consider the old Scots position in the case of *Muldoon v. Pringle.*[28] Here there was a contract for the making of drains to a depth of three-and-a-half feet and which had not to be covered up until they had been inspected by the employer or his representative; and further to be done to the satisfaction of a government inspector. The inspector failed to inspect and left almost everything to the employer's representative, but gave a certificate that the work had been duly executed, upon which the employer paid instalments. Subsequent investigation revealed that in no case were the drains of the agreed depth, and the majority were two feet eight inches to three feet deep. It was held by the Inner House that the contractor was not entitled to recover the balance of the price, but the employer, having a representative who had allowed the work to proceed without objection, was not entitled to have the work reconstructed or to damages.

4.16   The recent English cases that the quality of materials and workmanship are always inherently for the opinion of the architect, and not matters that have to be specially reserved for his approval, and that once finally certified any action against the contractor is prevented, seems to square with the old Scots position.

4.17   Also of interest is the First Division decision in *Chapman & Son v. The Edinburgh Prison Board*[29] where it was held that the contract to build to the entire satisfaction of the architect mutually bound the contractor and employer to that as by bargain. If the architect condemned work, that was an end of the issue: he had been chosen for his skill in these matters and did not have to receive evidence. There was no suggestion of improper conduct on the architect's part so as to disqualify him from acting as a referee. Also, the referral to his "entire satisfaction" was at the same time a submission to the architect: "No party ever entered into an agreement such as this — that he should execute work in such a way as should be found sufficient by a jury, but it would just come to that if such an agreement as the present were invalid." It is interesting to note how these issues have rumbled on down the years in relation to the position of an architect granting certificates.[30]

4.18   Recently in *Belcher Food Products Ltd v. Miller & Black*[31] Lord Gill considered at procedure roll the effect of final certificate provisions in relation to the JCT 63 contract (July 1977 revision, as amended by the Scottish Supplement), without the older Scottish cases apparently being cited. The employer sued *inter alios* the architect and the contractor. There were several issues concerning defective workmanship, such as a floor being

---

[28] (1882) 9 R. 916.
[29] (1844) 6 D. 1132.
[30] See Chap. 7 "Architects and the professional team".
[31] 1999 S.L.T. 142.

uneven and unsightly, water penetration at a junction, and whether the contractor had departed from the description in the bills in not using dust in the floor screed which meant that it became slippery. In relation to the latter point, the contractor argued that the final certificate was conclusive, and there was also an underlying question of proof as to whether the need for the dust, being a matter covered by a provisional sum, had been varied. Lord Gill said that the final certificate provisions were substantially the same as had been considered by the Court of Appeal in *Crown Estate Commissioners v. Mowlem*[32] but he distinguished that case. His view was that the ommission of dust would be a question of objective fact, and not a matter for which the architect certificate would be conclusive as between employer and contractor. The certificate would preclude the bringing of contrary evidence of the architect's satisfaction, but not that the certificate was conclusive for all purposes. Lord Gill then noted that the Court of Appeal had taken a wide view that all matters of quality of materials or standards were for the reasonable opinion of the architect, but declined to form a view of whether the other disputed matters in this case would be covered by that wide view. He declined on the basis that the point had not been pled, nor were the facts agreed, and that proof would be required.

The redraft in Amendment 15 purports to restrict the effect of the opinion of the architect when certifying.[33]

Clause 2 — Contractor's obligations

Having already begun to look at clause 2 as a consequence of clause 1, there is still the question of what the phrase "carry out and complete the Works in compliance with the Contract Documents" actually means. The question arises as to whether this creates an absolute obligation on the contractor to complete, as for example where a building collapses whilst he is working on its structure. This situation arose in *Morrison's Associated Companies Ltd v. James Rome & Sons Ltd.*[34] Here the relevant condition was from the General Conditions of Contract for Building Works in Scotland 1954 which read:

4.19

> "The contractor shall provide and do everything which may be necessary for the due and proper completion of the work included in the contract in accordance with the true intent and meaning of the signed drawings, specifications, schedules of quantities, and these conditions, and the works shall be carried out in accordance with the drawings, specifications and General Conditions of Contract and any modification thereof and any further drawings, details and instructions in explanation of same, and such directions as may from time to time be given by the architect."

---

[32] [1994] 70 B.L.R. 1; (1994) 40 Con. L.R. 36.
[33] See further comments in relation to these matters and cl. 8 at paras 4.58–4.59.
[34] 1964 S.C. 160.

The Lord Ordinary had held that this created an absolute obligation on the builders in contract for which they were liable in damages, although he held that specific proof of what caused the collapse was absent. He had actually rejected a claim that the collapse was due to the contractor's negligence. The Inner House held that the case in negligence had been rightly rejected, but reversed the Lord Ordinary on the finding that the clause created an absolute duty. The Lord President noted that:

> "This clause has been a standard clause in building contracts in Scotland for many years and I am not aware of it ever having been construed to involve so heavy an obligation on the contractor. A closer scrutiny of the language of the condition in my opinion demonstrates the unsoundness of the construction contended for. The important words are 'in accordance with the... drawings, specifications, schedules quantities'. All that the condition means, in my opinion, is that the contractor is to supply the labour and materials required to complete the work in accordance with the drawings, specifications and schedule of quantities. The 'due and proper completion of the work' does not involve any absolute or quasi-absolute obligation, but requires him to adopt the usual recognised standards and practice in the trade which a careful contractor would employ in carrying through the contract to its completion. 'Everything which may be necessary for the due and proper completion' does not mean ' is necessary in an absolute sense'. The phrase merely requires the contractor to do everything which according to good practice in the trade is required to be done."[35]

The Inner House did not close the door on cases where a building collapse may shift the burden of proof on to the contractor, but according to Lords Carmont and Guthrie it would have to be established that the building was sound to begin with. Lord Carmont was of the view that: "an obligation undertaken by the contractor to provide adequate shoring meant shoring adequate in quantity and strength for the job, but the contractors' obligation did not involve an insurance to keep the building standing."[36]

4.20   Safety issues which are relevant to a collapsing building are now dealt with in Amendment 14[37]; and, for example, it is now part of the contractor's obligations under clause 8.1.3 to carry out all work in accordance with the Health and Safety Plan.

4.21   Generally it is a term that would otherwise be implied that the work will be executed in a good and workmanlike fashion using the skill of a builder of reasonable competence.[38] In the context of JCT forms it should also be noted that Amendment 12 issued in July 1993 introduced a new clause 42 for Performance Specified Work. This provides that the Contractor shall exercise reasonable skill and care in the provision of Performance Specified Work (clause 42.17.1) and this clause shall not be construed so as to affect

---

[35]   *op.cit.* at 184.
[36]   *op.cit.* at 186.
[37]   See paras 4.49–4.52.
[38]   Erskine, *Institute*, III, iii, 1; Bell, *Commentaries*, I, 489,490; Bell, *Principles*, ss. 153, 154.

the obligations of the Contractor under this contract in regard to the supply of workmanship, materials and goods (clause 42.17.1.1), nor shall the contract entail a guarantee of fitness for purpose of the Performance Specified Work (clause 42.17.1.2). Clause 8 also raises issues of quality of workmanship, work (presumably something different?!) and materials and goods, which are examined below.[39]

The phrase "Contract Documents" is not defined to include either a   4.22 method statement or a specification, which are often imposed on a contractor as part of the Bill of Quantities. It is a moot point what effect these parts of the Bills may have when the Performance Specified Work provisions are not used. Neither is a programme a contract document, although, in terms of clause 5.3.2, a contractor has to produce one.

A problem can arise when the works in terms of drawings are not precise   4.23 enough and matters appear to be left to the contractor. Questions can arise as to whether there was consensus at all, whether the risk of the uncertainty rests with the contractor, or whether a Variation order under clause 13 should be issued. This question is discussed below in relation to variations.[40] In relation to a non-JCT agreement, in *Clement v. Gibbs*[41] a builder quoted for a shop front refurbishment on the basis of a sketch for the windows. A subsequent drawing with different dimensions for the windows was issued, and the difference was not noticed until the windows were made. It was held that the first drawing was an idea to be supported with further drawings, that the subsequent drawing was what the contractor had agreed to supply, and that the court would be reluctant to hold that a contract that was capable of performance was void from uncertainty from lack of exact dimensions.

Clause 2.3 deals with divergences between the Contract Drawings; Contract   4.24 Bills; drawings, documents or instructions issued by the architect; and the Numbered Documents. It appears from clause 2.3 that it is the Contractor's responsibility to bring these divergences to the attention of the Architect — if he finds them — who is then required to issue instructions in regard thereto. Any such instruction would constitute a Relevant Event for the purposes of an extension of time under clause 25.4.5.1 and a relevant matter for the purposes of calculating loss and expense under clause 26.2.3. Also, if the instruction is a variation then it should be valued under clause 13. There may be difficult issues if the consequences of any divergences are not discovered at a time when the Contractor should have discovered them, if he was exercising reasonable skill and competence,[42] and an architect's duty to warn his client of risks in the proposed method of construction.[43] Or if the works carried out are divergences, but matters of "constructional arrangement" and not departures from the contract.[44]

---

[39] See paras 4.56 *et seq.*
[40] See paras 4.76 *et seq.*
[41] 94/1393/B, December 5, 1995, C.A, unreported.
[42] See Chap. 5, paras 5.34 *et seq.*
[43] See *Wagner Associates v. Joseph Dunn (Bottlers)*, 1986 S.L.T. 267.
[44] See *Forrest v. Scottish County Investments Co.*, 1916 S.C. (H.L.) 28.

Clause 3: Contract Sum – additions or deductions – adjustment – Interim Certificates

4.25   This deals with additions and deductions from the Contract Sum in interim certificates. It requires an ascertainment.[45] Exactly how an ascertainment should be defined is difficult as this seems to be more than an estimate, although the clause allows for "partial ascertainment". There is a further potential difficulty in that the word "ascertainment" is also used in clause 26 relating to loss and expense, and the distinct word 'Valuation' is used in clause 13.4.1.1 for Variations, which Valuations are to be added to or deducted from the Contract Sum (clause 13.7). In practice Valuations are added to interim certificates also.

Clause 4: Architect's instructions

4.26   This allows the Architect, who is not a party to the contract, to issue instructions to the contractor under the contract: as such he is the general agent for the employer.[46] It would appear from the Court of Appeal in *Croudace v. London Borough of Lambeth*[47] that the employer has a contractual duty to appoint a replacement architect where necessary, and failure entitles the contractor to damages. Amendment 14 inserted a new clause 1.5 which requires the Employer to immediately notify the Contractor in writing of any replacement Planning Supervisor, who would normally be the Architect in any case. Architects' instructions are to be complied with "forthwith" if made with regard to matters "expressly empowered",[48] *i.e.*

> Clause 2.3 Discrepancies
> Clause 6.1.3 Statutory requirements
> Clause 7 Errors in setting out
> Clause 8.3 Opening up and testing
> Clause 8.4 Work not in accordance with the contract
> Clause 8.5 Exclusion of persons employed
> Clause 12 Confirmed clerk of work's directions
> Clause 13.2 Variations
> Clause 13.3 Provisional sums
> Clauses 17.2; 17.3 Defects
> Clause 23.2 Postponement
> Clause 34.2 Antiquities, and clauses 35 and 36 relating to Nominated Sub-Contractors and Nominated Suppliers respectively.

4.27   Questions arise as to whether any ostensible authority of the architect, or any implied agency, exists. Since the Architect is the general agent of the Employer, the Contractor is entitled to assume that an instruction of the

---

[45]   See *Alfred McAlpine Homes North Ltd v. Property and Land Contractors Ltd.*
[46]   *Black v. Cornelius* (1879) 6 R. 581.
[47]   [1986] 33 B.L.R. 20 (CA).
[48]   cl. 4.1.1.

Architect is within his authority at common law, provided it is not at variance with the building contract itself.[49] An architect, unless otherwise stated in the contract, has no power to instruct the contractor how he is to carry out his work, or to take particular precautions.[50] Clause 4.1.1 provides that the Contractor need not comply with a Variation if he makes "reasonable objection"; but clause 4.1.2 allows the Employer to employ other persons to execute any work whatsoever to give effect to an instruction. Under clause 4.2 the Contractor may ask the Architect to justify his authority under the conditions for an instruction, which the Architect must do "forthwith", and if the Contractor carries it out, it will be deemed a valid instruction. But what is the Contractor supposed to do when the Architect purports to justify his instruction, and the Contractor is still unhappy. It seems the answer is that the parties could go to arbitration immediately.[51] What could happen is that the Contractor merely refuses to carry out the instruction and rejects the justification and writes to the Architect accordingly, but the Employer gets someone else to do the work. The Contractor may well be in the right, and may initiate arbitration proceedings, but the conditions do not require the issue to be put on hold whilst an arbitration is pending. It is submitted that it is for precisely these types of issues that adjudication provisions were made compulsory by section 108 of the Housing Grants, Construction and Regeneration Act 1996. Clause 41A of the SBC (August 1998 revision) complies with section 108.

The issue of whether an architect may omit items of work which are covered   4.28
by provisional sums and then award the work to a third party was considered by the Official Referee in *Amec Building Ltd v. Cadmus Investment Co. Ltd.*[52] The decision of the Australian Supreme Court in Sydney in *Carr v. J. A. Berriman Pty Ltd*[53] was followed. In it, Fullagar J. said:

> "The clause is a common and useful clause, the obvious purpose of which —
> so far as is relevant to the present case — is to enable the architect to direct
> additions to, or subtractions in, or omissions from, the building as planned,
> which may turn out in his opinion, to be desirable in the course of performance
> of the contract. The words quoted from would authorize the architect... to
> direct that particular items of work included in the plans and specifications

---

[49] *Robertson v. Jarvie*, 1908 15 S.L.T. 703 at 707, 708, *per* Lord McLaren.

[50] *Clayton v. Woodman and Sons (Builders) Ltd* [1962] 2 Q.B. 53, [1962] 2 All E.R. 33, [1962] 1 W.L.R. 585 (CA); *AMF International Ltd v. Magnet Bowling Ltd* [1968] 2 All E.R. 789, [1968] 1 WLR 1028.

[51] This would be so under any pre-1998 SBC where there was an issue of what matters could not be arbitrated over until after practical completion, *e.g.* September 1997 revision, cl. 41.3.2. The August 1998 revision of the SBC allows the parties to choose arbitration or litigation: cll. 41B or 41C. However it seems likely that such disputes will be first dealt with by adjudication in terms of cl. 41A for the reasons given in the text.

[52] (1996) 51 Con. L.R. 105.

[53] (1953) 89 C.L.R. 327.

shall not be carried out. But they do not, in my opinion, authorise him to say that particular items so included shall be carried out not by the builder with whom the contract is made but by some other builder or contractor. The words used do not, in their natural meaning, extend so far, and a power in the architect to hand over at will any part of the contract to another contractor would be a most unreasonable power, which very clear words would be required to confer."

4.29   In clause 4.3.1 the procedure for issuing instructions is an attempt to impose a requirement for instructions to be in writing. But there is ambivalence on the part of the draftsman as to whose responsibility it is for putting the instructions in writing. There appears to be a shared responsibility, so that each can confirm a verbal instruction within seven days of its issue, and the Architect may confirm any instruction which has been complied with up to the issue of the Final Certificate. The question is whether the Contractor can ignore a verbal instruction. Keating[54] without citing any authority says no; but it is submitted that the terms of clause 4 create such doubt as to whose responsibility the confirmation of oral instructions is, that the matter can hardly be clear-cut. Often arguments about who instructed what and how it is to be paid for crop up. In *Tharsis Sulphur and Copper Co. Ltd v. McElroy & Sons*[55] the circumstances were that McElroy, who was to supply iron for a structure according to a specification, found that there was a risk of warping by casting the iron to the agreed specifications. To carry out the contract would have involved further research, or the use of thicker and heavier girders. The contractor chose to use more iron and the weight of the girders was noted and certified by Tharsis. It was held in the House of Lords (reversing the Second Division) that there had been no variation entitling extra payment to the contractor, and that certificates of the actual amount of metal brought onto the ground were not conclusive that a verbal agreement had been made to pay for extra work. The contractor had to bear the cost of the improved specification to meet his contractual obligations. The fact that the specification of the thickness and length could not be economically manufactured did not make the Tharsis Co. at fault; there was no fraud or deceit in ordering what they did. McElroy had accepted the risk of performance of the contract for a lump sum, and the change in the specification was for their benefit.

4.30   On the issue of writing, Lord Blackburn in *Tharsis* states at pages 175–176:

" It is very common in these contracts [lump sum contracts] that conditions are put in more or less stringent, that the engineer may require that the contractors do extra work at the same rates according to weights and measurements as they agreed to do the other work, and that he shall have the power to order them to do so; and in order to provide against the risk of the

[54]   May, *Keating on Building Contracts* (6th ed., 1995), p. 555.
[55]   (1878) S.C. 1119, revsd. (1878) 5 R. 171, HL.

parties being fixed with the cost of extra work which was not really ordered by them it is common enough to have provisions, as there are here, more or less stringent, saying that no extra work shall be paid for unless it is ordered in writing by the engineer; and if such conditions are properly made, and there is nothing fraudulent or iniquitous in the way they are carried out, these conditions would be quite sufficient and effectual".

Clause 5: Contract Documents — other documents — issue of certificates

This is a procedural clause concerning custody of the Contract Drawings and the Contract Bills which remains with the Architect — notice it is not with the Employer who may hold copyright in them. Copies are to be provided to the contractor free of charge, but again notice that this is to be done as soon as is possible after the execution of the contract, which may in practice be long after works have begun. Copies are to be kept by the Contractor on site and available to the Architect or his representative at all reasonable times (clause 5.5). Upon final payment the Contractor shall if so requested by the Architect forthwith return all drawings, details, descriptive schedules (which are not contract documents (clause 5.3.2)), and all other documents of like nature "which bear the name of the architect" (clause 5.6). There can be obvious difficulties if the meaning of such drawings, etc., are in dispute at arbitration, or if the contractor or sub-contractor claims that copyright in drawings, etc., remains with him, despite being approved by the architect. 4.31

The Contractor cannot use the drawings other than for the specific contract (clause 5.7). The Contractor's rates cannot be divulged by the Employer, the Architect or the Quantity Surveyor, except for the purposes of the contract (which presumably includes arbitration or adjudication). Clause 5.4 concerns the issue of further drawings or details as are reasonably necessary either to explain or amplify the Contract Drawings or to enable the Contractor to carry out and complete the Works in accordance with the condition "as and when from time to time may be necessary". Failure to provide further Contract Drawings "as and when from time to time may be necessary" (clause 5.4) has produced much litigation. Disputes tend to concern the need for further drawings and details, and this can be a complex matter of scheduling. Contractors are normally entitled to an extension of time (clause 25.4.6) where they have not received, in due time, necessary instructions, drawings or details or levels from the Architect for which the Contractor specifically applied. Does this mean that the Contractor is only entitled to an extension of time when additional drawings, etc., are provided for which the contractor specifically applied? If so, that would leave the contractor vulnerable to overruns due to design changes which he had no way of anticipating, or skill to second guess. 4.32

In *Holland Hannen and Cubitts (Northern) Ltd v. The Welsh Health Technical Services Organisation*,[56] under a JCT 63 contract, it was the 4.33

---

[56] (1987) 35 B.L.R. 1.

architect's responsibility to provide further drawings or details to the Contractor as a variation where the design of windows for a hospital by a nominated sub-contractor proved ineffective.

4.34   In *London Borough of Merton v. Stanley Hugh Leach*,[57] it was held that there were certain implied terms in the JCT 63 contract as follows:

> (i)   that the employer and/or architect or other agents of the employer would not hinder or prevent the contractor from carrying out its obligations in accordance with the terms of the contract and from executing the works in a regular and orderly manner;
>
> (ii) that the employer and architect or such other agent of the employer would take all steps reasonably necessary to enable the contractor to discharge his obligations and execute the works in a regular and orderly manner;
>
> (iii) that the architect would provide the contractor with full, correct and co-ordinated information concerning the works.

4.35   In *J. & J. Fee v. Express Lift Co.*,[58] it was held that the employer has an implied duty to provide the contractor with correct information regarding the works in such a manner and at such times as was reasonably necessary for the contractor to have and in order for the contractor to fulfil its obligations under the contract. The *Stanley Hugh Leach* case is widely quoted by contractors in their claims documents, at least under JCT contracts, although Lord Diplock took a much narrower view in relation to a non-standard engineering contract in *Needox Ltd v. Borough of Swinton and Pendlebury*.[59] He held that it was impossible to imply a term that the employers through their engineer would give the contractors all the details and instructions necessary for the execution of the works in sufficient time to enable the contractor to execute the works in an economic and expeditious manner and/or in sufficient time to prevent the contractor being delayed in execution and completion. Lord Diplock held that there was no more than an obligation to provide drawings within a reasonable time, and that was not solely to be judged by what was reasonable to the convenience and financial interests of the contractor.[60]

4.36   The Inner House had come to much the same conclusion that drawings had to be provided in a reasonable time as an implied term in *Robert McAlpine v. Lanarkshire & Ayrshire Railway Co.*[61] In this case there was the interesting point that the engineer who it was alleged was responsible for the delayed drawings was also the arbiter named under the contract. The contractor's claim was for damages in respect that they were put to the erection of considerable temporary works for a bridge because the permanent plans had not been forthcoming for the bridge. The Inner House held that

---

[57] (1985) 32 B.L.R. 31.
[58] (1993) 34 Con.L.R. 147.
[59] (1958) 5 B.L.R. 34.
[60] *ibid.* at 42.
[61] (1889) 17 R. 113.

this matter was not comprehended by the arbitration clause, which had to be construed strictly where the party alleged to be at fault would also be the arbiter; and also it was noted that under the law of Scotland an arbiter had no power to award damages[62] unless that power had been given as part of the submission to him, and that in this case the contractor's claim would clearly be for damages.

Recently, in the context of a sub-contract, where the main contract was   4.37
in the Model Form for Process Plants (1981 ed.) in *Scottish Power plc v. Kvaerner Construction (Regions) Ltd*[63] after a consideration of *Stanley Hugh Leach, J. & J. Fee*, and *Ductform Ventilation (Fife) Ltd v. Andrews Weatherfoil Ltd*,[64] it was held that there were the following implied terms:

(1) The [main contractors] owed to the [sub-contractors] a duty not to hinder or prevent them... [save in respect of the proper exercise of their contractual right to regulate the timing of the sub-contract works to suit the requirements of the main contractor's programme, and without a guarantee of continuous work]... from carrying out their obligations in accordance with the terms of the sub-contract or from executing and completing the sub-contract works in a regular and orderly manner.

(2) The [main contractors] owed to the [sub-contractors] a duty... [save in respect of the proper exercise of their contractual right to regulate the timing of the sub-contract works to suit the requirements of the main contractor's programme, and without a guarantee of continuous work]... to take all reasonable steps within their power which were reasonably necessary to enable the [sub-contractors] to discharge their obligations and to execute the sub-contract works in a regular and orderly manner.

(3) The [main contractors] owed to the [sub-contractors] a duty to provide or arrange for the provision to the [sub-contractors] of such full, correct and co-ordinated information concerning the sub-contract works as was or ought reasonably to have been known by the [main contractors] to be required by the [sub-contractors], and that in such manner and at such times as was reasonably necessary to enable the pursuers to fulfil their obligations under the sub-contract.

These implied terms were held to co-exist with the express terms of the contract, and suggest that current judicial reasoning in Scotland would also imply equivalent terms into JCT 80.

Where does this leave the contractor in a claim for late documents which   4.38
he has not requested in writing? Is there a condition precedent that he applies in writing? Clause 25 would appear to make it so, but despite this the courts seem to say that it is the architect's responsibility to deal with design matters.

---

[62] *Aberdeen Railway Co. v. Blaikie Bros* (1852) 15 D. (H.L.) 20. This is still the law of Scotland and a trap for the unwary.

[63] (1999) S.L.T. 721 (OH).

[64] *London Borough of Merton v. Stanley Hugh Leach* [1985] 32 B.L.R. 51; *J. & J. Fee Ltd v. The Express Lift Co. Ltd* (1993) 34 Con. L.R. 147; *Ductform Ventilation (Fife) Ltd v. Andrews-Weatherfoil Ltd*, 1995 S.L.T. 88.

It appears from the principles in *Merton v. Leach*, which was a JCT 63 contract, that the prime duty for granting an extension of time rests with the Architect; and this duty is owed not only to the Contractor but also to the Employer, who might lose his entitlement to deduct liquidate and ascertained damages if a proper extension of time is not given. Therefore the giving of notice by the Contractor is not a condition precedent, but the failure of the Contractor to notify could be taken into account by the Architect if the Architect was denied the opportunity of mitigating the effect of the delay. This decision may seem strange on a progressive reading through of clause 25, which at first sight would appear to place the onus of notification squarely on the Contractor. But on reading through, it is discovered that there is expressly stated to be a review period after Practical Completion where the Architect is to take account of Relevant Events, whether or not the Relevant Events have been specifically notified by the Contractor.

4.39   In relation to sub-contract conditions the view of Lord Macfadyen in *Scottish Power*[65] was that in principle the sub-contractor could not be in breach of contract where the sub-contract works were delayed as a result of the instruction of additional work or variations, which was not the same as saying that there had to be an implied right to an extension of time for the sub-contractor, particularly where there was no liquidated and ascertained damages clause in the sub-contract. Lord Macfadyen would not go so far as to imply a term that loss and expense not contemplated in the clause for valuing variations should be valued over and above the contractual provisions as a matter of implication. His view was that if the parties had made a bad bargain it was not for the court to rewrite it. Where the contract allowed for the main contractor to direct the progress of the sub-contractor no additional payment rights could be implied when operatives had to be removed from site.

4.40   Under JCT 80 in questions related to money rather than time, it is a condition precedent for the Contractor to give notice under clause 26.[66] As regards drawings that might be issued by other professionals, *e.g.* an engineer, the contract is silent. A Nominated Sub Contractor who is late in supplying drawings to the Contractor is dealt with later,[67] but suffice to say that in *H. Fairweather & Co. v. Wandsworth London Borough Council*,[68] that was held not to be the fault of the Employer or to give the Contractor an entitlement to an extension of time.

4.41   Amendment 18 introduces a new piece of documentation which is optional: the "Information Release Schedule". This is also referred to in the August 1998 revision of the SBC as something that has been provided to the contractor at the time of execution of the SBC, but which may be

---

[65] *op.cit.*
[66] See paras 4.281–4.286.
[67] Clause 35.2.4 of JCT 80 as altered by Amendment 18, discussed at para. 4.367.
[68] [1987] 39 B.L.R. 106, concerning JCT 63, cl. 3(4), the terms of which were materially identical to clause 5.4 of the unamended 1980 form.

deleted. The former clause 5.4 is renumbered as clauses 5.4.1 and 5.4.2, and the guidance notes to Amendment 18 state that the new clause 5.4.2 will apply where no Information Release Schedule is provided for. The Information Release Schedule is provided to the Contractor, and will therefore be set out to suit the Architect and not any over-optimistic programme prepared by the Contractor (similarly, if there is no Information Release Schedule, clause 5.4.2 provides for the provision of further information having regard to the Completion Date, not a foreshortened date)[69]; but the Architect is to *ensure* the release of such information at the time stated in the Schedule unless Employer and Contractor both agree: "which agreement shall not be unreasonably withheld or delayed". Failure on the part of the Architect becomes a Relevant Event for the purposes of extension of time under the redrafted clauses 25.4.6.1 and 25.4.6.2; and are relevant matters under the redrafted clauses 26.2.1.1 and 26.2.1.2 for the purposes of direct loss and/or expense.

Clause 6: statutory obligations, notices, fees and charges

This clause is on the face of it widely drafted and provides that the contractor shall comply with and give all notices required by any Acts of Parliament, any instrument, rule or order made under any Act of Parliament, or any regulation or byelaw of any local authority or of any statutory undertaker which may have any jurisdiction with regard to the works. All of these are lumped together and termed "the statutory requirements".   4.42

Interestingly, no specific mention is made of any precise legislation, be it planning legislation, environmental legislation, or much less E.U. legislation. In particular it is a moot point to what extent the provisions of clause 6 deal with matters of environmental law under, for example, the Environment Act 1995, the Environmental Protection Act 1990, or the Control of Pollution Act 1974. There are wide areas of risk in relation to environmental hazards, compliance notices under the Environmental Protection Act 1990, duty of care obligations under section 34 of that Act, and other notices from local authorities having jurisdiction for matters of planning law, or notices from such as waste management authorities which are not spelled out. It is regrettable that no comprehensive allocation of risk is attempted as the statutory and regulatory framework is fragmented to say the least.[70] However, the potential interplay of liabilities, both civil and criminal, would make this a daunting task for the draftsman, particularly having regard to such questions as who is the legal occupier of a construction site.[71] Suffice   4.43

---

[69] This confirms the basis of the decision in *Glenlion Construction Ltd v. Guinness Trust* (1987) 39 B.L.R. 89.

[70] For a useful text as an introduction to environmental law matters the author recommends Reid, *Environmental Law in Scotland* (2nd ed., 1997) which has tables of relevant statutory material.

[71] In *City of London Corp. v. Bovis Construction Ltd (A.C.)* [1988] 49 B.L.R.1, it was held that the management contractor was the correct person on whom to serve an injunction as being in possession of the site under the Control of Pollution Act 1974, s. 60. Compare *Moore v. Gleddon* (1869) 7 M. 1016.

to say that for almost every contract there will be issues relating to Integrated Pollution Control (IPC) of discharges into all environmental media, and waste management. What if the contractor is carrying out the work in a proper and workmanlike manner in terms of clause 8.1.3, but is contravening noise pollution provisions? In relation to noise pollution it has been held by a sheriff that a notice served by a local authority on a developer under section 60 of the Control of Pollution Act 1974 requiring restrictions on works carried out at certain hours was competent, even if no measurable noise level was specified, beyond "audibility" further than the site boundaries.[72] An application can be made under section 61 of the Control of Pollution Act 1974 by whoever intends to carry out construction works for prior consent from the local authority with respect to noise pollution, and the local authority must have regard to any relevant code of practice.[73] Any consent will not preclude an aggrieved occupier from taking action under section 82 of the Environmental Protection Act 1990, or possibly as a nuisance at common law.[74]

4.44   The relevant statute for building control in Scotland is the Building (Scotland) Act 1959 which is now administered by the new unitary local authorities introduced by the Local Government etc. (Scotland) Act 1994. Various statutory instruments are relevant.[75] The Technical Standards Regulations are arranged into parts as follows:

Part A   General, including: definitions, references to published standards, regulations 3–9, and schedules 1–5
Part B   Fitness of materials
Part C   Structure
Part D   Structural fire precautions
Part E   Means of escape from fire, facilities for fire-fighting and means of warning of fire in dwellings
Part F   Heat-producing installations and storage of liquid and gaseous fuels
Part G   Preparation of sites and resistance to moisture
Part H   Resistance to transmission of sound
Part J   Conservation of fuel and power
Part K   Ventilation of buildings
Part M   Drainage and sanitary facilities
Part N   Electrical installations
Part P   Miscellaneous hazards
Part Q   Facilities for dwellings
Part R   Solid waste storage, dungsteads and farm effluent tanks

---

[72] *Adam (Scotland) Ltd v. Bearsden and Milngavie District Council*, 1996 S.L.T. (Sh.Ct.) 21.
[73] See Control of Noise (Codes of Practice for Construction and Open Sites) Order 1984 (S.I. 1984 No. 1992).
[74] *Webster v. Lord Advocate*, 1985 S.C. 173; 1984 S.L.T. 13; 1985 S.L.T. 361, where the noise of erecting and dismantling scaffolding for the annual military tattoo at Edinburgh castle was a nuisance, but a delay was allowed for the organisers to find an alternative.
[75] Building (Scotland) Regulations 1990 (S.I. 1990 No. 2179) which consist of statements of requirements, supported by "Technical Standards" published separately. There have been several amendments to the 1990 Regulations: S.I. 1993 No. 1457 (s.191); S.I. 1994 No. 1266 (s. 65); S.I. 1996 No. 2251 (s.183); S.I. 1997 No. 2157 (s. 150).

Part S   Stairs, ramps and protective barriers
Part T   Access and facilities for disabled people

It can be seen that some of these matters are more properly design rather   4.45
than workmanship matters. Compliance and liability for compliance rests at
the design stage with the Employer and the Architect (clause 6.1.5) who apply
for a building warrant, but active compliance (clause 6.1.1) and notifying the
Architect of divergences should the Contractor find any, is the responsibility
of the Contractor. The cost of providing such notices was dealt with by SMM6
in a list of items which were to be included as provisional sums, *e.g.*
scaffolding, temporary roads, temporary fencing and many others including
noise and pollution.[76] The Contractor does not have to use any special care to
find divergences. Nor (clause 6.1.5) is the Contractor liable to the Employer
if the works do not comply with Statutory Requirements if the Works were
carried out in accordance with the documents listed in clause 2.3. The 1959
Act, however, at section 10(i) allows the local authority to serve a notice on
the person by whom or on whose behalf a building has been or is being
constructed to show cause why he should not be required to remove or make
the building conform to the Regulations. The Building Operations (Scotland)
Regulations 1975[77] are designed to protect the public while building or
demolition works are in progress. The 1959 Act contains provisions[78] that
have not yet been brought into force which create civil liability for damage,
including death or personal injury where the warrant provisions or building
operations regulations are not complied with. However, in *Forbes v. City of
Dundee District Council*[79] it was held that where the pursuer fell down stairs
which had been built disconform to building warrant that no action rested
against the issuing authority.

In *Townsends (Builders) Ltd v. Cinema News and Property Management*   4.46
Ltd[80] the Court of Appeal considered alterations that had been made so that a
WC could be accessed from two rooms, which was in contravention of the
building regulations. The builder had carried out the work according to plans
provided to him by the architect, but the builder had failed to serve a notice on
the local authority describing the work which he was carrying out. It was held
that the builder was still entitled to be paid as this was not a contract that was
"pervaded with illegality". Whilst the performance was illegal, the performance
could be made legal by partitioning. It was noted that the owner could recover
damages from the builder in this respect, even though it was the custom that the
architect saw to it that the works complied with the building regulations.
Although the decision does not explain why, it was also held that the builder
was entitled to be indemnified by the architect.

---

[76] There are no similar provisions in the current SMM7, but presumably these are to be
      covered in a provisional sum.
[77] S.I. 1975 No. 549.
[78] s. 19A.
[79] (1997) S.C.L.R. 682.
[80] [1959] 1 All E.R. 7 (CA).

4.47   Amendment 12, which introduced a Contractor's Statement for Performance Specified Work with clause 42, also introduced new clauses 6.1.6 and 6.1.7. Essentially any changes that are required for Performance Specified Work to comply with the Statutory Requirements are to be at no cost to the Employer, unless there is a change in the Statutory Requirements after the base date.

4.48   Clause 6.3 provides that a local authority or statutory undertakers executing such work in exercise of their statutory obligations are neither Domestic nor Nominated Sub-Contractors, but constitute a Relevant Event giving rise to an extension of time (clause 25.4.11) if they delay progress. However, a delay by a statutory undertaker can give rise to an extension of time under clause 25 but is not a reason for loss and expense under clause 26, *i.e.* the risks associated with a statutory undertaker are treated as neutral events, like bad weather.[81] Statutory undertakers are nowhere defined in JCT 80. Presumably these relate to services such as under the Sewerage (Scotland) Act 1968; the Water (Scotland) Act 1980; the Gas Act 1986; the Electricity Act 1989; the Roads (Scotland) Act 1984; and the relevant statutes for telecommunications and possibly cable broadcasting.

4.49   A new clause 6A has been imported into JCT 80 by Amendment 14 to take account of the Construction Design and Management (CDM) Regulations.[82] The CDM Regulations are essentially about goal-setting for good management of health and safety information from a design and pre-tender stage, throughout the project, and throughout the lifetime of the building. A team approach is introduced and instead of simply leaving safety to the contractor, the employer requires to appoint a competent planning supervisor (reg. 5) who acts as a sort of safety co-ordinator, and designers now have duties in respect to the safety of their designs. The co-ordination of the safety aspects on site will still largely be the role of the main contractor, who is termed the principal contractor in the CDM Regulations. Essentially, safety management documentation is now required to be produced by the planning supervisor in the form of a health and safety plan, at a pre-tender stage, and which the principal contractor develops into a construction phase plan which is intended by the legislation to be under constant review. Liability in terms of the CDM Regulations is under the criminal law, with the exception of two duties (reg. 21), namely:

(i)   failure by the client to ensure a suitably developed health and safety plan is in place before work commences (reg. 10);
(ii)   failure by the Principal Contractor to exclude unauthorised persons from the construction site (reg. 16 (1)(c)).

---

[81]   See discussion of clause 25.
[82]   The Construction (Design and Management) Regulations 1994 (S.I. 1994 No. 3140). These will apply, broadly, to construction works for more than 30 days or where more than 5 persons will be on the site at any one time; and wherever there is demolition or dismantling.

It remains to be seen whether the exception under regulation 10 will see actions against clients by contractors if losses arise for breach of duty, and the terms of clause 20.1 should be noted in this respect.

Clause 6 A.2 requires the Contractor where he is the Principal Contractor   4.50
(capitalised in the section but not in the Regulations) for the purposes of the CDM Regulations to "ensure that the Health and Safety plan (again capitalised) has the features required by regulation 15(4) of the CDM regulations". Regulation 15(4) is not set out as a footnote which would have been helpful, but it is as follows:

> " 15.–…(4) The principal contractor shall take all measures as it is reasonable for a person in his position to take to ensure that the health and safety plan contains until the end of the construction phase the following features:
>
> (a) arrangements for the project (including, where necessary for the management of construction work and monitoring of compliance with the relevant statutory provisions) which will ensure, so far as is reasonably practicable, the health and safety of all persons at work carrying out the construction work and all persons who may be affected by the work of such persons at work, taking account of —
>
> > (i)   risks involved in the construction work,
> >
> > (ii)   any activity specified in paragraph (5); and
>
> (b) sufficient information about arrangements for the welfare of persons at work by virtue of the project to enable any contractor to understand how he can comply with any requirements placed upon him in respect of welfare by or under the relevant statutory provisions."

An "activity" is widely defined as one that might affect persons' health and   4.51
safety.

Also, clause 6A.2 makes it a contractual requirement for the contractor   4.52
to comply with the requirements of a principal contractor under the CDM Regulations whilst he is so appointed; but if he is succeeded as principal contractor clause 6A.3 requires him to comply with all reasonable requirements of the principal contractor without the benefit of any extension of time. Compliance or non-compliance by the employer with his obligations under clause 6A.1 to ensure that the planning supervisor carries out his duties, or the principal contractor carries out his (where obviously he is not one and the same as the contractor), is a clause 25 "Relevant Event" (for an extension of time), and a clause 26 relevant matter (for direct loss and/or expense).

Clause 7: Levels and setting out of the Works

Clause 7 relates the specialism of setting out the Works at ground level.   4.53
It may be carried out by a specialist engineer, particularly in large and complex works. It is concerned with measurement and dimensions and layout of piled foundations, and such other structural matters. This is a crucial stage in the construction process. This clause provides that the

Architect shall determine levels and provide the Contractor with accurately dimensioned drawings. It is important to note that the architect may be liable at common law for the work of a specialist engineer if it is not the ordinary practice in the profession to delegate the work of design.[83] Clause 7 adds to the Contractor's obligations under clause 2 in that the Contractor has responsibility for and shall, at no cost to the Employer, amend any errors arising from his own inaccurate setting out. Note that it says amend — is this different from the common law position as regards defective building work.[84] This would appear to be so as clause 7 recognises that it might be better to live with certain errors. In *Ruxley Electronics & Construction Ltd v. Forsyth*[85] (which was not a JCT 80 case) a swimming pool was built for the defender which was to have a deep end of seven feet six inches, but which was built to a depth of six feet nine inches in and only six feet around the diving area. The House of Lords, reversing the Court of Appeal, held that the primary remedy was for diminution of value, and that where the reinstatement costs are out of all proportion but the principal objective of the contract had been satisfactorily achieved, an award of loss of amenity was the next appropriate award. Clause 7 allows that the Architect may instruct that such errors shall not be amended with the consent of the Employer and an appropriate deduction shall be made from the Contract Sum. What an appropriate deduction means is probably a payment in lieu of damages. But there may be questions of whether the employer has acquiesced in acceptance of the errors if an appropriate deduction is made and greater subsequent loss develops, thereby precluding any further recovery of damages. In clause 17.2 the same phrase is used. Under clause 17.2 if defects arise after Practical Completion they may be made good in the defects liability period at no cost to the employer. If these are not made good then an appropriate deduction is made. In *Emson Eastern Ltd (in receivership) v. EME Developments Ltd*[86] it was held that value of *de minimis* snagging matters after the Certificate of Practical Completion had been issued, but which were not made good by the insolvent contractor, should be abated from payments due at Practical Completion.

4.54   For clause 17 of a JCT Minor Works Contract it was held in *William Tomkinson v. Parochial Board Council of St Michael*,[87] that an appropriate deduction would be an amount "which the contractor could have remedied the matters for". The phrase, "appropriate deduction" also appears in clause 8, where work materials or goods which are not in accordance with the contract may be allowed to remain and an appropriate deduction be made. The deduction, it appears, should be made by the Quantity Surveyor according to the guidance notes to Amendment 5 of JCT 80. However, it is difficult to discern what contractual or delictual duties the Quantity Surveyor may have in such cases.

---

[83] *Moresk Cleaners Ltd v. Hicks* [1966] 2 Lloyd's Rep. 338. But see SFA/92 Conditions of Engagement which alter the position contractually.

[84] See *Ramsay v. Brand* (1898) 25 R. 1212.

[85] [1995] B.L.R. 73 (HL).

[86] (1991) 55 B.L.R. 114.

[87] 6 Const. L.J. 319.

A quantity surveyor's role had been judicially defined as "confined to   4.55
measuring and valuing... and not in any instance to determine liability" in
the case of *John Laing Construction Ltd v. County and District Properties
Ltd.*[88] In respect of the architect at least it has been held in *Wessex Regional
Health Authority v. HLM Design Ltd (No.2)*[89] that, after a settlement has
been finally agreed by the Employer and the Contractor under JCT 80, an
action is competent in contract and tort against the architect for the
employer's losses, including economic losses.

Clause 8: Work, materials and goods

In keeping with the tortuous history and drafting of this contract, clause 8   4.56
has been revised or redrafted by Amendments 4, 5, 9, 12 and 14. It also has
to be read along with clause 1.4 (Contractor's responsibility); clause 2
(contractor's obligations); clause 4 (Architect's Instructions); and clause 30
(Certificates and payments) — especially clause 30.10.1 added by
Amendment 15. Unfortunately, the reader will not, as in the ICE 6th contract,
find a proper index cross referencing these clauses.

Clause 8.1.1 states that all materials and goods shall, so far as procurable,   4.57
be of the kinds and standards described in the Contract Bills (notice, not the
Contract Documents which one might expect for consistency with clause 2).
Clause 8.1.2 also specifies that all workmanship shall be of the standard
described in the Contract Bills (again not the Contract Documents). It can
be difficult to assess what the word "standard" means, especially if the
Bills do not mention a "standard" as such, which would be quite normal. It
is also possible that if this clause were to be tested in the courts, that there
might be a difference between the workmanship standard of clause 8.1.1
and the Contractor's obligations under clause 2.1. It then continues "or to
the extent that no such standards are described in the Contract Bills, shall
be of a standard appropriate to the Works". What does this extraordinary
piece of draftsmanship mean, and is it inconsistent with clause 2.1? Does it
make the test for the standard of workmanship in some cases referable to
cost, value, or someone's opinion of quality or scale of the work? The normal
delictual standard of care that is implied by law and usually also in contract,
is that of the reasonably competent analogous practitioner. Therefore, a
surgeon's operation is judged to be negligent if it falls beneath the standard
of the reasonably competent surgeon. The surgeon's liability is not judged
against the "quality" of the individual upon whom he is carrying out the
operation, in the sense that a different standard is required for a national
health patient as opposed to a private one. On one interpretation this phrase
might mean that a standard might be expected for a garden hut and a different one
for a specialist floor, but this would get dangerously close to a fitness-for-purpose

---

[88] [1982] 23 B.L.R. 1.
[89] [1994] 71 B.L.R. 32; (1994) C.I.L.L. 991; 40 Con. L.R. 1.

standard. This drafting does not appear to have been judicially considered. In any event clause 8.1.3 provides that all work should be carried out in a proper and workmanlike manner.

4.58   One might have thought that the Architect's opinion was critical, as he can under clause 8.4.1 issue instructions in regard to the removal from the site all or any of such work, materials or goods not in accordance with the Contract (again, note not the Contract Documents). And, of course, clause 2.1 provides "that to the extent that approval of the quality of materials or of the standards of workmanship is a matter for the opinion of the Architect such quality and standards shall be to the reasonable satisfaction of the Architect". As we have seen in *Muldoon v. Pringle*[90] the Scottish courts would have held his opinion to be critical. Certainly, at least as regards the Final Certificate, the English courts generally did too[91] prior to Amendment 15 (July 1995) which now provides:

> "30.10   Save as aforesaid no certificate of the architect shall of itself be
>   conclusive evidence that
> 30.10.1   any works, materials or goods
> 30.10.2   any Performance Specified Work
>   to which it relates are in accordance with this Contract."

4.59   A similar "not conclusive evidence" clause is inserted at 30.9.1.1 as regards the Final Certificate, and clause 1.4 has been amended to keep the Contractor wholly responsible even if a Certificate of Practical Completion or the Certificate of Completion of Making Good Defects is issued. What then is the purpose and effect of clauses 8 and 2.1 speaking of approval of the quality of materials or the standards of workmanship being matters for the opinion of the architect, and why might it be provided that these are to be to the reasonable satisfaction of the architect who must express any dissatisfaction within a reasonable time from the execution of the unsatisfactory work (clause 8.1.1, clause 8.1.2, clause 8.2.2)? It might be suggested that the RIAS and the RIBA, who had a substantial interest from the professional negligence point of view in the drafting of Amendment 15, are attempting to give the architect authority without liability. Also, as was pointed out in the Latham Report[92] there was a need for a form of contract approved for use with other JCT contracts that specified the architect's role and that of other consultants. This is a matter which is currently being addressed by a JCT Working Party, although it is understood that consensus cannot yet be obtained. Why should the Architect have substantial powers to order opening up and testing of executed works (clause 8.3), and issue instructions for the removal from the site of any work, materials or goods

[90]   (1882) 9 R. 916.
[91]   *Crown Estates Commissioners v. John Mowlem & Co. Ltd* (1994) 10 Const. L.J. 311 (CA),
       approving *Colbart Ltd v. Kumar* [1992] 59 B.L.R. 89. See also *P & M Kaye Ltd v. Hosier
       & Dickinson Ltd* [1972] 1 All E.R. 121 (HL).
[92]   See Chap. 8 *passim*.

"not in accordance with this Contract" (clause 8.4); or issue Variations under clause 8.5 "where there is any failure to comply with clause 8.1.3 in regard to the carrying out of the work in a proper and workmanlike manner"; or enable the Employer to set in motion the determination provisions of clause 27; if the Architect's decisions in these matters are not conclusive (leaving aside any question of adjudication, litigation or arbitration)? Perhaps the answer is that his decision will be conclusive for matters that the architect must satisfy himself about, and some lesser standard of reasonableness will apply where he has not.[93]

It is submitted that the fundamental lessons of recent case law have not been fully thought through by the JCT, leaving a "black hole" of duties without contractual responsibilities and an incompatibility with the common law on the matter of agency, the discoverability of latent defects,[94] and the implied duties of the architect under delict. The central question of when has the Contractor performed his obligations under such a contract has been left up in the air; as has the role and liability of the Architect in supervising and certifying; both as agent of the Employer *vis-a-vis* the Contractor, and as a professional with duties under contract directly with the Employer, and perhaps in delict to the Contractor. The question of the architect's supervisory duties has been looked at in several recent cases.[95] It is unfortunate that the House of Lords in *P. & M. Kaye Ltd v. Dickinson Ltd*[96] elected not to deal with the matter fully when deciding that the issue of a Final Certificate under JCT 63 was conclusive, so that pre-existing disputes in court concerning defects were barred by the issue of a Final Certificate (Lord Diplock dissenting), and could not proceed to arbitration if the employer had not issued a notice of arbitration timeously. The House chose not to look at the wider issues of the meaning of architect's satisfaction and latent defects as the matter was not argued in the first place before the Court of Appeal. 4.60

The effect of final certificates is a question that is strewn with conflicting authorities[97]: *e.g.* Lord Diplock's dissenting judgment in *P. & M. Kaye Ltd*[98] was followed by an Official Referee in *H. W. Nevill (Sunblest) v. William Press,*[99] but the Court of Appeal in *Crestar v. Carr*[1] held that the Final 4.61

---

[93] See *Firholm Builders v. McAuley*, 1983 S.L.T. (Sh.Ct.) 105 *per* Sheriff Principal Bennett at pp 108–9. Note that in *Belcher Food Products Ltd v. Miller & Black*, 1999 S.L.T. 142 the *Crown Estates* case was distinguished, but the specific point made by the author was left undecided at 149 B-C.

[94] A problem highlighted by Lord Gill in *Belcher (ibid.)* at 148-L.

[95] *Corfield (Alexander) v. David Grant* (1992) 59 B.L.R. 102; *Gray (Trustees of the London Hospital) v. T.P. Bennett & Son (a firm)* (1987) 43 B.L.R. 63; and *Tesco Stores v. Norman Hitchcox Partnership* (1998) 56 Con. L.R. 42; *George Fischer Holding Ltd v. Multi Design Consultants Ltd*, 1998 C.I.L.L. 1361.

[96] *op.cit.*

[97] See *Firholm Builders v. McAuley*, 1983 S.L.T. (Sh. Ct.) 105; *Paterson (Robert) & Sons Ltd v. Household Supplies Co. Ltd*, 1975 S.L.T. 98; *Crown Estates Commissioners v. John Mowlem & Co. Ltd* (1994) 70 B.L.R. 1; (1994) 40 Con. L.R. 36; and more recently *Belcher Food Products Ltd v. Miller & Black*, 1999 S.L.T. 142.

[98] *op.cit.*

[99] (1983) 20 B.L.R. 78.

[1] (1987) 37 B.L.R. 113 (CA).

Certificate under a pre-1980 JCT Minor Works Contract had no conclusive effect. The highest Scots authority on the issue is to be found in the First Division decision in *Ayr Road Trustees v. Adams*[2] which was that the final certificate authorising payment by the employer was conclusive; and there is tentative authority from *Gloag on Contract* (2nd ed.) at pp. 704–705 to similar effect,[3] although he describes *Ayr Road Trustees* as "a very special one, and can hardly form a precedent...The real ground of judgement seems therefore to have been mere delay [a claim that work had been defectively carried out disconform to specification, and where there was more than three years between the raising of the action and final certification]". The "special circumstances" were that a resident engineer[4] appointed by the employer to supervise the contractor agreed with the contractor's site agent that concrete be substituted for ashlar in a foundation because the amount of water coming into the excavations made it impossible to lay ashlar when building a bridge at Ayr. The separately employed firm of civil engineers, who had the role of designing and certifying, were not made aware of the substitution by the resident engineer, but only of the depth of the foundations. The works were remeasured at the end by the resident engineer without the substitute materials being referred to by the resident engineer. The contractor made no attempt at deception and the final accounts were prepared on the basis of the resident engineer's reports, and both appeared to be acting in good faith. The problem was that the resident engineer did not have the authority to instruct replacement materials. One year after the expiry of the defects liability period foundation problems were discovered, *i.e.* they were washing away. This was probably due to cement being unskillfully put in place so that it did not get time to harden and so had washed away, or had been contaminated by clay and rendered inferior. The Lord President was of the opinion that: "if it was through his [the resident engineer's] conduct that this violation of the contract was committed, and this settlement made, I do not see who is to be answerable for this except the Pursuers".[5] And, *per* Lord Shand: "I am of the opinion that the pursuers cannot now question the settlement or open up these accounts."[6]

4.62   It is submitted that *Ayr Trustees* is authority for the proposition that if an architect's final certificate is conclusive then that should be the case *a fortiori* if a clerk of works with the power to reject or condemn any materials or workmanship is separately employed by the employer, as in JCT 80,

---

[2] (1883) 11 R. 326.
[3] Gloag does not appear to have considered *Chapman v. Edinburgh Prison Board* discussed at para 4.17.
[4] Note that in this case the resident engineer is referred to in Lord Mure's judgment as the clerk of works, and this case may have particular applicability for modern construction professionals such as project managers, who are employed for their expertise quite separately from the certifiers. Much will depend on the project manager's level of supervision of the works and whether he has power to issue binding instructions, which was held not to be the case for the resident engineer in this case.
[5] *op.cit.* at 345.
[6] *op. cit.* at 349.

clause 12, although JCT 80 clause 1.4, brought in by Amendment 5 (July 1988) makes the Contractor wholly responsible, notwithstanding inspection by the Clerk of Works.

In *Peddie v. Henderson* (1869) S.L.R. 608 there was an appeal to the Inner House. There had been two questions before a jury, (i) had work been properly carried out, and (ii) if not, had it been approved by the clerk of works. The jury answered the first question in the affirmative, therefore precluding discussion of the second. The charge to the jury by Lord Ormidale on the second matter had been:

4.63

> "they must in the first place, be satisfied that the drains were left open for some time, and if they were satisfied that they were seen by the clerk of works, and that he either knew or might be held to have known the condition of the pipes, and the manner in which they were laid, and the ground upon which they were laid, and that no objection was taken by him [the clerk of works] on the part of the pursuer, or by anyone else, then, in point of law, the pursuer was precluded from maintaining his present claim."

In the First Division Lord Dees gave a dissenting judgment that the jury's decision was in the "teeth of the evidence" and insupportable. His Lordship went on to say:

> "I do not concur with the law that the learned judge laid down to the jury— that if they were satisfied that the inspector was there and saw what was going on, that precluded the objections on the part of the proprietor. An inspector has very large powers: he has powers to make a great many variations on the work; but I have no idea that it will relieve a contractor from liability for making soil pipes and drains in the way that they ought to be made that the inspector does not object... I cannot hold that that relieves the contractor. But that is the contractor's view of the law. I have no idea that that is the law; and in the unqualified way that it was laid down to the jury I could not have concurred."

Gloag notes in relation to the other main authority, *Muldoon v. Pringle*, that no opinions were given:"and the case looks like one where the Court forced a compromise on the parties". Perhaps a solution to the continuing liability question, which probably boils down to whose insurance should cover defects that are found after the final certificate, lies in project insurance. This is a matter which has been the subject of proposals by the Latham Report, which suggests that compulsory project insurance be obtained,[7] but this proposal did not reach the statute books in the Housing Grants, Construction and Regeneration Act1996.

4.64

It is also worth noting that the modifier in clause 8.1.2 "so far as procurable" is not used for standards of workmanship but is under 8.1.1 for materials and goods. From a contractor's point of view a very real difficulty that might affect his progress is the unavailability of skilled labour — the

4.65

---

[7] See Chap. 8, para. 8.16.

so-called "skills shortage" — but there is no provision that might protect the contractor in those circumstances. Indeed, in *Davis Contractors Ltd v. Fareham Urban District Council*[8] shortage of labour led to a 14-month overrun which was held to have been at the contractor's risk; the contract had neither been frustrated, nor had a term of tender concerning adequate supplies of labour been incorporated into the contract.

4.66   There is a Code of Practice for opening up for inspection or testing work attached to JCT 80, which seeks to encourage agreement between the Architect and the Contractor. Clause 8 also gives the Architect power to issue instructions requiring the exclusion from the works of any persons employed thereon provided this is not done "unreasonably or vexatiously". This appears to impose two quite different standards, *i.e.* something might be unreasonable but not vexatious. Under clause 27, determination notices by the Employer also may not be given vexatiously or unreasonably, and this has been interpreted as meaning "unfair and almost amounting to sharp practice".[9] In *John Jarvis v. Rockdale Housing Association*[10] an identically worded provision was considered. "Unreasonably" was held to be a "general term which can include anything which can be objectively judged to be unreasonable". "Vexatiously" was said to connote "an ulterior motive to oppress, harass or annoy". In *J. M. Hill & Son v. London Borough of Camden*,[11] "vexatiously" was a different standard from "unreasonably", and together, as being "totally unfair and almost smacking of sharp practice".[12] The simplest way of avoiding such debates would be simply to have the word "vexatiously" deleted, if this can be successfully achieved (see comments on clause 2.2.2).

Statutory regime for the supply of materials

4.67   As regards the supply of goods, the Supply of Goods and Services Act 1982 has become part of Scots law by the Sale and Supply of Goods Act 1994, effective in relation to contracts made on or after January 3, 1995. This applies to building contracts as the 1994 Act applies whether or not services are provided under the contract.[13] Under section 11D (2) where "the transferor transfers the property in goods in the course of a business, there is an implied term that the goods supplied under the contract are of satisfactory quality". For the purposes of sections 11D and 11E (transfer by sample), "goods are of satisfactory quality if they meet the standard that a reasonable person would regard as satisfactory, taking account of any description of the goods, the price (if relevant) and all other relevant circumstances".[14] The question might arise as to whether the architect is

---

[8] [1956] 2 All E.R. 145 (HL).
[9] *J. M. Hill & Son v. London Borough of Camden* [1980] 18 B.L.R. 31.
[10] [1986] 36 B.L.R. 48 (CA)
[11] *op. cit..*
[12] *ibid.* at p. 149.
[13] s. 11A(3).
[14] s. 11 D(3).

the "reasonable person", or whether the architect is in a different position because of his professional status.

The implied term as to satisfactory quality does not extend to any matter   4.68
making the quality of goods unsatisfactory[15]:

(a)   where any matter of satisfactory quality is drawn specifically to the transferee's attention before the contract is made;
(b)   where the transferee examines the goods before the contract is made, which that examination ought to reveal; or
(c)   where the property in the goods is, or is to be, transferred by reference to a sample, which would not have been apparent on a reasonable examination of the sample.

Except as provided by sections 11D and E, there is "no implied term   4.69
about the quality or fitness for a particular purpose of goods supplied under a contract for the transfer of goods".[16] However in terms of section 11D(5), (6), (7), (8) and (9), there may be an implied term of reasonable fitness for purpose whether or not that purpose is one for which such goods are commonly supplied, if the transferor transfers in the course of a business, or as an agent, and the transferee, expressly or by implication, makes known to the transferee any particular purpose for which the goods are being acquired. The implied term will not apply where the transferee does not rely, or it is unreasonable for him to rely, on the skill and judgment of the transferor. Section 11E applies to transfer by sample and that the bulk will correspond with the sample in quality; that reasonable opportunity will be given for comparing the bulk and the sample; and that the goods will be free from any defect of unsatisfactory quality which would not be apparent on reasonable examination of the sample. Section 11F provides for remedies for breach of contract. The transferee may claim damages and, if the breach is material — which, in the case of a consumer contract as defined in the Unfair Contract Terms Act 1977, is a breach as to quality, or fitness for purpose, or correspondence to description or sample — may also reject any goods delivered and treat the contract as repudiated. Section 11L deals with the exclusion of these terms. A right, duty or liability which would arise by implication may be negatived or varied by express agreement, or by the course of dealing between the parties, or by such usage as binds both parties to the contract.

Quite how this will impact on building contracts in Scotland remains to   4.70
be seen. However, in England it has been held in *John Lelliot (Contracts) v. Byrne Bros (Formwork)*[17] that where a sub-contractor agreed to provide a temporary support system for steelwork for work at Lords cricket ground, and where the sub-contractors were specialists, the statutory implied term

---

[15]   s. 11 D(4).
[16]   s. 11 D(1).
[17]   31 Con. L.R. 89.

of reasonable fitness for purpose would be readily implied under the Supply of Goods and Services Act 1982, s. 9(4)–(6). However in *Rotherham Metropolitan Borough Council v. Frank Haslam Milan & Co. Ltd*[18] hardcore fill material which was within the specification of the contract, but which expanded causing concrete slabs above to crack was found by the Court of Appeal not to breach an implied term of merchantable quality as it was perfectly serviceable hardcore if used in another context. Nor was there an implied fitness for purpose where the employer had left no decision which was considered to be relevant to suitability unspecified, and the employer had not relied on the contractor's judgment.

4.71   A private employer under a building contract may deal as a consumer. However in *Chester Grosvenor Hotel Co. Ltd v. Alfred McAlpine Management Ltd*[19] an employer who had a series of refurbishment contracts with management contractors was not dealing as a consumer but as part of his business.

Clause 9: royalties and patent rights

4.72   If the Contractor is using and supplying patented articles or processes or inventions the Contract Sum is deemed to include these things. Interestingly there is no provision which deals with the other main areas where an intellectual property right may exist, *i.e.* copyright, registered designs, or trade marks. These questions of intellectual property law do not in practice appear to generate much case law in the construction context. The Contractor is contractually obliged to indemnify the Employer against any claims that might be made against the Employer by reason of the Contractor infringing any patent rights. This appears to be a wide indemnity, but it is difficult to imagine how an employer might infringe a patent in the typical construction context. Section 60 of the Patents Act 1977 defines the infringement of a patent. A patent may relate to a product or a process for making a product. Under section 60 of the Patents Act 1977 infringements are broadly related to the unauthorised use, disposal or importing of a patented invention. Infringement, therefore, is not likely to be something that the employer would be exposed to in the typical construction context. The remedies for infringement are given in section 61 and are injunction/ interdict, damages, an account of profits, an order for delivery up or destruction and a declaration that the patent is valid and has been infringed by the defender. Again, these are not matters that are likely to affect an employer, but even the fear of delivery up or destruction is not likely to be very real, as any disputes can be referred to the Comptroller of Patents if both parties are willing, and the remedies are limited to damages and/or a declaration. Damages were considered in relation to the use of a modified patented steel lintel in *Catnic Components Ltd v. Hill & Smith Ltd*[19a] in which the appropriate measure of damages was

---

[18] (1996) 78 B.L.R. 1 (AC).
[19] (1991) 56 B.L.R. 122.
[19a] [1983] F.S.R. 512, this action was a follow up to an action between the same parties which reached the Lords on whether there was an infringement, reported at [1982] R.P.C. 183.

lost sales of the patent holder. If anything the Employer might be more exposed than the Contractor if the Contractor is required to use or supply any patented article or process under clause 9.2. Clause 9.2 provides that if following an instruction leads to an infringement of patent rights, and if the contractor becomes liable for royalties or *damages* (author's emphasis) that these shall be added to the Contract Sum.

Clauses 10 and 12 can then be taken together. These deal with the people who are the main characters on site in practice.

Clause 10: person in charge/ Clause 12: clerk of works

In terms of clause 10, the Contractor "shall constantly keep upon the site a competent person-in-charge" who can then accept instructions given to him by the Architect, or directions from the Clerk of Works. He used to be known as the foreman-in-charge in the JCT 63 contract. He is normally referred to as the contractor's site agent. This clause in practice does not mean that a constant 24-hour presence is required. Clause 12 deals with the Clerk of Works. His duty is defined as "to act solely as an inspector on behalf of the Employer under the directions of the Architect". This definition would seem merely illustrative as the Clerk of Works is, of course, not a party to the building contract. The Clerk of Works may, however, give directions if it would be competent for the Architect to do so under the conditions and they will have the same status, provided the instructions are confirmed in writing by the Architect within two working days. Otherwise, the directions have "no effect". There would not appear to be an implied authority at common law for a clerk of works to issue instructions, either in respect of the architect or because he is paid by the employer.[20]   4.73

In the case of *Kensington & Chelsea & Westminster Area Health Authority v. Wettern Composites*[21] damages against the architect for a failure owed to the employer to discover defects were reduced by 20 per cent to take account of the contributory negligence of the clerk of works. He was referred to as the "chief petty officer" as opposed to the captain of the ship in that case.   4.74

The interphase between the supervisory role of the architect and the role of the clerk of works was discussed before the Second Division in *Jamieson v. Simon*.[22] The case involved the covering up of the bottoming of a cement floor in a small villa which had been constructed of improper materials and not according to specification. The architect was held in breach to his employer for inadequate supervision, although the architect had argued that site visits once a fortnight constituted general supervision. It was noted that a clerk of works would not normally have been employed for small works such as this. Lord Moncreiff said:

---

[20] *Ayr Road Trustees v. Adams* (1883) S.C. XI R. 326.
[21] (1985) 31 B.L.R. 57.
[22] 1899 36 S.L.R. 883.

" No doubt the architect is paid a commission of 2 1/2 % for supervision, but in return for that remuneration he cannot be expected to be constantly present, and even if he were to visit the work every day, scamping might go on when his back was turned, for which it would be unreasonable to hold him responsible... I do not wish to be understood as meaning that an architect is to be held responsible for all defective work which may be covered up during his absence. Not even a clerk of works could be expected to detect everything of that kind. My opinion proceeds on the ground that when one contractor had to follow another, and when the work done was about to be covered up so that it could not thereafter be inspected, the architect should, under the duty of supervision which he had undertaken, have ascertained either by personal inspection, or through an assistant, whether the bottoming had been done according to specification, and that in failing to do so he did not use reasonable care in the discharge of his duty."

Clause 11: Access for the architect to the works

4.75   This allows the Architect and his representatives (no one defined) reasonable access to the Works and to workshops or other places of the Contractor where work is being prepared for this Contract. The author is not sure how often it is invoked — but it may be used to go out and inspect specialist works, for example, pre-cast works off site. The Contractor is to ensure that a similar clause is incorporated in sub-contracts.[23] The right of access is not cross referenced to any particular powers that the Architect may have (or his undefined representatives — probably the Quantity Surveyor and Clerk of Works) under clauses 4, 8, 13, or otherwise at common law.

Clause 13: Variations and provisional sums

Clause 13A: Variation Instruction — Contractor's quotation in compliance with the instruction

4.76   Clause 13 is an altered version of clause 11 of JCT 63, and has been further redrafted by Amendments 4, 7, 9, 10, 12, 13 and 18. The result in the current SBC With Quantities (August 1998 revision) is tortuous to say the least. Amendment 4 (July 1987) for the avoidance of doubt gives the status of Variations to Architects' instructions making alterations to access, working space, working hours and sequence of working (clauses 13.1.2.1 to 13.1.2.4), and clarifies how the varied Nominated Sub-Contract work is to be valued. Amendment 7 (July 1988) deals with the valuation of Approximate Quantities and the expenditure of provisional sums for defined and undefined work; Amendment 9 redefined a Variation under clause 13.1 as a consequence of a redefinition of the Works in that Amendment; Amendment 10 was a consequential amendment due to the introduction of

---

[23] For example clause 3.12 NSC/C; cl. 25 DOM/1.

new nomination procedures for sub-contractors in that Amendment; Amendment 12 made consequential changes for the introduction of Performance Specified Work; and Amendment 13 introduced clause 13A which deals with quotations for variations by the Contractor, which the Employer may require, but which the Contractor is not bound to submit, being agreed by the Employer. This accepted quotation would then replace the valuation provisions of clause 13.4.1. The point of it is that it includes a confirmed and final sum for direct loss and/or expense under clause 26 in respect of that work. Amendment 18 (April 1998) replaces the above clause 13.4.1 and splits it into 13.4.1.1 and 13.4.1.2, so introducing provisions whereby a new Alternative A which the Contractor is free to adopt (allowing for a Contractor's Price Statement for such work) and a new Alternative B (the existing valuation rules of clauses 13.5.1 to 13.5.7) are now created. The Amendment provisions are optional and not necessary to comply with HGCRA, but they purport to follow a Latham Report recommendation that variations should be priced in advance. The Guidance Notes for Amendment 18 seem to indicate that the difference between these new alternatives and clause 13A is that under clause 13A the Contractor is not obliged to carry out the variation, but it appears to the author that the Contractor always has a right of reasonable objection to a Variation instruction in any case under clause 4.1.1.1.

Broadly speaking a Variation is the alteration or modification of the design, quality or quantity of the Works (clause 13.1.1); and the alteration of access, space, working hours, or the execution of work in any specific order (clause 13.1.2). It excludes nomination of a sub-contractor to do matters for which the measured quantities have been set out and priced in the Contract Bills to be done by the Contractor (clause 13.1.3). The Contractor in clause 13.2.2 has a right of reasonable objection as provided in clause 4.1.1, subject to the difficulties that we have noted with this. 4.77

The valuation rules are set out in clause 13.5.1. The Contract Bills are to be used where additional or substituted work is of similar character to, is executed under similar conditions as, and does not significantly change the quantity of, work set out in the Contract Bills (note, not the Contract Documents) under clause 13.1.1. The Bills, plus a fair allowance, are to be used to value work that is of similar character to that set out in the Contract Bills, but where the additional or substituted work is not carried out under similar conditions and/or significantly changes the quantities (clause 13.3.1.2). Fair rates and prices are to be used when all else fails and the additional or substituted work is not of similar character to work set out in the Contract Bills (clause 13.5.1.3). Understandably, there is much room for dispute as to the application of these rules.[24] Direct loss and/or expense, or disruption in respect of such variations is to be valued under clause 26. 4.78

---

[24] See P. R. Hibberd, *Variations in Construction Contracts* (1986); J. M. Arnott, "Quantifying Extra Work and Changed Conditions (Including Differing site Conditions) Claims", 1989 I.C.L.R. 158. For a case where an arbiter was found to have been in error for considering matters external to the contract to decide what the words "similar conditions" meant see *Wates Construction v. Bredero Fleet* [1993] 63 B.L.R. 128.

4.79   If additional or substituted work cannot be valued by measurement, clause 13.5.4 provides that it should be valued as a prime cost sum with a percentage addition. The reader of the contract is referred to an external document which is not published by the JCT for the "Definition of Prime Cost of daywork carried out under a building contract"[25] issued by the RICS and the Building Employer's Confederation (who are now called the "Construction Confederation"). Both of these are constituent bodies of the JCT Tribunal. There is often an attraction in having works paid on a dayworks basis if this would be more profitable to the contractor, as dayworks are calculated on the basis of hourly rates for labour, cost of materials and goods, and rates for plant (normally plant on site), plus a percentage for profit. The percentage for profit includes head office charges; site supervision; the additional cost of overtime (unless there is a separate agreement); and time lost for "inclement" weather.[26] The parties are free to define dayworks as they choose.[27]

4.80   In all Alternative B cases variations are to be valued by the Quantity Surveyor (but, peculiarly, the Quantity Surveyor has no contractual right to go on site — he requires to be given permission by the Contractor). In a non-JCT contract: *Burden Ltd v. Swansea Corporation*[28] Lord Radcliffe said: "But I do not see anything in the contract which suggests that the architect is bound to accept the surveyor's opinions or valuations when he exercises his own function of certifying sums for payment. At that point the architect remains master in his own field."

It is suggested in Walker-Smith, *The Standard Forms of Building Contracts*[29] that the precise provisions of clause 13.5 defeat the above decision.

4.81   It is the view of the authors of *Keating on Building Contracts* (6th ed.) at page 581 that the Architect cannot issue instructions requiring a Variation after Practical Completion, and this would require a separate agreement, presumably now a clause 13A procedure.

4.82   What constitutes a Variation is defined in clause 13.1 and clearly a Variation cannot alter a condition of the contract. But what of Variations that so alter the scope of the works so as to make the contract something other than what was contracted for. Under JCT 80 at least there is a specific stipulation that fair rates and prices are to be used for valuation of additional or substituted work of dissimilar character to that in the Contract Bills (clause 13.5.1.3, although still presumably measurable, or the dayworks clause would apply — clause 13.5.4); the Contractor has a right of objection

---

[25] Presumably the document referred to is the 2nd ed., published December 1, 1975.
[26] s. 6.1(a)–(d).
[27] *per* the introductory paragraph to the definition.
[28] [1957] 1 W.L.R. 1167 (HL).
[29] at p. 71/1/3.

to an instruction requiring a Variation (clause 13.2.1); and clause 13.2.5 explicitly provides that "No Variation required by the Architect or subsequently sanctioned by him shall vitiate this Contract". The status of an instruction requiring a Variation can be taken to arbitration without waiting for Practical Completion (clause 41.3.3) — and since Amendment 18, to adjudication — and a Variation gives the Contractor an entitlement to an extension of time (clause 25.4.5.1) and direct loss and/or expense (clause 26.2.7). Whilst a Variation may not vitiate[30] the contract, it is submitted that a welter of Variations that alter the scope of the works may entitle a contractor to say that the contract has been frustrated, and claim for payment for what had been done to that date on a *quantum meruit* basis. In non-JCT cases the problem for the contractor is whether to stop or carry on in such cases, in the hope that a fair payment will be made to him for what he goes on to do.

It was said in *G. MacKay & Son v. The Lord Advocate (War Dept.*[31]*)*:   4.83

> "It is not, of course enough for the pursuers to show that in the course of operations they met with serious difficulties which they were obliged to overcome at great additional cost. That is not a good ground for disregarding a written contract. Before they can succeed, they must prove that the work that they executed was not really of the nature and character which the contract contemplated at all."

In this case the contractor was put to considerable extra work when he discovered that drainage pipes that he was to lay had to be laid beneath water supply pipes for Edinburgh. Amongst other matters, this required tunnelling through over 1,100 feet of solid rock. The true position had been suppressed by the employer when inviting estimates, believing it to be a matter for the contractor to satisfy themselves on. It was held that the work as executed was so "peculiar, unexpected, and different[32] from what had been contemplated that it does not fall within the contract at all, and accordingly the contract... [was] not applicable as a basis of charge". In this case it was accepted by the judge that the negotiations that took place during the contract when difficulties arose made it clear that the contractor was not consenting to completing the contract on the given rates, and that the contractor had reasonable grounds for the belief that the contract prices would not be insisted upon.

Professor Gloag[33] states that the decision in *MacKay* seems irreconcilable   4.84
with the decision in the Lords in *Boyd & Forrest v. Glasgow and South-Western Railway.*[34] This latter case raised many issues but the facts seem to

---

[30] A word that does not appear to have been judicially defined but apears in clause 13.2.5.

[31] 1914 S.L.T. 33.

[32] This is the same formula of words that was applied by Lord Cairns in the English case of *Thorn v. London Corporation* (1876) 1 App. Cas. 120 at 127-128.

[33] W.M. Gloag, *The Law of Contract* (2nd ed.), p. 359.

[34] 1915 S.C. 20 (HL).

be that when more rock than was indicated in the specification was discovered by the contractors in 1902, they kept on working until completion in 1905. They accepted £5,000 when the discrepancy was discovered and a further £5,000 when the works were completed. The action was raised in 1907 for a further £106,000. The House of Lords reversed the Inner House and found that the contract was not induced by a misrepresentation creating essential error, and should not be set aside. Perhaps a distinction that can be drawn between *MacKay* and *Boyd & Forrest* is the acceptance of the payments of £10,000, and that in *Boyd & Forrest*, a material term of the contract was: "The particular attention of intending contractors is directed to the specification in regard to the following matters: The probability of more or less rock or soft material having to be excavated, as no allowance will be made should the material turn out to be different from what is calculated and given in the schedule." Therefore, in *Boyd & Forrest* the extra work did fall within the contract.

4.85   Professor Gloag[35] similarly doubts, in the light of *Boyd & Forrest*, the charge to the civil jury given by the Lord President in *Smail v. Potts*.[36] This was another case that involved the laying of drains, representations as to the ground conditions prior to the contract, and the contractor encountering rock and having to start again from different levels than those first provided to him. The pursuers apparently pled their case on the basis that they had been induced to enter the contract by misrepresentations, although they did finish the contract and came very near to the specification. Presumably it is this claim that Professor Gloag doubts after *Boyd v. Forrest*, as it is submitted that it was expressly held in *Boyd & Forrest* that that contract had not been induced by misrepresentation. Also in *Smail* the Lord President seems to have taken the view that the case was one of impossibility:

> "You [the jury] have to consider whether there did occur in the progress of the work, in consequence of a fundamental error in the measurements such a difficulty as rendered the completion of the contract impossible; and whether such unforeseen difficulty justified the contractor in beginning again at a lower level, and at an increased expense."

4.86   It has been said that *Boyd & Forrest* is "not a case of frustration at all",[37] and it is submitted that for a contract that comes to involve works that effectively overtake the meaning and intent of the contract this could be frustration.[38] The issue then is when does the contractor have to decide that the contract has been frustrated. Lord McCluskey had some views on this in *ERDC v. Love (supra)* at page 269:

---

[35] *op.cit.*
[36] (1847) 9 D. 1043.
[37] *Head Wrightson Aluminium Ltd v. Aberdeen Harbour Commissioners*, 1958 S.L.T. 12.
[38] See Lord Reid in *Davis Contractors Ltd v. Fareham Urban District Council* [1956] A.C. 696.

"It is perfectly possible to envisage situations in which the circumstances which entitle the contractors to conclude that the contract has been effectively frustrated, or the works transformed, by the employers' action might not become apparent or known and properly understood until the works themselves have been completed. And equally it may well be that during the performing of the works the contractors may have accepted substantial payments on contract terms. Accordingly, therefore, I do not consider the completion of the works or the acceptance of moneys payable only under the contract necessarily inhibits the contractors from repudiating the contract in relation to additional works (*i.e.* works not expressly included in the original contract) in respect of which no agreed payment has been accepted. It may even be, as senior counsel for the contractors submitted, that if the circumstances do not require the contractors to make an election before the works themselves have been completed, there is no necessity for the election to be made in any final way when the claim is presented whether through the courts or to an arbiter. It may well be that the claims may be advanced on the basis that they are alternatives. If that is so, it may be appropriate to plead a claim under the contract provisions such as those contained in cls. 11 and 24 [the variations and direct loss and/or expense clauses of JCT 63] as the principal claim and a claim for payment on a different basis as an alternative based upon the basis, 'esto the first claim fails'. But it appears to me that in advancing the claim on the basis of two such alternatives the contractors must claim that there has been a breach of contract giving rise to a claim for damages or alternatively that in the circumstances the contract has been repudiated by them on the ground of lately discovered material breach or breaches by the employers and that they are therefore entitled to claim on a *quantum meruit* basis."

Aside from any questions of frustration of contract, it may be that the contractor would wish his works paid for *quantum meruit* on the basis that the employer has been in material breach of contract and that therefore the contract price or rates no longer apply.

In *Gloag on Contract* (2nd ed.) at page 358 and under reference to the   4.87
Privy Council case of *Lodder v. Slowey*[39] the author states: "if the contractor can establish that the result of the breach has been so material as to make the work, as actually done, a different thing from that contracted for — necessarily a matter of degree — the contractor can also maintain that the contract is at an end, and that the work he has done must be paid for on the basis of *quantum meruit*."

First, where a claim to payment for variations is advanced by the   4.88
contractor under the contract itself, the contractor does so because the contract stipulates that he can do so (*e.g.* clause 11, JCT 63; clause 13, JCT 80). The contractor is not strictly speaking alleging that his entitlement is based on breach of contract. However as a matter of law in Scotland a contractor would be entitled to argue two or more inconsistent arguments in the same

---

[39] [1904] A.C. 442.

action as alternatives to each other, on an "esto the first claim fails" basis ("esto" merely means "if it be so that"). Therefore a contractor could simultaneously argue a claim due under a contract itself and alternatively a claim for damages for breach of contract. In Scots law certain breaches may be classed as material or not material. In the case of *Wade v. Waldon* [40] it was stated: "in any contract which contains multifarious stipulations there are some which go to the root of the contract that a breach of those stipulations entitles the party pleading the breach to declare that the contract is at an end. There are others which do not go to the root of the contract and which will give rise, if broken, to an action of damages."

4.89   The point was made again recently by the Lord Justice-Clerk (Ross) in a stated case from an arbiter in *ERDC Construction Ltd v. H.M. Love & Co.*,[41] where he quoted the Canadian case of *Morrison-Knudsen Co. Inc. v. British Columbia Hydro and Power Authority*[42] in the following terms as consistent with the law of Scotland:

> "The trial judge found many breaches of contract. However, it is not every breach which determines a contract and puts an end to contractual obligations. There are breaches compensable in damages only and fundamental breaches which can bring the contractual relationship to an end and free the parties from further performance. When faced with a fundamental breach the innocent party is put to an election. He may elect to affirm the contract and hold the other party to the performance of his obligations and sue for damages as compensation for the breach. He may, on the other hand, elect to treat the breach as a fundamental breach and treat it as such. Thus he would terminate the contract and thereafter be relieved of any further duty to perform and he could sue at once for damages or *quantum meruit* for performance to that point. It is essential that such an election, an election between inconsistent rights, be made promptly and communicated to the guilty party. Once made the election is binding and cannot be changed.... Where a plaintiff, having elected to accept the breach as a repudiation commences proceedings for his remedy, he may have, in a proper case, the right to *quantum meruit* as an alternative to the right to damages. His election between these alternatives is an election between alternative remedies and need not be made until judgment. The taking of judgment on one of the alternatives binds the plaintiff and he may not then have the other remedy."

4.90   So, a contractor can plead a claim under a contract itself where the contract so provides; alternatively, he may make a claim for damages for a non-material breach of contract, but otherwise both parties continue to perform their obligations; alternatively, he may hold a breach to be a repudiation of contract and sue for performance (presumably payment under interim certificates) and damages; and, further and alternatively, he may

---

[40]   1909 S.C. 571 at 576.
[41]   1995 S.L.T. 254 at 263.
[42]   Const.L. 1991 (Vol. 7), p. 227.

treat the breach as material and a repudiation, rescind the contract and sue for all damages (including loss of profit had the contract been completed) or for payment *quantum meruit*[43] for what work has been done to date. In the latter case he may not have both, *i.e.* hold the contract repudiated and claim damages *and* payment *quantum meruit*. If the contractor is reluctant to treat a breach as entitling him to rescind and claim damages (and who could blame him, for it could turn out that his rescission was unjustified and left him open to a claim for damages on the basis that he, not the employer, had repudiated), then the contractor can keep his powder dry and claim damages for non-material breach.

The difficulty for the contractor then is, if he is satisfied that variations   4.91
amount to a material breach and a repudiation, when must he rescind? In *Morrison-Knudsen* it was said that "it is essential that the election be made promptly".[44] As can be seen from the above quote, Lord McCluskey in *ERDC v. Love*[45] also identifies the principle of the "lately discovered material breach" which may give a contractor greater scope as to the time of making his election.

It may also be claimed by the contractor that the contract rates or price   4.92
should not apply and that payment should be made *quantum meruit* on the basis that there was no valid contract because consensus was tainted by error. In the sheriff court it has been held[45a] that where painters quoted a price per square metre believing that they were to paint flat surfaces, but where the structures turned out to be intricate three-dimensional objects at the Glasgow Garden Festival, there was a case of mutual error and the contract was void. There was an entitlement to payment *quantum meruit,* having particular regard to the rates quoted under the main contract. This case does not appear to have addressed the problem which was made clear in *Boyd & Forrest*[46] that a contract can only be reduced where *restitutio in integrum* is possible; in other words, the party seeking reduction must be able to restore the other party to the position in which he was before he entered the contract: "The work was done; the parties cannot in any sense be restored, in relation to this contract, to the position they occupied before the contract was entered into." For those reasons the decision of the sheriff may be doubtful.

A contractor may also claim a fair rate for what he did on the basis that no   4.93
consensus as to payment was reached. This has been so held in a letter of intent case, *British Steel Corporation v. Cleveland Bridge and Engineering Co. Ltd*[47] where a formal contract was expected but never entered into. Payment for the preparatory work that was done by the contractor was held due *quantum meruit.*

---

[43] *Quantum meruit* is described by Gloag on *Contract* (2nd ed.) at p. 358 as arising where a contractor "puts forward the claim that he is entitled to ignore the contract price and demand payment on the basis of quantum meruit, ie, on the basis of payment for the work he has done at the ordinary or market rates."

[44] *op. cit.*

[45] *op.cit.*

[45a] *Mathew Middleton v. Newton Display Group* 1990 G.W.D. 40–2305.

[46] *op.cit., per* Lord Atkinson at p. 28.

[47] [1984] 1 All E. R. 504.

4.94   In *Crown House Engineering Ltd v. AMEC Projects Ltd*[48] where
certificates had been issued but the basis of contract was challenged and a
claim *quantum meruit* was advanced, the Court of Appeal did not accept
the purported certificates as an "absolute bottom figure" for the purposes
of an Order 29 motion for interim payment. It was held that the gross figure
in the certificates could not be said to represent the value of the work, if the
value was claimed on a *quantum meruit* basis.

4.95   There is clearly a great deal of care necessary in deciding exactly how
an argument should be presented where there are extensive variations. Each
case may turn on its own circumstances, *e.g.* in *ERDC v. Love*[49] the arbiter
was not satisfied that the nature of the work had been so varied as to fall
outwith the provisions of the contract, but was satisfied that there had been
other material breaches which prevented the contractors from identifying
the need for further drawings, and from identifying what was being paid
for as variations. Or, a case may turn on how it is pled which may be a
narrow technical deficiency in pleading (*per* Lord McCluskey in *ERDC v.
Love* at p. 269). Essentially, *ERDC v. Love* is a case which turned on the
technical use of legal language, and what was fatal was that a claim *quantum
meruit* could not be advanced to "augment" sums already paid without, at
some stage, pleading a repudiation of the contract. The case was then referred
back to the arbiter, who, as master of procedure, could allow amendment to
the pleadings.[50]

4.96   The question of to what extent a welter of variations can amount to a
frustration of contract exercised the Court of Appeal in *McAlpine Humberoak
Ltd v. McDermott International Inc.*[51] The decision of the Official Referee
in this case which concerned a contract for the construction of deck pallets
for a North Sea oil rig had been that the contract had been frustrated three
months before it was even signed on the basis of variations issued. This
was so held even where there was a contractual mechanism for valuing
variations. The Court of Appeal overturned this, and distinguished the
circumstances from *Parkinson v. Minister of Works*[52] which the Official
Referee had relied on. *Parkinson* was held on appeal to turn on its own
facts which concerned the interpretation of a deed of variation executed
during the course of works. The deed provided that the contractors were
entitled to recover their costs, plus between £150,000 and £300,000 as
remuneration — the figures being based on between 3 per cent and 6 per cent
of the contractor's estimate of costs of £5 million. The employers ordered
extra work which was far greater in quantity, if not character, and raised the

[48]   [1989] 48 B.L.R. 32.
[49]   *op.cit.*
[50]   *ERDC v. Love (No.2)* 1997 S.L.T. 175.
[51]   [1992] 58 B.L.R. 1 (AC) although arguments of this kind are of long standing: see *MacKay v.
        Parochial Board of Barry* (1883) 10 R. 1046.
[52]   [1949] 2 K.B. 632.

costs figure to £6,683,056; and extended the contract by one year. It was held that there was an implied term that the employers would not be entitled to require work materially in excess of £5 million, but as they had done so they were required to pay for it *quantum meruit,* and the £300,000 ceiling did not apply. The Court of Appeal noted that there was nothing like the deed of variation in the *McAlpine* case, and also that it had been argued in *Parkinson* that the deed allowed an unlimited number of variations to be ordered at no extra cost which had been characterised by Singleton L.J. as "fantastic and absurd". A similar view had been reached in the Scottish case *MacBean v. Napier*[53] where it was said, in relation to a clause for the erection of a house where the contractor agreed to certain works "and also anything necessary to complete the work not mentioned in the specifications to be done free of any extra charge", that:

> "Of course, a fair and reasonable construction must be put on such a clause. It does not follow that because it exists in the contract, that therefore everything which is extra work is not to be charged for, but only everything which comes fairly under the original contract, and was omitted from the specification, either accidentally or of necessity."

Clause 14: Contract sum

Clause 14.2 provides that the Contract Sum shall not be adjusted or altered in any way whatsoever otherwise than in accordance with the express provisions of the Conditions, and subject to clause 2.2.2.2 any error whether arithmetic or not in the computation of the Contract Sum shall be deemed to have been accepted by the parties.[54] It is not clear to the author why this should be so, as Scots law recognises that the true agreement underlying a defectively expressed document can be given effect to.[55] Also, in terms of the Law Reform (Miscellaneous Provisions) (Scotland) Act 1985, ss. 8 and 9, the court can rectify a defectively expressed document.[56] Clause 2.2.2.2 provides that where there is any departure from the Standard Method of Measurement, 7th ed., or error in description, or in quantity, or omission of items, including provisional sums, then it shall be corrected and treated as a Variation.[57] At common law a

4.97

---

[53] 1870 8 S.L.R. 250, *per* Lord Deas at p. 253.

[54] The Scottish common law position where there is a lump sum and a schedule of rates for approximate quantities, and the work is to be remeasured, is that the contractor is not bound by an error in the bringing across of a calculation to form part of a lump sum: *Jamieson v. McInnes* (1887) 15 R. 17; and *Wilkie v. Hamilton Lodging-House Co.* (1902) 4 F. 951.

[55] *Krupp v. John Menzies Ltd*, 1907 S.C. 903.

[56] *Angus v. Bryden*, 1992 S.C.L.R. 626.

[57] This effectively negates the effect of the Court of Appeal decision digested in *Ford & Co. v. Bemrose & Sons Ltd*, 1902 9 S.L.T. 170. Materials in bills of quantities were insufficiently specified but that did not mean that the contractor was entitled to be paid more than his fixed lump sum, as no custom of trade could contradict a contractual provision. For comments and criticisms of contractors' claims based on discrepancies with the Standard Methods of Measurement see *Hudson's Building and Engineering Contracts* (11th ed.), paras. 8-024–8-036.

misrepresentation by the employer or his agent which has induced the contractor to enter into the contract may entitle the contractor to have the contract reduced if it created essential error and if *restitutio in integrum* was possible.[58] Damages could also be claimed if the misrepresentation was made fraudulently, but not if made innocently. Now in terms of the Law Reform (Miscellaneous Provisions) (Scotland) Act 1985, s.10, a negligent misrepresentation also gives rise to an action for damages provided the party who made the representation owed him a duty of care on *Hedley Byrne*[59] reliance principles, and that the misrepresentation caused him to contract.

4.98 It may not always be simple to suggest that a contractor is in a position of reliance. In *G. Percy Trentham Ltd v. Beattie Williamson & Pnrs*[60] the defenders were civil engineers and the contractors were excavating near a wall which they were to underpin. The space between the inner and outer wall was exposed to rain when its roof was removed, and it was alleged that the infill and rain caused the wall to collapse before the contractors had underpinned it. Neither the contractor nor the engineer were aware of the infill material. Lord Jauncey held that although part of the work was underpinning that did not mean that "the pursuers were entitled to rely on the defenders to provide them with all information relevant to the carrying out of the work even although the pursuers were entirely competent to and, through their control of the site, were in at least as good if not a better position than the defenders to provide that information for themselves."

4.99 ## Clause 15: value added tax-supplemental provisions

The current statutory position relating to the construction industry is to be found in the Value Added Tax Act 1994[61] and the Value Added Tax Regulations 1995[62] although the current printed edition of the JCT conditions has not caught up with this specific re-enactment. Regulation 93 is as follows:

> "SUPPLIES IN THE CONSTRUCTION INDUSTRY
> 93. Where services, or services together with goods, are supplied in the course of the construction, alteration, demolition, repair or maintenance of a building or of any civil engineering work under a contract which provides for the payment for such supplies to be made periodically or from time to time, a supply shall be treated as taking place at the earlier of the following times —
> (a) each time that a payment is received by the supplier where the consideration for the contract is wholly in money, or
> (b) each time that the supplier issues a VAT invoice."

---

[58] *Boyd and Forrest v. Glasgow and South-Western Railway Co.*, 1915 S.C. (H.L.) 20. *ose & Sons* 1902 10 S.L.T. 170.

[59] *Hedley Byrne & Co. Ltd v. Heller & Partners Ltd* [1964] A.C. 465.

[60] *G. Percy Trentham Ltd v. Beattie Williamson & Pnrs*, 1987 S.L.T. 449 (OH).

[61] c. 23.

[62] S.I. 1995 No. 2518. This replaces regulation 26 of the Value Added Tax (General) Regulations 1985.

Similar provisions relating to retention payments are to be found in regulation 89.   4.100
The Value Added Tax Act 1994 at section 30(2A) provides that the supply of goods or services as specified in Schedule 8 are zero rated. Schedule 8 refers to certain Groups, including "Group 5 — CONSTRUCTION OF BUILDINGS, ETC." which was substituted by the Value Added Tax (Construction of Buildings) Order (S.I. 1995 No. 280), art. 2, operative from March 1, 1995. The gist of this is that the construction of dwellings, or buildings designed for a relevant residential purpose, or a relevant charitable purpose, is zero rated, but this does not include consultants' services, furnishings (other than fitted kitchens), and the conversion, reconstruction or alteration of an existing building. Group 6 in Schedule 8 refers to "Protected Buildings", the approved alteration of which is zero rated if it is a dwelling used for charitable purposes and is a listed building or scheduled monument, but does not include repair or maintenance work. In relation to the provisions for protected buildings under the Value Added Tax Act 1983, the measuring and making of joinery and any subsequent site visits was an intrinsic part of the supply of goods where the joinery was not fitted, and was not zero rated, as a service.[63]

Clause 15.2 of JCT 80 provides that the Contract Sum is exclusive of VAT,[64]   4.101
and that the Contractor may recover VAT from the Employer under clause 15 and the VAT Agreement, which is entitled "Supplemental Provisions". Practice Note 6 is helpful in construing the Supplemental Provisions.

Clause 1 of the Supplemental Provisions brings JCT 80 under the   4.102
provisions of regulation 93 for the purposes of periodic payment, and clause 1.1 requires the Contractor to give a written provisional assessment of those goods and services which are included in each Interim and Final certificate that are taxable and zero rated. The Employer then calculates the tax and pays it to the Contractor within 14 days. If the Employer objects he must do so within three days and the Contractor must deal with the objection within three days (clause 1.2.2). As so few matters will be zero rated in practice there are alternative provisions in clause 1A,[65] whereby the Contractor merely notifies the legal rate of VAT seven days before the issue of the first Interim Certificate and this is applied to each payment (clause 1A.3). The Contractor requires to issue a receipt to the Employer (clause 1.4). Liquidate

---

[63] *Customs and Excise Commissioners v. Jeffs (t/a J. & J. Joinery)* [1995] S.T.C. 759. Note that the supply of building materials in these circumstances is now zero rated under item 3 of Group 6 of the Value Added Tax Act 1994, Sched. 8.

[64] It has been held that this would be the position by implication of custom and practice in any case where both parties are registered for VAT, see *Tony Cox (Dismantlers) Ltd v. Jim 5 Ltd* (unreported, Official Referee's Business, August 28, 1996, *per* His Honour Judge Bowsher Q.C.). Where no mention of VAT is made and one party is a consumer it has been held that the price is deemed to be inclusive of VAT, see *Franks and Collingwood v. Gates* [1985] 1 Con. L.R. 21.

[65] For example the first installation of double glazing ceased to be zero rated on June 1, 1984; see *APD Installations (Group) v. Customs and Excise Commissioners* (1987) V.A.T.T.R. 36, where manufacture before that date and supply after was not zero rated.

and ascertained damages that are deducted by the Employer under clause 24 of JCT 80 are to be disregarded by the Employer in calculating tax due to the Contractor (clause 2). Where there is an issue as to zero rating the Employer can request the Contractor to obtain a decision from the Commissioners of Customs and Excise when a final statement is issued to the Employer by the Contractor (clause 3). Any award by a court or an arbiter (as yet no mention is made of an adjudicator) which varies the amount certified for payment for goods and services supplied by the Contractor or that ought to have been certified are to be governed by the Supplemental Provisions (clause 5). H.M. Customs and Excise have issued guidance in relation to settlement agreements which embrace sums paid in respect of work carried out or services rendered, and sums paid in lieu of damages for breach of contract, including interest for late payment. The former element of the claim would attract VAT, whereas the damages part would not. Clause 7 states that the Employer "shall not be obliged to make any further payment" if the Contractor is in default in providing the receipt under clause 1.4, provided the Employer can show cause. Finally, clause 8 provides that if the employment of the Contractor is determined under clause 27.4 the Employer can reclaim from the Contractor additional tax that the Employer has had to pay by reason of the determination.

Clause 16: Materials and goods unfixed or off-site

4.103   Scots law with regard to goods which become fixtures is that they become the property of the owner onto whose heritable property they are fixed,[66] and this is so irrespective of non-payment, a valid retention of title clause, whether the goods were subject to a hire-purchase agreement, or in any competition with the interests of a floating charge holder, or liquidator.[67] The definition of a fixture excludes matters which are "mere juxtaposition to the soil"[68] and therefore the application of the rule has to be carefully considered in relation to goods or plant which are delivered to site and placed on it. There are certain exceptions to the rule relating to ease of removal (which may be relevant in relation to temporary works), prior agreement, and as between landlord and tenant, and in agricultural holdings.[69] Clause 16.1 however deals with unfixed moveables delivered to, placed on or adjacent to the Works, and there is no attempt to change the common law of fixtures. The SBC (currently August 1998 revision) has consistently deleted clause 16.2 relating to unfixed materials and goods off-site.

---

[66] *Inaedificatum solo, solo cedit* (a thing built on the ground goes with the ground).
[67] *Scottish Discount Co. Ltd v. Blin*, 1985 S.C. 216, 1986 S.L.T. 123; *Shetland Islands Council v. BP Petroleum Development Ltd*, 1989 SCLR 48, 1990 S.L.T. 8 (OH).
[68] *Brand's Trs v. Brand's Trs* (1876) 3 R. (H.L.) 16.
[69] *Scottish Discount Co., supra.*

The effect of statute

At Scots common law in relation to the sale of goods, property in 4.104 moveables passed where there was intention to transfer title *and delivery* of the moveables. This was fundamentally altered by the Sale of Goods Act 1893; and the current law on the passing of ownership is to be found in sections 16, 17, 18 and 19 of the Sale of Goods Act 1979 (as amended), which is a consolidating statute and which repealed and replaced the 1893 Act. In applying the statutory provisions much depends on whether goods are "specific" or "unascertained". Section 17 provides: "(1) Where there is a contract for the sale of specific or ascertained goods the property in them is transferred to the buyer at such time as the parties to the contract intend it to be transferred."

Prior to September 19, 1995, section 16 provided that where there is a 4.105 contract for the sale of unascertained goods, ownership does not transfer to the buyer unless and until the goods are ascertained. The Sale of Goods (Amendment) Act 1995 has changed the position for quantities of unascertained goods that form part of an identified bulk, so that when payment of some or all of the price is made, property in an undivided share of the bulk immediately passes to the buyer and the buyer becomes an owner in common of the bulk, unless the parties have agreed otherwise.

Section 18 allows for ascertaining the intention of the parties to transfer 4.106 ownership by applying five rules, when this intention cannot be taken from the terms of the contract or the conduct of the parties. Rules 1–3 apply to specific goods, rule 4 applies to goods delivered on approval and rule 5 applies to unascertained goods.

One of the main difficulties with the question of transfer of ownership 4.107 of moveables in building contracts is that, as we have seen, building contracts are normally contracts of location or executory sale,[70] and not contracts simply for the sale of goods.[71] The Sale of Goods Act would not normally be applicable as between an employer and main contractor, or main contractor and sub-contractor, but would be for any suppliers to them. Since January 3, 1995 the Sale and Supply of Goods Act 1994 has inserted a new Part 1A into the Supply of Goods and Services Act 1982, which does apply to Scotland. Section 11A(3) of the 1982 Act provides: "For the purposes of this Act in its application to Scotland a contract is a contract for the transfer of goods whether or not services are also provided under the contract." Therefore, the 1982 Act will apply to most building contracts. The 1982 Act provides that certain terms are to be implied in much the same way as under the Sale of Goods legislation in relation to title to transfer goods, and

---

[70] Chap.1.
[71] A point emphasised by Lord Upjohn who specifically observed that the passing of property differs as between contracts of sale and for work and materials in *Young and Martin Ltd v. McManus Childs Ltd* [1969] 1 A.C. 454 at 473, HL.

the quiet possession of the transferee. However the Supply of Goods and Services Act does not change the common law position of when title actually passes. Therefore there may be three areas of applicable law, at least, in questions related to the passing of property in a typical chain of building contracts and supplier's contracts: *i.e.* at common law in relation to title to goods as part of an executory contract; under the Supply of Goods and Services Act in relation to title to transfer and quiet possession; and under the Sale of Goods Act. This is to say nothing of title to retain goods under the law of pledge or impignoration[72]; the express terms of any contracts; and the law relating to retention of title clauses. Sections 20 and 21 of the Unfair Contract Terms Act 1977 applying to Scotland are also relevant to exclusions or restrictions of liability in respect of contracts for the sale of goods or the supply of goods and services.[73]

Common law on passing of title

4.108   We have already seen Professor Bell's comments that in respect of transfer of title in contracts for work and materials: "the act of delivery seems not to complete till the work be performed".[74] The matter was authoritatively dealt with by Lord Watson in the House of Lords in 1886 in *Seath v. Moore*[75] in relation to a shipbuilding case on the Clyde, and which it is submitted would apply *a fortiori* to a building contract on land: "Materials provided by the builder, and portions of the fabric, whether wholly or partly finished, although intended to be used in the execution of the contract, cannot be regarded as appropriated to the contract or as 'sold' unless they have been affixed, or in a reasonable sense made part of the corpus."

4.109   This was stated by Lord Watson to be the English law position also. As the case was a shipbuilding case, one of the issues was whether ownership of materials appropriated to part of the constructed vessel could pass by agreement before the vessel was completed — the "entire contract" question — and this was held to be so, whether or not there were instalment payments due and made, or inspection. Building contracts are, of course, different again as these are built on land. But it would appear from the above quote from Lord Watson that the appropriation question is the crucial one for both types of contracts. By way of comparison, *Reid v. MacBeth & Gray*[76] was another Scottish shipbuilding case in the Lords after the passing of the Sale of Goods Act 1893. In this there was a clause as follows:

---

[72] *Moore v. Gledden* [1869] VII MacPherson 1042.
[73] For example, see *Rees Hough Ltd v. Redland Reinforced Plastics Ltd* [1984] 27 B.L.R. 136.
[74] *Commentaries on the Law of Scotland* (7th ed., 1870), Part III, Chap. II at p. 193. See Chap. 1, para. 1-09.
[75] (1886) 13 R. (H.L.) 57 at 66.
[76] (1904) 6 F. (H.L.) 25.

"The vessel, as she is constructed, and all her engines, boilers and machinery, and all materials from time to time intended for her or them, whether in the building yard, workshop, river or elsewhere, shall immediately as the same proceeds, become the property of the purchasers, and shall not be within the ownership, control, or disposition of the builders; but the builders shall at all times have a lien thereon for their unpaid purchase money."

The shipbuilders became bankrupt, and there were lying at a railway station for the shipbuilders a quantity of steel plates from suppliers, which the shipbuilders intended to use in the construction of the vessel. The plates were claimed by the trustee in bankruptcy, and also the ship owners. The plates had been passed by a Lloyd's surveyor at the maker's works, and they were each marked by the makers (in accordance with the shipbuilder's instructions) with the number of the vessel, and with marks showing the position which each plate was to occupy in the vessel. Their Lordships agreed that there was only one contract which was for the purchase of the ship and no contract for the separate sale or purchase of the materials. The Lord Chancellor thought the inspection by Lloyds could not contractually appropriate the materials to the contract in any case, and approved the above quotation from Lord Watson in *Seath & Co. v. Moore*. Lord Robertson said:

"Article 4 of the contract seems to me to fall within subsection 4 of section 61 of the [Sale of Goods Act 1893] — that is to say, it 'is intended to operate by way of mortgage, pledge or other security'. The circumstance that it is inserted in what is a sale of a completed ship will not avail to make it a sale in the sense of the Sale of Goods Act. In fact the 4th article does not even purport to express a sale: it merely asserts to be the property of the purchaser of the ship what has no more relation to it than that it is intended by the builder for the ship. This as it stands is impossibly wide, and I agree with your Lordships that the respondents' attempts to make those materials 'specific' in the sense of the Sale of Goods Act, by saying that they had been passed by Lloyd's surveyors, is not warranted by the terms of the contract. The reference to Lloyd's in the first article cannot be strained to this effect. [1. That the builders will build for the purchasers, of the best materials and workmanship, a vessel and engines of the following dimensions, power, and class, *viz*.: — Class — Lloyd's 100 A1.] The truth is that the 4th article is simply a bold attempt to sweep into the net the whole of the materials required for the ship. The judgments of this House in *Seath & Co. v. Moore* negative the possibility of that being legally done."

We shall return to the pledge versus sale question.[77] The comments of Lord Watson in *Seath & Co. v. Moore* were again followed in *Dawber Williamson v. Humberside County Council*.[78]

---

[77] See *Moore v. Gledden* [1869] VII MacPh. 1042; and also paras 4.11–4.113.
[78] [1979] 14 B.L.R. 70.

Dawber Williamson v. Humberside County Council — the position of sub-contractors

4.110   In this case the plaintiffs were sub-contractors to supply and fix roof covering under the pre–1980 (non-nominated) standard form of sub-contract. Clause 1 of the sub-contract provided that the plaintiffs were deemed to have notice of all provisions of the main contract (which was the 1963 Form). The sub-contract made no provision for the passing of property in unfixed materials. Dawber Williamson delivered materials to site which were certified and paid for by the employers. The main contractors went into liquidation without paying Dawber Williamson. It was held that title in the unfixed materials had not passed to the main contractors under the sub-contract and that clause 1(1) of the sub-contract did not operate to make clause 14 of the main contract (substantially the same as clause 16 of JCT 80) part of the sub-contract. The employers accordingly had to pay twice.

4.111   The JCT responded with clause 19.4, by Amendment 1 to JCT 80, providing that any sub-contract shall have consistent provisions so that the Sub-Contractor "shall not deny that such materials or goods are and have become the property of the Employer". DOM/C/Scot provides accordingly at 4.15.2.2 and NSC/C provides accordingly at 4.15.4.2 (despite the fact that clause 19.4.2 of JCT 80 is deleted in the Scottish Building Contract April 1998 revision). It is questionable in the opinion of the author that such contractual conditions in the main contract would be effective anyway against a sub-contractor if not actually stepped down, as part of the *ratio* in *Dawber Williamson* emphasised that there was no privity of contract that bound the sub-contractor to the passing of title provisions of clause 14(1) of JCT 63. Part of the judgment was: "If title has passed to the main contractor from the sub-contractor, then this clause has force."

Right to use materials brought on site: retention and the pledge cases.

4.112   In *Kerr v. The Dundee Gas Light Co.*[79] a contractor became bankrupt during the course of works, having brought various materials, tools and plant, including a crane, which all belonged to him, on to the site. The employer refused to deliver these up to the bankrupt's trustee and claimed the right to retain them for the purposes of having the works completed by another contractor. The Lord Justice-Clerk gave judgment as follows:

> "Retention is a right of varying character, which is always to be measured according to the title on which that possession is held, which is the ground of the right of retention. Now, what was the nature of the defender's title? It was a title arising *ex contractu*. It is in vain to consider, to what extent, or in what sense, delivery of the materials into the possession of the defenders made

---

[79]   (1861) 23 D. 197.

them the property of the defenders. In one sense it did, and in another sense it did not. But in performance of the contract obligation, these materials were delivered; and, in any view, the right emerging to the defenders was, that they were entitled to retain them for those purposes of the contract for which they were brought there, viz. to be worked up into the work contracted to be executed. And, therefore, I come to the conclusion, without any difficulty, that the defenders were entitled to keep these materials, and to use them in building the tank. But, on the other hand, they must allow the pursuer the value of these materials; because, although they have paid for all the work done, they have not paid for these materials; and it is a condition of their right of retention of them that they shall pay their value.

But as regards the other portion of the sum...representing the value of the plant and tools brought on the defenders' premises, not to be permanently worked up into the work contracted for, but merely to be used temporarily in the execution of the work, it is obvious that there is, in point of fact and legal principle, a plain distinction between this part of the claim and the other. But here there is no longer the same right of retention on the part of the defenders, but a more limited right than they had over the stones and other materials; and it was more limited just in exact correspondence to the purposes for which the plant and tools were brought on the defenders' ground. Their right of retention arising on the contract was necessarily limited to the contract purposes; for the tools were there to be used for the purposes of executing the works contracted for, not to be exhausted in executing the work as the materials were, but to be used temporarily, and returned (no doubt deteriorated by tear and wear) as soon as the works were executed, and the contract obligation fulfilled by their means. And therefore, while they were entitled to retain the crane and other tools to be used in execution of the contract, on completion of the contract there arose to the trustee two rights. In the first place, a right to a reasonable consideration for the use of the tools, that being parallel to his right to payment of the value of the materials. But, secondly, there was a right on the part of the trustee to restoration of the plant and tools as they stood at the completion of the works contracted for."

Lord Benholme had an interesting point to make in concurring with the Lord Justice-Clerk:

"As to the materials, my view is, that while the contractor was solvent and able to perform the contract, I am not prepared to say that I would have interfered with him in the execution of his contract had he chosen to remove some materials in order to replace them with others. That would have been allowable during solvency, while he was in the active *bona fide* prosecution of the contract. But matters are very much altered, when, in consequence of insolvency, the work comes to a stand, and the company [the employer] are obliged to provide for the due and speedy execution of the work. Rights then come into existence, especially as regards the stones and other materials, which had not emerged before."

Moore v. Gledden[80]

4.113   In this case a railway construction contract provided:

> " And it is hereby specially stipulated and agreed that all materials, as well as tools, machinery, rails, scaffolding, wagons, horses, houses, sheds, and implements of every description, brought or left on or near to the site of the said works hereby contracted for, shall, from the time of their being so brought and left, be held to be the property of, and belong to, the company, and shall not, without their consent in writing, be removed or taken away therefrom; and it shall be in the power of the company to use or sell all the said materials, tools, machinery, rails, scaffolding, wagons, houses, horses, sheds, and implements of every description, either by public roup or private sale, as they shall think most expedient, and to impute the price or prices thereof *pro tanto* in extinction of the obligations of the contractors; but the said materials, tools, machinery, scaffolding, wagons, houses, sheds and implements shall, until default or bankruptcy as aforesaid, remain under the care and custody, and shall be entirely at the risk of, the contractors."

This case was decided by a majority of seven judges in the Inner House with one dissenting. The contractor became bankrupt and his trustee sought delivery of the plant and materials. Lord Neaves said:

> "In approaching this part of the case there are two propositions which might be taken as undeniable —
> 1.   The railway company could have no preference over this plant unless they had a real right of some kind or other, whether of property or pledge, duly constituted before bankruptcy.
> 2.   The railway company could have no such right in the plant, unless it was timeously completed by possession.... As to the contract or right here sought to be constituted, I need not enter into much detail or nicety of analysis. I consider it truly to be that of pledge or impignoration, with an additional agreement conferring an eventual right of use and a power of sale. Impignoration, with a power of sale, is an intelligible and well-known contract, though such a power is not generally implied with us in pledge, without special stipulation... The possession here, if there be possession, arises out of the transportation of the plant to the lands and ground of the railway company....It does not follow that everything the contractor brings to the ground thereby passes into the employer's possession".

Lord Neave then went on to find that the circumstances of this case were even stronger than those in *Kerr v. Dundee Gas Co.* because of the contractual stipulations.

Goods off-site

4.114   In *Stirling County Council v. Official Liquidator of John Frame Ltd*[81] a contract in the now defunct Scottish National Building Code Regulations provided that: "From the time they are placed upon the site... all materials delivered by the contractor for the execution of the works shall become and be the absolute property of the employer". It was held by the sheriff principal

---

[80]   [1869] VII Macph. 1042.
[81]   1951 S.L.T. 37.

that this was not a contract for the sale of materials and so the Sale of Goods Act had no application; also, that to complete the passing of property both the placing upon the site and delivery were necessary. The effect of that in this case was that even materials that had been paid for by the employer but stored off-site with his agreement could not become the property of the employer. The consequence of this decision is that where a main contractor is supplying materials as part of a building contract, unless there is a separate agreement for the purchase of materials that are kept off-site which would be relevant for the Sale of Goods Act, then property cannot pass to the employer until delivery. For this reason the Scottish Building Contract Committee delete clause 16.2 of JCT 80 and in clause 30.3 introduce provisions for the separate purchase from the contractor or any sub-contractor of any materials and goods prior to their delivery to the site. Both forms were last revised in 1991 (and are still drafted on the old basis for execution by two witnesses). In both of these agreements title to goods passes to the employer on payment of a first instalment representing the purchase price less a 5 per cent retention. The goods are made ascertained by describing where they are set aside and by their identifying mark. The contractor maintains an all-risks policy for the goods, and agrees that they shall not be removed except for use in the works. According to the instructions for use with these forms, the value of the goods is to be deducted from the contract sum, although no specific provision is made to enable this in clause 14.[82]

The clearly emerging line of authority from all the above cases is that (1) there can be no sale of materials under a building contract until they are "made part of the corpus" (*Seath, Reid*); (2) a catch-all clause claiming title to materials and plant will be ineffective as a sale, especially if the main contractor has no title to the materials brought to site by a sub-contractor (*Dawber Williamson*) and the materials and plant are unfixed (*Seith*; *Reid*); but the employer will normally have a right to use these materials, subject to payment (*Kerr*) with a possible right of sale[83] if the contract provides for

4.115

---

[82] This is probably a common law entitlement in any case: see *Newton v. Forster* 12 M. and W. 772; *Allinson v. Davies*, Peak's " Add. Cas.", 82; *Grainger v. Raybould*, 9 C. and P. 229 all referred to in Connell, *Law affecting Building Operations and Architects and Builders' Contracts* (1903) W. Green & Sons at p. 37.

[83] By way of comparison, the Court of Appeal in *Re Cosslett (Contractors) Ltd* [1997] 4 All E.R. 115, reviewed English authorities, and in relation to the wording of clauses 53(1), (2), (6), (7), and clause 63(1) of the ICE 5th contract, Millet L.J. said: "In the present case the council's rights in relation to the plant and materials are exclusively contractual, and are not attributable to any delivery of possession by the company. When the company brings plant and materials on to the site they remain in the possession of the company to enable it to use them in the completion of the works. There is no question of the company delivering possession at that stage, either by way of security (*i.e.* as a pledge) or otherwise (*i.e.* by way of lien)... In my judgment, therefore, the council's rights are derived from contract not possession." None of the above Scottish cases were cited in this case. But much the same outcome as in *Kerr v. Dundee Gas Co.* is reached as regards use of plant and then its return. In *Cosslett* it was held that any right to sell as such would be a floating charge under English law which would require registration, without which it was void as against a liquidator or administrator. It should be noted that in Scotland there is no such thing as a floating charge arising from the law of equity, only under statute, see *Stair Memorial Encyclopedia*, Vol. 4, para. 652.

it (*Moore*), and if the employer has possession of the materials on site (*Moore*). The issues then become more complex in relation to suppliers.

The position of the supplier under the Sale of Goods Act

4.116   *Thomas Graham & Sons Ltd v. Glenrothes Development Corp*[84] concerns a supplier of plumbing materials to a main contractor. The main contractor became insolvent at a time when it was averred that 80 per cent of the value of all goods placed on site had been paid for by the employer, but not passed on to the supplier. On insolvency, the employer sold the goods on to another contractor to use in completing the works. The supplier claimed that the employer had no title to sell these, as the contract with the main contractor contained a simple retention of title clause, and sought payment from the employer for the value of the materials. The employer claimed title by virtue of the provisions of section 25 of the Sale of Goods Act 1893; the Factors Act 1889, s. 2(1) and 5; and the Factors (Scotland) Act 1890, s.1(2). The employer further denied any prior knowledge of the retention of title clause.

4.117   Section 25 (2) of the Sale of Goods Act 1893 provides:

> "Where a person having bought or agreed to buy goods obtains, with the consent of the seller, possession of the goods... the delivery or transfer by that person... of the goods... under any sale... or other disposition thereof, to any person receiving the same in good faith and without notice of any lien or other right of the original seller in respect of the goods shall have the same effect as if the person making the delivery or transfer were a mercantile agent in possession of the goods... with the consent of the owner."

Section 25 (3) provides that a mercantile agent shall have the same meaning as in the Factors Acts.

4.118   The Factors Act 1889, by section 2(1), empowers a mercantile agent, if in possession of goods with the owner's consent, to give a valid title to them by sale or other disposition, provided that the purchaser acts in good faith and has no notice that the agent has no authority to do so. Section 5 of the 1889 Act provides that the consideration necessary for the validity of such a sale may be "either payment in cash... or any other valuable consideration", and the Factors (Scotland) Act 1890, which applied the 1889 Act to Scotland, provides that, in the application of section 5, a sale or other disposition shall not be valid unless made for valuable consideration.

4.119   It was admitted by the suppliers that possession in the goods had passed to the main contractors when the goods were unloaded by the main contractor's men on site. The court held that there was a relevantly pled case that there had been a "disposition" under section 25(2) to the employers by the main contractors by taking delivery, unloading the materials and placing them on site, as there was a necessary implication that the goods were only transferred to site by virtue of the building contract. The Lord President further went on:

---

[84]   1967 S.C. 284.

"Alternatively it could be argued... that there was a delivery within the meaning of s. 25(2) when [the main contractor's] employees unloaded the lorries and, having done so, placed them on the site, and the Corporation's architect, through his quantity surveyor, measured and did not reject them... In my opinion this could...amount to delivery within the meaning of s. 25(2)".

Lord Migdale agreed that measurement, inspection and approval of the goods would amount to delivery to the employer. "Delivery does not require a physical movement of the goods, and here the architect's assistant accepted these goods after measuring them... I think the same inspection and acceptance can amount to a delivery under a disposition." Lord Migdale said that payment of 80 per cent of the value to the main contractor would amount to "valuable consideration"; whereas the Lord President thought that the obligation to pay the price was "a sufficiently valuable consideration".

It seems therefore that the First Division were saying that title to goods could transfer under a contract with a building supplier as soon as they were delivered to site, thereby becoming the employer's property, even if there was a valid retention of title clause as between the supplier and the main contractor, so long as the employer was unaware of the retention of title. The supplier simply loses out, with no contractual way of protecting himself, once delivered to site. Title has passed, but the goods do not appear to have been sold — they have been transferred "by other disposition". This seems surprising given the comments of Lord Watson in *Seath & Co. v. Moore*[85] on the need for affixing or making the materials "part of the corpus", which were approved in the shipbuilding case of *Reid v. MacBeth & Gray*.[86] Differences between *Reid* and *Thomas Graham* are that in *Reid* the materials never reached the site at all, and that in *Reid* a shipbuilding contract as an entire contract of sale was upheld as a decisive issue. What is remarkable is that neither *Seath & Co. v. Moore* nor *Reid v. MacBeth & Gray* nor the pledge cases[87] are discussed at all in *Thomas Graham*. Nevertheless *Thomas Graham* was followed by Lord Mayfield in the Outer House in *Archivent Sales & Development Ltd v. Strathclyde Regional Council*.[88]

4.120

The Archivent case[89]

In the *Archivent* case a school was being built and ventilators were supplied with a retention of title clause between the supplier and the contractor. The contractor and the employer were under a standard form of JCT 1963 contract (July 1977 revision), clause 14 of which provided that

4.121

---

[85] *supra.*
[86] *supra.*
[87] *ante.* paras 4.112–4.113.
[88] 1985 S.L.T. 154.
[89] *ibid.*

where the value of goods has been included in an interim certificate and the contractor paid, property in the goods passes to the employer. The materials were measured and paid for under an interim certificate. A receiver was appointed to the contractor at a time when the supplier had not been paid. The employer did not know of the retention of title clause and had paid in good faith. The supplier sued the employer for delivery or payment, and claimed a right of retention of title under section 19 of the Sale of Goods Act 1979. The court followed the dicta of Lord President Clyde in *Thomas Graham* and decided the same way, putting particular significance on the inclusion of materials in interim payments and payment. Lord Mayfield concluded:

> "At the conclusion of his submissions the defender's counsel referred me to two cases, namely *Dawber Williamson Roofing Ltd v. Humberside County Council* and *Seath v. Moore* where suppliers had been successful. In the former case, however, no s. 25 defence was maintained. Without that the defenders could show no title to the goods. In the second case it was a matter of the construction of the particular contract. It was also a case prior to the 1893 Sale of Goods Act."

4.122   In *Dawber Williamson* counsel dropped any argument under section 25 as inappropriate for a supply and fix contract, which was commented upon as being correct by the judge. But, of course, *Seath v. Moore* was approved in the post-1893 cases of *Reid v. MacBeth & Gray* (which is very similar to *Thomas Graham* and *Archivent*, except that goods were on site in these cases), and in *Dawber Williamson* the main contract JCT 63 had a property passing on payment provision as in *Archivent*. The conclusion would appear to be that there is a separate rule for suppliers of materials only (exposed to risk of non-payment immediately on supply, especially if certified and the contractor is paid, unless any retention of title clause has been brought to the attention of the employer), and for supply and fix sub-contractors (risk of non-payment does not pass until materials incorporated), unless *Thomas Graham* and *Archivent* are wrong. Indeed recent Australian cases[90] have reached the same conclusions as Lord Watson in *Seath v. Moore;* and *Archivent* was not followed, or apparently even referred to, in *W. Hanson (Harrow) Ltd v. Rapid Civil Engineering Ltd.*[91]

The Hanson case[92]

4.123   In *W. Hanson (Harrow) Ltd* again the main contractor went into receivership, leaving an unpaid supplier. The supplier had a retention of title clause. There were three different contracts for works at three different

---

[90]   *Egan v. State Transport Authority* (1982) 31 S.A.S.R. 481; *R.J. Grills Ltd v. Dellios* [1988] V.R. 136, both referred to in *Hudson's Building and Engineering Contracts* (11th ed.), para. 11.031.

[91]   [1987] 38 B.L.R. 106.

[92]   *ibid.*

sites as between the employer and the main contractor. In two of these main contracts there was provision that property in materials would not pass to the employer until payment of relevant instalments. On that basis the Official Referee held that property had not passed to the employer as there had been no sale or "other disposition" in terms of section 25 of the Sale of Goods Act 1979 until the conditions regarding payment under the relevant main contracts had been met. The Official Referee then said with regard to the other contract:

> "With regard to the Gilbert Road contract, there was no provision relating to interim payments or to the passing of property in goods on site. I accept that there was an arrangement whereby interim payments would be made against the worth of work done and materials on site intended for inclusion in the development.[93] It is common practice in the industry for interim payments to be made on that basis against the contract price. However, valuation of work and materials for that purpose do [sic] not usually connote the purchase by the employer of site materials so valued. The assessment is merely a convenient means of determining the amount which should, in fairness to the contractor, be advanced to him from time to time against the contract sum. There is no evidence before me to justify the inference that there was any contractual departure from this established practice".[94]

It is not clear from the judgment whether any of the contracts were in JCT 80 terms. However, JCT 80 at clause 16.1 expressly provides property in goods passes with valuation and payment to the main contractor, which seems very similar. Indeed in *Archivent* the predecessor of clause 16 which was in materially the same terms was the relevant clause of the main contract. It seems therefore that the difference in *Archivent* was that the employer had paid the main contractor, although the fact of interim valuation was not thought by the Official Referee in the "Gilbert Road" contract to connote purchase. It is not clear but it seems it can be inferred from the Official Referee's view that valuation *and payment* would not have transferred title in a contract with no specific clause dealing with transfer of title.   4.124

There was also the question in *Hanson* as to whether the employer could exercise a contractual right to use the materials "of the contractor" on the determination of the main contractor's employment. In this case the Official Referee said there was no right to use the materials on site as they were not the property of the main contractor being subject to a valid retention of title clause. The current clause in the Scottish Building contract (August 98 revision) which deals with rights of the Employer on the determination of the contractor's employment is clause 27.5. Clause 27.5.1 allows the Employer to use "all temporary buildings, plant, tools, equipment, goods and materials   4.125

---

[93] It was held that on the facts no precise stages were identified, nor was a precise percentage figure agreed.

[94] *ibid.* at 113; similar observations were made *obiter* by Mervyn Davies J. in *Sauter Automation Ltd v. H.C. Goodman (Mechanical Services) Ltd* [1986] 34 B.L.R. 81 at 90–91.

intended for, delivered to and placed on or adjacent to the Works... provided that where the aforesaid temporary buildings, plant, tools, equipment and Site Materials are not owned by the Contractor the consent of the owner thereof to such use is obtained by the Employer". Site materials are defined in clause 1.3 as "all unfixed materials and goods delivered to, placed on or adjacent to the Works and intended for incorporation therein".

4.126   It is submitted that questions remain about the correctness of the decisions in *Thomas Graham* and *Archivent*, particularly on the point of what is meant by "or other disposition" in relation to section 25 of the Sale of Goods Act 1979. Emden[95] says that this phrase may be satisfied by a contract for work and materials. But it is submitted that it would be strange to bring what has traditionally been an entirely distinct type of nominate contract such as one for work and materials within the ambit of the Sale of Goods Act in such a shorthand way.

Supply of Goods and Services Act 1982 and retention of title issues

4.127   The Sale of Goods Act 1979 specifically provides in section 19 for title to be retained in goods after delivery, and this is a long-standing principle of law in any event. However, no such retention of title provisions are repeated in the Supply of Goods and Services Act 1982. Section 11B of the Supply of Goods and Services Act 1982 concerns implied terms as to title as follows:

> "11B—(1) In a contract for the transfer of goods, other than one to which subsection (3) below applies, there is an implied term on the part of the transferor that in the case of transfer of the property in the goods he has a right to transfer the property and in the case of an agreement to transfer the property in the goods he will have such a right at the time the property is to be so transferred.
>
> (2) In a contract for the transfer of goods, other than to one to which subsection (3) below applies, there is also an implied term that —
> (a) the goods are free, and will remain free until the time the property is to be transferred, from any charge or encumbrance not disclosed or known to the transferee before the contract is made, and
> (b) the transferee will enjoy quiet possession of the goods except so far as it may be disturbed by the owner or other person entitled to the benefit of any charge or encumbrance so disclosed or known.
>
> (3) This subsection applies to a contract for the transfer of goods in the case of which there appears from the contract or is to be inferred from its circumstances an intention that the transferor should transfer only such title as he or a third party may have.
>
> (4) In a contract to which subsection (3) above applies there is an implied term that all charges or encumbrances known to the transferor and not known to the transferee have been disclosed to the transferee before the contract is made.

---

[95] II, Chap. 4, para. 359.33.

(5) In a contract to which subsection (3) above applies there is also an implied term that none of the following will disturb the transferee's quiet possession of the goods, namely—

    (a) the transferor;

    (b) in a case where the parties to the contract intend that the transferor shall transfer only such title as a third party may have, that person;

    (c) anyone claiming through or under the transferor or that third person otherwise than under a charge or encumbrance disclosed or known to the transferee before the contract is made.

These provisions would appear to strengthen the employer's position in respect of any dispute over his quiet possession of goods which are claimed to be subject to a valid retention of title clause. In short, the employer who is in possession of goods has the implied contractual right not to have his quiet possession disturbed. This will be the case even where there appears to be a valid retention of title clause, so long as that clause is not considered to be a "charge or encumbrance".   4.128

In Scotland it has been held in *Armour v. Thyssen Edelstahlwerke A.G.*[96] that a retention of title clause is not to be confused with a right in security. In this case a German company that supplied steel to a manufacturer in Falkirk did so under a retention of title clause which retained property in the goods until all debts had been paid to them. This was held not to be an attempt to create a security in favour of the Germans over moveable property as the Falkirk company never obtained title to create a security in favour of the Germans. Nor had the Germans created a security in their own favour. A right in security could be given by a debtor to his creditor, but the Germans never became debtors to the Falkirk company. It was the Germans who were owed money. Accordingly the retention of title clause was held to be a valid contractual mechanism which reserved the right of disposal of the steel, but was not to be confused with the creation of a security over it.[97] On this authority it seems that a retention of title clause would not in Scotland be a "charge or encumbrance" which creates rights that could be used to interrupt the quiet possession of an employer under section 11B(2)(b) of the Supply of Goods and Services Act 1982.   4.129

However, in England in *Stroud Architectural Systems v. John Laing Construction*[98] it was held that a retention of title clause in a contract between a supplier of specialist glazing and a sub-contractor created a floating charge which, as it was not registered under section 395 of the Companies Act 1985, was void against the liquidator or administrative receiver of the sub-contractor.[99] The   4.130

---

[96] *ibid.*

[97] For a useful discussion of other matters related to retention of title clauses, such as sub-sales where there is a valid retention of title clause; where goods subject to a retention of title clause are made into something else, or attempts to set up a trust fund in relation to goods that are sold subject to a retention of title clause, see Greene and Fletcher, *Law and Practice of Receivership in Scotland* (2nd ed.), para. 5.19 *et seq.*

[98] [1994] B.C.C. 18.

[99] A similar decision was reached for a German supplier under a contract governed by German law to a company situate in England in *Re Weldtech Equipment* [1991] B.C.C. 16 which followed *Tatung (U.K.) v. Galex Telesure* [1989] 5 B.C.C. 325.

judgment sought to distinguish the Court of Appeal's decision in *Clough Mill Ltd v. Martin*[1] (which had been referred to with approval in *Armour v. Thyssen*) and to follow the earlier decision in *Re Bond Worth Ltd*.[2] In *Bond Worth* a clause with the sellers retaining "equitable and beneficial ownership" was held not to be a retention of title clause at all; legal title to the goods passed to the buyers, and it was held that an equitable charge had been created. This is strange territory to the Scots lawyer as floating charges in Scotland are entirely creatures of statute and do not arise from equity as happens in England.

4.131   A simple retention of title clause would however be a "hire purchase agreement" for the purposes of section 10(4) and section 251 of the Insolvency Act 1986, and therefore can be subject to the administration provisions of that Act preventing repossession of goods by the supplier from a main contractor in administration without leave of the court.

4.132   In relation to these problems, the standard form of JCT 80 conditions has a unique slant on the difficulties associated with title to goods that are unfixed on site or off-site that have been paid for by the employer. Clauses 16, 19.4 and 30.3 are the construction industry's unique slant on things.

THE JCT POSITION

4.133   In a nutshell clause 16.1 provides that title to materials and goods on site passes to the Employer on valuation and payment under an Interim Certificate (*N.B.* payment is qualified as the "amount properly due" and therefore may not be incompatible with set-off). Clause 19.4 requires that these provisions be stepped down to any Sub-Contractor who shall not deny that title has passed to the Employer. The fundamental problems therefore that are discussed above in relation to *Dawber Williamson* and *Hanson* of "making part of the corpus" of the works and what instalment payments mean in the context of passing title have not been addressed.

4.134   Clause 16 also creates a contractual restriction on removal of the materials brought on site so that they are not to be removed except with the consent of the Architect (which consent shall not be unreasonably withheld). Whether this is a pledge or lien or purely contractual right is difficult to assess given the analysis of the pledge cases above, and particularly the Court of Appeal position in relation to ICE 5th contract in *Cosslett*.[3] Despite the passing of property the Contractor remains responsible for loss and damage for the goods and materials subject to clause 22B or 22C (if applicable) (*i.e.* where the employer takes out All Risks insurance for the Works). As stated above, clause 16.2 in relation to off-site materials is deleted in the Scottish Building Contract and a direct purchase agreement is provided for in terms of clause 30.3. Risk in materials off-site under a separate purchase agreement remains with the contractor in terms of a Scottish amendment to clause 16.1.

---

[1]   [1984] 3 All E.R. 982.
[2]   [1980] 3 All E.R. 919.
[3]   *op.cit.*

Clause 17: practical completion and defects liability

There is no contractual definition of Practical Completion and the courts 4.135 have on occasion been asked to supply one. Defects similarly are not defined. The Defects Liability Period is defined, but only as a period of time in Appendix II of the SBC. Defects are linked to Practical Completion and there is a practice of snagging lists being given to the contractor which are to be made good before the certificate of practical completion is issued. The courts have attempted different definitions. In *Westminster City Council v. J. Jarvis & Sons Ltd*,[4] Lord Dilhorne said: "The contract does not define what is meant by practical completion. One would normally say that a task was practically completed when it was almost but not entirely finished, but practical completion suggests that it is not the intended meaning and what is meant is the completion of all the construction that has to be done."

In *Sworn Securities v. Chilcott*[5] the Lord President made, admittedly 4.136 *obiter*, remarks as to the meaning of "practical completion" under clause 15 of JCT 63. He viewed Viscount Dilhorne's remarks in *Jarvis* as effectively endorsing what was written in Hudson (10th ed.), p. 258:

> "It is submitted that the following definition framed for a somewhat unusual type of contract, cannot in fact be bettered for traditional building and engineering contracts, namely, 'apart from merely trivial defects, a stage of construction at which [the house] is ready for occupation in all ways relevant to the contract and is free from known omissions or defects'. It follows that a practical completion certificate can be issued when, owing to latent defects, the works do not fulfil the contract requirements, and that under the contract works can be completed despite the presence of such defects. Completion under the contract is not postponed until defects which became apparent only after the works have been finished, have been remedied."

The Lord President then said: "'practical completion' has not been achieved until there has been completion of all the construction work that has to be done and there are no apparent defects." In this case a certificate issued "subject to the making good of any outstanding items" was not a certificate under clause 15.[6]

There may be an issue about *de minimis* items, as in *Jarvis* Lord Justice 4.137 Salmon said:

> "I take these words to mean completion for all practical purposes, that is to say for the purposes of allowing the employer to take possession of the works and use them as intended. If completion meant completion down to the last detail, however trivial and unimportant, then clause 22 (the liquidate and ascertained damages clause) would be a penalty clause and as such unenforceable".

---

[4] [1970]1 All E.R. 943, HL.
[5] 1977 S.L.T. 86.
[6] This case is particularly important in relation to third parties who agree to buy subject to an architect's certificate. It was held that for this to mean a certificate under JCT 63 of practical completion this should be expressly stated, and that the certifying architect had to have knowledge of the third party contract.

Also, in *H.W. Nevill (Sunblest) Ltd v. William Press Ltd*,[7] Viscount Dilhorne spoke of practical completion where *de minimis* or trifling works had not been carried out, but where there were no patent defects. There may also be authority for this less strict view of practical completion in Scotland. In *Borders Regional Council v. J. Smart & Co. (Contractors) Ltd*[8] the Lord Justice-Clerk (Wheatley) said of clause 15 of JCT 63:

> "Section 15 (1) provides that such a certificate is to be issued when in the opinion of the architect the works have been practically completed. I take that as meaning that the works have been completed for all practical purposes, and the employers could take them over and use them for their intended purpose, as in fact occurred."

4.138   There is also the "law is not so pedantic" etc. quote of the Lord President in *Ramsay v. Brand*[9] in relation to payment under entire contracts, which could be used to support the less rigorous standard of what practical completion should be interpreted as.

4.139   Practical Completion is a landmark in administration of JCT 80 because:

  (i)   It marks the date at which the defects liability period begins.
  (ii) The contractor's liability for insurance ends.
  (iii) A moiety of the retention is released.
  (iv) Regular instalment certificates end.
  (v)   The period for the architect's first review of extensions of time begins under clause 25.
  (vi) Any reference to arbitration can be opened, at least prior to Amendment 18.

4.140   Since Amendment 4, issued in July 1987, there is now no doubt that there is no question of the Employer having to pay for the costs incurred by the contractor in making good his own defects, and if these are not instructed to be made good by the Architect with the consent of the Employer then an 'appropriate deduction' may be made from the Contract Sum.[10]

4.141   One might ask what the point is in having a defects liability period specifically referred to in the contract when the dicta above strongly indicate that a practical completion certificate should not be issued if there are patent defects, and that a latent defect will normally be a breach of contract, subject only to questions of whether a right to sue has prescribed[11] when the defect is discovered, and the meaning of a final certificate.[12] There are also the *"modo et forma"* comments of the Lord President in *Ramsay v. Brand.*[13]

---

[7]   (1982) 20 B.L.R. 78 at 87.
[8]   1983 S.L.T. 164 at167.
[9]   See para. 4.04
[10] See comments on this phrase in relation to clause 8 at para. 4.57, *ante.*
[11] See Chap. 3, paras 3.81 *et seq.*
[12] See paras 4.58–4.64.
[13] *op cit.*, see para. 4.04.

In the context of the design of computer software[14] it has been held that   4.142
"no buyer should expect a supplier to get his programs right first time",[15]
and that a beta version of a program was one which the developer considered
to be complete in every sense so as to be "bug free", although still subject
to testing before the purchaser released the same on to the market.[16] There
may be analogous thinking in relation to a practical completion certificate
in the construction context and the defects liability period, with the important
caveat that building contracts, of course, involve the fixing of work on
land. A similar notion appears to have been in the mind of Lord Diplock in
his dissenting speech in *P. & M. Kaye Ltd v. Hosier & Dickinson Ltd*[17]
when he said:

> "Upon a legalistic analysis it might be argued that temporary disconformity
> of any part of the works with the requirements of the contract even though
> remedied before the end of the construction period constituted a breach of
> contract for which nominal damages would be recoverable. I do not think
> that makes business sense. Provided the contractor puts it right timeously I
> do not think that the parties intended that any temporary disconformity should
> of itself amount to a breach of contract by the contractor."

This "temporary disconformity" was in the context of defects that had   4.143
been made right, but otherwise has been criticised as wrong or not intended
for universal application.[18] Why should the employer not be entitled to have
the work done by someone else or to simply sue for damages after it has
been found to have been defectively done by the contractor? It is suggested
that such clauses combine quite different concepts and possibly confuse
issues of mitigation of loss and breach of contract. A simpler analysis would
be that the contractor should have a continuing duty to carry out the work
properly throughout the contract period, as was held by the Official Referee
in *Surrey Heath Borough Council v. Lovell Construction Ltd.*[19] This would
be subject to the position under clause 8 where works disconform to
contract can be accepted. However, Lord Diplock said in relation to clause
15 of JCT 63:

> "Condition 15 imposes upon the contractor a liability to mitigate the damage
> caused by his breach by making good the defects of construction at his own
> expense. It confers upon him the corresponding right to do so. It is a necessary

---

[14] Albeit that in *Beta Computers (Europe) Ltd v. Adobe Systems (Europe) Ltd*, 1996 S.C.L.R.
      587, Lord Penrose said: "In my opinion the only acceptable view is that the supply of
      proprietary software for a price is a contract *sui generis* which may involve elements of
      nominate contracts such as sale, but would be inadequately understood if expressed wholly
      in terms of any of the nominate contracts."

[15] *Saphena Computing v. Allied Collection Agencies Ltd* 1989 [1995] F.S.R. 616.

[16] *Virgin Interactive Entertainment (Europe) Ltd v. Bluewall Ltd* [1998] Masons C.L.R. Rep.
      83

[17] [1972] 1 W.L.R. 146, at 165.

[18] *Lintest Builders Ltd v. Roberts* [1978] 10 B.L.R. 120.

[19] (1988) 42 B.L.R. 30.

implication from this that the employer cannot, as he otherwise could, recover as damages from the contractor the difference between the value of the works if they had been constructed in conformity with the contract and their value in their defective condition, without first giving the contractor the opportunity of making good defects."[20]

However, it has been held in *H. W. Nevill (Sunblest) v. William Press & Son*[21] by the Official Referee that the employer is still entitled to recover for consequential losses[22] as a result of the corrected defects which are made subject of a certificate of making good defects. Such losses may include the diminution in value (if there is any, in the sense of being "blighted") of the remedied works.[23]

4.144   It has recently been held in the Court of Appeal in *Pearce and High v. Baxter*[24] that the giving of notice under a JCT Minor Works contract was a condition precedent to the employer's right to require compliance with the defects liability clause, but this did not displace the common law remedies for breach of contract that might exist.

Clause 18: partial possession by employer

4.145   The JCT conditions talk in terms of the contractor being given "possession" of the site on the date of possession (clause 23.1.1). It has even been held in England that this gave the contractor an irrevocable licence to occupy the site until completion.[25] In terms of Scots law however no right of property is created under the JCT conditions in favour of the contractor. The contractor merely has a right of access and this is a personal right. This is clearly so from Lord Neaves in *Moore v. Gledden*[26]: "Land when let may reduce the proprietor's possession to civil possession, the tenant having natural possession. But a contractor coming on to the ground to do work has no possession. He has not even occupation. He has mere

---

[20] *Kaye (supra)* at 166.

[2]   (1983) 20 B.L.R. 78.

[22] Such losses are normally distinguished from losses which arise naturally and directly from a breach of contract, see *Croudace Construction Ltd v. Cawood Products* [1978] 8 B.L.R. 20, C.A. In this case a supplier's exclusion of consequential loss clause was not effective to exclude the losses suffered by the buyer's sub-contractors for delay to their works when materials were not delivered.

[23] *George Fischer Holdings Ltd v. Multi Design Consultants Ltd,* Official Referee's Business (February 10, 1998) C.I.L.L., April 1998, p. 1362. This case is also interesting as having an unusual clause which was construed as allowing for practical completion which was not inconsistent with some degree of outstanding or defective work (para. 163); http://tap.ccta.gov.uk/courtser/judgments.nsf/Referees+Court/By+Case+Reference

[24] C.A., February 15, 1999.

[25] *Hounslow London Borough Council v. Twickenham Garden Developments* [1970] 7 B.L.R. 81. This decision has been disapproved in New South Wales and New Zealand: see *Hudson* (11th ed.), para. 4.145.

[26] [1869] VII Macph. 1042 at 1046.

access, the employer being, as before, the sole possessor." The contractor and the employer can both be occupiers for the purposes of civil liability under the Occupiers' Liability (Scotland) Act 1960. But it is the responsibility of the principal contractor in terms of CDM regulation 16(1)(c) who is appointed for any project to take "reasonable steps to ensure that only authorised persons are allowed into any premises or part of premises where construction work is being carried out".[27] There is at common law, it is submitted, nothing to prevent the employer taking possession of works as they proceed, if it does not affect the contractor's access. Indeed recently in *Fischer v. Multi Design Consultants*[28] the Official Referee found as follows in relation to a particular contract:

> "I must summarise the relevant provisions of the building contract. By clause 28.1 the employer was on the date for possession to permit the contractor to occupy the site, 'but not so as to exclude the Employer', and the contractor was to complete the works on or before the date for completion, subject to the provisions for extension of time. The date for completion was 14 April 1990 and was not extended. The words quoted above are important, since much of the argument for [the defendants] proceeded on the assumption that the contractor, as is common under many standard forms of contract, had exclusive possession during the works and that the employer could not make any use of the premises until certificate of practical completion or the operation of provisions for partial possession. In my judgment the assumption is false; the plaintiff here did not need a certificate for that purpose, and indeed it is common ground that it was already using part of the premises before 14 April 1990. That use did not, as I understand it, involve excluding [the contractor]; there was provision in clause 21 for a formal process of taking partial possession which would have had that effect and carried other consequences, including a release of a proportionate part of the retention and a 'deemed practical completion' and the beginning of the maintenance period in respect of the relevant part of the premises, but clause 21 was not implemented."

Whatever possession might be construed to be in Scotland, clause 18.1   4.146
allows the Employer, with the consent of the Contractor (which may not be unreasonably withheld), to take possession of part of the site. The Architect is to issue a written statement identifying what has been "taken into possession" and the appropriate date. There are then provisions with regard to practical completion, insurance, and defects liability for that part. In practice, there is usually a trade-off as the Contractor will normally want issues regarding extensions of time and loss and expense agreed before allowing partial possession. There may also be the issue of liquidate and ascertained damages that might be due by the Contractor. Clause 18.1.4 attempts to keep the liquidate and ascertained damages clause (24) alive in

---

[27]   The Construction (Design and Management) Regulations (S.I. 1994 No. 3140).
[28]   *op.cit.*, para. 161.

the event of partial possession being taken by the Employer. Clause 18.1.4 provides for a ratio to be used based on the amount the part taken into possession bears to the Contract Sum. The idea presumably is that the Employer's damages might be unenforceable as a penalty if he actually has part possession of the works. But it is submitted that this need not always be so, and that a damages clause need have no relationship to a ratio based on the Contract Sum and the part taken into possession (if this could be worked out in any case). *Bramall & Ogden v. Sheffield City Council*[29] would at first sight appear to be the most ideal circumstances for carrying out such a reduction. The contract was in JCT 63 form, clause 16(e) of which is in substantially the same form as clause 18.1.4 of JCT 80. The Appendix to the contract stated a single date for completion and provided for liquidate and ascertained damages at the rate of £20 per week for each uncompleted dwelling. The employer took possession of dwellings as the works progressed. The employers then acted quite reasonably, they thought, in applying a weekly rate to each house that was left. It was held that this was neither what clause 16 provided for, nor was it provided for in the liquidate and ascertained damages clause which only provided for one completion date. Essentially there had been a draftsmanship problem that prevented the Council from doing what they did, as clause 16(e) did not provide for using the damages clause as a ratio: the contract sum was to be used as a ratio. In the absence of a sectional completion provision tied to sectional completion dates and rates for liquidated damages, the liquidate damages clause operated as a penalty and was unenforceable. However the judge held that ordinary damages at common law could still be claimed which would probably result in the outcome the employers wanted if the pleadings were amended. The conclusion would seem to be that it is difficult to see how in a more complex set of circumstances the liquidate and ascertained damages clause could be kept alive by clause 18.1.4.

Clause 19: Assignment and sub-contracts

4.147   The word "assignment" according to McBryde[30] if "found in a deed, perhaps of English origin, it should on Institutional authority, be treated as equivalent to 'assignation'". In fact in the Scottish Building Contract the term "assignment" is changed to "assignation" in the definitions section.

4.148   It is probably fair to say that the law relating to assignation in Scotland is undecided in relation to certain fundamental propositions. Lord Penrose in *Scottish Homes v. Inverclyde District Council*[31] found it unnecessary to express any view on the "fundamental proposition" that the contractor's obligations of performance cannot be assigned under an executorial contract.

---

[29] [1983] 29 B.L.R. 73.
[30] *The Law of Contract in Scotland* (W. Green & Son, 1987) at para. 17-02.
[31] Outer House, January 25, 1996, digested at G.W.D. 12-677.

Also, in the House of Lords in *Linden Gardens Trust Ltd v. Lenesta Sludge Disposals* and *St. Martins Property Corp. v. Sir Robert McAlpine & Sons*[32] the majority came close to, but chose to hold back from, formulating a general proposition that a building contractor in breach of his contract with his employer could be sued by the employer even if the employer no longer had an interest in the property, or did not suffer the cost of remedial works. In the particular circumstances of the *St. Martin's* case, the employer was held to be entitled to sue when a loss was incurred by another party. This of course has important commercial significance in relation to the sale of properties to third parties, and any attempt to assign rights to sue to those third parties.

Delectus persona

Naturally, contracting parties will have agreed obligations to each other.   4.149
An important matter will be whether there is an element of *delectus persona*. *Delectus personae* according to Gloag[33] is where the court finds an element of deliberate choice in who to contract with, for example where issues of set-off or compensation may arise.[34] At page 421 Gloag states:

> "Contracts for Work — A contract to do work may promise the personal exertion of the obligant and is then clearly unassignable. Nobody supposes that in a contract with A or B to paint a picture or write a book it is possible for A or B to say 'I will get somebody else to paint you the picture or write you the book, and that must satisfy you, and you must pay me the price'.[35] The same remark would apply where the skill involved was not literary or artistic, but manual or professional. And it is conceived that in such cases... there is delectus personae in the choice of an employer. But there are many contracts for the performance of work where it is known that the work cannot be performed by the obligant personally, but only through the agency of servants or workmen. Then unless there is an express or implied provision for personal superintendence,[36] the work may be delegated".

It has been held that there was *delectus persona* in the grant of a   4.150
permission to owners of land to erect a pier or jetty at Leith entirely at the owners' own expense. It was in fact built by a separate company formed for that purpose. The result was that the pier had to be demolished some 37 years later.[37] However, there was no *delectus persona* in a contract to supply

---

[32] Both cases decided together [1994] 1 A.C. 85.

[33] Gloag on *Contract*, p. 416.

[34] *Boulton v. Jones* (1857) 2 H. & N. 564. On compensation generally see Chap. 3, paras 3.52–3.68.

[35] *Cole v. Handasyde & Co.*, 1910 S.C. 68, 73, *per* Lord Dunedin.

[36] *Yorke v. Campbell* (1904) 12 S.L.T. 413.

[37] *Leith Dock Commissioners v. Colonial Life Assurance Co.* (1861) 24 D. 64. It is submitted that this case has little by way of opinion from the First Division, and can be of little general applicability.

materials, even though the supplier had been selected for his expertise, if the materials merely had to conform to, and satisfy, certain tests.[38] Nor was a contract adopted by a liquidator to pave King's Drive and King's Bridge in Glasgow which consisted "chiefly in manual labour" and maintenance over a five-year period *delectus persona*.[39] However, in *Scottish Homes v. Inverclyde District Council*[40] it was held that a maintenance contract could be *delectus persona* where the contract had been let under the "restricted" procedure required by the Public Works Contracts Regulations 1991 and was not assignable by the contractor; even where the employees of the contractor who would perform the work were all transferred to the new company. Lord Penrose held the provisions of the 1991 Regulations, when considered as a whole, involved a tendering process and selection of contractors that was carefully regulated, not only as to price, but according to criteria extending to skills, experience, resources, reliability and the degree of quality control exercisable by the contractor.

4.151   An assignation may be an attempt to do any of several things. Gloag says that whilst it will be a matter for the court to interpret the intention of the assignation, "there is no general principle of law by which a party who has entered into a contract can get rid of the liabilities it may involve by assigning it to a third party."[41] Gloag states that a contract may be assignable in three senses or degrees:

> "(1) The contract may be so completely assignable that the original party may not only transfer his contractual rights to the assignee, but also free himself from his contractual liabilities. (2) It may be assignable in the sense that an assignee acquires the right to tender performance and sue for its counterpart, the cedent nevertheless remaining liable if the contract be not implemented. (3) It may be assignable only in the sense that one or other party may fulfil the obligations he has undertaken through the agency of a third party, without giving the third party any right to enforce the contract or introducing him into the contractual relationship."[42]

Novation and delegation

4.152   If entirely new contractual obligations by consent are substituted for existing ones, then this is properly termed novation[43] and extinguishes all liability under the previous obligations, but no new parties are introduced. This would not therefore be the same as assignation. Erskine writes[44]:

---

[38] *Cole v. Handasyde*, 1910 S.C. 68.
[39] *Asphaltic Limestone Concrete Co. Ltd v. Glasgow Corporation* 1907 S.C. 463.
[40] Outer House, January 25, 1996, digested in 1996 G.W.D. 12-675; and which distinguished *Asphaltic Limestone Concrete Co. Ltd v. Glasgow Corporation, ibid.*
[41] *op.cit.,* p. 416.
[42] *ibid.*
[43] Stair I, xviii, 8; Erskine's *Institutes* III, iv, 22; Bell *Prin.* para. 576.
[44] *ibid.*

"Delegation, which may be accounted a species of novation, is the changing of one debtor for another, by which the obligation which lay on the first debtor is discharged; [for example] if the debtor in a bond should substitute a third person, who becomes obliged in his place to the creditor, and who is called in Roman law *expromissor*, this requires not only the consent of the *expromissor*, who is to undertake the debt, but of the creditor; for no debtor can get quit of his obligation without the creditor's consent, except by actual performance; and no creditor can be compelled to accept of one debtor for another against his will. Neither novation or delegation is to be presumed; for a creditor who has once acquired a right ought not to lose it by implication; and consequently the new obligation is [in doubtful cases] to be accounted merely corroborative of the old."

Delegation in this sense would therefore be obtained with consent, and is not something that can be unilaterally done. The above quotation was approved in *W.J. Harte Construction v. Scottish Homes*.[45] The circumstances were that following a company reorganisation, a building contract undertaken by one company that was part of the group was performed by another. There had been correspondence between the pursuers and defenders seeking their consent to this change, which was given. The wording of the correspondence was held to indicate consent to performance being carried out by the pursuers but not the substitution of the pursuers as parties to the original contract, as that would have required express language. 4.153

A question remains as to how the first of Gloag's degrees of assignation could take place without consent. This would not it appears be consistent with English law,[46] nor the Scots case of *Stevenson v. Maule & Son*[47] which Gloag refers to at the same page *per* the opinion of Atkin J.: "Under ordinary circumstances it is quite clear that a contracting party cannot assign a contract so as to relieve himself of its burdens. He cannot, against the consent of the other party, substitute for himself a person who is put under the sole obligation to perform the contract." Lord Penrose in *Scottish Homes* thought that Gloag's first degree indicates that Scots law is different from English law in that assignation could take place in Scotland without consent, and approves remarks by Professor Walker[48] to that effect. However Professor Walker cites no authority to that effect. Lord Penrose went on: "If on a sound construction of its terms, express or implied, a contract entitles a contracting party to substitute another in his place both as regards performance and the benefits of the contract, there is in my opinion, no rule of Scots law which would prevent that from having effect." These remarks do seem consistent with another of Gloag's general propositions and might have been cited by Walker: 4.154

45 1992 S.C. 99 at 111.
46 See Bingham L.J. in *Southway Group Ltd v. Esther & Morris Wolff, The Times*, May 21, 1991, C.A.
47 1920 S.C. 335.
48 Walker, *The Law of Contract and Related Obligations in Scotland* (3rd ed.), para. 29.35.

"If there is no element of *delectus personae* such as to demand personal and not substituted performance there would seem to be no reason why the party to whom performance may be delegated should not have the contract assigned and with it the title to sue. Within this rule should fall all executory contracts when the obligations are limited to performance on one side, payment on the other."[49]

Lord Penrose decided the *Scottish Homes* case as one of *delectus persona* in any event.

Sub-contracting and assignation

4.155   In relation to the second of these degrees of assignation this should be distinguished from sub-contracting, because a sub-contractor normally has no rights to tender performance or to sue the employer for payment in relation to the sub-contract works. Nor is the second degree of assignation comparable to the position of a nominated sub-contractor.[50] In both cases the potentially confusing similarity with Gloag's second degree is that the main contractor remains responsible to the employer for the work of a domestic or nominated sub-contractor. In relation to the third degree of assignation, this is the normal domestic or nominated sub-contractors' position. Confusion can arise as the third degree of assignation is often called delegation too, but it is submitted that it should be termed sub-contracting to avoid confusion with Erskine's definition *supra,* which means substitution and replacement with consent. JCT clause 19.2 actually uses the expression "sub-let" in relation to Domestic Sub-Contractors.

4.156   A common way of analysing contractual obligations in relation to assignation is to identify whether it is a matter of significance or indifference to the debtor who he makes performance to, or who makes performance to him. Therefore the benefit arising under a contract is assignable, in the absence of an express provision to the contrary.[51] This benefit will arise when the contract stipulations have been executed, and nothing remains except payment of money, or delivery of an item, for example.[52]

Intimation and consent

4.157   As stated above, at common law the contractor can assign the benefit under a contract, *i.e.* payment; and all that would be required would be an intimation of the assignation to convey it, not consent to the assignation from the employer.[53] Intimation completes the assignee's right, fixes the point of time of the assignation, and after intimation payment to the former creditor will not discharge him in any question with the assignee.[54]

---

[49]   *op. cit.,* p. 418.
[50]   For the peculiarities of nominated sub-contracting see paras 4.364–4.373.
[51]   *Aurdal v. Estrella,* 1916 S.C. 882; *Whiteley v. Hilt* [1918] 2 K.B. 808.
[52]   Stair, III, i, 3.
[53]   See *Stair Memorial Encyclopaedia,* Vol.15, para. 858, p. 555.
[54]   See Walker, *op.cit.* at para. 29.31.

Assignation and proprietary rights

The employer may sell the land on which construction has taken place   4.158
or is on-going. Gloag states:

> "In general, the acquisition of property does not carry with it any right to sue
> on contracts to which the acquirer was not a party.... Where a tenant had
> undertaken to lay a certain quantity of lime on the land annually, and failed
> to do so, it was held that a singular successor of the landlord had no title to
> call him to account in respect of the years before his own title to the subjects
> had been acquired."[55]

This raises difficult questions for building contracts, of whether a transfer   4.159
of a property interest can also involve the assignation of rights to sue in
respect of a building contract relating to that property, and if so, what losses
can be recovered.

GUS Property Management Ltd v. Littlewoods[56]

The House of Lords considered this point in *GUS Property Management*   4.160
Ltd v. Littlewoods, with Lord Keith warning of the absurdity of a claim
for damages disappearing into some legal "black hole".[57] Here, the Lords
reversed the Inner House and held that the right to sue in respect of a
property that had been damaged through the negligence of a third party
could be assigned when the property was transferred, and the loss
recoverable would be the cedent's estimated cost of making good the
damage, or the diminution of value of the property. The Inner House
had held that as the property had been transferred between related
companies in a group for book value that the cedents had not suffered
any loss. As the cedent had suffered no loss the assignee could not sue
to recover any such loss, as the assignee only had as good a claim as the
cedent *(assignatus utitur jure auctoris).* The Lords however said that
the book value transfer could be ignored and seen in the same way as if
it was a gratuitous alienation, having no bearing on the actual loss
suffered by the cedent.

Prohibition on assignation: Linden Gardens & St. Martin's Property Corp.

In relation to assignation or assignment under standard forms of building   4.161
contract, the House of Lords has given far-reaching judgments in recent
years in *Linden Gardens Trust Ltd v. Linesta Sludge Disposals Ltd* and
St Martin's Property Corporation Ltd v. Sir Robert McAlpine.[58]

---

[55]   *op. cit.,* 224-225 with reference to *Hamilton v. Fleming* 1793, Hume, 787.
[56]   1982 S.C. 157, HL.
[57]   *ibid.* at 177.
[58]   [1994] 1 A.C. 85.

Whilst the facts are slightly different in both cases, the essence of the cases was the same: if the contract contained a prohibition on assignment which was not overcome when the employer purported to effect an assignment, who, if anyone, had the right to sue the contractor for defective performance which occurred either before or after the assignment?

4.162   In both cases clause 17 of JCT 63 read:

> "(1) The employer shall not without the written consent of the contractor assign this contract. (2) The contractor shall not without the written consent of the employer assign this contract, and shall not without the written consent of the architect (which consent shall not be unreasonably withheld to the prejudice of the contractor) sublet any portion of the works".

These cases raised the "legal black hole" point made by Lord Keith in *GUS Properties*[59] although in that case the issue was whether a delictual right to sue for negligent damage to a property was lost, not a claim for contractual defects. Also, in *GUS* there was no prohibition on assignation, nor apparently any question of whether the assignation had to be consented to by the wrongdoer.

4.163   The *Linden Gardens* case involved a contract to remove asbestos from the owner's building in Jermyn Street, London. It was alleged that the contractor had failed to remove all the asbestos and was in breach of contract, so the proprietor initially sued the relevant nominated sub-contractor for the costs of having another do the work. This remedial contract also had a clause which prohibited assignment. The proprietor, who paid the remedial contractor, then sold the leasehold on the property, for full market value and on the assumption that the asbestos had been removed, and purported to assign all rights in the existing action and all other rights of action to the buyer. As a matter of fact the original leaseholder continued to occupy the premises under a licence thereafter. No consent to the assignation was obtained from either contractor. It was then alleged that the replacement contractor had not done the work properly either, and the assignee (*Linden Gardens*) paid for more remedial works and sued both previous contractors, and the original main contractor, taking over the first action from the cedents. It was held that the contractual prohibition prevented all assignations of all rights which the original leasehoder had, not merely sub-contracting by the main contractor, and that *Linden Gardens* had no title to sue. The Lords thereby reversed the Court of Appeal.

The prohibition on assigning the contract was said to be imprecisely worded and meant assign the benefit of the contract as *per* Lord Browne-Wilkinson: "every lawyer knows the burden of a contract cannot be assigned".[60] The prohibition also barred assignment of accrued causes of

---

[59]   See note 324.
[60]   *op.cit.* at p.103. Note that this proposition was regarded by Lord Penrose in *Scottish Homes v. Inverclyde District Council*, O.H., January 25, 1996 as to "suggest a difference of approach to the basic issue which one would follow safely only after a much more exhaustive study of the comparative rule of contract law in the two countries than was carried out in this case and than the circumstances of the case would have justified". See the author's comments at para. 4.154.

action before the assignment. His Lordship thought that a prohibition against assignment might not always mean that "the fruits of performance", *e.g.* payment or the right to sue for payment, were also prohibited, but did in this case. He did so almost on the basis of a *delectus persona* argument, as in building contracts which he said were "pregnant with disputes" that "some employers are more reasonable than others in dealing with disputes". Also that a confused position would arise if assignment of the right to sue took place before final payment, involving the employer still being bound to pay under the contract but the assignee having the rights relevant to set-off. More confusion still could arise if before completion of the works the right to sue was assigned and separated from the right to insist on further performance which was said to be unassignable (presumably on the basis of *delectus persona*). If the contractor then committed a repudiatory breach of contract who could accept the repudiation? His Lordship described such an implied intention as "perverse", although a result which could be obtained by careful drafting.[61]

It is interesting then to note the position under clause 19 of JCT 80 and   4.164
under the Scottish Building Contract (August1998 revision). Clause 19.1.1 says that "Neither the Employer nor the Contractor shall, without the written consent of the other, assign this contract." This clause then is much the same as clause 17 of JCT 63 as regards the employer's position. However, a new clause 19.1.2 was added by Amendment 4 in July 1987. Clause 19.1.2 is deleted in the Scottish Building Contract and replaced as follows:

> "Where Clause 19.1.2 is stated in Appendix II to apply, then in the event of the Employer alienating by the sale or lease or otherwise disposing of his interest in the Works, the Employer may at any time after the issue of the Certificate of Practical Completion assign to the person acquiring his interest in the Works, his right, title and interest to bring proceedings in the name of the Employer (whether in arbitration or court proceedings) to enforce any of the rights of the Employer arising under or by reason of breach of this Contract."

This therefore provides for assignation without consent of the contractor of parts of the benefits of the contract when other matters remain outstanding, notably the final payment, release of half of the retention sums, and the defects liability period. Whether this drafting will achieve the intended result, particularly in relation to any counterclaim by the contractor remains to be tested.

The *St. Martin's* case was slightly different again. Following a corporate   4.165
restructuring the employer, under a building contract to develop shops, offices and flats, which were on completion to be leased to a local authority,

---

[61] A similar position was reached in *Flood v. Shand Construction, The Times*, January 8, 1997, CA where assignment without consent of a sum due under a building contract did not cover any preliminary steps that were required to establish that a particular quantified sum was due and payable.

purported to assign: "the full benefit of all the contracts and engagements whatsoever entered into by the assignor and existing at the date hereof for the construction and completion of the development". The building contract was JCT 63, and again no consent from the contractor was obtained. There were alleged breaches of contract by the contractor, but these took place after the purported assignment. However in this case the assignee and the cedent both sued the contractor. As in *Linden Gardens* the prohibition on assignment was fatal to the claims of the assignee, but rather remarkably, it was held that the purported cedent could sue to recover damages in respect of the costs of remedial work that the assignee sustained. Quite why in principle this should be possible was not decided on the basis of any prevailing fundamental rule of law, but as a new category of exception. Indeed this case might be seen as the Lords making the law up, for no other reason than to provide "a remedy where no other would be available to a person sustaining loss which under a rational legal system ought to be compensated by the person who has caused it".[62] Their Lordships refrained from working out a general principle, although Lord Griffiths went the furthest without taking all his brethren with him. It may be that this principle is confined to building contracts, especially those which prohibit assignment to anyone, including ultimate purchasers, and where it is clear that there will be an ultimate purchaser. Of course, ultimate purchasers could arrange to obtain warranties from the contractor, but this case seems to say that they do not need to, the original employer can recover if they cannot.

4.166   These cases leave a number of important questions unresolved. In *Linden Gardens* there appears to be no clear answer about what happens next. Can the original purported cedent still sue for the breaches by both contractors. It seems the answer to that is yes, although this is not answered — indeed there seems a clear error at the second paragraph of page 116 in Lord Browne-Wilkinson's judgment which confuses matters — as the breaches were in respect of binding contracts to which they were a party, and as in *St. Martin's*, they could sue for substantial losses. Again what these losses might be is not spelled out but would seem to be those which result from defective performance. There is also an anomaly created by the *St. Martin's* decision as the purported assignee was the party that lost out, but it was indicated that any damages that are recovered by the cedent are a distinct matter and not to be held in any "constructive trust" for the other.

Darlington Borough Council v. Wiltshire Northern Ltd[63]

4.167   The question of whether such damages are to be held in trust has since been considered for the purposes of English law by the Court of Appeal in *Darlington Borough Council v. Wiltshire Northern Ltd.* The circumstances

---

[62] *ibid.* Lord Browne-Wilkinson at p. 115.
[63] [1995] 1 W.L.R. 68.

were that Darlington sought to fund the construction of a leisure centre to be constructed by Wiltshire. They did so by an arrangement whereby Morgan Grenfell (Local Authority Services) Ltd were made the employer of Wiltshire under a JCT 63 contract. Various agreements were then put in place, including one which allowed Darlington to make a wide call for the assignment of any rights of action that Morgan Grenfell might have against Wiltshire, who, it seems, were aware of this arrangement. Therefore a different situation again arose from that in *Linden Gardens* (prohibition of assignment was fatal to the claim of the assignee), and that in *St. Martin's* (prohibition of assignment left the original contracting party free to sue for the losses sustained by the purported assignee); the difference being that a different legal black hole argument arose, which went as follows. As assignment is permitted, Morgan Grenfell could not sue for damages sustained by Darlington in the exceptional way that *St. Martins* could, and as Darlington could have no better right than Morgan Grenfell had, no damages could be recovered. To make matters worse, as Morgan Grenfell never had a property interest, it was not their property that was subject to defective construction — and so they could have no loss to assign. So we would have another legal black hole through which the wrongdoer would escape scot-free. Dillon L.J. however took the "rational legal system" end result of *St. Martins* by a different route. Morgan Grenfell he said stood in a fiduciary relationship to Darlington and were constructive trustees for them of the benefit of any rights under or for breach of the building contracts. As Morgan Grenfell could have sued in that capacity, there was something to assign, and Waite L.J. concurred. The bases of these opinions in the law of "constructive trust", is entirely novel from a Scots law point of view in circumstances such as these, and should be approached with caution.[64] Steyn L.J. found it unnecessary to consider the question of 'constructive trust,' and seemed to regard this case as one to be approached on the same broad principles of Lord Browne-Wilkinson's speech in *Linden Gardens,* and indeed the wider principle of Lord Griffiths in that case.

The wider principle can be broadly stated that if an employer engages a builder to perform specified work, and the builder fails to render the contractual service, the employer's loss is recoverable irrespective of whether he owns or has an interest in the property which requires the remedial work, *i.e.* the loss is not only that of the proprietor, but of the employer who did not get what he bargained for. Steyn L.J. said it was of no concern to the contractor who was in breach what the employer intended to do with those damages, by analogy with sale of goods cases, nor even that the employer proposed to undertake the necessary repairs. This last point that the employer need not even propose to carry out the repairs went much further than even Lord Griffiths in *Linden Gardens,* and would appear to be unsettled.

---

[64] For the concepts of "constructive trust" generally see T.B. Smith, *Short Commentary*, p. 561; Burgess, "Thoughts on the origin of the trust in Scotland" (1974) J.R. 196 at 210; Norrie, K., and Scobie, E., *Trusts* (W. Green, 1991), pp. 53–58.

4.168　　This difficult area of law has been taken further in *Alfred McAlpine Construction Ltd v. Panatown Ltd*[65] where the Court of Appeal held that the employer under a building contract who was not the owner of the land could sue for damages, even where the contractor had entered into a separate warranty with the owner of the land.

Scottish response

4.169　　However, *St. Martins* has been cited in argument in Scotland in *Steel Aviation Services v. H. Allan & Son Ltd*.[66] In *Steel* the pursuers ran a concession from premises at Glasgow Airport which was owned by Glasgow Airport Ltd, and for which Steel had no lease. Steel entered into a building contract for works to the premises, works were allegedly defectively done, and Steel subsequently sued for losses for the diminution in value of the premises as a business asset. The pursuers were at the debate stage allowed to sue although they had no proprietary interest in the property, making this case closer to the *Darlington* one. The court did not require to analyse the Scottish position as the defenders dropped their arguments against Steel's right to sue in this case.

4.170　　In Scotland, it is well settled that what might almost be called the converse[67] of the *St. Martin's* position exists. This is the *jus quaesitum tertio,* where the contracting parties provide that a third party should have the right to sue under that contract.[68] Indeed in the *Darlington* case, Steyn L.J. thought that the absence of the power to create such a right for a third party was a factor in the need to find a solution to the "black hole" problems in assignment cases.[69] The efficacy of the *jus quaesitum tertio* is probably rather limited in the context of most construction contract arrangements as currently drafted, as in *Strathford East Kilbride v. HLM Design Ltd*[70] in circumstances where the employer had been the Ford Motor Company, and a car dealership was constructed to be operated by the pursuers as tenant and an affiliate company of the employer, the *jus quaesitum tertio* was rejected. It is precisely in these sort of circumstances that the need for so-called "collateral warranties" between contractor and tenant or funder have become prevalent.[71]

---

[65]　(1998) 58 Con. L.R. 47, AC.

[66]　1996 G.W.D. 28–1699.

[67]　MacQueen, "Assignation and Breach of Contract" (1997) 2 S.L.P.Q.

[68]　See *Scott Lithgow Ltd v. GEC Electrical Projects Ltd*, 1989 S.C. 412.

[69]　*op.cit* at 76–78. The Law Commission of England and Wales has published a comprehensive overview of the current position and published a draft Bill to remove the difficulties of privity of contract and assignment in "Privity of Contract: Contracts for the benefit of Third parties (Law. Comm. No. 242), July 31, 1996: http://www.gtnet.gov.uk/lawcomm/library/lc242/app-a.htm. The Contracts (Rights of Third Parties) Bill had reached Committee stage on February 2, 1999. It is not to apply to Scotland.

[70]　1997 S.C.L.R. 877.

[71]　In Scotland the SBCC publish Standard Forms of Agreement for a Collateral Warranty by a Main Contractor to a Purchaser or Tenant, 1994 ed. MCWa/P&T/Scot (Purchaser and Tenant) August 1998 revision; also to a funder, MCWa/F/Scot (Funder) (August 1998 revision). It has recently been suggested that greater use should be made of the *jus quaesitum tertio* rather than collateral warranties in Scotland: see Macauley and Wedderburn "Collateral Warranties — An Unnecessary Encumbrance?" 1999 S.L.T. 23.

Sub-Contracting

Clause 19.2.1 provides that where any portion of the works is sub-let, other than to a Nominated Sub-Contractor, that person is to be referred as a "Domestic Sub-Contractor". Clause 19.2.2 provides that the contractor shall not, without written consent of the Architect (which consent shall not be unreasonably withheld), sub-let any part of the Works.

Clause 19.3 provides for a sort of hybrid between domestic sub-contracting where the contractor chooses the sub-contractor, and nominated sub-contracting under Part 2 of the JCT conditions. Clause 19.3 provides for the appointment of a Domestic Sub-Contractor, who must carry out the part of the Works, from a list of three contained in the Contract Bills at the sole discretion and choice of the Contractor. This list may be added to by consent of both Employer and Contractor. This is a sort of back-door nominated sub-contracting, what used to be called "named sub-contracting". The difference is that under this sub-clause, the Contractor makes the decision, whereas under clause 30 (for Nominated Sub-Contractors), the Employer makes the decision. Clause 19.4 stipulates conditions that shall exist for Domestic Sub-Contractors which relate to automatic determination of the sub-contract on determination of the main contract. As has been discussed above[72] such provisions have to be "stepped down" and will not readily be implied. Amendment 18 introduces a new step-down provision in clause 19.4.3, which is optional, relating to interest on unpaid sums due to a sub-contractor. This corresponds to the new provision in clause 30.1.1.1 *vis-à-vis* the Employer and the Contractor.[73] Clause 19.4.2 in relation to property in unfixed materials and goods is deleted in the Scottish Building Contract.

The Scottish Building Contract Committee has recently published its own forms of sub-contract documentation (revised in August 1998), to replace the existing form DOM/1, copyright in which rested with the Building Employer's Confederation (now the Construction Confederation). It remains to be seen whether JCT will publish its own form of domestic sub-contract or will adopt a recently revised DOM/1. The current Scottish revision of Domestic Sub-Contract Conditions (Dom/C/Scot) takes into account the payment and notice provisions of the Housing Grants, Construction and Regeneration Act 1996 . The current Scottish Domestic Sub-Contract forms follow the style and procedure for letting nominated sub-contracts, in that there is an invitation to tender document (Tender Dom/T/Scot/Part1), a tender document (Tender Dom/T/Scot/Part 2), an agreement called the Scottish Building Sub-Contract (Sub-Contract Dom/A/Scot), and Domestic Sub-Contract Conditions (Dom/C/Scot). It should be noted that the use of these forms was provided for in the Scottish Building Contract

4.171

4.172

4.173

---

[72] See paras 3.19–3.22.
[73] See comments on clause 30.1.1.1.

September 1997 revision, by the insertion of a new clause 19A, but this clause 19A has been deleted by the April and August 1998 revisions. There is a side note added that the Scottish Building Contract Committee "publish standard forms of domestic Sub-Contracts and collateral warranties along with appropriate enabling clauses". The most recent Guidance Notes in respect of these documents issued by the SBCC provide that the documentation is not appropriate where the Domestic Sub-Contractor has design responsibilities. The SBCC Standard Form of Employer/Sub-Contractor Warranty Agreement (December 1997 ed., August 1998 revision) does provide for a warranty by the Sub-Contractor that he has exercised and will exercise all reasonable skill and care in the design of the Sub-Contract works in so far as they are designed by him.

4.174   The general position on liability is that the Contractor remains liable for carrying out and completing the works where any part is sub-let, either to a Domestic Sub-Contractor (clause 19.2.2) or a Nominated Sub-Contractor (clause 19.5.1). Indeed the Scottish Building Contract (August 1998 revision) also provides that the Employer shall not be liable to any Domestic Sub-contractor under clause 19; and features a highly ambiguous clause that seems to indicate that the Contractor will not be liable to the Employer if the SBCC Employer/Sub-Contractor Warranty is used. There may be particular problems if a Nominated Sub-Contractor repudiates and these are considered *post*.[74] But clause 19.5.2 provides that subject to clause 35.2 the Contractor is not himself required, unless otherwise agreed, to supply and fix materials or goods or to execute work which is to be carried out by a Nominated Sub-Contractor.

4.175   Amendment 18 introduced a new clause 19.4.3 in relation to Sub-Contracts and corresponds to the new provisions in clause 30.1.

Clause 20: Injury to persons and property and indemnity to Employer

Clause 21: Insurance against injury to persons or property

Clause 22: Insurance of the Works

4.176   These clauses deal with the often difficult questions of indemnity and insurance under JCT 80. Perhaps the first thing to note is that there is no requirement that a form of insurance be taken that insures that the works as completed will be free of latent defects. Such policies do exist and the Latham Report had proposed a legislative change so that a standard 10-year liability period be backed by single project insurance.[75] This was not enacted in the Housing Grants, Construction and Regeneration Act 1996.

---

[74] See paras 4.369–4.372.
[75] Recommendations 28 and 29 for Building Users Insurance Against Latent Defects (BUILD). The Government did not see a convincing argument for treating liability periods under construction contracts any differently from other cases, pending a Law Commission examination of limitation periods.

JCT indemnity and insurance provisions are concerned with questions 4.177
of liability during the course of the Works, which may extend only to
Practical Completion,[76] or beyond to the expiry of the Defects Liability
Period.[77] If what has been constructed causes death or injury, or damage to
other property, or poses a risk of these, after Practical Completion, then
separate questions arise concerning the effect of final certificates,[78]
prescription and limitation,[79] and the delictual liability associated with
defective buildings.[80]

Broadly a number of risks can be foreseen for which insurance is relevant. 4.178
The works may be damaged because of a design fault; the works may be
damaged as they progress by contractors' or sub-contractors' negligence at
common law or in the performance of the contract; the works may be
damaged through no fault (as for example where the works cannot be
sustained by the site), *force majeure* (or to use the more Scottish terminology
damnum fatale), or matters for which no insurance cover can be obtained.
Persons on site may die or be injured as a result of fault or breach of a
statutory duty. Other property adjacent to the Works may be damaged as a
result of the contractor's or sub-contractor's fault, or faulty design, or through
no fault. It is also possible to foresee that if the works are damaged they
will be delayed, with consequent financial losses.

The JCT 80 approach is for the Contractor to give a wide fault-based 4.179
indemnity under clause 20.1 for personal injury or death, and a wide fault-
based indemnity under clause 20.2 for damage to property (which does not
include the Works or Site Materials). Clause 21 then refers to two types of
insurance cover: the first to be taken by the Contractor for death or personal
injury, and damage to property; the second as instructed by the Architect
for damage to property to be taken in joint names with the Employer, broadly
for nuisance or stability risks to other property excluding the Works. In
relation to the Works themselves, Specified Perils have to be insured against
in joint names of the Employer and Contractor (with any Nominated Sub-
Contractors being recognised also) under "All Risks Insurance", and
differentiation is made between the erection of new buildings and works to
existing structures.

---

[76] *e.g.* clauses 22A.1, 22B.1 (erection of new buildings); and clause 22C.1 (insurance of
existing structures).

[77] Practice Note 22 says: "The Tribunal recommends Contractors and Sub-Contractors not to
terminate their insurance cover taken out in accordance with clause 2.1 until at least the
expiry of the Defects Liability Period or the date of the issue of the certificate of Completion
of Making good Defects whichever is the later. In no circumstances should such cover be
terminated at the date of Practical Completion and it may well be prudent to keep the cover
in force until the issue of the Final Certificate."

[78] see paras 4.15–4.18.

[79] see Chap. 3, paras 3.81–3.89.

[80] see Chap. 6.

4.180   In much the same way as the insurance industry markets "comprehensive" policies in motor insurance, so too in the area of construction projects there are a number of so-called "Contractor's All Risk" policies, which prompted Sir Godfray Le Quesne Q.C. in *Cementation Piling Foundations Ltd v. Aegon Insurance Company Ltd and Commercial Union*[81] at first instance to note: "Policies all bearing the title 'Contractors' All Risks Insurance' vary considerably in their terms." All Risks Insurance is defined in clause 22.2, as is what is to be excluded and required under the contract in terms of clauses 22A, B or C. The definition has been amended by Amendment16.

4.181   Most of these so-called "CAR" policies seek to exclude claims involving the repair of the contractor's defective work, or resulting from its design (under JCT 80 the Contractor would not normally be responsible for design in any case). For example, clause 22.2.2 excludes the cost necessary to repair, replace or rectify: "any work executed or any Site Materials lost or damaged as a result of its own defect in design, plan, specification, material or workmanship or any other work executed which is lost or damaged in consequence thereof where such work relied for its support or stability on such work which was defective".

4.182   In the *Cementation* case[82] the plaintiffs were sub-contractors in a land reclamation project where various quays were constructed at an existing dock. The works involved the depositing of sand over a large area to form a berm which protruded above sea level. Walls of concrete were then constructed in the sand. Once the walls for the quays were in place, the surrounding sand was dredged up so that sea water could flow into the newly constructed docks. It was found that sand was escaping into the dock because side panels of a piled diaphragm wall had parted due to defective design, materials and workmanship. *Cementation* were required to carry out remedial works to remove the sand from the docks, fill the voids that the sand had escaped from, and fix the joints, all at a cost of £442,000.

The Commercial Union policy was in the following terms:

> "The Insurers shall not be liable in respect of the cost of replacing or rectifying defects in design, materials or workmanship *unless the property insured suffers actual loss, destruction or damage as a result of such defect.* However *additional costs* of introducing improvements, betterment or corrections in the rectification of the design, materials or workmanship causing such loss or damage shall always be excluded [emphasis added]."

The Commercial Union had accepted the cost of removing the sand as damage to the dock, and the cost of filling the voids, as damage to the berm. They denied liability for fixing the joints on the basis that these had not been right in the first place, so that any repair was betterment. The fact

---

[81] [1993] 1 Lloyds Rep. 526; case was appealed [1995] 1 Lloyd's Rep. 97; 47 Con. L.R. 14.

[82] *ibid.* In which the judge at first instance described the relevant policy as a "perplexing document".

was that the other two parts of the work could not be successfully carried out till the gaps were fixed. The Court of Appeal did not think that in itself meant that the repairs to the joints were covered. However, the court held that the word "additional" was crucial in relation to betterment. This suggested something extra, and so did not preclude the costs of remedying the works to the condition they should have reached in the first place.

Similarly in *Kier Construction v. Royal Insurance (U.K.)*[83] the plaintiffs 4.183
had contracted to carry out pile-driving into the beach for the Sizewell B power station. In terms of the contract the employer required to take out a single site insurance policy in which all contractors and sub-contractors were named as insured parties. Part of the plaintiffs' works was the construction of two cofferdams using sheet steel piles. The piles were damaged arising out of ground conditions and the cofferdams were not watertight. It was held that the damage to the piles was an insured loss, and not a workmanship matter that might have been reasonably expected by the contractors. The exception in the policy for defective workmanship did not arise on the facts; and the term in the policy that the plaintiffs should at all times take reasonable precautions to prevent accidents or loss meant that they should not be reckless. Notice had not been given to the insurers "as soon as possible" as required by the policy, as there had been a four-week delay, but the insurers were held to have waived their objection by not complaining until two years after notification. Also, the excess of £500 on each occurrence related to each state of affairs on which the claim was based, not for each damaged pile.

Also, in *Hitchins (Hatfield) Ltd v. Prudential Assurance Co. Ltd*[84] the 4.184
contractor claimed under a contractor's combined policy when landslip occurred at a terraced site for a housing development. The houses were not damaged but the slopes had to be reinstated. The landslips were due to the presence of discrete shear surfaces within the clay on which the development took place. The plaintiffs argued that they had been put to the cost of de-watering the works by installing piling and drainage. The relevant clauses provided that insurance included: "damage to the property insured or any part thereof arising out of any fault defect error or omission in design plan specification material or workmanship". The clause continued: "(iv) no amount shall be admitted... due to redesigning... any part which is defectively designed." The Court of Appeal held that proviso (iv) did not refer back to the general cover, and that it could not be held to cover redesign where there was absence of negligence in the design. This was because different terminology was used: "defectively designed" may imply negligence, whereas a "fault... in design" may not. In this respect the Court of Appeal reversed the judge at first instance, and also said that as there

---

[83]   30 Con. L.R. 45.
[84]   [1991] 2 Lloyd's Rep. 580; 60 B.L.R. 51.

was ambiguity, that should be resolved in favour of the insured on the *contra proferentum* principle.[85]

4.185   The normal rule of law relating to insurance contracts that they are contracts *uberrimae fidei* applies in the construction context. In *St Paul Fire & Marine Insurance Co. (U.K.) Ltd v. McConnell Dowell Constructors Ltd*[86] it was held that there had been material non-disclosure so that the insurers could avoid the policy. Material non-disclosure did not mean that the insurers had to prove that the risk was increased in the light of the true facts, only that their estimate and appreciation of the risk would have been affected had they been aware of the true facts. In this case the contractors had built on shallow foundations which they described as piled foundations. It did not avail the contractors under the policy that there was a body of opinion that the foundations should have been adequate to prevent subsidence. There was a body of opinion also against the contractors, and in fact subsidence took place.

4.186   Clause 20.1 is a wide indemnity which the Contractor gives the Employer in respect of personal injury or death from carrying out the Works,[87] except "to the extent" due to neglect or fault for which the employer is responsible. The "to the extent" phrase was added by Amendment 2 in 1986. *Keating*[88] suggests that this change means that the Contractor's indemnity will still apply even where the Employer is partly liable with the Contractor for death or injury. This view accords with Guidance Note 22.[89]

---

[85] Note that for clause 22.2.2 the wording reads: "as a result of its own defect in design". In this respect the decision in *Queensland Government, Railways and Electric Power Transmission Pty Ltd v. Manfacturers Mutual Insurance Ltd* [1969] 1 Lloyds Rep. 214 would be relevant, *i.e.* "faulty design" being more comprehensive than "negligent design". Peculiarly in the light of the above decisions a footnote to clause 22 (which does not appear to have been deleted by Amendment 16) states: "In any policy for 'All Risks Insurance' taken out under clauses 22A, 22B or 22C.2 cover should not be reduced by the terms of any exclusion written in the policy... thus an exclusion in terms 'This policy excludes all loss of or damage to the property insured due to defective design, plan, specification, materials or workmanship' would not be in accordance with the terms of those clauses and of the definition of 'All Risks Insurance'". This note would seem to have misunderstood the decision of the Court of Appeal in *Hitchens (Hatfield)* illustrated in the text.

[86] [1996] 1 All E.R. 96; 45 Con. L.R. 89.

[87] On construction sites there is a 1:300 chance of being killed at work (Health and Safety Executive, "Key facts, Injuries in the Construction industry 1961–1996", p. 3); and the chances of being disabled by injury or serious illness are close to 1:100 . In the European Community as a whole 7% of employees work in construction but it accounts for 30% of fatal accidents: see E. Oliver Taylor, "Health and Safety in the Construction Industry", p. 7.

[88] 6th ed. at p. 609.

[89] The author tentatively doubts whether the rewording is unambiguous enough in this respect to defeat the decision in *AMF International v. Magnet Bowling* [1968] W.L.R. 1028; where the former wording "provided always that" meant the contractor's indemnity did not apply where the employer was also partly liable.

In fact, safety issues on construction sites are a highly regulated matter.[90]   4.187
But it is important to note that the regulatory framework is essentially
concerned with criminal liability, and indeed there is a specific exclusion of
any right of action in civil proceedings arising from breaches of:

   (a)   breaches of the general duties imposed by sections 2–8 of the Health &
        Safety at Work Act 1974 (s.47);
   (b)   breaches of any duty imposed by the Management of Health and Safety
        at Work Regulations 1992 (S.I. 1992 No. 2051);
   (c)   breaches of any duties imposed by the Construction (Design and
        Management) Regulations 1994, with the exception of two duties
        (regulation 21), namely —
       (i)   failure by the client to ensure a suitably developed health and safety
           plan is in place before work commences (regulation 10);
      (ii)   failure by the Principal Contractor to exclude unauthorised persons
           from the construction site (regulation 16(1)(c)).

In respect of other regulations that pertain to construction, on September   4.188
2, 1996 over 100 existing regulations were revoked and replaced by the
Construction (Health, Safety and Welfare) Regulations 1996.[91] The 1996
Regulations incorporate into U.K. law the requirements of Annex IV of the
European Directive 92/57[92] on the minimum health and safety requirements
at temporary or mobile construction sites, the first part of which was
introduced as the Construction (Design and Management) Regulations 1994.
These CDM Regulations were incorporated into JCT 80 by Amendment 14
(March 1995) and Practice Note 27 was issued.[93]

Although the statutory regime is largely concerned with criminal liability, the   4.189
common law position as regards general delictual duties of care to one's neighbour
remain.[94] Often a statutory duty, can be reformulated as a common law duty and
will succeed.[95] In other breach of statutory provisions cases, where civil liability
has not been specifically excluded, a claim for breach of a statutory duty can
succeed if it can be established that the statutory duty was imposed for the benefit
of the protection of a specific class of persons, and not the general pubic at large.[96]

---

[90] Any wide discussion of safety requirements and regulations is beyond the scope of this
    book. Readers are referred to the following loose leaf publications : Construction Industry
    Training Board *Construction Site Safety; Construction Health and Safety Manual*, Vols 1
    and 2 published by Construction Industry Press Ltd; and the very useful *Croner's
    Management of Construction Safety*, Croner.
[91] (S.I. 1996 No. 1592). The only construction regulations which remain are: Construction
    (Lifting Operations) Regulations 1961 (S.I. 1961 No. 1581); Construction (Head Protection)
    Regulations 1989 (S.I. 1989 No. 2209).
[92] [1992] O.J. L245.
[93] See comments for clause 6A at para. 4.49.
[94] For example, where pipes to be installed under a public road were left so that children might be
    attracted to them and so form a hazard if rolled, it was held a breach of a common law duty might
    be established after proof: *Galbraith's Curator ad Litem v. Stewart*, 1997 S.L.T. 418.
[95] Typically such duties might rest with employers, contractors and sub-contractors, and designers.
[96] See *Murphy v. Brentwood District Council* [1991] 1. A.C. 398; also *Pullar v. Window
    Clean Ltd*, 1956 S.C. 13.

4.190   As regards property other than the Works, clause 21.2.1 provides that insurance at the option of the Employer may be required to be taken by the Contractor in Joint Names[97], as defined to include others who are "recognised". Insurance is to be for any expense, liability, loss, claim or proceedings which the Employer may incur caused by such matters as collapse, subsidence, heave, vibration, weakening or withdrawal of support or lowering of ground water. There are certain exclusions which are to reflect model exclusions which the Association of British Insurers have compiled. These are: damage for which the Contractor is liable under clause 20.2; damage attributable to errors or omissions in the designing of the Works, which can be reasonably foreseen to be inevitable having regard to the nature of the work to be executed or the manner of its execution; damage which it is the reponsibility of the Employer to insure under clause 22C.1 (if applicable), and damage arising from war or the Excepted Risks.

4.191   In *Duncan's Hotel (Glasgow) Ltd v. J. & A. Ferguson Ltd*[98] a fire in a shop which was underneath a hotel led to the reconstruction of the shop. Specialist sub-contractors were instructed initially to sink a pile to bedrock. If this proved successful the piling contractors were to be nominated for the rest of the work. As a result of the piling works the upper storeys owned by the hotel suffered settlement. The piling work was done all the while without a building warrant having been granted. The pursuer chose not to sue the piling contractor, but to sue the employer, main contractor and structural engineers. It was held in the Outer House that the piling contractor had not been negligent:

> "The decision to pile was not theirs, all they were concerned with was whether piling was feasible. They thought it was, and their experience with the first pile confirmed them in that view. What the consequences of the operation might be was a matter not for them, who were simply carrying out instructions, but for those who instructed it, *viz.* the engineers."

Lord Stott did however hold that the works as carried out and continued with were a nuisance and the piling contractors could not point to the instructions of the engineers to absolve them. The employers were liable because they could not avoid responsibility for this nuisance on the basis that they had appointed independent contractors. In addition the work had been illegal as it had been carried out without first obtaining a building warrant. However the main contractors were not similarly liable for the hazardous works of the piling contractor:

---

[97] The need for joint names insurance was exemplified in *Gold v. Patman & Fotheringham Ltd* [1958] 1 W.L.R. 697 (AC) where it was held that where there were building operations which without negligence caused damage to adjacent property, there was no implied duty on the contractor to insure so as to protect the employer.
[98] 1974 S.C. 191.

"No doubt, in a sense, the contractor in employing a sub-contractor is appointing someone to do part of his work for him. But the work is being done not for him but for the building employer, and there is no compelling reason to assume that in delegating part of the work to a sub-contractor he is to be taken as accepting responsibility for the sub-contractor's delicts. His obligations, unlike those of the employer, do not stem from occupation or possession or interest in the end-product of the work, but merely from the terms of his contract, and if the terms of the contract do not include an acceptance of the sub-contractor's delicts, it is difficult to find any principle of law apt to impose such a liability on him.' No liability without *culpa'* is a principle well rooted in the law of delict, and, outmoded and anomalous as the principle may be, it must remain the criterion for determination of liability in delict until Parliament decides otherwise."[99]

With Lord Stott's words in mind, the question is why has clause 20.2 been   4.192
drafted the way it has? Is this an attempt to change the common law responsibility of a contractor for the negligence of a sub-contractor or not? *Keating*[1] says the point is not free from difficulty.

The law in the area of damages for nuisance caused to adjoining   4.193
landowners has changed recently, as the House of Lords has held that *culpa* or negligence is also essential to establish a claim in nuisance.[2] And since *Kennedy v. Glenbelle Ltd*[3] in Scotland, any invasion of another's land, such as in this case where there had been the removal of a load bearing wall, must exceed what is reasonably tolerable for there to be a remedy in nuisance. In England it has again been held in the Lords[4] that it is necessary that the harm done to neighbouring landowners' property be foreseeable before there could be recovery of damages under the rule of strict liability in *Rylands v. Fletcher.*[5]

Under clause 22A, where new buildings are being erected, the Contractor   4.194
is required to take out a Joint Names Policy for All Risks for the full reinstatement value of the works, plus a percentage to cover professional fees[6] stated in the Appendix (Appendix II in Scotland). The policy is to be maintained up to the date of issue of the Practical Completion Certificate or up to and including the date of determination of the employment of the Contractor

---

[99] This decision was recently followed in the Outer House by Lord Abernethy in *MTM Construction Ltd v. William Reid Engineering Ltd* 1997 S.C.L.R. 778. In this case a fire was started allegedly through the negligence of a welding sub-sub-contractor, and Lord Stott's opinion was said to fit with the Court of Appeal in *Honeywill and Stein Ltd v. Larkin Brothers Ltd* [1934] 1 K.B. 191.

[1] May, *Keating on Building Contracts* (6th ed.), p. 610.

[2] *RHM Bakeries (Scotland) Ltd v. Strathclyde Regional Council*, 1985 S.C. (H.L.) 17.

[3] 1996 S.C. 95.

[4] [1994] 1 All E.R. 426.

[5] (1868) L.R. 3 H.L. 330.

[6] A professional who provides, for example, engineering services, would not normally be covered as a contractor under a contractor's All Risks Policy otherwise: *Hopewell Project Management Ltd v. Ewebank Preece Ltd* (unreported), C.I.L.L. October 1997, p. 1310.

under clause 27 or clause 28 or clause 28A (whether or not the validity of the determination is contested), whichever is the earlier. Provision also exists for the furnishing of proof of the taking out of such a policy, or the Employer may take over that obligation. Where a claim is made, the occurrence of such loss shall be disregarded in computing any amounts due to the Contractor. The Contractor then has to restore the damaged works, replace or repair any Site Materials which have been lost or damaged, remove and dispose of any debris and proceed to complete. The Contractor shall be paid for this under interim certificates only from those monies recovered under the policy. Under clause 22B, still for the erection of new buildings, the Employer rather than the Contractor takes out an All Risks policy with similar provisions to 22A applying. Under clause 22C, the Employer is required to take out a Joint Names policy where the works are alterations of and extensions to existing structures, and also insure in respect of their contents for full reinstatement, repair, or replacement of loss or damage[7] due to one or more of the Specified Perils up to Practical Completion, determination etc. The Specified Perils in the definitions section include fire, lightning, explosion,[8] storm,[9] tempest, flood bursting or overflowing of water tanks,[10] apparatus or pipes, earthquake, aircraft or other aerial devices or articles dropped therefrom, riot and civil commotion, but excluding Excepted Risks. If the Employer defaults in taking out such a policy, the Contractor may do so, and any premiums are added to the Contract Sum (clause 22C.3).

In the case only of existing buildings it seems, in terms of clause 22C.4.3.1 the employment of the contractor may be determined within 28 days of the occurrence of such loss or damage at the option of either party "where it is just and equitable to do so", which is, since Amendment 18, a matter that may be challenged under the new procedures for the resolution of disputes or differences.

4.195   The provision requiring a Joint Names Policy is the construction industry's way of getting round the difficulties of subrogation in insurance contracts, which normally give the insurer the rights to seek recovery of sums paid to the insured from the party at fault by effectively having the right to pursue the matter under the cloak of the identity of the insured. A joint names policy has the effect of creating a closed circle of protected parties[11] and has been said to enable continuity amongst the contracting parties, without the risk of the party in

[7]   This has been held not to mean a requirement to obtain compulsory insurance by the employer for loss of profit from and increased cost of working in a business carried on in those structures: the contractor remains liable, *Kruger Tissue (Industrial) Ltd v. Frank Galliers Ltd*, 57 Con. L.R. 1.

[8]   *Commonwealth Smelting v. Guardian Royal Exchange* [1986] 1 Lloyd's Rep. 121.

[9]   *Glasgow Training Group (Motor Trade) Ltd v. Lombard Continental plc*, 1989 S.L.T. 375; 1989 S.C. 30: a heavy fall of snow constituted a storm causing a roof to collapse.

[10] To be construed intransitively, *i.e.* not negligently fractured as when a purlin was dropped — *Computer & Systems Engineering plc v. John Lelliot (Ilford) Ltd and EWG Stoddart Ltd* [1991] 54 B.L.R. 1.

[11] *Petrofina (U.K.) Ltd v. Magnaload Ltd* [1983] 3 All E.R. 35.

default going into insolvency because of exposure to such risks. However the courts have sometimes been a little hard to follow on this question of circuity of insured parties on the basis that there is a reluctance, for example, to let a contractor who negligently burns down a building escape the cost of reinstating it where he has given an indemnity to the employer for any expense, liability, loss, claim or proceedings etc. arising from his negligence; such as in clause 20.2 of JCT 80.

In order to follow the current JCT position it is necessary to consider the changes in wording which clause 20 has gone through, and particularly the effect of Amendment 2 issued in November 1986 following the House of Lord's decision in *Scottish Special Housing Association v. Wimpey.*[12] Amendment 2 is a substantial amendment and with the accompanying Practice Note 22 and Guide it is noted in the Foreword that the JCT had not until then reviewed these provisions, and that they had been substantially the same in JCT 63. As noted above, clause 20.1 provides that the Contractor shall indemnify the Employer in wide terms for death or personal injury caused by the carrying out of the works except where the Employer, or those for whom the Employer is responsible, are negligent. Clause 20.2 would, at first sight, appear to do the same for damage to property belonging to the Employer, including the Works,[13] but the Contractor's obligation is now qualified by clause 20.3.1 (introduced by Amendment 2, November 1986) which defines such property as not including the Works up to Practical Completion, or determination of the Contractor's employment, and that the Contractor's obligation is also subject to clause 22C.1 (existing structure where Employer takes out a Joint Names Policy) *where applicable* (emphasis added). Quite what "where applicable" meant in Amendment 2 was open to interpretation, and replaced the original 1980 wording which was effectively considered in *Scottish Special Housing Association v. Wimpey* (although a JCT 63 case).

In *Scottish Special* the Lords had to decide if the insurance provisions of the contract meant that, even if a fire to existing structures (where fire is a Specified Peril and as such a risk to be insured by the Employer) is caused by the negligence of the Contractor, has the Employer agreed to exempt the Contractor from the consequences of his own wrong and any indemnity? A court of six judges held it did, reversing the Inner House, and the Contractor was not liable when he caused the fire. Amendment 2, straight after that (November 1986), changes the wording of the Contractor's indemnity clause 20.2 from "except for such loss and/or damage as is at the sole risk of the Employer under clause 22B or 22C (if applicable)" to "The Contractor

4.196

4.197

[12] [1986] 1 W.L.R. 995.
[13] As held in *Surrey Heath Borough Council v. Lovell Construction* [1990] 48 B.L.R. 108 (CA) — a decision on the identical pre-Amendment 2 terms in the 1981 JCT with Contractor's Design form.

shall, subject to clause 20.3 and, where applicable, clause 22C.1 be liable for...". So, in the redrafting the Employer's "sole risk" phrase has vanished for Specified Perils; and in clause 22C.1 for insurance to existing structures a Joint Names Policy becomes required for the existing structures and contents against the Specified Perils; and under clause 20.3 the Works and/or Site Materials were excluded property for the purposes of the contractor's indemnity; but under clause 22C.2 a Joint Names All Risks policy is required which necessarily would have to cover work executed and Site Materials according to the definition of all risks in clause 22.2. The question is would the *Scottish Special Housing Association* case be construed differently if the same circumstances — damage to existing structures — were to arise under the Amendment 2 wording.

4.198   *Keating*[14] states: "The effect of the change of wording does not appear to be great. If the existing structures are damaged by a Specified Peril, such damage remains, it is thought, at the sole risk of the Employer whether or not caused by the negligence of the Contractor."[15] The JCT have tried again with Amendment 16 issued in July 1996 to clarify the point, so that amended clause 20.2 removes the Amendment 2 verbiage of "where applicable, clause 22C.1" discussed above, and now says that the Contractor's indemnity clause excludes loss or damage caused by a Specified Peril if insurance of the existing structures clause is taken in terms of the contract. Therefore the conclusion in *Scottish Special Housing* has been accepted by the JCT as correct.

4.199   As regards sub-contractors who negligently set fire to existing structures there has also been considerable judicial activity. In *Aberdeen Harbour Board v. Heating Enterprises (Aberdeen) Ltd*,[16] Aberdeen Harbour Board owned property which it let, and which in turn was sub-let to Ferrranti, the employer under a JCT 63 contract. Heating Enterprises were nominated sub-contractors for plumbing works, under the July 1976 revision of the standard form, and allegedly caused a fire as a result of their own negligence in the use of blow torches. As in the *Scottish Special*[17] case, under the main contract, fire was a specified peril which was at the sole risk of the employer

---

[14]   *Building Contracts* (6th ed.) at pp. 607–608 and at p. 622.
[15]   With respect to the learned author, it is submitted that the Employer's sole risk for Specified Perils was simply dropped, in favour of the simple resolution to the problems of *res perit domino*, or if the peril is the result of negligence, by requiring a Joint Names Policy. Nevertheless, Keatings' view was approved in *Kruger Tissue (Industrial) Ltd v. Frank Galliers Ltd*, 57 Con. L.R. 1 at p. 6. The Lord Chancellor in *British Telecommuniations v. Thomson*, December 10, 1998 (House of Lords web page) said: "It is true that insofar as the existence of the obligation on the Employer to take out insurance against the Specified Perils in respect of existing structures relieves the main contractor from responsibility that he otherwise would have had for the negligence of sub contractors under clause 20.2, the risk of [a domestic sub contractor's] actions causing such loss as part of the responsibility of the main contractor will be covered." Printed copy: 1999 S.C. (H.L.) 9.
[16]   1989 S.C.L.R. 716; 1990 S.L.T. 416.
[17]   1986 S.L.T. 599.

and for which he was to insure the existing structures under clause 20 [C]. Heating Enterprises argued that as they were deemed to have knowledge of the main contract terms by the sub-contract, they were entitled to have it implied into their sub-contract that the employer bore the sole risk of fire, and should indemnify them. Under clause 18 of the main contract the contractor had a general obligation to indemnify the employer against damage or injury as a result of carrying out the works, subject to the sole risks under clause 20 for which the employer was to insure, including fire. The House of Lords in *Scottish Special Housing* had held that for precisely the same main contract conditions, the main contractor was indemnified from the consequences of his own negligence. Heating Enterprises said they should be in the same position *vis-a-vis* the employer. However it was held, at first instance by Lord Clyde, that the circumstances here were different. The difference was that here the employer was not the owner of the premises: it was the owner who was suing for losses and clause 20 [C] was not framed to cover his losses, and from the defender's point of view clause 20[C] was inappropriately drafted to give the defender the protection sought as it did not require both employer and owner to insure. In any event it was held that an obligation on the employer to insure did not lead to the necessary implication that a positive obligation to indemnify was to be implied in favour of a sub-contractor. Clause 20 [C] required insurance, but only in the name of the employer and not, as in clause 20[A], in the joint names of employer and contractor. This suggested to Lord Clyde that clause 20 [C] was for the employer's benefit, and not for the benefit of creating a right of relief under the policy for the main contractor or sub-contractors; especially so as regards a sub-contractor with whom the employer had no direct contractual relationship. Lord Clyde also was of the view that clause 20[C] did not cover such matters as the owner's losses, such as loss of rent from the employer. Lord Clyde said (pp. 766–767):

> "The problem in the present case appears to have arisen because of the fact that the employer was the occupier of only part of the larger premises and indeed was not even the proprietor of that part. When the Employer owns and occupies the whole premises the whole interest in the property will be his and the clause should operate without difficulty. No question of indemnity would arise. The loss would be that of the employer and he having undertaken the whole risk there is no liability on the Contractor or the Sub-Contractor even for their own negligence. Where there are other persons than the Employer interested in the building then the clause may be ill suited to cover the situation... in my view they should have amended the standard condition at the time of entering the contract and the court should not try to improve the contract for them."

The case was appealed[18] and Lord Clyde was upheld, but several other 4.200 interesting points were made. Lord Dunpark said that "the existing

---

[18] *Aberdeen Harbour Board v. Heating Enterprises Ltd*, 1990 S.L.T. 416

structures" used in clause 20[C] were not defined, but should be construed as qualified by the phrase "together with the contents thereof owned by him or for which he was responsible", so that the tenant/employer must also own or be responsible for the existing structures and the contents before having to insure them. At the very least the existing structures could not include parts of the building not occupied by the employer. Lord Cullen was of the opinion that if there had been an insurable interest then the employer could not recover from the sub-contractor even for the nominated sub-contractor's own negligence (p. 423 J-K). His Lordship agreed with the decision in *Norwich City Council v. Harvey*[19] that if the sub-contractor had contracted on the basis that the employer had accepted the risk of fire it was neither just or reasonable to regard a sub-contractor as being under a duty of care to the employer in regard to loss or damage caused by the sub-contractor's negligence.[20] This last delictual point was to re-emerge in *British Telecommunications plc v. James Thomson & Sons (Engineers) Ltd.*[21]

4.201　　This was another case which dealt with a fire, again caused by a sub-contractor's negligence (this time a domestic sub-contractor) to existing structures. This main contract was JCT 80, including Amendment 2. The Inner House (Lord Morison dissenting) approved Lord Rodger's[22] decision at first instance when he said:

> "It seems to me, applying the approach of Lord Clyde and Lord Cullen in *Aberdeen Harbour Board* and the Court of Appeal in *Norwich City Council*, that in the circumstances averred the court should not impose upon the defenders a duty of care to BT since the result of doing so would be to allow BT to sue the defenders in negligence for a loss for which BT had in effect agreed to look to their insurers, as the defenders must have known from the terms both of their tender and of the order. Such a claim in delict would cut across the commercial arrangements embodied in the main contract and the sub contract by exposing the defenders to a liability which did not accord with those arrangements and against which defenders would have been entitled to insure".

4.202　　However, in the Lords the Amendment 2 language was used as the basis for distinguishing the previous cases. It was held that the joint names policy did not specifically have to provide for domestic sub-contractors, and in this case did not. Indeed clause 22.3.2 provided for recognition of domestic sub-contractors but not where clause 22C.1 applied for existing structures. In short there was no reason in fairness why there should not be a duty of

---

[19] (1988) 4 Const. L.J. 217.

[20] It should also be noted that this case only concerned issues between the employer and the sub-contractor; the sub-contractor still had rights against the main contractor under clauses 4 and 5 of the Standard Form of Subcontract for Nominated Subcontractors (July 1976 revision).

[21] 1997 S.L.T. 767; overruled by House of Lords on December 10, 1998, see House of Lords web page. Printed copy: 1999 S.C. (H.L.) 9.

[22] Currently Lord President Rodger.

care owed by the domestic sub-contractors to the employers. Although the point does not appear to have been raised, this is precisely what is stated in Practice Note 22. The fact that there could then be double insurance covering the main contractor, and if separately taken out the domestic sub-contractor, was thought not to be a bar against imposing the duty of care on the domestic sub-contractor. The insurers of the main contractor could adjust their premium accordingly depending on whether they retained subrogation rights or not.

The wording used in the JCT Minor Works form (January 1987) differs   4.203
again from JCT 80, and in *National Trust for Places of Historic Interest v. Haden Young Ltd*[23] the Court of Appeal held that for a sub-contractor who was negligent in leaving a blow torch unattended there was no circularity with the employer who had a contract with the main contractor. There was an overlap of insurance, and *Scottish Special Housing Association* was distinguished. *Haden Young* was recently followed in the Court of Appeal for another Minor Works contract (October 1988 revision) in *Barking and Dagenham London Borough Council v. Stamford Asphalt.*[24]

Lastly, and rarely seen by the author in practice, the Architect may under   4.204
clause 22D require the Contractor to obtain insurance against the Employer's loss of liquidated damages in the event of an extension of time, because of a Specified Peril for which the Employer is responsible, such as fire. The existence of clause 22D, whether operated or not, has been held to be no bar to the recovery by the Employer of consequential losses which are covered by the Contractor's indemnity.[25]

Amendment 16 issued in July 1996 makes significant changes to the   4.205
insurance provisions of JCT 80. The definition of All Risks Insurance now includes "the reasonable cost of the removal and disposal of debris and of any shoring or propping of the Works which results from such physical loss or damage." The Joint Names Policy has been redefined; the only cryptic guide from the Guidance Notes is that the change was made "in view of a recent court decision". The changed wording now reads "Joint Names Policy: a policy of insurance which includes the Employer and the Contractor as the insured and under which the insurers have no right of recourse against any person named as an insured, or, pursuant to clause 22.3, recognised as an insured thereunder."

Amendment 17 issued in May 1997 introduces a new clause 22FC in   4.206
respect of compliance with the Joint Fire Code which is published by several parties as defined.

It is perhaps not often realised that the JCT when issuing Practice Note 22 also provided various model clauses where the Employer does not insure and takes the risk or the sole risk for the Works and/or existing structures.[26]

---

[23]   (1994) 72 B.L.R. 1 (CA).
[24]   *The Times*, April 10, 1997.
[25]   *Kruger Tissue (International) Ltd v. Frank Galliers Ltd* (1998) 57 Con. L.R. 1.
[26]   Model Clauses 22E, 22F, 22G, 22H, 22J, 22K; and also corresponding clauses for nominated sub-contracts.

Clause 23 Date of Possession, completion and postponement

4.207   This clause deals with the giving of possession of the site to the Contractor, which should be distinguished from access to the site.[27] Clause 23.1.1 involves another restatement of the Contractor's obligations in addition to those in clause 2 (in compliance with the Contract Documents) and clause 8 (proper and workmanlike manner) so that on the Date of Possession "the Contractor... shall thereupon begin the Works, regularly and diligently proceed with the same and shall complete the same on or before the Completion Date." Clause 23.1.2 allows the Employer to defer the giving of possession of the site for a period not exceeding six weeks. This is a "Relevant Event" for the purposes of an extension of time under clause 25.4.13, and a matter that requires the Architect to ascertain the amount of direct loss and/or expense to the Contractor under clause 26.1, or for any Nominated Sub-Contractor under clause 26.4.1.

4.208   Under clause 23.2 the Architect may issue instructions in regard to the postponement of any work to be executed under the contract, which has similar time and money consequences as clause 23.1.2. There is no stipulation as to reasonableness for the Employer deferring possession or postponing work, and the Employer would appear to be bound to pay direct loss and/or expense however innocently he acts in invoking these clauses. It may be that at common law a claim would only otherwise lie against an employer if he acted unreasonably. In *G. Mackay & Son v. Police Commissioners of Leven*[28] there was a clause which allowed the employer to reserve the right to appoint the time when the contractors could enter on the lands and proceed with the works subject to an extension of time. As the employer was negotiating over a compulsory purchase of the land, there was a delay of six months for giving possession of part of the site at first, and ultimately more than 12 months for giving possession of the entire site. Lord Adam in the First Division said: "But it is not said that they [the employer] acted in any way unfairly, or for the purpose of delay, in acquiring possession of the ground."[29] It was held that in terms of the contract there was no room for an award of damages to the contractor in the absence of any special grounds being pled.

4.209   Were there not a deferral of possession clause it is arguable that, in the absence of an express provision, failure to give possession of the site at the contractual date would not be a material breach of contract, entitling the contractor to rescind in any case.[30] But perhaps the extent of deferral would make matters material, or if the contractor specified a future date during a period of unreasonable delay as one which would become material or "of the essence".[31] It does seem plain however that where there is an act or

---

[27] See earlier discussions in relation to clause 18 at paras 4.145–4.146.
[28] (1893) 20 R. 1093.
[29] *ibid.* at 1101.
[30] See Lord Dundas in *T. & R. Duncanson v. Scottish County Investments*, 1915 S.C. 1106 at 1113.
[31] For a general illustration of the point and discussion of the similarity of Scots and English law see: *Visionhire v. Britel Fund Trustees Ltd*, 1991 S.L.T. 883 at 886–888, *per* Lord President Hope.

omission by the employer through which he does not give the contractor: "possession of the subjects within a reasonable period after the execution of the contract, the contractor is not bound by the original time limit fixed; nor is the contract time necessarily only extended by the period during which the employer's omission has continued."[32] A contractor will be liable to the employer for the delays of his own sub-contractors, but there is a special difficulty where other contractors are working alongside him, that were not chosen by him. In *Duncanson v. Scottish County Investments*[33] where it was argued by an employer that a joinery contractor who had agreed to complete his part of the works on a specific date, but was prevented from so doing by separate trades (specifically the plasterer), who were late in carrying out other "departments" of the works, was nevertheless bound to complete by the date which the joiner agreed. This was rejected in the Inner House. Lord Dundas said: "it seems to me that the pursuers were entitled, as a condition precedent, to obtain timeous access to the physical subject on which their work was to be performed; and that, if this were withheld from them by any cause, they would be proportionally freed from the operation of the time limit." Lord Dundas also added *obiter dicta* that if the delay was due to frost preventing another trades contractor completing an antecedent part of the works, that would release the time limit too; even though bad weather would normally be at the risk of the contractor. Lord Salveson considered this whole question of co-ordinating trades to a time limit, including associated risks with weather, "a very difficult question of law" and appeared disinclined to accept Lord Dundas' view:

> "It is however in evidence that the pursuers were informed at the time when they entered into the contract as to the dates when the mason and other tradesmen were taken bound to finish; and it was on that footing that they undertook the obligation with regard to time to which I have already referred. Had, therefore, the case depended entirely on our accepting the pursuers' construction of the contract, I should have hesitated to affirm it. I think it would have been more reasonable to hold in such a case that each contractor took the risk of the other fulfilling his contract by the stipulated date, than that the building owner, who had bound each of them to a specified time, should take the risk. The tradesmen who are jointly engaged upon a building are necessarily in constant touch with each other; and it would be their duty to see that each fulfilled his part of the obligation so as to enable his successors to fulfil theirs, rather than that the duty should be laid upon the building owner who has bound each of them to a specified time. There appears to me to be nothing essentially unjust in this; for, if the joiner is made responsible, I see no reason why he should not have relief against the tradesman who was actually to blame, although it is true there is no express contractual relation between them. On paying such damages as were due to the failure to complete

---

[32] *Duncanson v. Scottish County Investments, op. cit., per* Lord Salvesen at 1117.
[33] *ibid.*

by the stipulated date he would probably be entitled to an assignation of the building owner's contractual rights against the other tradesmen. Be this as it may, all that could be said would be that the joiner had made an improvident contract, and had accepted risks in order to obtain the contract which had resulted in his having to pay damages on which he had not reckoned. Certainly the building owner would have more prospect of obtaining his house by the stipulated time, if each contractor knew that he would be held responsible and would not be able to blame all or any of the others who were associated with him. I do not find it necessary for the decision of this case to solve this very difficult question of law."

Lord Salvesen's eventual decision was that the contractor was not bound to the completion date because the employer had failed to tie the preceding trade to an exact date. Lord Guthrie's decision was that he agreed with both Lord Salvesen and Lord Dundas' reasons for not holding the contractor to the time period, and his Lordship found particular support for Lord Dundas' judgment from American decisions: "A person employing another person to do certain work impliedly agrees to keep such work far enough in advance to enable such person to perform his work in the time agreed upon, and the builder is not liable when the owner does not do so."[34]

4.210   Clause 23.3 was inserted by Amendment 2 issued in November 1986 and covers partial use or occupation of the site by the Employer with the Contractor's consent prior to Practical Completion. This clause is similar in effect to partial possession under clause 18 which was also changed by Amendment 2. The common aim of these two clauses appears to be to allow partial possession or use by an Employer of part of the site prior to Practical Completion without invalidating the insurance cover.[35] Accordingly for the Employer to occupy part of the site for storage or otherwise (no help is given as to what "or otherwise" means) the consent of the insurers is necessary. Clause 23.1 provides: "For the purposes of the Works insurances the Contractor shall retain possession of the site and the Works" (up to Practical Completion). This again raises the question of insurable interest[36] and the basis in Scots law of whether the contractor has any property right over the site, which is relevant to transfer of title of goods amongst other matters.[37]

Clause 24: Damages for non-completion

4.211   This is the liquidated and ascertained damages (L&AD) clause, which as will be seen is closely linked in practice with the succeeding clause 25 which deals with extensions of time. To that extent the clause heading is misleading, as clause 24 is not concerned with total failure to complete, but rather failure to complete on time.

---

[34] *Nash's Cyclopaedia of Law Procedure* (1903, New York), Vol. 6 at page 72, citing *Taylor v. Renn* 79 Illinois, 181.
[35] See JCT Practice Note 22 at p. 28.
[36] See Lord Dunpark's comments in *Aberdeen Harbour Board v. Heating Enterprises* at para. 4.200.
[37] See generally, comments regarding clause 16 *ante*.

A substantial body of case law concerning L&AD clauses has built up   4.212
in the U.K. and abroad.[38] In the twentieth century there has been less judicial
opposition to such clauses than in the nineteenth, probably for good policy
reasons. Generally, if parties have agreed at the outset of the contract that
in the event of some failure that a "genuine pre-estimate of damage" shall
be recoverable, then the courts will give effect to the intentions of the parties
on normal rules for the interpretation and construction of contracts. This
saves the courts time.[39] It also makes for a greater degree of certainty between
the parties as to their likely exposure to risk than in attempting to predict
how the courts will interpret the recurringly difficult task in practice of
deciding what losses flow naturally from a breach of contract as general
damages, and what special damages might apply, on the principles classically
expressed in *Hadley v. Baxendale*,[40] and by Bell as follows:

> "The general rule is, that if one bound absolutely becomes, without fraud or
> fault, unable to fulfil his engagement, damages are due; the damages being
> the indemnification for that which the obligee has directly lost or been
> prevented from gaining, with the expense of proceedings for obtaining
> reparation. Whenever a breach of contract is proved, damages follow, although
> if no loss or inconvenience be proved the damages will be nominal. Under
> such claim for damage will fall lawful interest in pecuniary obligations, as
> the damage for money not paid: the loss sustained on the thing itself or
> foreseen, or naturally in the contemplation of the parties as the natural result
> or consequence to be reasonably expected from the breach: But not collateral
> or consequential damage; unless either such damage has by special stipulation
> of the parties, been brought into view; or unless it be a loss on the thing
> itself, as by the rise or fall of markets."[41]

The question of reasonable foreseeability of loss can be a difficult matter   4.213
in normal circumstances, as for example in *Balfour Beatty v. Scottish Power.*[42]
Balfour Beatty were building a by-pass near Edinburgh in 1985 and also
had to build an aqueduct to divert a canal. They were using batched concrete
and required a continuous supply of electricity. As a result of a power cut
the batching was interrupted and what had been built required to be
demolished at a cost of £229,000. The Outer House said that these damages
were too remote.[43] On appeal the First Division reversed this,[44] but the Lords
upheld the Outer House in finding that such damages under the first limb
of *Hadley v. Baxendale* were not reasonably foreseeable.[44a]

---

[38] See particularly chapter 10 of *Hudson's Building and Engineering Contracts* (10th ed.).
[39] Bell, *Commentaries* (6th ed.) III.I; VIII.III.
[40] (1854) 9 Ex. 341. For an interesting discussion on these issues see MacQueen, "Remoteness and Breach of Contract", 1996 J.R. 295.
[41] Bell, *Principles of the Law of Scotland* (10th ed.), s. 31.
[42] 1994 S.L.T. 807.
[43] 1992 S.L.T. 811.
[44] 1993 S.L.T. 1005.
[44a] 1994 S.L.T. 807.

4.214   But in permitting so-called L&AD clauses, the Scottish courts in their equitable jurisdiction may modify the amount if it is exorbitant, but that may require proof of loss if the facts are not simple.[45] Accordingly the courts may enforce, or not, such clauses in a range of circumstances. L&AD clauses in construction contracts are normally for a fixed sum for an identifiable period in given circumstances, but may also provide for the forfeiture of plant and machinery.[46] In general the courts are more chary of the latter.[47] The identifiable period may be as narrow as each day of delay.[48] Typically, enforceable liquidate and ascertained damages clauses are linked with a single contractual failure, *i.e.* to complete on time.[49]

4.215   The courts have refused to enforce L&AD clauses traditionally where such clauses are deemed to be penal (whether or not the word[50] penalty or some such is actually used[51]) and are *in terrorem*. At times it appears to the author that an almost Shakespearean quality is reflected in this area of law.[52] Put simply: "The court will give effect to the bargain if it be reasonable that damages be paid. But if the penalty be truly a penalty — that is, a punishment — the Court will not allow that, because the law will not let people punish each other."[53]

4.216   Recently, in *Philips Hong Kong Ltd v. Attorney General of Hong Kong*[54] the Judicial Committee of the Privy Council held that oppression was the critical factor militating against such clauses. The frequently cited classic distinction between penalties and valid L&AD clauses is found in the speech of Lord Dunedin in *Dunlop Pneumatic Tyre Co. Ltd v. New Garage and Motor Co. Ltd.*[55] This was not a construction case, and involved penalties for breach of many and various conditions in an agreement to resell tyres. To paraphrase: the test is one for the courts, whatever the actual words used; the essence of liquidated damages is a genuine pre-estimate of loss; such sum must not be extravagant or unconscionable having regard to the greatest loss that could conceivably be proved; a sum will be a penalty if the breach consists in not paying a sum of money and the sum stipulated is for greater than that; and there is a presumption of penalty when one sum is payable for one or more or all events, some of which are serious and some trifling. However, Lord Dunedin then went on to restate the jurisprudentially most far-reaching point, that where a genuine pre-estimate is almost impossible that the parties may yet bargain for one and stipulate it.

---

[45] *Forrest & Barr v. Henderson* (1869) 8 M. 187; 42 J. 89; 7 S.L.R. 870.
[46] For example, clause 63 ICE 5th contract.
[47] The above-noted forfeiture clause was not upheld in *Cosslett (Contractors) v. Bridgend County Council*, 1997 C.I.L.L. 1279.
[48] *Beattie & Son v. Ritchie & Co.*, 1901 9 S.L.T. 2 (OH).
[49] *Johnston v. Robertson* (1861) 23 D. 646.
[50] *Lord Elphinstone v. Monkland Iron & Coal Co.* (1886) 13 R. 98 (HL).
[51] *Crux v. Aldred*, 1866 14 W.R. 656.
[52] "And where thou now exact'st the penalty, Which is a pound of this poor merchant's flesh", *Merchant of Venice*, Act IV, Scene 1.
[53] *Robertson v. Driver's Trustees* (1881) 8 R. 555 at 562, *per* Lord Young.
[54] (1993) 61 B.L.R. 41, PC.
[55] (1915) A.C. 79 at 86–88, HL.

An earlier illustration of this last stipulation point can be seen most clearly   4.217
in the case of *Clydebank Engineering & Shipbuilding Co. Ltd v. Don Jose
Ramos Yzquierdo y Castaneda*.[56] There were two contracts to deliver four
torpedo boat destroyers with a "penalty" for late delivery at the rate of £500
per week. The value of the contracts was around £67,000 for each vessel.
The boats were delivered late and the Spanish Government claimed £67,500
for that period. Clydebank argued that there had been no loss. If they had
delivered these at the contractual time then they would have been sunk by the
American fleet along with the greater part of the Spanish fleet. Also, it was
argued that a war ship had no commercial value as compared to a commercial
ship. Both of these points were rejected, and in particular were criticised
strongly as "absurd" or at least "a striking example of defective jurisprudence".
The Spanish Government was entitled to the full sum of £500 per week for
each vessel. The sum of £500 could be related to other tenderers and the time
periods within which they would have agreed to deliver the completed ships:
i.e. the quicker, the more expensive.

It is in relation to the problem of what the real losses actually are that   4.218
much litigation can take place. In the most recent analysis of the law in the
matter in *Philips (Hong Kong)*,[57] Lord Woolf, in the Privy Council, said:

> "It will normally be insufficient to establish that a provision is objectionably penal
> to identify situations where the application of the provision could result in a larger
> sum being recovered by the injured party than is actually lost... so long as the sum
> payable in the event of non-compliance with the contract is not extravagant, having
> regard to the range of losses that it could reasonably be anticipated it would have to
> cover at the time the contract was made, it can still be a genuine pre-estimate of a
> loss... and so a perfectly valid liquidated damage provision".

There is Scottish authority in *Beattie v. Ritchie*[58] in relation to a building   4.219
contract that where there was a fixed day rate of damages for failure to
complete of £20, and another fixed sum of £5,000 as a penalty for any
breach in the same contract, but only the day rate was claimed, the £20 per
day rate was still recoverable. In the *Philips (Hong Kong)* case[59] a minimum
penalty clause was upheld even though the rest of the liquidate damages
provisions were very detailed and applied a sliding scale as against how far
completion of installation of security devices by Philips had reached.

Liquidate and ascertained damages can perhaps be criticised as a legal   4.220
fiction because they are supposed to be "a genuine pre-estimate of loss"
but may still apply if no loss actually occurs.[60] Indeed it is probably irrelevant
to try to lead evidence that no loss actually occurred.[61]

---

[56]   [1905] A.C. 6, *per* Lord Halsbury at 7–9.

[57]   *op.cit.*

[58]   (1901) 9 S.L.T. 2.

[59]   *op.cit.*

[60]   *BFI Group v. DCB Integrated Systems Ltd*, 1987 C.I.L.L. 348.

[61]   *Clydebank Engineering, op.cit, per* Lord Davey; but it seems evidence can be led to show what
        was reasonably expected at the time the contract was made: see *Philips (Hong Kong) op.cit.*

4.221   There are also interesting questions where the contractor fails to complete at all. In *British Glanzstoff Manufacturing Co. Ltd v. General Fire and Life Assurance Corporation Ltd*[62] the pursuers, who were a foreign-based company, contracted to have a factory built at Flint. The defenders had granted a bond for the contractor. The pursuers required the factory built by January 31, 1910 and had set up various contracts to commence thereafter. There was a liquidate damages clause at £250 for the first two weeks delay and £500 for each week thereafter, all linked to an extension of time provision. In addition there was a bonus payment provision for early completion, and a separate clause in the event of suspension of the works by the contractor. Under the latter clause the employer had a lien over the contractor's plant until the works were completed, and property in any materials on site would then pass to the employer. The works were then to be completed by the employer without undue delay or expense. On completion of the works the architect would then certify the amount of expenses properly incurred "consequent on and incidental to the default of the Contractor...in completing the works by other persons. Should the amount so certified as the expenses properly incurred be less than the amount which would have been due to the contractor upon the completion of the works by him, the difference shall be paid to the contractor by the employer; should the amount of the former exceed the latter, the difference shall be paid by the contractor to the employer". It was held at every stage of the court process that when the contractor became insolvent and his receivers gave up the contract, liquidate damages were not an appropriate remedy, standing the wording of the suspension clause. Damages were to be calculated in accordance with the suspension clause for extra or under cost; as were any other damages which were not construction related. Liquidate damages based on the number of weeks it took the replacement contractor to complete the works was inappropriate. This was particularly so when the replacement contractor was to work to an earlier date than the original contractor. The Lord President said that the liquidate damages clause applied only when the works were finished by the original contractor. Lord Johnston had interesting things to say about damages, and does not appear to accept what the author sees as a legal fiction in *Clydebank* and Lord Dunedin's speech in *Dunlop, i.e.* that a genuine pre-estimate will be upheld where otherwise it would be impossible to predict damages. Lord Johnstone said at p. 599:

> "The contractors are ex hypothesi in breach, and that breach does not necessarily affect only the cost of completion. There may be other damage to the employers. And while the contract does provide for ascertainment of the balance, one way or the other, of the cost of construction, it neither provides for nor precludes a claim for other loss and damage consequent on the breach.

---

[62]   1912 S.C. 591; affd [1913] A.C. 143, HL.

Such other damage may result purely from the delay occasioned, or may involve other considerations. But it is evidently a matter which could not be measured by liquidate damages. Neither does the clause stipulating damages apply to it, nor could such clause very well have been framed, because the data involved are not necessarily mere loss from delay, but may be other matters neither definite nor capable of being foretold. Hence damage must be ascertained in the ordinary way."

Similarly, in *Chanthall Investments Ltd v. F.G.Minter Ltd*[63] the above   4.222
case was followed where extensive remedial work was required due to structural defects in a building caused by the contractor's alleged negligence in following the specification. The contractors resisted a very large claim by the owners for the additional cost of completion and other damages on the basis that the L&AD clause set a cap on the damages recoverable. It was held that the L&AD clause only applied to the contractor being late in completion and the owners were entitled to recover other losses, such as finance charges and loss of rents and profits.

A similar argument had also failed in *Dingwall v. Burnett*,[64] and although   4.223
not a construction case, it was held that an amount of damages of £50 for failure to implement parts of an agreement in a lease was a penalty and not a genuine pre-estimate of loss, but that did not stop a greater sum being claimed as damages.

This line or reasoning has been taken further in England in the case of   4.224
Turner & Sons Ltd v. Mathind[65] where the Court of Appeal held that where there was one date for completion which regulated a claim for L&ADs, it might still be possible to claim unliquidated damages for failure to meet contractual completion dates for other sub-areas which preceded the date for completion, otherwise there would be no remedy for a breach.

It may be however that the existence of a L&AD clause will have the   4.225
effect of capping the amount of damages,[66] even if such damages exceed the pre-agreed amount; or if the pre-agreed amount is stated to be "nil".[67] In relation to capping, it was held in the House of Lords in *Cellulose Acetate Silk Company v. Widness Foundry (1925) Ltd*[68] that where in negotiations which moved from a position of accepting no liability whatsoever for delay, to a position where liquidated damages were agreed at £20 per week, and where it must have been obvious to the parties that the actual damage would be more than £20 per week, that the agreed figure capped damages. This was so in the circumstances of this case even when the agreed figure was clearly not a pre-estimate of actual damage: it was better than nothing at

---

[63] 1976 S.C. 73.
[64] 1912 S.C. 1097; 2 S.L.T. 90.
[65] 1986 5 Const.L.J. 273.
[66] *Cellulose Acetate Silk Co. Ltd v. Widnes Foundry (1925) Ltd* (1931) 2 K.B. 393.
[67] *Temloc Ltd v. Erril Properties Ltd* (1987) 39 B.L.R. 30, 12 Con. L.R. 109, CA.
[68] *op.cit.*

all. Their Lordships however left open the question of whether in different circumstances it might be appropriate to ignore a penalty which was less than the prospective damages, and to sue for the actual amount. It is interesting to note that the Supreme Court of Canada in *Elsley v. Collins Insurance Agencies Ltd 1978*[69] held in a case for damages for breach of a restrictive covenant on the sale of a business, that even where the L&AD clause fails, the amount so stated will form the upper limit of sums recoverable. (See *Hudson*, para. 10.016.)

4.226   The question of a "nil" liquidated damages clause may however be a matter that would be decided differently in Scotland and England. In England, in *Temloc v. Errill*[70] JCT 80 was used, and "£ nil" inserted in the Appendix against clause 24.2 in respect of liquidated damages. The Completion Date was extended to November 14, 1984 and Practical Completion was certified on December 20, 1984. The defendant Employer argued that he was still entitled to deduct damages for delay, as the use of the word "nil" only had the effect of deleting the liquidated damages clause, leaving the normal remedies for breach of contract intact. This argument was rejected on the basis that a true interpretation of what the parties intended was that no damages for delay were intended to be recoverable, whether liquidated or otherwise. The Employer then argued that as his Architect had failed to certify a later Completion Date within the 12-week period from the date of practical Completion, that invalidated the operation of the L&AD clause, so that normal damages could then be claimed. This argument was rejected by the Court of Appeal. In particular it was stated that the time period within which the Architect was to act was "directory only and not something that would invalidate the calculation and payment of liquidated damages."

4.227   In Scotland, the same reasoning was followed in *John Maxwell & Sons (Builders) v. Simpson*,[71] but in *Stanley Miller v. Ladhope*[71a], Lord Prosser decided the use of the word "nil" in similar circumstances was ambiguous and that there should be a proof before answer. *Hudson* in the 10th edition doubts that the *Temloc* case would be definitive authority where similar wording is used, and therefore seems to support the view of Lord Prosser; and Keating (6th edition) cites an Australian case *Baese Pty Ltd v. R.A. Bracken*[72] to the effect that the word "nil" did not provide an exhaustive remedy and that the *Temloc* and *Cellulose* cases involved materially different contracts.

4.228   A L&AD clause may nevertheless become inoperable. If, for example, there has been some act of prevention on the part of the employer for which he is unable to grant a valid extension of time under the contract then the employer will be unable to rely on the L&AD clause. In *McElroy & Sons v. Tharsis Sulphur and Copper Co.*[73] the contract period was 12 months, with

---

[69]   83 D.L.R. (3d) 1, at 15.
[70]   *op.cit.*
[71]   1990 S.C.L.R. 92 (Sh Ct).
[71a] 1988 S.L.T. 514, OH.
[72]   52 B.L.R. 130.
[73]   (1877) 5 R. 161 (reversed upon other points (1878) 5 R. (H.L.) 171).

liquidated damages of £50 per week. Due to delays by other contractors or sub-contractors possession could not be given, and work could not begin. It was held that the contract was one to complete the works within 12 months from the date of possession; that the date of possession was a contractual date that could be of commercial importance to the contractor; and the L&AD clause was avoided, leaving the employer to show actual damage.

In *Steel v. Bell*[74] the Inner House overturned the decision of the sheriff   4.229 which was that where instructions are given by an architect for variations after the date set for the completion of works, this *per se* invalidated the liquidate damages clause. This particular case seemed to cause two of their Lordships considerable difficulty, as the time overrun for the works, which was to build a house, was 14 months; and the value of the job rose by about 70 per cent. There had been no extension of time granted by the architect, but it was held that it was up to the pursuers to prove that non-completion was due to the employer, who had made performance impossible by his act or omission; especially where it was contended for the employer that the contractor had been to blame for delays from the start of the contract. Professor Gloag rather surprisingly suggests that this case is authority for the proposition that it is the builder's duty to obtain a certificate from the architect,[75] but it is submitted that this is something that is beyond the contractor's control. It may only be authority that it is the contractor's obligation to take steps to obtain an extension where there is a mechanism to obtain one in the contract.

There is however some doubt as to whether in Scotland an L&AD clause   4.230 could be enforceable when it would be almost impossible to complete the works in the time specified. Gloag at page 339 suggests that the contractor could so bind himself, and cites *Steel v. Bell* as his authority. It is submitted that *Steel v. Bell* is not authority for that proposition at all. Indeed this would mean that the Scots courts would not follow the English Court of Appeal in *Dodd v. Churton*,[76] a case that was expressly distinguished in *Steel* on the basis that in *Steel* there was a clear contractual position that allowed the architect to certify extensions of time. In addition the Inner House in *Robertson v. Driver's Trs*[77] were required to construe a contract for alteration of the front of a house by making four oriel windows which included inconsistent terms for the time periods for completing parts of the building works. It was held that if the entire works were to be completed in seven weeks, that was inconsistent with a separate stipulation for the masonry work to be completed within six weeks. Effectively an impossibility would have been created on any way of analysing the construction process, as no proper account had been taken for the time for plaster to dry. The Lord Justice-Clerk

---

[74]   (1890) 3 F. 319, 8 S.L.T. 381.
[75]   Gloag, *The Law of Contract* (2nd ed.), p. 339, n. 6.
[76]   L.R. 1897, 1 Q.B. 562.
[77]   (1881) 8 R. 555.

said: "The Court will not enforce a penalty where the thing undertaken could not possibly be done in the time." In effect the contractor was entitled to the full time periods which were specified for the completion of each stage, even if this had the effect of making the final completion date impossible.[78]

4.231   Clause 24 of JCT 80 has caused difficulties of interpretation, such that Amendment 9 was issued in July 1990 to clarify the question of the issue of certificates and of failure to complete by the Completion Date. These questions were considered in *A. Bell & Son Paddington v. CBF Residential Care and Housing Association*.[79] It was held that fresh certificates of non-completion were necessary with each extension of time, and any failure precluded deduction of liquidated and ascertained damages. In this case the architect was *"functus officio"* as he had issued his Final Certificate and had no residual power to issue a further non-completion certificate. Since Amendment 9, there is a specific provision in clause 24.1 that if a new completion date is fixed: "the Architect shall issue such further certificate under clause 24.1 as may be necessary." This would appear to coincide with the decision in *Bell* that each and every notice under clause 24.1 is a condition precedent to the deduction of liquidated and ascertained damages. The point seems further confirmed by the rewording of clause 24.2.1 in terms of Amendment 18. This rewording also seems to make it plain that the Employer's notice of his intention to deduct L&ADs is also a condition precedent.[80] It would appear from the language of clause 24.2.3 that the Employer need not issue fresh notices of intention to deduct liquidated and ascertained damages with each fresh certificate. What should be contained in the Employer's notice requiring payment to be valid is a moot point. In *J. F. Finnegan v. Community Housing Association*[81] it was held that a remittance advice showing a deduction for L&ADs, such that the number of weeks damages applied for could be deduced by the simple arithmetic of dividing the sum by the weekly rate, was inadequate as too uncertain. Conversely, in *Jarvis Brent Ltd v. Rowlinson Construction Ltd*[82] it was held that a letter prepared by a quantity surveyor and sent by the employer to the contractor showing calculations for L&ADs, coupled with cheques with the relevant sums deducted, was a valid notice. In Scotland it has been held that the issue of a certificate of non-completion on a weekday, when the completion date fell on a weekend, was invalid.[83]

---

[78] There is English authority that it is the contractors' right to the whole period for performance in *Wells v. Army and Navy Co-Operative Society* 1902, 86 L.T. 764; H.B.C. (4th ed.), Vol.2, p. 353, CA.

[79] [1989] B.L.R. 102.

[80] There had been conflicting decisions on this matter in *Bell v. Paddington* 46 B.L.R. 102; *Jarvis Brent Ltd v. Rowlinson Construction Ltd* (1990) 6 Const. L.J. 292; and *J. F. Finnegan Ltd v. Community Housing Association Ltd* [1993] 65 B.L.R. 103.

[81] *ibid.*

[82] *op.cit.*

[83] *G.A. Group Ltd v. Scottish Metropolitan Property plc*, 1992 G.W.D. 16–899.

In terms of section 111(1) of the Housing Grants, Construction and 4.232
Regeneration Act 1996 a party to a construction contract may not withhold
payment after the final date for payment of a sum due under the contract
unless he has given an effective notice to withhold payment. Amendment 18
to JCT 80 therefore amends clause 24.2.1 (and clauses 30.1.1.4 and 30.8.3
relating to interim and final certificates) to comply.

In *Peak Construction Liverpool v. McKinney Foundations*[84] it was held 4.233
in the Appeal Court that liquidate damages and extensions of time clauses
in printed forms of contract must be construed *contra proferentem, i.e.*
against the person putting it forward and who seeks to rely on it where
there is an ambiguity. Conversely, it should be remembered that JCT
contracts are arrived at by a consensus across the construction industry,[85]
and in *G. A. Estates Ltd v. Caviapen Trs Ltd*[86] it was held an L&AD clause
may not be construed *contra proferentem* where parties of equal bargaining
power negotiate a contract. The *contra proferentem* issue was raised in
Balfour Beatty Building Ltd v. Chestermount Properties Ltd[87] where it was
unsuccessfully argued for the Contractor that a Variation instruction could
not be issued after the Completion Date in JCT 80 without the Employer
losing his entitlement to L&ADs, at least from the date of the Variation
onwards. Coleman J. whilst rejecting the Contractor's analysis of the scheme
of risk in JCT 80 in relation to instructions/omissions/extensions of time
and L&ADs, also said: "In this respect the contract is not so ambiguous or
so unclear as to call for application of the *contra proferentum* [*sic*] rule or
the resolution of nicely-balanced issues of construction in favour of the
employers for whose benefit the liquidate damages regime is introduced."[88]

Clause 24.2.2 provides for repayment by the Employer of liquidate 4.234
and ascertained damages if certificates are superseded, but whether interest
is also due is not expressly stated. In the case of the *Department of the
Environment for Northern Ireland v. Farrans Construction*,[89] the employer
was required to pay interest on repaid liquidated damages under a JCT
1963 form, even though no interest provision was provided for in the
contract. Surprisingly Amendment 18 does not clarify the point, when
elsewhere a new right to interest on overdue payments is created in
clauses 19.4 (in favour of Sub-Contractors) and 30.1.1.1 (in favour of the
Contractor).

---

[84] [1971] B.L.R. 114.
[85] In relation to a standard engineering form which was the result of industry consultation, the *contra proferentem* rule was held to have no application: *Terson's Ltd v. Stevenage Development Corporation* [1963] 5 B.L.R. 54.
[86] 1993 S.L.T. 1051 at 1057, *per* Lord McCluskey.
[87] [1993] 62 B.L.R. 1.
[88] *ibid.* at 28.
[89] [1981] 19 B.L.R. 1.

Clause 25: Extensions of time

4.235   This is the extension of time clause and replaces JCT 63, clause 23 (for the interpretation of which clause see particularly *London Borough of Merton v. Leach (Sanley Hugh)*).[90] Perhaps the first question that might be asked is what this provision is for. Similar provisions have been common in construction contracts for many years,[91] and it would appear that the main purpose is to preserve the liquidate and ascertained damages clause from becoming unenforceable in the event of a delay to the progress of the works due to the employer or those for whom he is responsible. Indeed, from the decision in *Steel v. Bell*[92] it is arguable that where delays are caused by the employer, and where there is a mechanism to obtain an extension of time in the contract, it is the contractor's obligation to take steps to obtain an extension. Otherwise the full amount of liquidated damages from the original completion date might be obtained from the contractor. In terms of *Merton v. Leach*,[93] this notification is probably not a condition precedent for the architect to issue an extension of time, at least under JCT 63. The matter was specifically left undecided by the First Division in *John L. Haley Ltd v. Dumfries and Galloway Regional Council*[94] where it was held that the arbiter had been wrong to accept site minutes as constituting notice. It is submitted that notice is not a condition precedent for an extension of time under JCT 80, although a failure to give notice in good time to enable the architect to make omissions, for example, may not be the contractor using best endeavours to prevent delay in terms of clause 25.3.4.1.

4.236   It is often assumed that an extension of time is to be given for events that would otherwise constitute a breach of contract by the employer, or for any act for which the employer is responsible that prevents the contractor completing on time. The corollary would then seem to be that as the contractor would prima facie be entitled to damages for breach of contract, the contractor is entitled to compensation if an extension of time is granted. On closer inspection this is not the case, either at common law or in terms of clause 26 of the contract which follows and is headed: "Loss and expense caused by matters materially affecting the regular progress of the Works".

4.237   This might appear strange as clause 25.2.1.1 begins: "If and whenever it becomes reasonably apparent that the *progress of the Works* [emphasis added] is being or is likely to be delayed..."; and clause 26.1 states: "and as soon as the Architect is of the opinion that the direct loss and/or expense has been incurred or is likely to be incurred due to any such deferment of giving possession or that the regular *progress of the works* [emphasis added] or of any part thereof has been or is likely to be so materially affected as set out

---

[90]   [1985] 32 B.L.R. 51.
[91]   See, for example, *Steel v. Bell* (1890) 3 F. 319, 8 S.L.T. 381.
[92]   *ibid.*
[93]   *op.cit.*
[94]   November 8, 1988 — unreported.

in the application of the Contractor...". Clause 25 on extensions of time as amended by Amendment 18 lists 18 "Relevant Events" in clause 25.4 (with two new ones related to Amendment 18 and the Information Release Schedule in clauses 5.4.1 and 5.4.2; and the right of the Contractor to suspend performance pursuant to clause 30.1.4). Clause 26 lists 10 "matters" in clause 26.2 which affect the regular progress of the works. Some "Relevant Events" are identical to clause 26 "matters". The "Relevant Events" in clause 25.4 which give rise to extensions of time do not always give rise to a claim for loss and expense under clause 26. For example, clause 26 does not include force majeure,[95] or exceptionally adverse weather. The Contractor would appear to bear the financial risk of these. He may get an extension of time which protects him from L&ADs being deducted, but he does not get any money under clause 26. It should be noted however that clause 26.6 provides that the preceding provisions of the clause are "without prejudice to any other rights and remedies which the Contractor may possess".[96]

The absence of a causal link between clause 25 and 26 matters has   4.238
recently been judicially confirmed in Scotland at procedure roll in *Methodist Homes Housing Association Ltd v. Scott & McIntosh*,[97] where it was held to be "self evidently correct" that a certificate of extension of time issued under clause 25 had no direct bearing on a claim based on disruption under clause 26; even when counsel had argued that "the extensions of time granted and the claim proceeded on exactly the same 'Architect's Instructions'". Prior to Amendment 18, there were identically worded clauses where the Contractor had not received in due time necessary instructions in clauses 25 and 26. Amendment 18 deletes the former identical clauses and replaces them with two new identical clauses relating to the release of information. It is doubtful that this Amendment would make any difference to the *ratio* in *Methodist Homes.*

The rather peculiar agglomeration of "Relevant Events" in clause 25 is   4.239
a mixture of matters which would otherwise be supervening events (force majeure, weather, statutory changes, terrorism, the work of statutory undertakers); or breaches of contract by the Employer or those for whom he is responsible (discrepancies in the documentation, provision of information,

---

[95] For interpretation in a construction context see *Bilton v. Greater London Council* [1982] 20 B.L.R. 1 at 14 (HL).

[96] See comments on clause 26.6 at para. 4.273 and the comments of Vinelott J. in *London Borough of Merton v. Stanley Hugh Leach Ltd* [1985] 32 B.L.R. 5: "But the contractor is not bound to make an application under clause 24.1[of JCT 63]. He may prefer to wait until completion of the work and join the claim for damages for breach of the obligation to provide instructions, drawings and the like in good time with other claims for damages for breach of obligations under the contract. Alternatively he can, as I see it, make a claim under clause 24.1 in order to obtain prompt reimbursement and later claim damages for breach of contract, bringing the amount awarded under clause 24.1 into account."

[97] (unreported), Lord Marnoch, Outer House, May 2, 1997. This case may actually be more concerned with the pleading of delay and disruption, and the problem of incorporating claims documents wholescale into pleadings.

provision of materials, delays by Nominated Sub-Contractors or Nominated Suppliers, the execution of work by the Employer himself, failure to give access or egress, deferment in giving possession); or what might at first sight be assumed to be the Contractor's risk (in securing labour or materials)[98]; and matters relating to the Employer reserving the right to change matters (Variations, provisional sums and approximate quantities) or inspect matters (unless the inspected work is found not to be in accordance with the contract). It is the author's perspective in relation to the traditional draftsmanship of contracts so as to apportion risk, that clause 26 does correspond to the extension of time matters which would otherwise be the Employer's fault, or a consequence of the Employer's reservation of matters to himself as the works proceed. This does not appear to have been the view of the court in *Methodist Homes Housing Association Ltd v. Scott & McIntosh.*[99] Certainly it does appear plain that extensions of time are not simply for matters that are associated with fault by the Employer, and therefore it would not be appropriate for the Employer to be required to pay damages for breach of contract at common law, or to pay direct loss and/or expense under clause 26 whenever there is an extension of time.[1] Also, the risk of delays by a Nominated Sub-Contractor or Nominated Supplier is borne by the Employer under clause 25.4.7, but there is no corresponding right to the Contractor for loss and/or expense. The Contractor has to look to recover from the Nominated Sub-Contractor or Nominated Supplier. In some construction contracts if the event on the employer's part signalling an extension of time has not been specifically included in the contract then the employer will have no common law right to extend the completion date by implication.[2] One of the major difficulties with these clauses is therefore that, as a matter of logic, one sort of analysis would be proper for an extension of time, taking into account questions of causation which each "Relevant Event" has with another; and one sort of analysis would be

---

[98] Securing materials, where the contractor has taken due care in ordering these goods, was held in *Taylors v. Maclellans* (1891) 19 R. 10 not to be at the contractor's risk where there were strikes and sickness among workmen caused by a heatwave affecting a supplier in Belgium.

[99] *ibid.*

[1] In *Henry Boot v. Central Lancashire New Town* [1980] 15 B.L.R. 1 the scheme of allocation of risk in the JCT conditions was said to reflect that in some cases the "loss lies where it falls": *i.e.* the employer gives an extension and loses L&ADs, and the contractor is not compensated for delay.

[2] See for example *Peak Construction (Liverpool) Ltd v. McKinney Foundations* [1970] 1 B.L.R. 111; and *Rapid Building v. Ealing Family Housing Association* [1984] 29 B.L.R. 5, where Lloyd L.J. said he was "startled" that a contract did not make provision for the employer's failure to give possession of the site, and the employer consequently lost the right to recover L&ADs, leaving recovery only of damages that could be proven if the contractor had failed to complete within a reasonable time, and such damages would probably be capped by the L&AD clause had it been effective — although this last point was not actually decided.

proper for an award of loss and/or expense, or common law damages, which assess the causative effect of delays which are essentially due to the employer, on the contractor's financial position. At times the two analyses will coincide, at others they will not, creating a cat's cradle of connections between time to complete the works and the contractor's losses. Clause 26.3 does not particularly clarify the matter, but provides: "If and to the extent that it is necessary for the ascertainment under clause 26.1 of loss and/or expense the Architect shall state in writing to the Contractor what extension of time, if any, has been made under clause 25 [in respect of employer's risk matters]". An "ascertainment" from time to time under clause 26 shall be added to the Contract Sum (clause 26.5) and therefore becomes due under the payment provisions of the contract; as distinct from damages for breach of contract which are a separate common law remedy. Thus a further layer of differentiation is possible between a claim under the terms of the contract and a claim for breach of the contract.

If this were not complicated enough, this is still without factoring in that the contractor might be at fault for all or part of the delay; that certain delays by employer or contractor might be concurrent with each other; that certain delays might then bring supervening events into play that would otherwise have been avoided (winter working, strikes); that the contractor might have planned his resources so as to finish before the completion date by including "float" in his planned progress; and that the contractor has a duty to mitigate the consequences of a breach of contract at common law, and under clause 25.3.4.1: "shall constantly use his best endeavours to prevent delay in the progress of the works, howsoever caused, and to prevent the completion of the works being delayed or further delayed beyond the Completion Date." Also, and fundamentally, the Contractor under JCT 80 is not required to show at any time when tendering just how he intends to apply his resources to complete on time and make a profit. So, how does the Contractor truly show that he has suffered a loss? The unenviable tasks of giving a "fair and reasonable" extension of time, and of "ascertaining" direct loss and/or expense, are given to the Architect (who may, of course, himself have been the cause of either one of these[3]). 4.240

How then should the Architect give an extension of time? The Contractor, in terms of clause 25.2.1.1, "if and whenever it becomes reasonably apparent that the progress of the Works is being or is likely to be delayed... shall forthwith give written notice to the Architect of the material circumstances including the cause or causes of the delay and identify in such notice any event which in his opinion is a Relevant Event." 4.241

Clause 25.1 provides "that any reference to delay, notice or extension includes further delay, further notice or further extension of time" and clause 25.2.1.1 is drafted in terms of the identification of causes of delay affecting "progress", which are "Relevant Events". A distinction is drawn between 4.242

---

[3] Note particularly the comments of Sir John Donaldson M.R. in this respect in *Northern Regional Health Authority v. Crouch (Derek) Construction Co.*[1984] 2 All E.R. 175 at 188–189.

cause of delay affecting progress (clause 25.2.1.1), and causes of delay which can be estimated to affect the completion of the works beyond the Completion Date "whether or not concurrently with delay resulting from any other Relevant Event" (clause 25.2.2.2). The Architect is then to look at the Completion Date. If the Architect thinks that any such event is a Relevant Event and the completion of the works is likely to be delayed beyond the Completion Date he shall grant an extension of time by fixing such later date as the Completion Date as he then estimates to be fair and reasonable (clause 25.3.1). The Architect should do so: not later than 12 weeks from the receipt of the notice and of reasonably sufficient particulars and estimate; or where the period between receipt thereof and the Completion Date is less than 12 weeks, not later than the Completion Date (clause 25.3.1). Note, that in terms of *Temloc v. Errill*,[4] and despite the apparently mandatory language of the clause and use of the word "shall", such time limits on the Architect have been described as "directory only", and do not render L&ADs at large for the technical breach of not acting within the period stated in the contract. In any case the Architect is to act "'if reasonably practicable having regard to the sufficiency of the aforesaid notice" (clause 25.3.1). There is a fall-back position in terms of clause 25.3.3, so that the Architect shall "upon reviewing a previous decision or otherwise and whether or not the Relevant Event has been specifically notified by the Contractor" fix such later Completion Date not later than the expiry of 12 weeks after the date of Practical Completion. This would appear to confirm the author's view that the Contractor's notice is not a condition precedent to an extension of time. JCT Practice Note 16 at note 6 states: "It is therefore desirable for this reason[5] among others that the Architect shall communicate his decisions on extensions of time before the current Completion Date has passed."

4.243   The problem for the Contractor is what should he best include in any delay notice he gives. A delay in receiving information, for example, may cause a chain of events which may or may not have been reasonably foreseeable consequences of that delay; particularly if that delay becomes concurrent with others. Any such notice would seem to be tentative at best, yet as noted above, it has been held that the historical recording of events in site minutes was held not to constitute notice.[6] No particular criteria or formula is prescribed for the "sufficiency" of a Contractor's notice, nor is one prescribed for the Architect, if he thinks it insufficient. However a retrospective view of events from the date of Practical Completion would seem the most appropriate vantage point to judge a fair and reasonable extension of time. Indeed on the interpretation of JCT 63 and whether the architect had the right to make a retrospective extension of time at all Lord Denning said:

---

[4]   *op.cit*
[5]   The reason relates to the "freezing" of fluctuation amounts under clauses 38.4.7, 39.5.7 and 40.7 as inoperative until the Architect has made his decision on every application from the Contractor under clause 25.
[6]   *John L. Haley v. Dumfries and Galloway Regional Council* (Inner House), November 8, 1988 (unreported).

"Or take a cause of delay such as we have in this case, due to labour and materials not being available. That may cause a continuous delay operating partially, but not wholly, every day, until the works are completed. The works do not stop. They go on, but they go on more slowly right to the end of the works. In such a case, seeing that the cause of delay operates until the last moment, when the works are completed, it must follow that the Architect can give a certificate after they are completed."[7]

An important distinction should be noted in relation to the same events   4.244 and for any entitlement to direct loss and/or expense. Clause 26.1 speaks of direct loss and/or expense which has been incurred or is likely to be incurred. This seems to comprise losses actually incurred which should be indemnified, and also the expected loss on the bargain where such losses are not too remote from the breach. All eventual losses, as so often in cases of damages for breach of contract, cannot be as readily scanned from a final fixed point in time looking backwards, as can delay to a building which is eventually completed. The answer to the question how long did it actually take to complete the works can be answered relatively easily. The answer to the question, how was the Contractor's economic position affected throughout, would involve a series of financial snapshots in time involving projections of loss likely to be suffered, and an assessment of whether such losses are too "remote". Clause 26.1 requires an ascertainment to be made "from time to time". As any number of financial loss models could be devised there is just as much difficulty in ascertaining loss as there is in granting extensions of time. Part of the problem is in the word "ascertain" itself. As Lloyd J. put it, in *Alfred McAlpine Homes North Ltd v. Property and Land Contractors Ltd*[8]: "'to ascertain' means 'to find out for certain'[9] and it does not therefore connote as much use of judgment of the formation of an opinion had 'assess' or 'evaluate' been used. It thus appears to preclude making general assessments as at times have to be done in quantifying damages recoverable for breach of contract." All this without any added complexities, such as that the Contractor might be at fault concurrently with the Employer; that losses actually are more or less than expected due to some perceived chain of events; or that the Contractor might have made a loss on the contract from the start because of inefficient pricing.

A lawyer would be expected to approach the time and loss issues of delay and disruption by applying legal principles of causation and remoteness of damage. These are perennially difficult areas,[10] and sometimes the courts have admitted to have decided remoteness of damage on an "instinctive feeling".[11] The

---

[7] *Amalgamated Building Contractors Ltd v. Waltham Holy Cross UDC* [1952] 2 All E.R. 452 at 454.

[8] (1995) 76 B.L.R. 59 at 88.

[9] The footnote to Lloyd J.'s judgment reads: " It is defined in the *Oxford English Dictionary* (2nd ed.) as 'to find or learn for a certainty by experiment, examination, or investigation, to make sure of, to get to know' and this is stated to be the only current use of the word."

[10] For a deep analysis of the complexities of causation see Hart and Honore, *Causation in the Law* (2nd ed., 1985).

[11] *Lamb v. Camden London Borough Council* [1981] Q.B. 625 at 647, *per* Watkins L.J.

construction industry has sought to develop its own solutions to the problems of delay by applying "critical path analysis" or "retrospective delay analysis".

Causation and remoteness of damage

4.245   Problems of causation have exercised philosophers, and, indeed, the Judicial Committee of the House of Lords. Lord Wright in *A/B Karlshamns Oljefabriker v. Monarch Steamship Co.*[12] said:

> "If a man is too late to catch a train, because his car broke down on the way to the station, we should all naturally say that he lost the train because of the car breaking down. We recognise that the two things are causally connected. Causation is a mental concept, generally based on inference or induction from uniformity of sequence as between two events that there is a causal connection between them. This is the customary result of an education which starts with our earliest experience: the burnt child dreads the fire. I am not entering upon or discussing any theory of causation. Those interested in philosophy will find modern philosophic views on causation explained in Russell's History of Western Philosophy in the Chapter on Hume, Book III, ch.xvii. The common law, however, is not concerned with philosophic speculation, but is only concerned with ordinary everyday life and thoughts and expressions".

In this particular case a vessel called the *British Monarch* was declared unseaworthy and delayed in port. Its destination was Karlshamns in Sweden. When it set sail war broke out, and the ship was diverted by the Admiralty to Glasgow. A clause in the charterparty was that the chartered ship should be seaworthy, and that compliance with government orders would be deemed the fulfilment of the voyage. Had the ship been seaworthy it would not have been caught up in the events of war, and arrived in Sweden weeks before the outbreak of war. Lord Wright noted that a fitter ship would have sailed through the peril unscathed, therefore the ship owner was debarred through his own fault from relying on the diversion clause as satisfying his obligations under the contract. His Lordship said unseaworthiness was the decisive or "dominant" cause. Damages were due for transhipment to another port.

4.246   It is submitted that the application of this reasoning could apply to JCT 80 when the progress of the Contractor is delayed by the Employer's fault, and is then delayed further beyond the Completion Date by a supervening event for which JCT 80 provides an extension of time, but no loss and/or expense, such as the use or threat of terrorism and/or the activity of the relevant authorities in dealing with such use or threat (clause 25.4.16). The Contractor would then have a claim for damages, it is submitted, if the terrorism was a serious possibility. Judge Fox-Andrews in *Fairweather v. Wandsworth*[13] seems to be of the same view. He gave an example of a contract being

---

[12]   1949 S.C. 1 at 24.
[13]   *Fairweather & Co. Ltd v. London Borough of Wandsworth* (1987) 29 B.L.R. 112 at 118–119.

extended as a result of a variation order and a strike then occurring two weeks before the new completion date, when the contractor was on time, and which lasted for six months. When work resumed the contractor took two months instead of the expected two weeks to finish because the contractor had no opportunity to protect his machinery during the strike. The judge said: "If the Architect grants an extension of time of eight months only... I can see no reason why the contractor under the Contract cannot still recover all his direct loss and/or expense under [the variations clause]."

Another shipping and insurance case is instructive on the question of causation. In *Leyland Shipping v. Norwich Union Fire Insurance Society*[14] a ship was torpedoed by enemy action. She was taken to port, storms blew up, and after two days when she went to ground with each ebb tide and floated again with the flood, her bulkheads gave way and she sank. It was held that the dominant cause was not that which was closest in time, *i.e.* the storms, but that the ship had been torpedoed. This was not a risk the insurers had covered. Again in the context of a construction contract it is submitted that an employer's fault which then causes a delay into a period of bad weather, which would otherwise have been avoided, would give the contractor an entitlement to claim for any loss.[15] Lord Shaw of Dunfermline at p. 369 said: 4.247

> "To treat *proxima cause* as the cause which is nearest in time is out of the question. Causes are spoken of as if they were distinct from one another as beads in a row or links in a chain, but — if this metaphysical topic has to be referred to — it is not wholly so. The chain of causation is a handy expression, but the figure is inadequate. Causation is not a chain but a net. At each point influences, forces, events, precedent and simultaneous, meet; and the radiation from each point extends infinitely. At the point where these various influences meet it is for the judgment as a matter of fact to declare which of the causes thus joined at the point of effect was the proximate and which was the remote cause."

Conversely, if no work could have proceeded anyway because of bad weather, the existence of an employer's fault may not be the dominant cause of delay. This would seem to follow from delict cases where, for example, the injured person would have died from arsenic poisoning anyway, even though a doctor had failed to treat him.[16] The same might be said for a strike. Surprisingly though, Lord Denning in the context of an earlier form in *Amalgamated Building Contractors v. Waltham Holy Cross UDC*[17] said: "Take a simple 4.248

---

[14] [1918] A.C. 350.
[15] It has however been held that where a contractor had fallen behind on his programme, although still proceeding "regularly and diligently", and the works were then affected by a period of "exceptionally inclement weather" under JCT 63, that the contractor was still entitled to an extension of time: *Walter Lawrence & Son v. Commercial Union Properties (U.K.) Ltd* [1984] 4 Con. L.R. 37.
[16] *Barnett v. Chelsea and Kensington Hospital Management* [1969] 1 Q.B. 428.
[17] [1952] 2 All E.R. 452.

case where contractors, near the end of the work, have overrun the contract time for six months without legitimate excuse. They cannot get an extension for that period. Now suppose that the works are still uncompleted and a strike lasts a month. The contractors can get an extension of time for that month".

Lord Denning's view was not expressly criticised by the lower court in *Balfour Beatty v. Chestermount,* but an analogy that was given *obiter dicta* would not sit squarely with it[18]:

> "There may well be circumstances where a relevant event has an impact on the progress of the works during a period of [the contractor's] culpable delay but where the event would have been wholly avoided had the contractor completed the works by the previously-fixed completion date. For example, a storm which floods the site during a period of culpable delay and interrupts progress altogether if the contractor had not overrun the completion date. In such a case it would be hard to see that it would be fair and reasonable to postpone the completion date to extend the contractor's time."

4.249   One of the many problems with causation in construction contracts, particularly with regard to delay as to time, and leaving aside for the moment any question of loss, is that there may be a series of delaying events, and any one of several might be selected as the dominant cause. In *Fairweather & Co. Ltd v. London Borough of Wandsworth*[19] a major issue of the case was concerned with whether an extension of time was a condition precedent to an award of direct loss and/or expense under JCT 63. Not surprisingly, it was found not to be, although it was noted that the contractor who was refused an extension by the architect would be unlikely to succeed with the same architect on an application for direct loss and/or expense. The selection of one dominant cause alone by the arbitrator, a strike for which the contractor would not be compensated under the contract, as the basis for an extension of time was judged an error; and the matter was remitted back to him for an allocation of delay under the various contractual heads in JCT 63.

4.250   There are numerous, almost endless, variables over the course of construction works where "fault"[20] on either side may cause delay.[21] But in JCT 80 the possible "faults" on the Employer's part are in the main provided for in the contract, so that these "faults" are not breaches of contract as such. Also, delay in progress by the Contractor is a matter that cannot be judged against interim dates as the only binding date on the Contractor is

---

[18] (1993) 62 B.L.R. 1 at 34–35.

[19] (1987) 39 B.L.R. 106.

[20] The term "fault" is used loosely in the manner of Edgar Fay J. in *Henry Boot Construction Ltd v. Central Lancashire New Town Development Corporation* 18 B.L.R. 1 *passim*, and particularly at p. 12.

[21] "The number of variables in most delay claims tend to make weather forecasting look simple", Naughton P., *Management of Time in Construction Contract Policy,* edited by Uff and Capper, Centre of Construction Law and Management, Kings College, London (1989), p. 254.

the Completion Date.[22] The practical approach of the industry has been to examine with ever-increasing computerised sophistication the results of delay caused by the contractor, employer, or neutral events (or all of these), on so-called "critical" activities; so that if these "critical" activities are delayed then consequent activities must necessarily be delayed. A certain logic on a "critical path" can then be demonstrated by considering simple precedence in activities, for example, that a wall cannot be painted until it is built. But sometimes assumptions about buildability have to be made in accepting what is critical and what is not amidst many interlinking activities; and where, for example, criticality can change as part of the works unexpectedly become critical because of some major delay, and any of several critical paths have to be redrawn through it, showing a relationship to the completion date. But no matter how sophisticated the original programming, or the delay analysis based on criticality, on-site matters can simply become chaotic, so that everything and nothing becomes critical from one period to the next. A similar but different set of problems arise in the effect of delay on damages or direct loss and/or expense, where delays on a critical path may be used by the contractor to demonstrate a claim for direct loss and /or expense; only to be met by a counter-claim by the employer for damages.[23]

The main legal difficulty is where delay is partly caused by the employer's 4.251 fault and partly caused by the contractor's fault. A further refinement would be where in addition a third party or a "no-fault" event also contributes to delay. Also on either side of this "window" there may have been delays which were solely the fault of the employer, the contractor, or a "no-fault" event. Writers on these issues often refer to them as concurrent delays, without necessarily agreeing on definitions.[24]

The first principle would seem clear from Salmon L.J. in *Peak* 4.252 *Construction (Liverpool) Ltd v. McKinney Foundations*[25]:

> "If the failure to complete on time is due to the fault of both the employer and the contractor, in my view [the extension of time] clause does not bite. I

---

[22] It is rare for a programme to be made contractually binding, especially if the programme is provided by the employer, but it is possible, see *West Faulkener Associates v. London Borough of Newham* (1993) Const. L.J. 232. A contractually binding programme or method statement may in some cases be provided by the contractor, see *Yorkshire Water Authority v. Sir Alfred McAlpine & Son (Northern) Ltd* [1985] 32 B.L.R. 114. Similar decisions were reached in *Holland Dredging (U.K.) Ltd v. Dredging & Construction Co. Ltd* [1987] 37 B.L.R. 1; *Blue Circle Industries plc v. Holland Dredging (U.K.) Ltd* (1987) 37 B.L.R. 40 and *Havant Borough Council v. South Coast Shipping Company Ltd* [1996] C.I.L.L. 1146. For JCT 80 the difficulty in making such documents contractual will be in relation to clause 2.2.1.

[23] The authors of *Keating on Building Contracts* (6th ed.), p. 210 refer to this as "the obverse problem".

[24] See, for example, Galloway and Nielsen, "Concurrent Schedule Delay in International Contracts", I.C.L.R. (1990) 7 (4); Pickavance, *Delay and Disruption in Construction Contracts*, LLP 1997 at Chap. 12; Bramble and Callahan, *Construction Delay Claims* (2nd ed., 1992), Wiley Law Publications at Chapter 1.4.

[25] [1970] 1 B.L.R. 111 at p. 121.

cannot see how, in the ordinary course, the employer can insist on compliance with a condition if it is partly his own fault that it cannot be fulfilled. *Wells v. Army and Navy Co-Operative*[26]; *Amalgamated Building Contractors*[27]; and *Holme v. Guppy*.[28] I consider that unless the contract expresses a contrary intention, the employer in the circumstances postulated is left to his ordinary remedy; that is to say to recover such damages as he can prove flow from the contractor's breach. No doubt if the extension of time clause provided for the postponement of the completion date on account of delay caused by some breach or fault on the part of the employer, the position would be different. This would mean that the parties had intended that the employer could recover liquidated damages notwithstanding that he was partly to blame for the failure to achieve the completion date. In such a case the architect would extend the Date for Completion, and the Contractor would be liable to pay liquidated damages for delay as from the extended Completion Date."

4.253   Further, if there is no contractual basis for giving an extension of time for a matter that constitutes prevention by the employer, it does not appear open to the employer to give a reasonable or commonsense extension and so preserve entitlement to L&ADs. Lloyd L.J. in *Rapid Building v. Ealing*[29] said:

"Like Phillimore L.J. in *Peak Construction (Liverpool) v. McKinney Foundations Ltd*, I was somewhat startled to be told in the course of the argument that if any part of the delay was caused by the employer, no matter how slight, then the liquidated damages clause in the contract, clause 22, becomes inoperative.

I can well understand how that must necessarily be so in a case in which the delay is indivisible and there is dispute as to the extent of the employer's responsibility for that delay. But where there are, as it were, two separate and distinct periods of delay with two separate causes, and where the dispute relates only to one of those causes, then it would seem to me just and convenient that the employer should be able to claim liquidate damages in relation to the other period.

In the present case the relevant dispute relates to the delay, if any, caused by the presence of squatters. At the most that could not account for more than... a period of some 24 days. It ought to be possible for the employers to concede that there is a dispute as to that period, and then deduct the 24 days from the total delay... and claim liquidated damages for the balance. But it was common ground before us that that is not a possible view of clause 22 of the contract in the light of the decision of the Court of Appeal in *Peak's* case, and therefore I say no more about it".

4.254   What then should the employer do if he is partly to blame for delay in respect of a matter covered by the contract, and the contractor is also in delay. Does the employer ignore the contractor's delay, and scrupulously

---

[26] [1903] *Hudson's Building Contracts* (4th ed.), Vol. 2, 346.
[27] [1952] 2 All E.R. 452.
[28] (1838) 3 M. & W. 387.
[29] *Rapid Building Group Ltd v. Ealing Family Housing Association* (1984) 29 B.L.R. 5.

give extensions in respect of his own faults? It would seem from *Balfour Beatty v. Chestermount*[30] that the contractor should get no such "windfall". In this case the Employer under JCT 80 was entitled to have the appropriate time to carry out a Variation instruction issued after the Completion Date added to the existing Completion Date. It was no drawback that in effect the contractual provisions would then make the Contractor bound to complete the Variation works at a time before the instruction was issued, because otherwise the contractor would have had the slate wiped clean in respect of his current delay.[31]

In *Balfour Beatty* it was stated at page 25:

> "The underlying objective is to arrive at the aggregate period of time within which the contract works as ultimately defined ought to have been completed having regard to the incidence of main contractor's risk events and to calculate the excess time, if any, over that period, which the contractor took to complete the works. In essence the architect is concerned to arrive at an aggregate period for completion of the contractual works, having regard to main contractor's risk events and to calculate the extent to which the completion of the works has exceeded the period".

In the light of this decision it appears that the scheme of the extension of time provisions as they affect the Completion Date and therefore the Employer's entitlement to L&ADs is to focus on the Contractor's risks, and keep them with the Contractor. There is no analysis of causation or concurrency in the judgment. Indeed, having decided the matter in that way, Coleman J. felt there was no need to form a view on "conceptual difficulties",[32] presumably related to causation and concurrency, if all or part of the employer's claim became for unliquidated damages.[33]   4.255

The "conceptual difficulties" alluded to by Colman J. in *Balfour Beatty* are indeed problematic. These might be summarised in the following question: 4.256

(a) What legal basis for the analysis of "fault" on the part of either the employer or contractor, or both of them, should be applied in reaching a decision on damages; (b) particularly as the "fault" on the employer's side is likely not to be a breach of contract, but something specifically provided for in the contract; (c) where the contractor's fault as regards progress can normally only be contractually related to a single completion date at any give time; (d) and also where the contract does not speak of damages but of an ascertainment of direct loss and/or expense?

---

[30]   *Balfour Beatty Building Ltd v. Chestermount Properties Ltd* [1993] 62 B.L.R. 1.
[31]   Although the Inner House decision in *Steel v. Bell*, 1901 S.L.T. 381 was not cited, this would appear to be the Scottish position too, see para. 4.229.
[32]   *ibid.* at 35.
[33]   As had been held in New Zealand in *Baskett v. Bendigo Gold Dredging Company* (1902) 21 N.Z.L.R. 166; and in the Supreme Court of Victoria in *SMK Cabinets v. Hill Modern Electrics Pty Ltd* [1984] V.R. 391.

Part (d) of the question will be looked at in relation to clause 26. As regards parts (a) and (b) of the question, the first issue is that of "fault". It seems that neither contract law nor the law of negligence provide a single answer by way of analogy for a "fault" that is provided for in the contract. A contract law analysis would normally first involve identifying a breach of contract, and then what financial effects the breach causes. If these financial effects amount to a loss which is not too remote, judged from the perspective of the time the contract was made, the loss can be recovered from the party responsible for the breach. If there are mutual breaches of contract, each party would be required to prove his claim on a balance of probability, and ultimately, by the rules relating to set-off or compensation; damages could be set-off by each of the parties against the other. A party who has suffered loss can only recover those losses which he could reasonably have been expected to have mitigated the effects of. If a loss is caused partly by one party's breach of contract and partly by a supervening event, the law will look to the "dominant cause". If a loss is caused partly by one party to the contract and partly by the other there is authority that liability can be apportioned.[34]

4.257 An analysis of fault under the law of negligence would first seek to identify whether a duty of care was owed by one party to the other. The nature of the loss suffered would be identified as the law of negligence is predominantly concerned with damage to property and injury to the person, although pure financial loss can in some circumstances be recoverable. If the fault "materially contributed" to the loss then all the losses could be recoverable. It is a moot point whether the same rules as in contract for remoteness of damage apply, or whether recovery can be claimed for the actual loss that occurred provided some loss was foreseeable. Awards of damages can be reduced by statute for contributory negligence. In the law of negligence you take your victim as you find him, even if he is more susceptible to the loss than an ordinary person might be. In short, the rules of causation and remoteness of damage are probably different for both branches of law; mitigation of loss is a feature of contract law only; and there is arguably a difference relating to apportionment of liability where there is contributory fault. It is tempting to suggest that the construction

---

[34] This last point may be a moot point, and some might argue that contract law has an "all or nothing" approach to breach of contract. But it is submitted that that is the effect of the decision in *Tennant Radiant Heat Ltd v. Warrington Development Corporation* [1988] 1 E.G.L.R. 41 (AC), and which was followed in *W. Lamb Ltd v. J. Jarvis & Son plc*, 1998 C.I.L.L. 1427. It is true that the Court of Appeal in *Bank of Nova Scotia v. Hellenic Mutual War Risks Association (Bermuda) Ltd* [1990] 1 Q.B. 818 said: "the scope and extent [of *Tennant*] would have to be a matter of substantial argument if the principle there applied were to arise for consideration in another case." See also the Law Commission Report, *Contributory Negligence as a Defence in Contract* (Law Com. No. 219) 1993; and also *Barclays Bank plc v. Fairclough Building Ltd* [1995] 1 All E.R. 2289 (AC): contributory negligence was not a defence to a claim for damages founded on a strict contractual obligation.

industry is not holding its breath waiting for an answer to these "conceptual difficulties" and that in practice there is a tendency to keep such matters away from the courts, by means of settlement of claims or recourse to arbitration. An industry approach on how to analyse delay in relation to critical path analysis, and then demonstrate loss as a result, seems to have developed independently of the promptings of the courts or lawyers. There are relatively few legal decisions on these matters, and yet millions of pounds worth of claims are settled in the industry each year. Whether or not lawyers like it, much of the negotiation of these issues is carried out by claims consultants, who are normally a multi-disciplinary group of persons whose first qualifications will be in the construction field. At least one of these companies is now listed on the Stock Exchange.[35] A typical construction claim will now include a retrospective delay analysis.

Retrospective delay analysis

In *McAlpine Humberoak Ltd v. McDermott International Inc. (No. 1)*[36]   4.258 there had been a 92-day trial at first instance on the effects of a welter of variation orders on a contract for the construction of nine steel pallets for an oil platform in the Shetland basin. The trial judge had found that the effect of the variations was to frustrate the contract and render time for completion "at large". The Court of Appeal overturned that decision. Whilst the case did not involve JCT 80, some guidance on the question of assessing the effect of variations on delay on any construction contract can be taken from the decision of the Court of Appeal. There was criticism of the judge's approach and the analysis of delay which was presented by an expert witness for the plaintiffs. The judge had said:

> "The concatenation of causes of delay and disruption in this case were almost infinite. They all boil down in the end to two basic causes; the issue of the additional drawings and their impact on the lump sum element of the work; and the inordinate time which it took McDermott to respond to TQs [Technical Queries] to approve working drawings, and in the case of lifting beams, to approve their design."[37]

The judge was criticised in the Court of Appeal as follows:

> "Yet the judge made no detailed findings, or indeed any findings at all, as to any of these matters, save for his generalised conclusion that the time taken as a whole was reasonable, and that therefore the plaintiffs were entitled to recover the whole of their costs plus 10% profit. This hardly did justice to the painstaking analysis by the defendant's experts of what actually happened."[38]

---

[35]   James R. Knowles plc (the author's mentors for five years).
[36]   (1992) 58 B.L.R. 1 (AC).
[37]   *ibid.* at 17.
[38]   *ibid.* at 20.

And at page 28:

> "The judge dismissed the defendant's approach to the case as being 'a
> retrospective and dissectional reconstruction by expert evidence of events
> almost day by day, drawing by drawing, TQ by TQ and weld procedure by
> weld procedure, designed to show that the spate of additional drawings which
> descended on McAlpine virtually from the start of the work really had little
> retarding or disruptive effect on its progress.' In our view the defendants'
> approach is just what the case required."

4.259   Whilst this case should be seen in context, and not strictly concerned
with an extension of time to preserve liquidated damages, it does appear
that the courts will look for some analysis of cause and effect when
considering questions of delay, at least in so far as loss and/or expense, or
damages are concerned. The expert's approach in this case: "that if one
man was working for one day on a particular VO [Variation Order], the
whole contract was held up for that day", was described as defective.[39]

4.260   Similarly, but in the context of JCT 80, in *John Barker Construction v.
London Portman Hotel*[40] the Recorder, Roger Toulson Q.C., stated:

> "In my judgment his [the architect's] assessment of the extension of time
> due to the plaintiffs was fundamentally flawed in a number of respects,
> namely... [the architect] did not carry out a logical analysis in a methodical
> way of the impact which the relevant matters had or were likely to have on
> the plaintiff's planned programme.... He made an impressionistic rather than
> a calculated assessment of the time which he thought reasonable for the
> various items individually and overall".

The architect was under a duty to act fairly, and the grounds of challenge
were not simply limited to "bad faith or manifest excess of jurisdiction". In
evidence the architect had indicated that he had tried to identify critical
delays, but this was not something which he had been consistent about
when he gave the extension.

4.261   What appears to be gaining credence in the construction industry is the
belief that a "critical path analysis" is necessary to establish an entitlement to
an extension of time. This follows on from the American experience,[41] although
no such requirement is specifically called for in JCT 80. Various computer
software programmes are available to demonstrate critical paths,[42] and expert
witnesses known as "planners", who are generally quantity surveyors by

---

[39] *ibid.* at 25.
[40] (1996) 50 Con. L.R. 43.
[41] See Bramble & Callahan, *Construction Delay Claims* (1992, Wiley Law Publications);
      particularly at 212 quoting the decision in *Minmar Builders Inc.,* GSBCA No. 3,430, 72–2
      BCA (CCH), para. 9,599 (1972).
[42] A legal definition of a critical path was given in *Haney v. United States* 230 Ct. Cl. 148,
      167–168, 676, F. 2D 584, 595 (1982), quoted in full by Pickavance, *Delay and Disruption
      in Construction Contracts* (1997) at 172.

training, have come to dominate this area. There does not appear to be standardisation of methodology or terminology for such analyses, and considerably different results can be obtained from different approaches.[43]

Critical path analysis[44]

A critical path for a set of activities is a time and resource management 4.262 technique based on simple arithmetical modelling for complex projects.[45] The constituent parts of the project may be started and stopped independently of others. Logically some activities must precede others in whole or in part, so-called precedent activities and dependent activities. Each activity has a duration based on the resources available to carry it out, and obviously, each activity must have a start and a finish. The beginnings and ends of each activity can be put into a logical relationship — based on buildability in the context of construction — with other succeeding activity or activities, by comparing starts and finishes. There are only four basic possibilities: until the first is finished the second cannot start (F-S); until the first starts the second cannot start (S-S); until the first starts the second cannot finish (S-F); and until the first is finished the second cannot finish (F-F). A precedence network is thus created showing the relationship of starts and finishes between activities. Refinements can be built into these start to finish links, as, for example, there may have to be a lag between the finish of one activity and the start of another, as when plaster has to dry. Conversely, where separate trades follow others round a building there may be an overlap in one starting before the other has actually finished.

Buildability may mean that there are many possible precedence networks 4.263 between linked activities. Buildability can establish what resources can be used for each activity (*e.g.* two men for five days or five men for two days). Each activity, once resourced, can be separately studied to discover four things for it: the earliest start date; the latest start date; the earliest finish date; and the latest finish date. Where there is no difference between these the activity will be critical. It is said to have "zero float". The critical path will be the sequence of such critical activities that would take the longest time, as by definition any delays to it will control the soonest completion of all the works. It may be possible to shorten the critical path by targeting more (and more effective) resources to critical activities, although this may mean that the critical path then shifts to go through other jobs. Much of the advance in this area of analysis is due to computer software programmes which make graphical representations of these matters readable, normally by what is called the cascade diagram method — a sort of linked bar chart

---

[43] For the most recent and fullest exposition on the topic from a U.K. perspective see Pickavance, *Delay and Disruption in Construction Contracts* (1997) *passim*.

[44] The current British Standard is BS 6064 "The Use of Network Techniques in Project Management".

[45] A review of the technique in a study for a construction project is in Levy, Thomson, Wiest, "The ABC's of the Critical Path Method", *The Harvard Business Review* 41 (4) 1963, 98–108.

— and the processing of resource levelling algorithms automatically.[46] Accordingly, a project manager can manage resources on various activities consistently, without simply deciding to expedite everything wildly. The packages vary in capabilities to handle between 10,000–100,000 activities and teams of planners may be involved. However actually operating the software is often remarkably easy to learn (half a day, with built-in teaching "wizards"),[47] but the underlying construction experience is where the real expertise lies.

4.264 A retrospective delay analysis based on analysis of critical paths and how they alter can then be carried out. For example, delays can be added to a network, normally the "as built" network, and the resultant delay to the completion date shown; or an "as-built" network can have the delaying factors subtracted. The former tend to be called "impact analyses", and the later "collapsing" or "but-for analyses". Great care should be taken in factoring in delaying events as these will probably shift the critical paths and widely differing results of analysis are possible. The responsibility for each delaying activity as between employer, contractor and neutral event, and the "conceptual difficulties"[48] of causation would have to be considered in the light of the scant legal authority reviewed above.

4.265 There are also other legal factors that have not yet been considered. As noted above, critical path analysis involves the analysis of float, with zero float activities being critical. It is therefore possible that certain delays will not be critical for the purposes of delay because there is scope in the precedence network as to when they can start or finish with given resources: they have "float" built in. In relation to delay the question that is sometimes asked is "who owns the float"? But this question by focusing on the float tends to overly simplify causation and concurrency issues, and fails to distinguish between extensions of time under clause 25 and the "obverse problem"[49] under clause 26. In *Hounslow v. Twickenham Garden Developments*[50] Guy J. said in relation to JCT 63, clause 23:

> "If a contractor is well ahead with his works and is then delayed by a strike, the architect may, nevertheless, reach the conclusion that completion of the works is not likely to be delayed beyond the date of completion.... If a strike occurs when 2/3 of the work has been completed in 1/2 the contract time, I

[46] A 1994 survey by Aouad, Ghassan and Price, Andrew D.F., "Construction Planning and Information Technology in the U.K. and U.S. Construction Industries: A Comparative Study" (1994) *Construction Management and Economics* 12, 97–106, found that the software package Pertmaster was the most popular in the U.K. (31%) and Primavera in the U.S. (67.5%).
[47] *ibid.*
[48] See note 32.
[49] May, *Keating on Building Contracts* (6th ed.) at 210. See note 23.
[50] [1970] 7 B.L.R. 89 at 113.

do not think that on resuming work a few weeks later a contractor is then entitled to slow down the work so as to last out the time until the date for completion (or beyond, if an extension of time is granted) if, thereby, he is failing to proceed with the work 'regularly and diligently'."

These comments seem to the author highly questionable. How best to 4.266 manage the construction works must be a matter for the contractor,[51] particularly in the light of modern critical path analysis and resource levelling. The judge was concerned with whether to grant an injunction excluding the contractor from the site, on the basis that the contractor's employment had been validly terminated for failing to proceed "regularly and diligently" under JCT 63. What would constitute a failure to proceed "regularly and diligently" was not indicated by the judge, however he did say: "but I find great difficulty in forming any clear conclusion merely from the number of workers. Nor under this head do I find much help in the value of the certificates".[52] In any event he refused the injunction on a balance of convenience, saying that what was involved was the application of an uncertain concept to disputed facts.

In *Glenlion Construction Ltd v. The Guinness Trust*[53] the question arose 4.267 as to whether there was an implied term under JCT 63 for the employer to enable the contractor to complete ahead of programme. It was held that whilst the contractor was entitled to complete ahead of programme, he was not obliged to. Therefore such an implied term would impose an obligation on the employer and not the contractor and could not be implied: "The contractor cannot unilaterally determine what is a reasonable time." This adopted the reasoning of Diplock J. in *Needox v. Swinton & Pendelbury*[54] in relation to an engineering contract that what was a reasonable time for the issue of instructions should include the point of view of the engineer and his staff and the employer. Also, in *Glenlion* the extension of time provisions were noted to apply to the date for completion stated in the contract, not any earlier date. The *Glenlion* decision did not mention the question of float in a programme or critical path methodology, but dealt with the question of early completion by four weeks. Without discussing questions of float Fox-Andrews J. said: "A fair and reasonable extension of time for completion of the works beyond the date for completion stated in the appendix might be an unfair and unreasonable extension from an earlier date." This suggests to some that a contractor's float should be disregarded for extension of time purposes, but if that is correct, it entirely discounts all questions of concurrency and causation.

---

[51] *Greater London Council v. Cleveland Bridge and Engineering Co.* 34 B.L.R. at 78.
[52] *op.cit.* at 120.
[53] *Glenlion Construction Ltd v. The Guinness Trust* 11 Con. L.R. 126.
[54] *Needox Ltd v. The Mayor Alderman and Burgesses of the Borough of Swinton and Pendelbury* (1958) 5 B.L.R. 34.

4.268   It is submitted that an architect who has accepted the methodology of a critical path would have an implied obligation to release information so that the contractor might keep to the critical path, if the critical path terminates at the completion date. If that were not so, the reasoning of *Glenlion* would mean that critical path methodology was meaningless as a tool for project management, extensions of time, and for direct loss and/or expense claims. This submission is based on the decision in *London Borough of Merton v. Stanley Hugh Leach*[55] where Vinelott J. said:

> "A document that sets out in diagrammatic form the planned programme for the work and indicates the dates by which instructions, drawings, details and levels are required could be a specific application to meet the requirements of clause 23 and clause 24 [of JCT 63]. Such an application might be made at the commencement of the work for all the instructions that the Contractor could foresee would be required in the course of the Works provided that the date specified for delivery of each set of instructions met the requirements of not being unreasonably distant from or close to the relevant date. If the Works do not progress strictly in accordance with the plan, some modification may be required to the prescribed timetable and the subsequent furnishing of instructions."

4.269   Further, in *GLC v. Cleveland Bridge and Engineering Co.*[56] it was held by the Court of Appeal that there was no obligation on the contractor to "conduct his programme and his commencing dates as to afford the best advantage to the employer". *GLC v. Cleveland Bridge* concerned the operation of a pricing formula, and the interpretation of the phrase "due diligence" in respect of the contractor's progress. Parker L.J. said this:

> "Suppose that it takes or could take ten months to make a particular gate [of the Thames barrier]. Suppose also that the interval between the time when it ought to be ready and the beginning of the contract is four years. It is now conceded, although it was not originally, that the manufacturer is perfectly entitled if he wishes to manufacture or fabricate that gate during the last ten months of the contract."[57]

Parker L.J. continued at page 78:

> "if the contractor deliberately delayed the last slap of paint in order to prolong the manufacturing period,... he may perfectly well, as it seems to me, say, 'I am going to conduct matters so that I do none of the painting of any of the gates until the last possible moment.' That might result in a gate being fabricated save for painting at an early stage, but if the contractor says, 'I will hold the painting on that and do all the painting on all the gates at a later stage because I find that the best way to conduct my work', I can see no possible reason why he should not."

---

[55]   (1985) 32 B.L.R. 51.
[56]   *op.cit.*
[57]   *ibid.* p. 76.

The relevant clause in JCT 80 is clause 25.3.4.1, which provides that the 4.270 Contractor: "shall use constantly his best endeavours to prevent delay in the progress of the Works, howsoever caused, and to prevent the completion of the Works being delayed or further delayed beyond the Completion Date". This particular clause does not appear to have been judicially considered, but it is submitted that it would be construed in much the same way as in *GLC v. Cleveland Bridge.* Whilst this clause bears a passing resemblance to the common law duty to mitigate loss sustained by the party who suffers a breach of contract, reflection shows that the extension of time clause is for the Employer's benefit as regards preserving the L&ADs clause. If there is a culpable delay by the Contractor the Employer should be entitled to L&ADs. If the Contractor fails to "mitigate" delay the penalty against him would be the same: L&ADs. The "obverse" problem[58] that delay by the Contractor's fault may entitle the Employer to L&ADs is not specifically catered for in clause 25, nor in clause 26.

One way of mitigating delay is for the architect to omit work. In *Balfour* 4.271 *Beatty v. Chestermount,*[59] whilst directly concerned with net extensions of time, the position of how variations omitting work should affect the completion date was considered *obiter dicta.* Colman J. said: "If [the completion date] is advanced by reason of an omission instruction the consequence may well be that the adjustment required by way of reduction of the time for completion is sufficiently substantial to justify refixing the completion date before the issue of the instruction." These remarks are relevant when there is delay to the Completion Date because otherwise JCT 80 only allows the fixing of an earlier completion Date under clauses 25.3.2 and 25.3.3 to extended Completion Dates (*i.e.* not the Date for Completion stated in the Appendix). Nor can the Architect shorten the Completion Date where a 13A Quotation has been given and the length of time for such has been stated in a confirmed acceptance of a 13A Quotation.

Where the Architect omits part of the works which is covered by a 4.272 provisional sum the Contractor has no remedy in respect of loss of profits. However if the omitted item covered by a provisional sum is then given to a third party to execute, the Contractor is entitled to loss of profit.[60]

Clause 26: Loss and Expense caused by matters materially affecting regular progress of the Works

This clause, following on from the extensions of time and L&AD clauses, 4.273 is another of the construction industry's peculiar and important clauses. This clause, properly operated, allows the Contractor to be paid "direct loss and/or expense" under the terms of the contract, and in interim payments,

---

[58] See notes 49 and 23.
[59] (1993) 62 B.L.R.I.
[60] *Amec Building Ltd v. Cadmus Investment Co. Ltd* (1997) 13 Const. L.J. 50.

when certain "matters" which are specified in clause 26 arise. It should be noted at the outset that clause 26.6 specifies that the provisions of clause 26 "are without prejudice to any other rights and remedies which the Contractor may possess." Therefore if there are breaches of contract that might give rise to a damages claim, these can also be pursued.[61] Some sophisticated legal reasoning then is necessary to see that two avenues of claim can be pursued by the contractor both under the contract, and for breach of contract at common law.

4.274   Claims clauses differ in wording from standard form to standard form, and a host of difficulties can occur as to what should be properly recoverable. Should "direct loss and/or expense" mean cost to the Contractor or cost plus lost profit, or are they interchangeable? Should it include losses of a supplier or sub-contractor that are being laid at the door of the contractor?[62] This brings us into the minefield of how a contractor arrives at a lump sum price in the first place, and what use the bill of quantities should be in construing what should be recoverable. Disputes can arise as to whether a claim properly arises under a particular part of clause 26, or should be valued under the variations clauses 13.5.1 to 13.5.7; whether a claim is supported by sufficient evidence; whether a claim was made timeously; and most importantly, what the true relationship should be of cause and effect between delay and effect on resources. The central problem in any such analysis is that the activities in a construction project for a lump sum are not in reality uniquely costed and marked up with a profit, which is known to be recoverable if a certain amount of time is spent doing that activity. Bills of quantities are simply not designed to show this: they are essentially for measuring what has been done or should be done.

4.275   A financial claim made by a contractor will normally also be for an extension of time under clause 25, with all the permutations of culpability and criticality that we have seen above. Also, there is always the contractor's obligation to constantly use his best endeavours to prevent delay in the progress of the works, howsoever caused, and to prevent the works being delayed or further delayed beyond the Completion Date (clause 25.3.4.1); and to do all that may be reasonably required to the satisfaction of the Architect to proceed with the Works (clause 25.3.4.2).

---

[61] Not all building contracts have such a clause, *e.g.* MF/1 General Conditions of Contract. The absence of such a clause was held to preclude a claim based on breach of contract or, under English law, the Misrepresentation Act 1967; see *Strachan & Henshaw Ltd v. Stein Industrie (U.K.) Ltd (No. 2)* 87 B.L.R. 52 (CA) where an instruction to move tea cabins on site half a mile away was not a variation and the contractor was not compensated for "walking time".

[62] In the context of ICE 5th ed. a fair valuation under clause 51 (2) must include loss of profit claimed by a sub-contractor or supplier whose contract is cancelled as a result of a variation ordered by the engineer, see *Tinghamgrange Ltd (trading as Gryphonn Concrete Products) v. Dew Group Ltd and North West Water Ltd* (1995) 47 Con. L.R. 105 (CA).

Almost inevitably the Contractor will seek an extension of time to the date of 4.276 Practical Completion, to protect himself against the deduction of L&ADs, and seek direct loss and/or expense under clause 26 on a full-cost-to-him basis, "because the regular progress of the Works or any part thereof has been or is likely to be materially affected by any one or more of the matters referred to in clause 26.2", or due to deferment of giving possession of the site under clause 23.1.2.

A clause 26 claim therefore has to establish what direct loss and /or expense 4.277 means in relation to the contractor's price; what "regular progress" should be regarded as, when he has no positive contractual obligation to carry out the works to a programme (clause 5.3.2), merely to provide a programme (clause 5.3.1.1) and to prevent delay (clause 25.3.4.1) and to proceed regularly and diligently with the works (clause 27.2.1.1); what "materially affected" means; and what the clause 26.2 "matters" are.

Recently in the case of *Ogilvie Builders Ltd v. City of Glasgow District* 4.278 *Council*[63] Lord Abernethy in the Outer House stated:

> "direct loss in terms of this clause [26.1] of the contract is, in my opinion, the same as loss arising naturally in accordance with the first branch of *Hadley v. Baxendale*. There is no doubt that that is the conclusion reached by the Court of Appeal in *Minter*[64] and followed by the same court in *Rees & Kirby*[65] (see also *Keating on Building Contracts* [5th ed.], at p. 583)."

This case concerned another common aspect of claims in the construction industry: claims for finance charges. If a contractor incurs loss and expense and there is a delay in making payment of that, the contractor will argue that he has effectively financed the employer for the period that he has withheld the money, either by the contractor incurring overdraft interest himself, or losing out in making use of that money. The question in the *Minter*[66] case of whether such a claim would qualify as direct loss and/or expense payable under the contract was actually conceded by counsel as payable under the first limb of *Hadley v. Baxendale*; but no such concession in the *Ogilvie* case was made. Lord Abernethy at page 23 after reviewing Scottish authorities notes:

> "But all these cases turned on their own facts and circumstances, which were different from the facts and circumstances in this case, and I do not read any of them as indicating any general proposition that claims for financing charges, if recoverable at all, can only be recovered under the second branch of the rule in *Hadley v. Baxendale*. Moreover circumstances may change with the times. And if they do the law must recognise that and adapt. So what at one point may be considered an extravagant proposition, to use Lord Hunter's phrase in *Tiffney*,[67] is not necessarily to be considered so for all time. These things are not cast in tablets of stone. In the recent case of *Margrie*,[68] the

---

[63] 1995 S.L.T. 15.
[64] *F.G. Minter Ltd v. Welsh Health Technical Services Organisation* (1980) 13 B.L.R. 1.
[65] *Rees & Kirby Ltd v. Swansea City Council* (1985) 30 B.L.R. 1.
[66] *op.cit.*
[67] *Tiffney v. Bachurzewski*, 1985 S.L.T. 165; 1984 S.C. 108.
[68] *Margrie Holdings Ltd v. City of Edinburgh District Council*, 1994 S.L.T. 571.

court had *Minter* before them. But there is nothing in the opinion of the court given by the Lord President which indicates disagreement with the approach taken in *Minter* that in appropriate circumstances financing charges of the kind claimed there could arise naturally according to the usual course of things and so be recoverable under the first branch of the rule in *Hadley v. Baxendale*. The financing charges claimed in this case are of the same kind as claimed in *Minter*. I see nothing extravagant in the averments made in art. 5 of the condescendence in support of the claim under this branch of the rule in *Hadley v. Baxendale*. Indeed it seems to me compatible with sound financial strategy in the construction industry that the pursuers should incur these financing charges."

Lord Abernethy noted that the defenders had regularly ingathered and collated financial information about prospective tenderers for local authority work and went on: "it is also to be borne in mind that these parties are not strangers to one another nor are their respective positions with regard to these financing charges unknown to one another."

4.279   The decision in the *Ogilvie* case is consistent with a case which preceded it before the sheriff principal at Falkirk but which was reported subsequently: *W. M. Nelson Cladding Ltd v. Murray Williamson (Builders) Ltd.*[69] In that case the defenders counterclaimed against a roofing sub-contractor for finance charges incurred due to the late payment to them by the employer caused by rectification works to the sub-contract works which were admittedly defective and in breach of contract. Although the case gives no details as to what contractual conditions prevailed in either the main contract or the sub-contract, the sheriff principal held that financing charges were a loss occasioned by the pursuer's breach of contract and must be held to have been in the reasonable contemplation of the parties at the time they made the contract. He said:

"it must have been known to any contractor in the building trade that such a breach of contract could well result in the withholding of an architect's certificate and consequent delay in funds becoming available to the contractors. The loss caused by funds not being timeously available is in my judgment a loss which not only arises naturally from the pursuer's breach of contract but also and in any event must also be held to have been in the reasonable contemplation of these parties at the time they made the contract".

It is interesting to note in the report of this case that there is no indication that the parties were not strangers to each other in the sense commented on in *Ogilvie*, or that there was any notice given as regards these charges actually being incurred. The position with respect to interest on unpaid certificates is now explicitly possible under JCT 80 since Amendment 18 introduced clause 30.8.[70]

---

[69] 1995 S.L.T. (Sh. Ct.) 86.
[70] See comments at para. 4.342.

Written Application

Clause 26 of JCT 80 begins: "If the Contractor makes written application   4.280
to the Architect stating that he has incurred or is likely to incur direct loss
and/or expense (of which the Contractor may give his quantification [words
in brackets *per* Amendment 18]) in the execution of this contract for which
he would not be reimbursed by a payment under any other provision of this
contract...". The clause does not go on to state what such written application
should contain or even give a specimen for such application. The clause
would also appear be to predicated on the making of such application, but
the timing of any such notice can be confusing as the Contractor's application
can be for either direct loss and/or expense that has been incurred, and
future or even contingent loss and/or expense that may or may not be
incurred. It would seem that the Contractor is the appropriate party to identify
such a claim, as the Architect would scarcely be in a position to identify the
Contractor's loss.

As for the cause of the loss, this may be: "due to deferment of giving
possession of the site under clause 23.1.2 where clause 23.1.2 is stated in
the Appendix to be applicable or because the regular progress of the Works
or any part thereof has been or is likely to be materially affected by any one
or more of the matters referred to in clause 26.2". The cause of loss would
appear to be an objective one for the Architect to decide.

However, it is "provided always" that the Contractor is to make
application in terms of clause 26.1.1 "as soon as it has become, or should
reasonably have become, apparent to him that the regular progress of the
Works or of any part thereof has been or was likely to be affected as
aforesaid." (Note the word "materially" vanishes in clause 26.1.1 for no
apparent reason.) This is an issue related to time and resources.

So what does the Contractor have to identify first to make a valid   4.281
application a loss; a likely loss; a clause 26.2 matter (remembering that
clause 26.2 does not cover all possible breaches of contract at common
law); a delay to progress; or a likely delay to progress; or a combination of
these; or must all coincide? The cause or clause 26.2 matter would appear
the logical starting point, but that is a matter for the Architect to identify,
and he will probably not know the effect of the cause on the Contractor.

In the case of *Rees and Kirby v. Swansea City Council*[71] which dealt   4.282
with clause 11(6) of JCT 63, Robert Goff L.J. stated: "It seems to me that,
in the ongoing relationship between a contractor and an architect carrying
out their functions under a contract in this form, a sensible and not too
technical attitude must be adopted with regard to the form of such an
application."

In the *Minter* case which was dealing with the JCT 63 contract and   4.283
clauses 11(6) and 24(1), being the variations and loss and expense clauses

---

[71] [1985] B.L.R. 1.

respectively, with the wording slightly amended so that applications had to be made "not more than 21 days" as opposed to "within a reasonable time", the question of the timing of such applications was considered. Stephenson L.J. was of the view that interest lost or expended before an application some three weeks previously was still direct and recoverable, but that regular applications under this contract still had to be made. He noted that:

> "It is, I suspect, to meet the difficulties...by the need for successive applications that the 1980 edition of the Standard Contract has been redrafted (clause 26.1) to require applications to be made 'as soon as it has become, or should reasonably have become apparent to him [the Contractor] that the regular progress of the works or any part thereof has been or is likely to be affected' by specified events (including instructions requiring Variation) and to state 'that he has incurred or is likely to incur direct loss and/or expense'; and also to require the Architect to ascertain the amount of such loss and/or expense which has been or is being incurred by the Contractor."

4.284   It would appear therefore that under JCT 80 successive applications need not be made, nor that a back-dated claim for finance charges will be invalid. In *Minter* a compounded interest charge on an overdraft was also regarded as direct. The important point to grasp is that finance charges, which look very like interest on a debt, will be recoverable: whereas any interest on a debt is only recoverable in restricted circumstances in Scotland; notably where it can be shown that there has been wrongful withholding of monies; under Amendment 18, clause 30.8; or under the Late Payment of Commercial Debts (Interest) Act 1998.[72]

4.285   A distinction between JCT 63 and 80 is that the latter requires that the Contractor shall in support of his application submit to the Architect *upon request* such information as would reasonably enable the architect to form an opinion (clause 26.1.2). It seems that lack of particularity of a claim under clause 26 will not defeat it if the Architect does not request it. However, for the purposes of adjustment of the Contract Sum (clause 30.6.1): "not later than 6 months after Practical Completion of the Works the Contractor shall provide the Architect, or, if so instructed by the Architect, the Quantity Surveyor, with all documents necessary for the adjustment of the Contract Sum...".

4.286   However in *Croudace Ltd v. London Borough of Lambeth*[73] it was held that the Architect's failure to ascertain the amount of direct loss and/or expense under clause 26 was a breach of contract for which the Employer may be liable in damages. Also in *Rees & Kirby Ltd v. Swansea City Council (supra)* which dealt with JCT 63, it appears that notice that an element of the claim concerns financing charges should be given, and that there is no cut-off point at Practical Completion for finance charges.

---

[72] See comments at para. 4.342.
[73] (1986) 33 B.L.R. 20, CA.

The clause 26 matters are, to paraphrase: 4.287

(1) delay in receipt of instructions, drawings, details and levels, from the Architect;
(2) opening up of work for inspection and testing, where the work opened up conforms to contract;
(3) discrepancies or divergences between or amongst Contract Documents, for example Contract Documents and Contract Bills and/or Numbered Documents;
(4) the carrying out of work by other persons employed directly by Employer (*N.B.* not Nominated Sub-Contractors);
(5) postponement of work;
(6) failure of the Employer to give ingress or egress from the site at the appropriate time;
(7) authorised Variations and for the expenditure of provisional sums;
(8) the execution of work for which an Approximate Quantity is included in the Contract Bills which is not a reasonably accurate forecast of the quantity of work required;
(9) failure to comply with an Information Release Schedule;
(10) suspension of the performance by the Contractor under Amendment 18, clause 30.1.4.

Interestingly no correlation has been introduced between clause 26 and the new priced Activity Schedule introduced by Amendment 18 and as defined in clause 1.3.

What is normally found in claims?

Typically, contractors categorise different types of direct loss and/ 4.288 or expense as either prolongation costs or disruption. For prolongation there is normally claimed to be an extension of time entitlement also under clause 25. For disruption there need not have actually been a delay to the works, merely that the contractor has been unable to use his resources as profitably as he might have done were it not for the specified matters. The term "prolongation" has not been judicially defined, nor has "disruption", although it normally features along with "delay and/or disruption". It has been held that under clause 23.2.1 of NSC/4a set-off provisions related to delay claims also applied to disruption claims.[74] The term "forced overrun" into winter working was judicially approved as a head of claim, albeit *obiter dicta* by Lord Maxwell in *Wimpey Construction (U.K.) Ltd v. Martin Black & Co. (Wire Ropes) Ltd.*[75]

---

[74] See *Pillar (P.G.) Ltd v. Higgins* (1986) 10 Con. L.R. 46; 34 B.L.R. 43 (CA).
[75] 1982 S.L.T. 239 at 244.

4.289   A list of prolongation items might be as follows:

> remuneration of site staff and incidental travelling expenses;
> plant and scaffolding retained on site;
> temporary power distribution and lighting;
> temporary offices and storage accommodation;
> any local authority charges;
> electricity accounts for the delay period;
> additional insurance premiums;
> attendances on sub-contracts over a longer period;
> inflation costs;
> security, lighting and protection — especially against vandalism;
> safety and welfare matters;
> site clearance and maintenance of temporary works; and
> head office overheads.

This last item is often thought to include for management and clerical staff:

> salary, bonuses and allowances;
> pension contributions;
> national insurance;
> holiday pay;
> travelling expenses;
> car allowances; and
> fixed overhead costs which increase or which are not adequately recovered
> due to delay.

4.290   It should be noted that in *Minter* the loss of a generous productivity bonus paid by a contractor to his men was thought to be indirect. The hire of plant and machinery would appear to be straightforward, but if the contractor owns his own plant then the cost of depreciation might be recoverable (see *Sunley v. Cunard White Star*).[76] But in *Property and Land Contractors Ltd v. Alfred McAlpine Homes (North) Ltd*[77] plant which was owned by a contractor could not be claimed for on the basis of assumed or typical charges, but only as actual loss.

4.291   The contractor's claim for head office overheads will normally represent the cost of permanent fixed assets such as running and administration costs of their head office; including non-site-based employees and management time. This will be on the basis that the Contract Sum included for such matters and, had his resources not been tied up by the prolongation of the contract he might have redeployed his head office resources to recover such overheads and profit on other jobs. Even if we accept that such a loss would be reasonably foreseeable, and how realistic the opportunity of recovering such losses elsewhere might be, there is also the difficulty of proof of how such head office resources were actually tied up by the delay. Also, a

---

[76] [1940] 1 K.B. 740.
[77] (1995) 76 B.L.R. 59.

contractor's claim will not just seek to recover overhead costs but also argue that he has lost the opportunity of making a profit from such overhead costs, as the only way that he can recover these costs is from his profit percentage of turnover, which, if eroded, represents a loss. This questionable head of claim is, surprisingly perhaps, frequently paid in practice on the basis of certain formulas which have been judicially considered. The most widely used formula is found in *Hudson*. This takes a profit percentage for the under recovery of head office overheads and another fraction representing the overrun of the contract period and multiplies the contract sum to arrive at a figure of loss:

Head office overheads and profit percentage x Contract Sum x Period of Delay
Contract Period

The profit percentage is the profit built into that specific contract. This   4.292
formula has had some judicial approval in *Finnegan v. Sheffield City Council*[78] (where peculiarly the judge seemed to approve the *Hudson* formula but interpreted the meaning of the profit percentage as an annual average); and in the Supreme Court of Ontario in *Ellis-Don v. Parking Authority of Toronto*[79] and in *Whittal Builders v. Chester-le-Street D.C.* (unreported — see *Keating* (6th ed.), p. 230).

In Scotland however in *Wimpey Construction (U.K.) Ltd v. Martin Black*   4.293
& Co. (Wire Ropes)[80] the Outer House judge refused to accept, albeit *obiter dicta,* an overhead rate of 12 per cent as an across-the-board figure as applied to various costs that arose as a result of delay caused when a pile that was being lifted by a crane was dropped because a wire rope sling failed. The backlash effect of the sling failure caused serious operational damage to the crane of a jack-up barge. The barge was then out of commission for 86 days which was a critical matter to progress. The case was decided on questions of whether a valid claim for damages due to negligence could be made when another party's property was damaged. Wimpey owned the pile, but another company in the joint venture owned the barge. The judge found that there had been no evidence that the salvage operation delayed the programme, also that such losses as attributed to delay to the works would have been too remote as Wimpey had no possessory interest in the barge which was damaged.[81] This may have caused injustice in the case of a joint venture where:

> "to an exceptional degree the application of the rule... gives rise to a distinction between the claims of two joint venturers respectively which is likely to appear unreal and even unjust. However in my opinion that is what inevitably arises sooner or later when the law draws a line, not so much on

---

[78] [1988] 43 B.L.R. 124.
[79] [1978] 28 B.L.R. 98.
[80] 1982 S.L.T. 239.
[81] *Dynamco v. Holland & Hannen & Cubitts (Scotland) Ltd*, 1971 S.L.T. 150; 1972 S.L.T. 38; 1971 S.C. 257 followed.

the ground of principle but because of the dictates of policy or practical expediency."

The 12 per cent figure had been applied to all salvage costs, delay to the construction programme, costs of overrun into the winter months, and other miscellaneous charges, including insurance and retained services of monthly paid staff. Lord Maxwell stated at page 245:

> "In my opinion the 12 1/2 % claims in all the actions should be disallowed. The percentage is a notional figure used for accounting purposes within the companies or groups of companies in question. It is no doubt also a figure reasonably used for example in pricing tenders, but does not purport to represent a calculation or even a broad estimate of any loss actually sustained or any cost actually incurred by anyone as a result of the accident. If one takes, for example, item 1.2 of the Wimpey claim, 'salvage vessels', this is largely concerned with the cost of hiring two large floating cranes for salvaging the pile. I can see no logical reason why a figure for head office expenses based on a percentage of that cost should be allowed. If the cranes had cost twice as much or half as much as they did in fact cost I see no reason why head office expenses in hiring them, if any, should correspondingly be doubled or halved. It may be somewhat easier to figure the theoretical basis for the claim in relation to loss for delay. No doubt the administrative centre of a large company is financed by its productive units and it might be said that if a productive unit is rendered unproductive for 86 days there must be some loss in the financial provision it can make to the central administration. Nevertheless it appears to me that the 12 1/2 per cent or any other percentage applied in this way is a purely notional figure not related to any quantifiable reality. I get some support for this view from the fact that neither side were aware of any case in which an award of damages to a company has included an element of this kind. I do not know why the insurers in this and perhaps in other cases accept, according to Mr. Buist, a ten percent addition to a claim for indemnity but the fact that they do is not a reason for the court to include it in a claim for damages."

Although this case was appealed, it was appealed on a matter of the expenses of experts giving evidence. It has appeared to the author that the overall decision was a strange one, particularly as in a joint venture there is only one contractor.

4.294   In a note given by Lord Morton of Shauna in *Rotary Services Ltd v. Honeywell Control Systems*[82] a 15 per cent mark-up across the board with little specification was allowed in the amount of damages which a sub-contractor was allowed to recover from a sub-sub-contractor for the cost of remedial works for which the defenders were liable. This was allowed on the basis that the pursuers pled that the mark-up did not include any profit, and it was held that it was for the defenders to show that it did. It is the author's view that this is a questionable decision.

4.295   Assuming a buoyant market-place where the market is chasing contractors (and not vice versa to get over the problem of foreseeability),

---

[82] 1993 S.L.T. 781.

there is still the problem of causation: *i.e.* was an actual loss of profit caused because of under-recovery of head office overheads; what relationship have head office overheads to overall profitability on the contract; or even generally as part of the contractor's business? Indeed some contractors may have recovered profit through the valuation of extra work. Again we come back to the inherent difficulty of how a contractor assesses his profit as discussed above.

Another leading textbook, *Emden*, has its own formula which follows   4.296
the *Hudson* formula, but instead of profit on the contract, a head office percentage profit for the contractor's year is used. In *Property and Land Contractors Ltd v. Alfred McAlpine Homes North Ltd*[83] a claim under the *Emden* formula was considered. It was held that the pre-conditions for the applicability of the *Emden* formula had not been satisfied. The contractors in this case were in effect a single contract company, normally dedicated to carrying out contracts for its parent company, and not looking to expand. However it was held that the arbitrator had been correct in applying a logic which largely corresponded to a formula in use in the USA, *viz*. the *Eichleay* formula.[84] The arbitrator had accepted on the facts that fixed overhead expenditure, for example rent, was a direct expense as a result of a postponement of the works under clause 23 of JCT 80. Also it was held that even if the Contractor had been on a less unusual business footing they: "would have been entitled to recover as a 'loss' the shortfall in the contribution which the volume of work was expected to have made towards the fixed overheads but which because of a reduction in volume and, it is assumed, in revenue, was not made."

Despite the qualified approval[85] that has been given to these formulae   4.297
the facts of the particular case will be crucial to the application of any formula.[86] As discussed above a contractor will typically make up his tender price by adding a percentage for profit to the cost to him of labour, plant and materials. Both the *Hudson* and *Emden* formulas however apply the percentage to the contract sum which already includes profit and overheads. Therefore there can be an element of double recovery. These formulas can also over compensate a contractor in other ways.[87] If on a £1 million contract for 52 weeks 95 per cent of the works have been certified for payment

---

[83] (1995) 47 Con. L.R. 74; 76 B.L.R. 59.

[84] Described in *Hudson's Building and Civil Engineering Contracts* (11th ed.), paras 8–182 to 8–189.

[85] Also in *St Mowden Developments Ltd v. Bowmer and Kirkland Ltd* (1996) C.I.L.L. 1203 a formula was approved by Fox-Andrews J. where the experts for both parties had used identical styles of formula for calculating head office overheads and profit and it was accepted that the construction industry was booming.

[86] See *City Axis Ltd v. Daniel P. Jackson* [1998] C.I.L.L. 151.

[87] For a telling analysis of how different figures are reached by applying different formulas see: Pettet, J., "Claims for Head Office Overheads and Profit in the Construction Industry", Construction Paper No. 93 (1998) (The Chartered Institute of Building).

leaving only external landscaping works which have been delayed, and the contractor sub-contracts these and is only involved in minor supervision, head office overheads should form only a negligible part of the claim. Perhaps in practice it is recognised that this head of claim is suspect and is often used as a gambit in the negotiations to settle.[88]

4.298   As regards disruption claims, if the contractor can demonstrate output before a disrupting event and a demonstrable drop afterwards then a figure for direct loss and expense can be fixed. This method was judicially approved in *Whittal Builders v. Chester-le-Street.*[89] Life however is seldom that simple as there can be many overlapping disrupting causes, and also the comparison sample might be subject to criticism. Also what may have been disrupted at one part of the job may be counter-balanced at another, or should have been. What tends to be produced are lots of different ratios to show that in a particular period the contractor had to pay his men the same for less performance. Even if the principle behind a claim based on ratios is accepted, very often the information making up the ratios can be juggled. For example, where there is a job involving the pouring of concrete which was due to be completed on November 30, but was not completed till the end of May the following year, an allowance for falling productivity due to winter working is normally claimed due to the failure of the architect. A contractor will normally have records of how many labour hours were involved for how much pour at a given period. How these figures are creatively handled can produce large claims for under-recovery. The contractor may himself have been partly responsible for the overrun into the winter period; he may have been unable to secure labour, the labour may not have been diligent, or may have had to go back to rectify errors.

4.299   Also a contractor may be faced with claims from his suppliers in respect of factory costs that have been incurred due to design changes and which the contractor seeks to pass up the line to the employer. The possibilities of any assessment of direct loss and/or expense can spiral into almost unimaginable difficulties by applying the strict legal theory of cause and effect, which, standing the cases on "global claims" discussed below, is the tool which lawyers will always seek to use to make sense of the position. Contractors however tend to favour a total cost plus profit approach and, the author suspects, often find legal theory of cause and effect artificial. There is something to be said for both views. In large engineering projects, for example in the supply of a diesel power generator or a tunnel boring machine, the disruption can run into millions of pounds. The key seems always to be to keep the best possible records of costs, factory space used, labour and supervision used, and output and hope that some consensus as to the extent of the loss will be accepted as demonstrated.

---

[88]   Indeed in *Amec Building Ltd v. Cadmus Investments Co. Ltd* (1996) 51 Con. L.R. 105 where records were scarce a formula was applied with a smaller percentage than claimed only to specific items.

[89]   40 B.L.R. 82.

Global Claims

As there is something to be said for both a lawyer's analysis, and the   4.300
contractor's desire to obtain a full extension of time to practical completion
and all his costs paid plus a percentage for profit, it is hardly surprising that
construction law has generated ways of its own. In *J. Crosby and Sons v.
Portland Urban District Council*[90] where the arbitrator had awarded the
contractor a rolled-up sum in relation to various heads of claim for delay
and disruption, and when the arbitrator had found it "impracticable, if not
impossible, to assess the additional expense caused by delay and
disorganisation due to any one of these matters in isolation from the other
matters", Lord Donaldson (as he then was) said:

> "The respondents say that the contract provides a most elaborate code whereby
> prices and rates can be varied or prescribed in almost every eventuality. They
> say that this code is intended to operate in relation to each piece of work
> separately and no provision is made for a variation of the contract price
> generally. Whilst they concede that an arbitrator at the end of the day may
> make an award of a lump sum, they insist that this lump sum must be
> ascertained simply by adding together the individual amounts which he finds
> to be due under each head of claim. This results, they say, from the fact that
> the code in the contract provides different bases of assessment for diferent
> claims....
>
> The claimants... say that where you have a series of events which can be
> categorised as denial of possession of part of the site, suspension of the work,
> and variations, the result is, or may be, that the contractor incurs the extra
> costs by way of overhead expenses and loss of productivity: these extra costs
> are all recoverable directly... or indirectly [under certain clauses].... Since
> however, the extent of the extra cost incurred depends upon an extremely
> complex interaction between the consequences of the various denials,
> suspensions and variations, it may well be difficult or even impossible to
> make an accurate apportionment of the total extra cost between the several
> causative events. An artificial apportionment could of course be made; but
> why, they ask, should the arbitrator make such an apportionment that has no
> basis in reality?
>
> *I can see no answer to this question* [emphasis added]. Extra costs are a
> factor common to all these clauses, and so long as the arbitrator does not
> make an award which contains a profit element, [which was not permissible
> under certain of the clauses under consideration] and provided that he ensures
> that there is no duplication, *I can see no reason why [the arbitrator] should
> not recognise the realities of the situation and make individual awards in
> respect of those parts of individual items of the claim which can be dealt
> with in isolation and a supplementary award in respect of the remainder of
> these claims as a composite whole* [emphasis added]."

The *Crosby* contract was on ICE conditions. However, following *Crosby*,   4.301
there was a prevailing view that the onus of proving cause and effect had

---

90   [1967] 5 B.L.R. 121.

been removed, but this would be to go too far. It is still a fundamental basis of written pleadings in Scotland and England that fair notice of the case against him should be given to the defender, and it is for the pursuer to prove his case on a balance of probabilities. In *Merton v. Leach*[91] Vinelott J., whilst following *Crosby*, interpreted what Lord Donaldson said as follows: "I think I should nonetheless say it is implicit in the reasoning of Donaldson J., first that a rolled up award can only be made in the case where the loss and expense attributable to each head of claim cannot, in reality, be separated." He went on:

> "If application is made [under more than one contractual provision] for reimbursement of direct loss and expense attributable to more than one head of claim and at the time when the loss or expense comes to be ascertained it is impracticable to disentangle or disintegrate the part directly attributable to each head of claim, then,... the architect must ascertain the global loss directly attributable to the two causes, disregarding... any loss or expense which would have been recoverable if the claim had been made under one head in isolation and which would not have been recoverable under the other head taken in isolation... a rolled up award can only be made in a case where the loss or expense attributable to each head of claim cannot in reality be separated and, secondly, that a rolled up award can only be made where apart from that practical impossibility the conditions which have to be satisfied before an award can be made have been satisfied in relation to each head of claim."

4.302   In *Wharf Properties Ltd v. Eric Cumine Associates (No. 2)*[92] there was a £60 million claim for loss and expense laid against the architect. There had been a huge overrun in a property development in Hong Kong and the question arose how to show that £60 million was due to the delays by the architect. There were two problems, namely the lack of specification and the lack of a nexus (link) between cause and effect. The pleadings in this case were called "hopelessly embarrassing" and the case was dismissed without any evidence being heard. Lord Oliver stated:

> "[The cases of *Crosby* and *Merton*] establish no more than this, that in cases where the full extent of extra costs incurred through delay depend upon a complex interaction between the consequences of various events, so that it may be difficult to make an accurate apportionment of the total extra costs, it may be proper for an arbitrator to make individual financial awards in respect of claims which can conveniently be dealt with in isolation and a supplementary award in respect of the financial consequences of the remainder as a composite whole. This has, however, no bearing upon the obligation of the plaintiff to plead his case with such particularity as is sufficient to alert the opposite party to the case which is going to be made against him at the

---

[91] *London Borough of Merton v. Leach (Stanley Hugh)* (1985) 32 B.L.R. 51 at 98 *et seq.*
[92] (1991) 52 B.L.R. 1 (P.C.).

trial. ECA are concerned at this stage not so much with quantification of the financial consequences — the point with which the two cases referred to were concerned — but with the specification of the factual consequences of the breaches pleaded in terms of periods of delay. The failure even to attempt to specify any discernible nexus between the wrong alleged and the consequent delay, provides, to use [counsel's] phrase, 'no agenda' for the trial."

Whether there is a special rule for pleading a pursuer's case for building contracts is a matter that has not been finally determined in the highest courts, as in *Wharf Properties* Lord Oliver said:

"At the hearing of the petition for special leave it was thought that the appeal raised a point of general significance in building cases... having regard particularly to the impact which it was suggested that it might have upon two decisions of the High Court of England... [*Crosby* and *Merton*]... As the argument has progressed, however, it has become apparent that the case... rasies no question of any general importance, so that... their Lordships' Board has been... concerned with a pure point of pleading to the particular dispute in which the parties are engaged."

In *ICI v. Bovis Contractors*,[93] his Honour Judge Fox-Andrews was   4.303
required to examine a Scott Schedule which purported to show the cause of delays linked to direct losses. Again architects and also engineers were being sued for massive cost overruns which took the estimated cost from almost £30 million to almost £54 million. About one-half of the judgment is taken up with his criticisms of the Scott Schedule. Typical amongst his criticisms of the four-volume schedule was: "I found it palpable nonsense that £840,000 would be the cost of repositioning a fire bell". However in this case the judge allowed a revised Scott Schedule to be served. He said: " The history of this matter is quite different from that in *Wharf*. There is no question here of debarring ICI from pursuing their claim. But the present substitute schedule is inadequate in so many respects... that a fresh schedule must now be served."

More recently, and for another ICE contract, in *Bernhard's Rugby*   4.304
Landscapes Ltd v. Stockley Park Consortium Ltd[94] the Official Referee held that a party was entitled to present its case as it thought fit, and was not to be directed as to the method by which it was to plead or prove its claim, but a defendant was entitled to know the case it had to meet. In order to ensure fairness and observance to the principles of natural justice, a court might require a party to spell out its case with sufficient particularity, and where its case depended upon the causal effect of an interaction of events, to spell out the nexus in an intelligible form. A party would not be entitled to prove at trial a case which it was unable to plead having been given a reasonable

---

[93]   (1992) 32 Con L.R. 90.
[94]   (1997) 82 B.L.R. 39.

opportunity to do so since in that event the other party would be faced at trial with a case which it did not have a reasonable and sufficient opportunity to meet. A cost-effective balance had to be struck in assessing the degree of sufficient particularity. The plaintiff should identify those variations, events or acts and omissions which were relied upon as critical or crucial to the costs claim, so that the defendant knew which of the events were said to rely on a critical part and which costs were caused by those key elements.

Clause 27: determination by employer

4.305   In the Scottish Building Contract, clause 27 of JCT 80 is entirely deleted and replaced in Appendix 1 (the Scottish Supplement). The common law position for rescission of the contract if it has been materially breached by the Contractor and so repudiated is retained by clause 27.7, which states that clauses 27.2 to 27.6 are without prejudice to any other rights and remedies which the Employer may possess.[95]

4.306   Clause 27.2.1 provides that before the date of Practical Completion if "the Contractor shall make a default in any one of the following respects" (which may or may not mean the same as a breach at common law) then the Architect may give a notice specifying the default or defaults. The first of these is where the Contractor, without reasonable cause, wholly or substantially suspends the carrying out of the Works (clause 27.2.1.1). This clause has been retained despite the Amendment 18 right to the Contractor to suspend the works, although the new clause 30.1.4 provides that a suspension under that clause shall not be a suspension for the purposes of clause 27.2.1.1 or a failure to proceed regularly and diligently for the purposes of clause 27.2.1.2. For the contractor the wrongful withholding of payment under certificates does not generally at common law give the right to suspend the works — see *Lubenham Fidelities and Investments Co. Ltd v. South Pembrokeshire District Council*[96] where it was held that where there was an arbitration clause and the employer had not interfered with or obstructed the issue of certificates, the employer was not to pay more than the amount on the certificate; even when the architect had wrongfully purported to deduct L&ADs on the face of a certificate and was said to be doing "his incompetent best".

4.307   Secondly, if the Contractor fails to proceed regularly and diligently with the works (clause 27.2.1.2) a notice may be served. But note that in *Loke Hong Kee Pte Ltd v. United Overseas Land*[97] failure to comply with an

---

[95] If notice provisions are not followed by the employer that may amount to a repudiation on his part, unless there existed common law rights of determination which were not expressly excluded: see *Architectural Installation Services v. James Gibbon Windows* (1990) 16 Con. L.R. 68.

[96] (1986) 33 B.L.R. 39.

[97] (1982) 23 B.L.R. 35, PC.

intended work programme did not necessarily imply failure to proceed regularly and diligently. *Keating*[98] is of the view that this ground for determination applies before and after the date for completion. The comments made in connection with the phrase "regularly and diligently" for clause 23.1 *supra* apply. In particular in *Hounslow Borough Council v. Twickenham Garden Developments Ltd*[99] Megarry J. said:

> "These are elusive words on which the dictionaries help little. The words convey a sense of activity, of orderly progress, and of industry and perseverance; but such language provides little help on the question of how much activity, progress and so on is to be expected. They are words used in a standard form of building contract and in those circumstances it may be that there is evidence that could be given, whether of usage among architects, builders and building owners or otherwise, that would be helpful in construing these words. At present, all that I can say is that I remain somewhat uncertain as to the concept enshrined in these words."

More recently in *West Faulkner Associates v. London Borough of Newham*[99a] it was held that the words "regularly and diligently" should be construed together, and that in essence contractors must go about their work in such a way as to achieve their contractual obligations. This requires them to plan their work, to lead and to manage their workforce, to provide sufficient and proper materials and to employ competent tradesmen, so that the works are fully carried out to an acceptable standard, and that all time, sequence and other provisions of the contract are fulfilled. This would now appear to be a very wide definition, perhaps leaving the contractor more exposed to a determination under this clause than might have been previously thought. In this case both the architect and the quantity surveyor were unsure whether the contractor had failed to proceed "regularly and diligently" and accordingly did not certify a failure. The result was that the employer sued the architect for breach of his obligations. The employer had to negotiate with the contractor to leave the site in circumstances where the contractor generally had sufficient men on site but progress was very slow, they were disorganised and inefficient. Judge Newey Q.C. held that as the contractor's failures were so very extreme the architects were in breach of contract in failing to give a notice to that effect under clause 25 of JCT 63.

4.308

Thirdly, a notice may be served if the Contractor refuses or neglects to comply with a written notice or instruction from the Architect/Contract Administrator requiring him to remove any work, materials or goods not in

4.309

---

[98] May, *Keating on Building Contracts* (6th ed.) at 660. This may be a partial oversight in relation to current amendments, as although that edition includes the text of Amendment 11 which makes it clear that clause 27.2.1 specifically applies before the date of Practical Completion, that amendment is simply commented upon as "new" at 664.

[99] [1970] 7 B.L.R. 81.

[99a] (1992) 31 Con.L.R. 105 at 139, *The Times*, November 11, 1994 (CA).

accordance with the contract and by such refusal or neglect the works are materially affected (clause 27.2.1.3). Clearly, what materially affected means will be a matter that may be contentious. There is also open to the Employer in terms of clause 4.1.2 the slightly less divisive right to pay other persons to execute any work whatsoever to give effect to an instruction which the Contractor does not comply with within seven days of receipt of a notice to comply. It should be noted that clause 4.1.2 seems quite independent of the determination clause. Prior to Amendment 4 this clause read "persistently neglects" which suggests that only one written notice for one neglect will now suffice. However there is always the provision of clause 27.2.4 that subsequent notice of determination under clause 27.2.2 or 27.2.3 shall not be given unreasonably or vexatiously.

4.310   Fourthly, notice may be served if the Contractor fails to comply with the provisions of clause 19.1.1 or 19.2.2, which forbid assignation or sub-contracting without consent.

4.311   Fifthly, if the Contractor fails pursuant to the conditions to comply with the requirements of the CDM Regulations which were introduced by Amendment 14 (March 1995).

4.312   Clause 27.2.2 provides time limits that are to apply as follows:

> "If the Contractor continues a specified default for 14 days from receipt of the notice under clause 27.2.1 then the Employer may on, or within 10 days from, the expiry of that 14 days by a further notice to the Contractor determine the employment of the Contractor under this Contract. Such determination shall take effect on the date of receipt of such further notice."

4.313   Clause 27.2.3 continues:

> "If the Contractor ends the specified default or defaults, or the Employer does not give the further notice referred to in clause 27.2.2 and the Contractor repeats the specified default (whether previously repeated or not) then, upon or within a reasonable time after such repetition, the Employer may by notice to the Contractor determine the employment of the Contractor under this Contract. Such determination shall take effect on the date of receipt of such notice."

4.314   It is submitted that the time periods should be strictly followed, although there is some conflicting case law on this point.[1] The most recent case law in Scotland on stipulations as to time noted that these are generally "in a special position because of the hardship which may arise if, for example, a party is held to be in material breach where he is just one day late in doing something which the contract requires"; but "there is room for consideration of the nature of the contract and the circumstances in order to decide whether or not a stipulation is material and, as such, is of the essence of the contract".[2]

---

[1]   See *Central Provident Fund Board v. Ho Bock Kee* [1981] 17 B.L.R. 21 and *J. M. Hill & Sons v. London Borough of Camden* (1980) 18 B.L.R. 31, CA, and generally *Hudson*, pp. 1266–1274).

[2]   *Visionhire Ltd v. Britel Fund Trustees*, 1991 S.L.T. at 888 E–G.

It may seem strange and possibly contrary to natural justice that no separate   4.315
notice for a repetition is necessary, which leaves the Employer with the difficulty
of deciding whether to give another notice which might be construed as non-
contractual, as outwith the provisions of clause 27.2.3. However in *Hounslow,
London Borough Council v. Twickenham Garden Developments*,[3] Megarry J.
said: "for the rules of natural justice to apply there must... be something in the
nature of a judicial situation". An architect's administrative decision under a
contract was not a matter to which the rules of natural justice applied. In any
case it is possible to imagine a situation where a contractor might deliberately
abuse a system that requires an almost endless series of notices.

Contractor insolvency

The insolvency of a contractor during the course of a contract is a crisis event,   4.316
and is a matter which is provided for in JCT 80 and the Scottish Building Contract.
Amendments 4 (July 1987), 11 (July 1992) and 13 (July 1994) have considerably
altered the original form of clause 27 in 1980, which was substantially the same
as clause 25 of the 1963 form. However, in Scotland, the SBCC appear to have
gone their own way to an extent, for reasons that are not particularly apparent to
the author, given that one of the stated objectives of the SBCC is to bring about
conformity in contracting conditions north and south of the border.
    A contractor may trade as a sole trader; a partnership (possibly also in
Scotland as a limited partnership, although these have been very rare)[4]; or
as a limited company (whether a public limited company, or a private limited
company, or a company limited by guarantee — which last type of limited
company would almost certainly never be found for a contractor). Insolvency
affects each type of trading entity differently.
    A sole trader or a partnership in Scotland may be sequestrated.[5] As regards   4.317
limited companies the statutory provisions governing their insolvency is to
be found in the Insolvency Act 1986. One of the aims of the Act was to
provide a new alternative to the drastic remedy of liquidation; and this was
achieved by introducing the new concept of the administration order. If a
company becomes insolvent in Scotland or runs into severe financial
difficulties, three separate and distinct legal procedures can apply: winding
up; administration; and receivership. The first major effect of any of these
is to shift control of the company from its board of directors to the liquidator,
administrator, or receiver. Also, a voluntary arrangement may be entered
into between a company and its creditors and such an arrangement can
precede any of the above procedures or take place during them.

---

[3] (1971) 7 B.L.R. 81.
[4] They may be less so in future with new proposals for reform of the Limited Partnership Act 1907.
[5] For the sake of brevity it is intended to discuss only corporate insolvency in this text as it
     is the most common for contractors. For an introduction to the Scots law of bankruptcy,
     currently found in the Bankruptcy (Scotland) Act 1985, see Gloag and Henderson *The Law
     of Scotland* (10th ed.), Chap. 54.

4.318 **Legal effect of a winding up order.** A winding up order operates for the benefit of all creditors and contributories (Insolvency Act, s.130(4)) and is deemed to be equivalent to completed diligence.[6] The property of the company is in the control of the liquidator (or the court if there is no liquidator — Insolvency Act, s. 144). The directors' powers in relation to the assets and business of the company (and those of any other agent or servant having authority to act in its name) cease on the granting of a winding up order, but only to the extent that such powers have passed to the liquidator. The powers to act in the name of the company which do not pass to the liquidator and remain vested in the directors include the power to appeal against the winding up order itself, or to seek recall of the liquidator's appointment.[7] The appointment of the liquidator does not affect the power of a receiver to enter into contracts in respect of that part of the property and undertaking of the company comprised in the charge under which he was appointed.[8]

4.319 Contracts other than contracts of employment are not automatically terminated by liquidation, in the absence of a specific term to that effect. The liquidator has the option to take over any such contract, irrespective of his decision on any other contract, or to terminate it and concede a claim for damages.[9]

4.320 A winding up order or a resolution for voluntary winding up is presumed to constitute constructive notice of termination of all contracts of employment with the company. If the winding up is on the grounds of insolvency, an employee is entitled to leave the services of the company immediately and to claim damages. If he continues in the services of the company a separate contract may arise expressly or by implication between the liquidator and the employee.[10] A liquidator is not personally liable for the obligations of the company. A liquidator who enters appearance and defends an action warrants the sufficiency of the company's assets to meet any expenses to which the pursuer may be found entitled, and thereby incurs personal liability if the assets are found to be insufficient. As regards bonds and other guarantees, if a company which is being wound up is insured against liabilities to third parties, and a liability is incurred, the company's rights against the insurer are transferred to the third party.[11] In the light of the House of Lords decision in *Trafalgar House*[12] concerning the wording

---

6   Bankruptcy (Scotland) Act 1985, s.37(1) as applied by the Insolvency Act, s.185.
7   *Mettoy Pension Trs Ltd v. Evans* [1990] 1 W.L.R.1587.
8   Insolvency Act, s. 55 and Sched. 2.
9   *Gray's Trs v. Behar Coal Co.* (1881) 9 R. 225; *Asphaltic Limestone Concrete Co. Ltd v. Glasgow Corporation* (1907) S. 463; 14 S.L.T. 706; *Clyde Marine Insurance Co. v. Renwick*, 1924 S.C. 113; S.L.T. 41; *Turnbull v. Liquidator of Scottish County Investment Co.*, 1939 S.C. 5; 1938 S.L.T. 584.
10   *Day v. Tait* (1900) 8 S.L.T. 40.
11   Third Party (Rights Against Insurers) Act 1930, s. 1.
12   [1995] 3 W.L.R. 204 (HL).

of the common form of bond, it is doubtful if this provision will assist an employer in most cases. The creditor requires to maintain his claim against the liquidator until his claim is established.[13] The insurer cannot claim set-off in respect of unpaid premiums.[14]

The specific provisions of clause 27.3.2 of the SBC provide that in a series of insolvency events, both corporate and personal, the employment of the Contractor will be *forthwith automatically determined.* Excluded from these automatic provisions is the appointment of a provisional liquidator, which is a matter of optional determination on giving notice (clause 27.3.1), and included is the appointment of an administrator.   4.321

The JCT position is different again, as it provides for the identification of a series of insovency events (clause 27.3.1), of which the Contractor must give notice to the Employer (clause 27.3.2). The employment of the Contractor is *forthwith automatically determined* in only some of these events (clause 27.3.3), *viz.* the appointment of a provisional liquidator; the appointment of a trustee in bankruptcy; a winding up order being made; or in the event of (except for the purposes of amalgamation or reconstruction) a resolution for voluntary winding up passed.   4.322

In both contracts the employment of the Contractor may be reinstated by agreement. In England the appointment of the provisional liquidator marks automatic determination, but not in Scotland — perhaps because the appointment of a provisional liquidator may be recalled; and in Scotland "*amalgamation*" is omitted for whatever reason, in the context of a winding up order. Special care needs to be taken to distinguish between the different positions of an administrator, a receiver, and an administrative receiver in Scotland and England.   4.323

The administration order procedure made its first appearance in Chapter III of Part II of the Insolvency Act 1985 and was consolidated as Part II of the Insolvency Act 1986 (ss. 27–44 inclusive). This procedure developed out of the experience of receivership where, in some cases, it was possible for a receiver to initiate a corporate rescue. Before looking more closely at administration orders, it is appropriate to look at what is meant in the Scottish context by an "administrative receiver". This means a receiver appointed under the Insolvency Act 1986, s. 51 where the whole (or substantially the whole) of the company's property is attached by the floating charge.[15] However, in practice a floating charge over all of the company's assets will be taken almost always. If there is an "administrative receiver" in office an administrator cannot be appointed without the consent of the holder of the charge,[16] unless the court is satisfied that any security constituted by the charge is to be invalidly released. After an administration order has been granted an "administrative receiver" cannot be appointed, and any other proceedings to enforce a charge-holder's security are prohibited.[17]   4.324

---

[13] *Vickers Oceanic Ltd v. Ross (Liquidator of Speedcranes Ltd)*, 1985 J.L.S. s. 85.
[14] *Murray v. Legal and General Assurance Society* [1970] 2 Q.B. 495.
[15] Insolvency Act 1986, s. 251, definition (b).
[16] Insolvency Act, s. 9 (3) (a).
[17] Insolvency Act, s. 11.

4.325   One has to be careful with the terminology as the office of receiver in Scotland is different in many respects from its English counterpart. In England a receiver and manager of the entire undertaking is known as an "administrative receiver" *per* the Insolvency Act 1986, sections 29(2) and 251 (whereas s. 51 has the relevant definition for Scotland, as noted above). In *Palmer's Corporate Insolvency in Scotland*[18] at p. 67 the principal differences between the office of receiver in Scotland are:

(a) only the holder of a floating charge may appoint or secure the appointment of a receiver;

(b) while it is possible for the instrument creating the floating charge to add to or limit his powers, the powers of a Scottish receiver under statute are extensive and will generally be sufficient;

(c) express power to appoint a receiver need not be taken in the instrument; and

(d) the law relating to receivers in Scotland is wholly statutory, with no origins in common law.

4.326   An administration order may be made if the court is satisfied that a company is, or is likely to become, unable to pay its debts (which can involve taking into account prospective and contingent liabilities) under section 8(1)(a); and that the making of an administrative order would be likely to achieve one or more of the following purposes, *per* section 8(3):

(a) the survival of the company, and the whole or any part of its undertaking, as a going concern;

(b) the approval of a voluntary arrangement under Part I of the Insolvency Act;

(c) the sanctioning under section 425 of the Companies Act 1985 of a compromise or arrangement between the company and any such persons as are mentioned in that section; and

(d) a more advantageous realisation of the company's assets than would be realised on a winding up.

However, an administration order may not be made after the company has gone into liquidation (s. 8(4)).

4.327   In *Re Harris Simons Construction Ltd*[19] a contractor sought an administration order after increasing its turnover from £830,000 in 1985 to £17 million in 1987 and £27 million in 1988. Almost all the increase was due to one major client, and when the disputes arose and substantial sums were withheld the contractor was unable to pay its debts as they fell due. Their customer proposed a rescue plan whereby, if an administration order was pronounced, the customer would fund the completion of four contracts if the contractor was removed from the dispute sites. Hoffman J. accepted that there was a "real prospect" that one or more of the specified purposes of the administration order would be achieved.

---

[18]   David Bennett, W. Green, Edinburgh, 1993.
[19]   [1989] 1 W.L.R. 368.

The effects of an administration order petition being presented to the 4.328
court, and before any hearing to allow it are:

(a) no resolution may be passed or order made for the winding up of the
company;
(b) no steps may be taken to enforce any charge on or security over the
company's property, or to repossess goods in the company's possession
under any hire-purchase agreement, conditional sale agreement, chattel
leasing agreement or retention of title agreement, except with leave of
the court and subject to such terms as the court may impose;
(c) no other proceedings, and no execution of any other legal process may
be commenced or continued except with leave of the court;
(d) in Scotland, diligence cannot be carried out or continued without leave
of the court and subject to such conditions as the court may impose;
(e) there is created a statutory moratorium over the company's affairs.

If the administration order is made, the moratorium is continued and
extended for the period of the administration order. All managerial power
is transferred to the administrator and the directors are suspended for the
duration of the administration order.

The status and powers of an administrator are modelled closely on those 4.329
of an administrative receiver but are slightly more extensive. Just as for an
administrative receiver, the administrator is deemed to be acting as an agent
of the company. This means the company is bound by, and liable in respect
of, all acts validly performed by the administrator. It has been held that
there is no analogy between an administrator and a receiver, or an
administrator and an administrative receiver, as far as concerns the rights
of the administrator not to fulfil the company's outstanding contracts.[20]
The administrator has very wide powers to do "all such things as may be
necessary for the management of the affairs, business and property of the
company" (s. 14(1)(a) of the Insolvency Act) and without prejudice to that
generality in Schedule 1 to the Insolvency Act *inter alia* to do all such
things (including the carrying out of works) as may be necessary for the
realisation of the property of the company.

In *McPhail v. Lothian Regional Council*[21] it was held that the receiver 4.330
(and presumably, administrator) could sue in his own name for sums
recoverable to the company, and any plea of compensation or set-off was
not maintainable against the receiver. However a conflicting decision was
reached in *Taylor Petr*,[22] and it was also held in *Taylor* that set-off of a debt
incurred after receivership was possible. This latter view has since been
disapproved,[23] and further clarification by the courts would be beneficial.

---

[20] *Astor Chemical Ltd v. Synthetic Technology Ltd* [1990] B.C.C. 97.
[21] 1981 S.L.T. 173; 1981 S.C. 109.
[22] 1982 S.L.T. 172.
[23] *William Loudon & Son Ltd v. Cunninghame District Council*, 1985 S.L.T. 149; *Myles J.*
Callaghan Ltd v. City of Glasgow District Council, 1988 S.L.T. 227; 1987 S.C.L.R. 627.

The management of the company by the administrator is to be done in the first instance in accordance with any directions given by the court, and thereafter in terms of his approved proposals.

4.331   In the light of the many advantages for a contractor of administration, notably:

(i)   hostile claims which eat up resources can be suspended;

(ii) creditors can be deprived of their retention of title advantage, which an employer might be glad of, and which could be used by the contractor as a good negotiating tool with the employer;

(iii) where there has been wrongful set-off the contractor can get a breathing space to improve cash flow (see *Smallman Construction Ltd v. Redpath Dorman Long Ltd*[24]); and

(iv) pressure comes off the contractor to settle claims;

it is surprising that the SBCC have gone a different route from the JCT. In terms of clause 27.3.2 an application made under the Insolvency Act 1986 for the appointment of an administrator will mean that the employment of the Contractor shall be forthwith automatically determined. Employment may be reinstated by agreement with the Employer in Scotland under clause 27.3.3. The same applies if a receiver or administrative receiver is appointed in Scotland, but in neither case will there be automatic determination in England — only if a provisional liquidator or a trustee in bankruptcy is appointed — and this may also be reinstated by agreement. However in England there is clause 27.3.4 which does not exist in Scotland where the Employer may determine at any time merely by giving notice, effective on the date of receipt of such notice. This was inserted by Amendment 11 issued in November 1992 and would appear to apply if an administrator or administrative receiver was appointed. If this clause had applied in Scotland, then it is submitted that it could not be interpreted as a termination-at-will clause and that a valid reason under clause 27 would be necessary.[25]

4.332   The question has arisen as to whether a termination on insolvency clause might be invalid in any case. In the case of administration the beneficial ownership of the company's property remains with the shareholders. The court can restrict the issue of proceedings to enforce contractual rights. However, in the English case of *American Express Europe Ltd v. Adamson*[26] it was held that a notice terminating a contract was not "proceedings" or "other legal process" requiring leave under section 11 of the Insolvency Act 1986. This might appear strange given the grounds on which an administration order may be ordered, and in practice may make it impossible for the contractor to continue trading.[27] The validity of clause 25(2) of JCT 63, which automatically

---

[24] (1988) 47 B.L.R. 15.

[25] *Frank's Howden Ltd v. Hamilton Brothers Oil and Gas Ltd*, 1991 G.W.D. 32–1890.

[26] [1993] B.C.C. 154.

[27] Mark Homan, "A Survey of Administrations under the Insolvency Act 1986: the result of Administration Orders made in 1987", Institute of Chartered Accountants in England and Wales (1989).

terminates the employment of the contractor on his entry into compulsory winding up, was expressly upheld, although there does not appear to have been argument on this issue in *Westminster City Council v. Rema Construction Ltd (No. 2).*[28] In the absence of a termination clause, a liquidator is entitled to continue the contract provided it is desirable for the beneficial winding up of the contractor, and he will not be personally liable to creditors or contributories unless negligent, which cannot be maintained (in the absence of fraud or the concealment of material facts) where the court or liquidation committee has sanctioned the act complained of.[29]

As regards receivership in Scotland there appears little doubt that an 4.333 automatic determination provision on receivership will be valid. In *F.G. Cullis Construction Ltd v. HMV Fields (Properties) Ltd*[30] where there was a development agreement whereby the contractor was receiving payments under a funding agreement at the end of which the contractor would become the beneficial owner of the development, which agreement incorporated the JCT conditions by reference, it was held that the automatic determination on receivership provisions was not only valid, but rendered all other respective obligations unenforceable. (*N.B.* it is not clear from the report what precise JCT conditions were incorporated by reference.)

Clause 27.4 of the SBCC contract also allows the Employer to determine if 4.334 there has been corruption in relation to the obtaining or execution of the contract or any other contract. This includes offences under the Prevention of Corruption Acts 1889 to 1916, or where the Employer is a local authority — section 68 of the Local Government (Scotland) Act 1973 as amended or re-enacted. Presumably this will include the Local Government etc. (Scotland) Act 1994, and that the reference to the 1889 Act is supposed to be the Public Bodies Corrupt Practices Act. 4.335

Clause 27.5 sets out the respective rights and duties of the Employer and the contractor on determination, where the Contractor's employment has not been reinstated. Clause 27.5.1 raises the issues of the use of temporary buildings, plant, tools, equipment, goods and materials "intended for, delivered to and placed on or adjacent to the Works". This raises the issues of title to materials, pledge and retention of title clauses that are discussed elsewhere in the text.[31] Clause 27.5.2.1 continues with an obligation on the insolvent contractor to assign the benefit of "any agreement for the supply of materials or goods and/ or for the execution of any work for the purposes of this Contract to the extent that the same is assignable". This raises thorny issues which are also raised elsewhere in the text.[32] There follows the strangely-drafted clause 27.5.2.2 which attempts to allow direct payment by the Employer to any supplier or sub-contractor, which is also fraught with difficulty and discussed at Chapter 3.[33]

[28] (1990) 24 Con. L.R. 26 at 32.
[29] *Highland Engineering Ltd v. Anderson*, 1979 S.L.T. 122.
[30] 1989 G.W.D. 20–830 (OH); (1990) G.W.D. 13–637 (Ex Div).
[31] See paras 4.112–4.115.
[32] See commentary on cl. 19 at paras 4.147 *et seq.*
[33] See Chap. 3, paras 3.76–3.80.

The clause continues with a strange apparent right to sell goods, etc., which the Contractor does not remove or arrange for others to remove. Again this raises difficult questions relating to title and pledge noted above. The next sub-clause is one of those which Lord Penrose thought indicated that retention sums could not be held in trust notwithstanding the language of the contract in *Balfour Beatty v. Britannia Life*.[34] Clause 27.5.4 says that no further release of retention shall apply.

4.336   Clause 27.5.5 provides that further accounting to the Contractor is to take place "upon the completion of the Works and the making good of defects"; but that "direct loss and/or damage [note, not the more familiar clause 26 pairing of direct loss and/or expense] caused to the Employer as a result of the determination" shall be set out in a statement. This does not appear to have been revised in Amendment 18 to take account of the new statutory and contractual provisions with respect to payment that are discussed in relation to clause 30 below. Clause 27.5.6 has the difference as a debt payable by the Contractor to the Employer, or vice versa.

Clause 28: Determination by the Contractor

4.337   Clauses 28 and 28A are concerned with determination by the Contractor and were redrafted by Amendments 11 (July 1992) and Amendment 18 (April 1998). Again these provisions are stated to be without prejudice to any other rights and remedies which the Contractor may possess (clause 28.5). Broadly, determination is triggered by certain Employer's defaults, certain suspension events precluding the Contractor's progress, or the Employer's insolvency. Amendment 18 has made one of the Employer's defaults failure to pay by the final date for payment the amount properly due to the Contractor. Therefore, the Contractor now has clear options at his disposal: both suspension under clause 30.1.4, and determination under clause 28. There is thus a peculiar double-use of the words "suspension" and "specified suspension events" that mean quite different things.

4.338   The determination provisions depend on notices of specified defaults, or specified suspension events and determination by notice thereafter. Many of the same criticisms that were made in relation to notices under clause 27 can equally be applied to clause 28. The other defaults are interference or obstruction with the issue of any certificate under the contract (clause 28.2.1.2), and assigning the contract without consent (clause 28.2.1.3). In Scotland clause 28.3.1 has been redrafted to take account of the different perspective the SBCC has as regards the appointment of a provisional liquidator, so that the Contractor may determine if the Employer goes through insolvency events. The determination is not automatic, but the Contractor's obligations are suspended (clause 28.3.3). The consequences of determination are set out in clause 28.4. Again the phrase "direct loss and/or damage" is used, but in the context of the determination by the Contractor the phrase has been

---

[34] See Chap. 3, paras 3.69–3.73.

interpreted to include loss of profit where the Contractor had only worked a few weeks out of a 60-week contract when works were suspended.[35]

Clause 28A: Determination by Employer or Contractor

This clause is concerned with what happens when the Works are   4.339
suspended by reason of any of six events for a continuous period stated in the Appendix. The events allow either party to determine and accordingly might be considered neutral events. However, one of the events is loss or damage to the Works occasioned by any one or more of the Specified Perils, and the Contractor may not serve notice if the Specified peril was caused by the negligence or default of the Contractor, or the confusing list of servants and agents that are familiar from clause 20.1. This exception is because the succeeding provisions of the consequences of determination under clause 28A are very much in favour of the Contractor, who is otherwise entitled to direct loss and/or expense under clause 26, and direct loss and/or damage under clause 28A.5.5.

Clause 29: Works by Employer or persons employed or engaged by Employer

This clause allows the Employer to engage others to carry out and   4.340
complete work. This is in the author's experience a seldom employed clause, at least in so far as it would enable the Employer to employ others direct, rather than as named (clause 19.3) sub-contractors or Nominated Sub-Contractors under clause 35.

Clause 30: Certificates and Payments

This clause is a crucial and much-revised one.[36] Issues surrounding   4.341
the architect's role as certifier in relation to interim and final certificates are also discussed elsewhere in the text; so too common law set-off, and the status of retention sums; the effect of a final certificate; and the provisions of HGCRA — and the Scheme for Construction Contracts (Scotland) Regulations — relating to dates for payment and notice of intention to withold payment. All of the foregoing have a bearing on this clause.

Amendment 18 has introduced particular novelties. The combination of   4.342
the effect of section 110 of HGCRA and the ninth recommendation of the Latham Report[37-41] has led to a revision of clause 30.1.1. This clause seeks to conform to section 110 of HGCRA, which requires that interim payments

---

[35] *Wraight Ltd v. P.H.& T.(Holdings) Ltd* (1968) 13 B.L.R. 27.
[36] Amendments 2, 4, 5, 7, 10, 12, 13, 15, 16, and 18; and is also amended in the Scottish Building Contract.
[37-41] Latham, *Constructing the Team* (1994) at para. 5.18.

specify what any amounts to be paid relate to, and how they are calculated. Clause 30.1.1 seeks to do this through Interim Certificates and as such purports to be an "adequate mechanism"[42] under that section; and also specifies that a "final date" for payment is to be 14 days from the date of issue of each Interim Certificate. Latham recommended that there should also be a sufficiently heavy interest entitlement to deter late payment, and this option is given in the redraft of clause 30.1.1. A rate for simple interest is specified as 5 per cent over the base rate of the Bank of England. It is perhaps worth noting that this rate is less than the new statutory right to interest introduced by the Late Payment of Commercial Debts (Interest) Act 1998,[43] which is 8 per cent above the official dealing rate of the Bank of England.[44] That Act came into force on November 13, 1998 and only applies to companies that have 50 full-time employees or fewer ("small business") and who are owed monies by companies that have more than 50 full-time employees ("large business"). The 1998 Act would cover many construction contracts, and detailed provisions are given for working out how the number of employees should be calculated.[45] It may be in practice that many contractors will qualify as a small business by these criteria, so it should be noted that by section 8(1) and (2) the exclusion of this statutory right shall be void unless a "substantial remedy" is agreed. If the 5 per cent above base figure is not a "substantial remedy", then there will be questions about how the 1998 Act, and particularly section 11 dealing with interest on obligations to make advance payments, interphases with HGCRA, s.110, and the whole "entire contract" issue.[46]

4.343   Clause 30.1.1.2 has been slightly redrafted by Amendment 18, but it is submitted that on the basis of Lord Penrose's decision in *Balfour Beatty Ltd v. Britannia Life Ltd*[47] the redrafting contributes nothing to the problem of the status of retention monies as a trust in Scotland.

4.344   Clauses 30.1.1.3, 30.1.1.4, and 30.1.1.5 are the Amendment 18 way of making JCT 80 comply with HGCRA, s.109 (Entitlement to stage payments); s. 110 (Dates for payment); and s. 111 (Notice of intention to withhold payment). The gist[48] of these sections of HGCRA is that whilst there is now an entitlement to stage payments, the parties are free to agree amounts, intervals and circumstances for stage payments; failing which a fall-back position will apply under the Scheme for Construction Contracts.[49]

---

[42] See comments on "adequate mechanism" at Chap. 8, para. 8.32.

[43] c. 20.

[44] The Late Payment of Commercial Debts (Rate of Interest) (No. 2) Order 1998 (S.I. 1998 No. 2765), art. 4.

[45] (S.I. 1998 No. 2479), art. 2(2), Sched. 2.

[46] See paras 4.04–4.12.

[47] 1997 S.L.T. 10. See Chap. 3, paras 3.69–3.73.

[48] s. 109 (2) and (3).

[49] The Scheme for Construction Contracts (Scotland) Regulations 1998 (S.I. 1998 No. 687).

The fall-back position envisaged by the Scheme for interim payments is: 4.345

← each 28-day period[50] → 8 days later payment becomes due (*i.e.* on the expiry of 7 days)[51] → 17 days later is the final date for making payment.[52]

A statutory notice is required in all cases under section 110(2) of HGCRA   4.346
specifying the amount of payment made or proposed to be made, and the basis on which that amount was calculated, irrespective of any questions of set-off under the contract or other contracts, "abatement",[53] or whether contractual obligations had been carried out. Such notice shall be given "not later than five days after the date on which a payment becomes due". Based on the above diagram, such notice would be valid not later than day 41, *i.e.* 28 + 8 + 5.[54]

A notice of intention to withhold payment, which is a statutory requirement   4.347
in all cases under section 111 of HGCRA, must be given not later than the prescribed period before the final date for payment, which period may be subject to agreement; but in absence of such agreement, not later than seven days before the final date for payment. This "not later than *x* days before [date]" formulation was considered in *Main v. City of Glasgow District Licensing Board*.[55] The date in that case was the date when a meeting of the Licensing Board was to take place. Lord Morison held that this meant not later than *x* days before the start of the day of the meeting, *i.e.* midnight. As for the fall-back position under the Scheme, based on the above diagram and Lord Morison's view, a section 111 notice must be given not later than day 46, *i.e.* 28 + 8 + 10.[56]

It is important to note that section 115 leaves the parties free to agree on the   4.348
manner of service; otherwise service may be "by any effective means".[57] Postal service shall be effective if addressed, pre-paid *and delivered* (author's emphasis).[58]

---

[50] *ibid.*, regs 2(1) and 12.
[51] *ibid.*, reg. 4; or, confusingly, later, if a claim is made by the payee after the expiry of 7 days; see comments at para. 8.32.
[52] *ibid.*, reg. 8.
[53] This term is used without reference to existing Scots legal terminology, see Chap. 3, paras 3.56 *et seq.*
[54] *ibid.*, reg. 9, which reiterates the language of s.110(2).
[55] 1987 S.L.T. 305 (OH), Lord Morison. See also D.C. Coull, "'Not Later Than' Defined", 1987 S.L.T. (News) 353.
[56] Scheme For Construction Contracts *op.cit.*, reg. 10. Regrettably HGCRA, s.116 which provides for reckoning periods of time does not define the issue. The calculation in the text is based on the interpretation of "not later than seven days before" as meaning that the sixth day before is the first "illegal" notice day.
[57] s. 115 (3). It is suggested that this may include fax (see by way of comparison the cases on telexes: *Entores v. Miles Far East Corp.* [1955] 2 Q.B. 327; *Brinkibon v. Stahag Stahal und Stahlwarenhandels GmbH* [1983] 2 A.C. 34). At the time of writing it is doubtful whether e-mail would be considered an "effective means", but matters are changing fast at European law level and with the Government's current proposals for a Secure Electronic Commerce Bill. It is noteworthy that the clause 41A.5.2 provisions of the SBC (August 1998 revision) provide for e-mail and fax referral to an adjudicator, followed by other steps "for record purposes".
[58] s. 115 (4). This is contrary to the well-known rule for the conclusion of contracts by post, where the posting of an acceptance, not the receipt, concludes the bargain: *Jacobsen, Sons & Co. v. E. Underwood & Son* (1894) 2 R. 654.

4.349   HGCRA therefore requires two new notices under sections 110(2) and 111, and also section 110(1) requires that every construction contract provides an adequate mechanism for determining what payments become due under the contract, and when; and that there be a final date for payment in relation to any sum which becomes due. Also, section 111 of the HGCRA provides that payment may not be withheld after the final date for payment unless an effective notice of intention to withhold payment has been given. Clause 30.1.1.5 *per* Amendment 18 makes a contractual stipulation to that effect. HGCRA makes no mention of interim certificates, nor is there a definition of what constitutes an "adequate mechanism". JCT 80 clings to the familiarity of the use of Interim Certificates, but their status becomes even more confusing. The logic of the Act and Scheme is that where work is carried out within a given period, then an entitlement to payment for that work arises at a time afterwards. A notice should then be given showing the basis for the calculation of such an amount, irrespective of any disputes about the work. A final date for payment for such works then comes into being. The post-Amendment 18 JCT 80 position now becomes that Interim Certificates are to be issued at "the Period of Interim Certificates specified in the Appendix", *per* clause 30.1.3; that the Interim Certificates should state the basis on which that amount was calculated, *per* clause 30.1.1.1; that the final date for payment shall be 14 days from the issue of each Interim Certificate, *per* clause 30.1.1.1; but in addition not later than five days after the issue of an Interim Certificate a notice shall be given of the amount of payment proposed to be made in respect of the Interim Certificate, *per* clause 30.1.1.3.

4.350   It is submitted that the logic of the HGCRA is fractured by these revisions, because JCT confusingly equates the issue of Interim Certificates with the contractor's entitlement to payment (a status they do not appear to hold),[59] whereas in HGCRA entitlement to payment is a time-related matter, and a final date for payment runs from the section 110(2) notice.

4.351   There is a new clause 30.1.1.6 which is optional and for use with private versions of JCT 80 only. It introduces an option for the Employer to make an advance payment to the Contractor. The guidance notes with Amendment 18 explain that this provision is to comply with paragraph 5.18, sub-paragraph 13 of the Latham Report.[60] The Latham Report said that where appropriate

---

[59]   See comments on set-off at Chap 3. In so far as the existence of an interim certificate is a condition precedent to payment to the contractor, it is submitted that is not the issue which HGCRA addresses. Although the point was decided in Scotland in the context of the ICE 5th contract by the Inner House that a contractor's claim was contingent on the issue of an interim certificate in *Costain Building and Engineering v. Scottish Rugby Union*, 1994 S.C.L.R. 257, and by the Court of Appeal in relation to JCT 63 in *Lubenham Fidelities & Investment Co. v. South Pembrokeshire District Council* [1986] 33 B.L.R. 39 that an interim certificate is a condition precedent to payment to the contractor; the same can probably safely be said for JCT 80, subject to any issues such as to fraud, or interference with or obstruction (clause 28.2.1.2): see *Burden v. Swansea Corporation* [1957] 3 All E.R. 243 (HL).

[60]   See Chap. 8, para. 8.07.

there should be provision for advance mobilisation payments, which might be bonded, for such matters as off-site prefabricated materials. The Guidance Note does not clarify what matters the JCT think might be the subject of such payments, but the Appendix is amended so that an amount or a percentage of the Contract Sum might be inserted. This is then to be reimbursed to the Employer in amounts and at times to be inserted. Quite why reimbursement should be chosen as the contractual mechanism rather than a deduction from the Contract Sum seems cumbersome to the author, and probably not what will happen in practice. It has already been noted that the SBCC issue their own forms of purchase of materials off-site[61] from the main contractor, or any sub-contractor for use with the SBC, both of which provide for such sums to be deducted from the Contract Sum. The new clause 30.1.1.6 requires that a bond be given by the Contractor for any such advance payment, but as yet there is no tie-up with any such requirements in the Scottish purchase documentation. The terms of the bond are set out in Amendment 18 and have been agreed between the JCT and the British Bankers' Association. It is to be construed in accordance with the laws of England and Wales! In Scottish terms it would be construed as an indemnity and not as caution at all, as the parties are the surety and the Employer.[62] It appears to be payable on demand, in the form of demand that is attached. The Surety's liability is a decreasing one based on the amount that has been repaid to the Employer.

Clause 30.1.2.1 provides that the Quantity Surveyor is to make interim valuations for the purpose of ascertaining the amount to be stated as due in the Interim Certificate. Clause 30.1.2.2 *per* Amendment 18 is also new and provides that the Contractor may submit an application to the Quantity Surveyor "not later than seven days before the date of the Interim Certificate" setting out the amount of the gross valuation pursuant to clause 30.2, and act similarly for any Nominated Sub-Contractor. To the extent that the Quantity Surveyor disagrees with these amounts he shall give the Contractor a statement identifying such disagreement. It is not clear why this amendment was considered necessary, as the procedure is "without prejudice to the obligation of the Architect to issue Interim Certificates". 4.352

Clause 30.1.3 remains unamended, and provides for Interim Certificates to be issued for the period stated in the Appendix up until Practical Completion, thereafter "as ascertained" with reference to the later of the expiry of the Defects Liability Period or the Certificate of Completion of Making Good Defects, but not within one calendar month of a previous Interim Certificate. Whether any Interim Certificates at all are appropriate after Practical Completion will presumably depend on what constitutes Practical Completion in any particular case, but it is submitted that any 4.353

---

[61] See para. 4.114.
[62] Chap. 3, para. 3.38.

such Interim Certificates should seldom be necessary (save in relation to Nominated Sub-Contractors: clause 30.7); the Final Certificate being the only certificate which the Architect is required to issue (clause 30.8) in respect of the Contractor.

4.354   Clause 30.1.4 is introduced by Amendment 18 to make JCT 80 comply with section 112 of HGCRA. Prior to section 112 it had been held that there was no general common law right for a contractor to suspend his works for want of adequate interim certificates under JCT 63[63]; the contractor's remedy under that form of contract was to go to arbitration.[64] Section 112 now creates a right to suspend performance where a sum due to be paid by the final date for payment has not been paid and there is no effective notice to withhold payment. Section 112(2) requires "at least seven days' notice of intention to suspend performance" with a statement of grounds. Section 112 continues that the right to suspend ceases when the payment is made and that any contractual time-limit be adjusted accordingly. The new clause 30.1.4 incorporates the new statutory provisions and makes it clear that a suspension shall not permit the Employer to determine on the basis of clauses 27.2.1 or 27.2.1.2. Amendment 18 makes suspension a Relevant Event for an extension of time (clause 25.4.18) and a relevant matter for direct loss and/ or expense (clause 26.2.10), provided the suspension was not "frivolous or vexatious".[65] Notice that, in terms of the Guidance Notes, suspension applies to all obligations, including, for example, insurance. It is not clear whether there would be any legal bar on the Employer and the Contractor agreeing not to comply with the suspension provisions of HGCRA.

4.355   Amendment 18 makes a small change to clause 30.2 for ascertaining the amounts due in Interim Certificates, so that any advance payments under clause 30.1.1.6 are to be deducted from the gross valuation. Presumably in most cases the Appendix will be completed so as to provide for advance payments to be deducted from Interim Certificates. The gross valuation is to be applied "up to and including a date not more than seven days before the date of the Interim Certificate".

---

[63] *Lubenham Fidelities v. South Pembrokeshire District Council* 6 Con. L.R. 85 at 110 (AC). See also *Eurotunnel v. TML* [1992] C.I.L.L. 754, *per* Staughton L.J.: "It is well established that if one party is in serious breach, the other can treat the contract as altogether at an end; but there is not yet any established doctrine of English law that the other party may suspend performance, keeping the contract alive." That may not have been the Scottish position as in *Duncanson v. Baylis* (1869) 7 S.L.R. 139, when the contractor ceased to work on site because of the employer's default until such time as the employer re-established the position to enable the contractor to proceed, this was not a repudiation by the contractor. Interestingly, in relation to the issues that are discussed above in relation to clause 16 concerning whether a building contract should properly be considered a sale of goods transaction, the Sale of Goods Act 1979 provides that unless a different intention appears from the terms of the contract, stipulations as to time of payment are not of the essence of a contract of sale at s.10.

[64] *ibid.* at 100, *per* May L.J.

[65] See comments on the use of the word "vexatiously" at para. 4.66. Note that here vexatious is wedded for the first time to "frivolously".

Clause 30.2.1 provides what is to be included in the "gross valuation" 4.356
and that it should be subject to retention. Amendment 18 has not altered the
basic position that "the total value of the work properly executed" is to be
included. The confusion as to what "properly executed" means remains,
and as we have already noted in the context of a Final Certificate, there
have been problems as to how conclusive any such Final Certificate might
be. What does appear plain, however, in the context of Interim Certificates
is that one of these cannot be the last word on whether work has been
completed so as to discharge the Contractor of all liability. Whilst it is
possible to draft a contract to achieve that end, it is more likely that a court
will construe Interim Certificates as little more than a measuring device to
facilitate what are effectively payments on account for work and materials.[66-67]
Clause 30.2.1.1 goes on to provide that Variations under the Amendment
procedures are to be subject to retention, but not restoration or repair work
under the insurance provisions. What changes the new Activity Schedule
makes is unclear, as interim payments are to be in proportion to work
properly executed for each activity.

The rules in relation to the retention in clauses 30.4 and 30.5 are left 4.357
unaltered by Amendment 18, which is perhaps surprising given the decision
of Lord Penrose in *Balfour Beatty Ltd v. Britannia Life Ltd.*[68]

Clause 30.7 also remains unchanged in relation to the final adjustment 4.358
or ascertainment of Nominated Sub-Contract sums, which is to be as soon
as practicable but not less than 28 days before the date of issue of the Final
Certificate. The issue of the Final Certificate clause 30.8 is changed by
Amendment 18 to make JCT 80 comply with HGCRA.

Clause 30.9.3 makes a Final Certificate conclusive for the purposes of 4.359
clause 30.9.1 unless challenged at arbitration or adjucation or other
proceedings within 28 days of its issue in England, and peculiarly 60 days
in Scotland in the SBC August 1998 revision. The effect of the Final
Certificate clause (clause 30.9.4) now provides for a referral to arbitration
or litigation of an adjudicator's decision given after the date of issue of the
Final Certificate. Section 108(3) of HGCRA provides that a construction
contract "shall provide that the decision of the adjudicator is binding until
the dispute is finally determined by legal proceedings, by arbitration... or
by agreement". Clause 30.9.4 provides that such arbitration (but no mention
is made of litigation by the SBC) *may* (author's emphasis) be commenced
within 28 days of the date of the adjudicator's decision. It is not clear if, by
using the word "may", this is an absolute time bar.

The SBC (August 1998 revision) then goes on to add some of its own 4.360
amendments to clause 30. It is not clear to the author what the purpose of

---

[66-67] This was the view of the Lord Chancellor, Lord Cairns, in *Tharsis Sulphur and Copper Co. v. McElroy and Sons* (1878) 5 R. (H.L.) 171 at 173, to which Lord Hatherly agreed at 175, as did Lord Blackburn at 178.

[68] 1997 S.L.T. 10. See Chap. 3, paras 3.69–3.73.

the SBCC's new clause 30.11 is, as it appears that the deduction of L&ADs from the Final Certificate is a matter already provided for in clause 24.2.1. There is then a series of entirely unique provisions which allow for an application to be made by the Contractor direct to the Employer if the Architect does not issue an Interim Certificate (clauses 30.12.1 to 30.12.5). It is presumed by the author that this is an attempt to deal with perceived difficulties concerning an Interim Certificate probably being a condition precedent to payment.

Clause 31: Finance (No. 2) Act 1975 — statutory tax deduction scheme

4.361   This clause is concerned with payment by the employer if the employer is also a contractor, otherwise the provisions do not apply. In any event there is a new Construction Industry Scheme at the time of writing to come into effect on August 1, 1999 regarding taxation and payment to contractors which the JCT will no doubt take account of in their next amendment.[69]

Clauses 32 and 33: numbers not used

4.362   These formerly related to Outbreak of Hostilities and War damage respectively but were deleted by Amendment 11 (July 1992).

Clause 34: Antiquities

4.363   Clause 34 deals with loss and/or expense to the Contractor if his progress is disrupted by the finding of fossils, antiquities or other objects of interest or value. The contract then goes on to say that such will become the property of the Employer — which may or may not be the case in law depending on what is found and whether it is covered by statute, *e.g.* gold, coal etc.

PART 2: NOMINATED SUB-CONTRACTORS AND NOMINATED SUPPLIERS

Clause 35

4.364   Nomination of sub-contractors is a matter where the courts have often found themselves at odds with the industry as to what the object of this arrangement is. In the increasingly sophisticated world of construction processes, the basic principle underlying nomination is that the employer reserves to himself the option of selecting a sub-contractor and the terms of the sub-contract, perhaps because there is to be a substantial element of design left to the sub-contractor, or because of price or quality considerations; whilst still keeping the traditional chain of contractual responsibility between employer, main contractor and sub-contractor intact. The system has several

---

[69] For further details see www.inlandrevenue.gov.uk/cis

points in its favour. The main contract can be let by the employer at a stage long before the detailed design has been carried out, especially as regards the sub-contract works, on the basis of prime cost sums inserted in the bills or provisional sums included in a nominated sub-contract. The main contractor then is entitled to mark up the prime cost of the nominated sub-contract work with a percentage for pure profit, and also to charge for attendances on nominated sub-contractors, and to charge what is called a "cash discount" for prompt payment of what is due to the nominated sub-contractor. These features and the fact that a contract may often be let with up to 60 per cent of the works to be done by nominated sub-contractors can make nomination an attractive way of business for a main contractor. These features are particularly argued in *Hudson*[70] as having been lost sight of by the courts in decisions where the main contractor has been absolved from liability to the employer in the event of a defaulting nominated sub-contractor. Indeed, *Hudson* says the practice of having the nominated sub-contractor enter into direct warranties with the employer can lead to: "bewildering complications into the interpretation of the express or implied responsibilities of the various parties for defaults of the other parties in what will essentially be triangular relationships".[71]

Perhaps it is partly because of these "bewildering complications" that 4.365 *Keating*[72] recommends that nomination be avoided (especially because of exposure to risk on the part of the employer), and the Latham Report[73] recommended that it should not be followed as a normal procedure.

Notwithstanding the analysis of the purpose of nomination and criticisms in 4.366 *Hudson*, triangular relationships are exactly what we have under the nomination procedures of JCT 80. This is because a direct warranty is entered into between the Nominated Sub-Contractor, and the Architect has a decisive role in the administration of key aspects of the Nominated Sub-Contract. Prior to Amendment 10 there were two forms of nomination: the basic method and the alternative method. Now since March 1991 the method following Amendment 10 is simplified. In Scotland clause 35.4 of JCT 80 is deleted so as to take into account Scottish versions of the nomination forms which are identified by the suffix "/Scot", *e.g.* NSC/T/Scot. The Standard Conditions of Nominated Sub-Contract (NSC/C) are left unaltered for Scotland, *i.e.* without the suffix.

Put simply, the new procedure involves the Employer inviting a tender from the sub-contractor (NSC/T/Scot) and his completing of a warranty to the Employer (NSC/W/Scot). The Architect or Employer then approves the tender, signs the warranty, instructs the main contractor who he has to have as Nominated Sub-Contractor (NSC/N/Scot), and the main contractor enters into an agreement with the Nominated Sub-Contractor (NSC/A/Scot) on the Standard Conditions for Nominated Sub-Contractors 1991 ed. (NSC/C).

[70] Wallace, *Hudson's Building and Engineering Contracts* (11th ed.) at 1309.
[71] *ibid.* p. 1310.
[72] May, *Keating on Building Contracts* (5th ed.) at 319.
[73] *Constructing the Team,* July 1994, see Chap. 8, para. 8.05.

4.367   There are several specific problem areas in respect of nomination. For example, as the Nominated Sub-Contractor has effectively been imposed on the Contractor (although he has the right to reasonable objection under clause 35.5), to what extent should the Contractor be liable for the Nominated Sub-Contractor's work, especially where that involved a specialised design aspect, which even the Architect would normally dilute his own responsibility to the Employer for?[74] Clause 35.21 as altered by Amendment 18 now provides:

> "35.21 The Contractor shall not be responsible to the Employer for:
> .1   the design of any nominated sub-contract works insofar as such nominated sub-contract works have been designed by a Nominated Sub-Contractor;
> .2   the selection of the kinds of materials and goods for any nominated sub-contract works insofar as such kinds of materials and goods have been selected by a Nominated Sub-Contractor;
> .3   the satisfaction of any performance specification or requirement insofar as such performance specification or requirement is included or referred to in the description of any nominated sub-contract works included in or annexed to the numbered tender documents enclosed with any NSC/T [/Scot] Part 1;
> .4   the provision of any information required to be provided pursuant to Agreement NSC/W[/Scot] *(Employer/Nominated Sub-Contractor Agreement)* in reasonable time so that the Architect can comply with the provisions of clauses 5.4.1 and 5.4.2 in respect thereof.
> Nothing in this clause 35.21 shall affect the obligations of the Contractor under this Contract in regard to the supply of workmanship, materials and goods by a Nominated Sub-Contractor."

4.368   The position of the Employer in relation to a Nominated Sub-Contractor is stated in clause 35.20 to be that : "Neither the existence nor the exercise of the powers in clause 35 nor anything else contained in the Conditions shall render the Employer in any way liable to any Nominated Sub-Contractor except by way and in terms of the Agreement NSC/W [Scot]."

4.369   A matter that has caused particular difficulties has been who bears the risk when the nominated sub-contractor does not complete his works.[75] The House of Lords considered the position in *Bickerton v. N.W. Metropolitan Hospital Board.*[76] This was a JCT 63 contract where the nominated sub-contractor for heating went into voluntary liquidation before completing their works, and by agreement between employer and the contractor, the contractor completed them, but at a cost that exceeded the original sub-contract package. In the absence of specific provisions in the main contract

---

[74]   See Standard Form of Agreement for the Appointment of an Architect (1992 RIBA ed.), clause 4.2.5.
[75]   For a discussion on these points see the chapter, "Nominated Sub-Contracts and Repudiation — The *Bickerton* Albatross" in Wallace, *Construction Contracts: Principles and Policies in Tort and Contract* (1986).
[76]   [1970] 1 W.L.R. 607 (HL).

for renomination in such circumstances,[77] Lord Reid said: "I can find nothing anywhere to indicate that the principal contractor can ever have in any event either the right or the duty to do any of the prime cost work itself. That would, I think, be contrary to the whole purpose of the scheme, and it would be strange if the contractor could have to do work for which it never tendered and at a price which it never agreed." It was an implied term that the employer had to renominate at his risk as to price. But if the contractor wrongfully repudiates the nominated sub-contract, the contractor will be liable to the employer in damages.

JCT 80, clause 35.24 now sets out the precise position where renomination   4.370
is necessary and in each case the amount properly payable to the re-nominated sub-contractor shall be included in Interim Certificates and added to the Contract Sum; unless the Nominated Sub-Contractor had validly determined his contract where such sums will be deducted from the Contractor. The grounds for determination of NSC/A/Scot are set out in clause 7.1 of NSC/C. It is still unclear who bears the cost of the Contractor's direct loss and/or expense as a result of renomination. JCT 80 is not explicit on the point. In *Fairclough Building v. Rhuddlan B.C.*[78] it was held that, again for the JCT 63 form, where a renomination was objected to by the main contractor as it did not refer to remedial work that was necessary, the objection was justified on the basis of *Bickerton*.

Clause 35.24.10 makes it clear that the obligation to renominate is to be   4.371
carried out within a reasonable time, which confirms the term implied in *Percy Bilton v. GLC.*[79]

In Scotland in *Borders Regional Council v. J. Smart & Co. (Contractors)*   4.372
Ltd,[80] a JCT 63 (1971 revision) contract with Scottish Supplement (July 1971) was considered. Bill no. 9 related to floor screeding, and a particular sub-contractor who was the only accredited operator of a particular branded rapid-drying concrete was selected in the bills, *i.e.* they were named, not nominated. The sub-contractor was to provide a 10-year guarantee to the main contractor and this was to be assigned to the employer. The main contractor had not wanted this particular sub-contractor and had suggested someone cheaper, using a different process. Eventually, the floor screed cracked and the sub-contractor admitted liability for defects, but before any remedial works were carried out, the sub-contractor went into voluntary liquidation. The pursuer argued, relying heavily on *Bickerton*,[81] that there was an obligation on the employer to renominate a sub-contractor, that the main contractor had no authority to correct the defects and was entitled to

---

[77] JCT 80 does at clause 35.24; no doubt prompted by the stinging criticism of Lord Reid in *Bickerton ibid.* that the failure in draftsmanship had "caused a long and expensive litigation in the present case".
[78] [1985] 30 B.L.R. 26 (CA).
[79] [1982] 1 W.L.R. 794 (HL).
[80] 1983 S.L.T. 164 (Second Division).
[81] *op.cit.*

an extension of time, and the employer was liable for the cost (a certificate of practical completion had been issued subject to shrinkages and defects being fixed). It was also a matter of agreement that the sub-contractors were not nominated within the meaning of clause 27. It was held that what fell to be done was not the carrying out of the specified works but the remedying of defects in the completed specified works. This was the ultimate responsibility of the contractor. It was for them to secure that remedial work was done, and to secure that works were completed satisfactorily. An argument that the contractor had been frustrated was rejected as it was not said to have been physically impossible to have the remedial works carried out. "Frustration is not to be lightly invoked as the dissolvement of a contract." *Bickerton* was distinguished as it involved a nominated, not specified, sub-contractor who went into liquidation, and liquidation occurred at an earlier stage so that the distinction between practical completion and rectification of defects did not arise.

4.373   The Nominated Sub-Contractor is entitled to extensions of time for his works under NSC/C 2.2. Delay on the part of the Nominated Sub-Contractor entitles the Contractor to an extension of time under clause 25.4.7, and constitutes a breach of clause 3.3.2 of NSC/W, giving rise to an entitlement to damages to the Employer. If the Nominated Sub-Contractor fails to complete the sub-contract works to time, and this is certified by the Architect under clause 35.15, then "loss and/or damage" can be recovered from the Nominated Sub-Contractor (clause 2.9 NSC/C).

Clause 36: Nominated Suppliers

4.374   The law of property as it affects the transfer of title in materials: implied terms as to title, quality and quiet possession; delivery; reservation of title; and the common law and statutory positions, have all been considered at length in relation to clause 16. It was central to the author's analysis that a typical supply-and-fix building contract should be distinguished from a contract for the supply of materials only. Clause 36 is concerned solely with contracts which the Contractor may be required to enter into with Nominated Suppliers. Accordingly this clause introduces something of the complexity of nomination of sub-contractors, against a statutory background for the sale of goods. Suppliers to a main contractor may be either nominated or domestic. Suppliers to a sub-contractor will be domestic. There is no attempt to regulate supplies by domestic suppliers. There is uniquely for Scotland a Standard Form of Tender for use in Scotland by a Nominated Supplier (January 1992 revision), incorporating Schedules 1 and 2; and Schedule 3: Warranty Agreement for use by a Nominated Supplier (January 1992 revision). These would not appear to be "construction contracts" for the purposes of section 104 of HGCRA and have not required amendment. Much the same problems for nomination in the context of sub-contractors arise for suppliers, *i.e.* responsibility for design, and also quality and fitness for purpose.[82] However certain matters such as liability for delay, or renomination, are not covered. What is plain is that clause 36.5 prevents any suggestion that the Contractor should have a wider liability for materials to the Employer, than the Nominated Supplier has in turn to the Contractor[83]; and a list of nine essential clauses for the supplier's contract is given in clause 36.4.

PART 3: FLUCTUATIONS

Notwithstanding that JCT 80 Private With Quantities ed. is often referred to   4.375
as a lump sum contract plus or minus variations, in fact it is not. Part 3 of JCT 80 provides that price fluctuations[84] are to apply, whether prices rise for the Contractor or Sub-Contractor, or fall so that the Employer benefits. Under JCT 63 the relevant provisions were set out in full in the contract. Under JCT 80 they are printed separately, although these should not be ignored as they can significantly affect the Contract Sum. In short, a choice of clauses 38, 39 or 40 may be made and specified in the Appendix, but clause 37 provides "that clause 38 will apply where neither clause 39 nor 40 is identified in the Appendix". Clause 38 is the minimum category of fluctuation and is limited to adjustment to the Contract Sum arising from statutory contribution, levy and tax fluctuations; but clause 38 is not appropriate for use with the Approximate Quantities ed. Clause 38.2 provides for payment or allowance in respect of tax changes that affect the price of "import, purchase, sale, appropriation, processing or use of the materials, goods, electricity and, where so specifically stated in the Contract Bills, fuels, specified in a list submitted by the Contractor and attached to the Contract Bills under or by virtue of any Act of Parliament." A separate provision to provide for landfill tax is now added by Amendment 18 as clause 38.2.3. In what might become a contentious issue, but based on the policy that the landfill tax was to encourage other effective means of waste disposal, clause 38.2.3.3 provides that no payment shall be made if the Contractor could reasonably have disposed of the waste other than to a licensed landfill site.

Clause 39 allows for fluctautions in relation to labour and materials costs   4.376
and tax fluctuations. The prices in the Contract Bills are deemed to have been calculated in accordance with the rules or decisions of the National Joint Council for the Building Industry or other wage-fixing body, and includes Productivity Incentive Schemes and/or Productivity Agreements,

---

[82] See Chap. 5, paras 5.19–5.20 and *Young & Marten Ltd v. McManus Childs Ltd* [1969] 1 A.C. 454 (HL); *Gloucestershire County Council v. Richardson* [1969] 1 A.C. 480 (HL); *IBA v. EMI and BICC* (1980) 14 B.L.R. 1 (HL).

[83] A suggestion that was disapproved in *Gloucestershire ibid.*

[84] For judicial consideration of fluctuations clauses see *John Laing Construction Ltd v. County and District Properties Ltd* (1982) 23 B.L.R. 1 and *Jefco Mechanical Services Ltd v. Lambeth London Borough Council* (1983) 24 B.L.R. 1, CA.

and Annual and Public Holiday Agreements. Clause 39.7.2 defines "materials" and "goods" as including timber used in formwork but they do not include other consumable stores, plant and machinery (save that electricity and, where specifically so stated in the Contract Bills, fuels are dealt with in clause 39.3). These provisions will apply to 'workpeople' as defined, and to others who do not fit that definition if they are on site for at least two days in any week.[85] On top of all this the Contractor will be entitled to a fixed percentage which is stated in the Appendix, on the basis that Procedure Note 7 issued by the National Joint Consultative Committee for Building (Fifth revision, September 1989) indicated that experience shows that a "full fluctuation" clause rarely results in full reimbursement:

> "This is due to the exclusion from adjustment of many elements of costs, some of the more significant being:
> .1   labour which is not paid for in accordance with the rules and decisions of the NJCBI or other appropriate recognised body;
> .2   supervisory staff;
> .3   plant;
> .4   consumable stores;
> .5   head office and depot overheads."

If the contractor is in culpable delay and has not been awarded an extension of time the fluctuations clause is frozen (clause 39.5.7).

4.377   As an alternative to clauses 38 and 39, use may be made of a price adjustment formula under clause 40. The appropriate Formula Rules are also published separately. These involve the classification of Works into Work categories to which an algebraic equation is applied based on monthly published indices. There are formulas which apply to certain Specialist Engineering Installations carried out by the contractor, *e.g.* electrical installations; heating ventilation and air conditioning installations; and structural steelwork installations. As these calculations and indices are rather complex, specialist advice from a quantity surveyor is normal.

PART 4 — SETTLEMENT OF DISPUTES — ADJUDICATION — ARBITRATION —
COURT PROCEEDINGS

4.378   Traditionally disputes under construction contracts were disposed of by arbitration and there were many good reasons for this, such as the expertise of the arbiter, informality, and generally finality of an arbiter's award.[86] Indeed there were a line of decisions in England following the decision in *Northern Regional Health Authority v. Crouch*[87] to the effect that a court

---

[85]   For the previous JCT 63 wording the Court of Appeal had held that self-employed persons were not covered by the fluctuations provisions: *J. Murphy & Sons v. Southwark London Borough Council* [1982] 22 B.L.R. 41.
[86]   See discussion at paras 4.384–4.393.
[87]   [1984] 2 All E.R. 175 (CA).

had no inherent power to revise certificates that were issued by the architect, only an arbitrator; which generally made it pointless to eschew arbitration in favour of court proceedings. *Crouch* has recently been overruled by the Lords in *Beaufort Developments (N.I.) Ltd v. Gilbert-Ash (N.I.) Ltd.*[88] However it had become plain that the construction industry had developed a highly adversarial culture, which resulted in arbitration being perceived as generally too slow or cumbersome to cope with some of the powerplay that took place in the administration of building contracts. Arbitration was also generally a costly matter, as the procedures at arbitration tended to follow those of formal court proceedings as soon as lawyers became involved. The author can recall from personal experience a small joinery client being driven to bankruptcy when he had not been paid as he should, but was unable to lodge caution for expenses to go through the protracted legal hurdles of ever-more detailed pleading that the main contractor's advisors insisted upon. A word was even coined for this in the industry, *viz.* "subbie-bashing". The Latham Report at paragraph 5.18 said that a modern contract should: "While taking all possible steps to avoid conflict on site, provide for speedy dispute resolution if any conflict arises, by a pre-determined impartial adjudicator/referee/expert." These suggestions then became law in HGCRA, s.108. At around the same time as the construction industry was questioning access to justice, Lord Woolf in England produced a report on the court system generally.[89] Scotland had seen similar initiatives with the introduction of special rules of procedure for commercial actions in the Court of Session[90] and a report by Lord Cullen.[91] In the light of all this JCT introduced its adjudication provisions in clause 41A (redrafted by the SBCC); kept the arbitration provisions, now in clause 41B (again redrafted by the SBCC); but gave the option of deleting the arbitration clause and allowing the parties to proceed to court (in the SBCC redrafted clause 41C, to the Court of Session).

Clause 41A: Adjudication

This is discussed in a later chapter.[92]   4.379

Clause 41B: Arbitration

Whilst there is no statutory definition of arbitration in Scotland, it is essentially a quasi-judicial process where certain disputes are agreed as a matter of contract to be referred to the decision of a certain person or persons for a binding decision.[93] The disputes are taken away from the ambit of the   4.380

---

[88] [1998] 2 All E.R. 778.
[89] The Rt. Hon. Lord Woolf M.R., *Access to Justice* (HMSO, 1996).
[90] Act of Sederunt (R.C.S. 1994 Amendment No. 1) (Commercial Actions) 1994 (S.I. 1994 No. 2310).
[91] The Rt Hon. Lord Cullen, Review of the business of the Outer House of the Court of Session (1995) Scottish Courts Administration.
[92] See Chap. 8, paras 8.22–8.30.
[93] See for example Lord Moncreiff in *Brakinrig v. Menzies* (1841) 4 D. 274 at 283. See also Erskine, *Institute*, IV, iii, 29; J. C. Irons and R. D. Melville, *The Law of Arbitration in Scotland*.

courts by agreement of the parties for the private decision of an arbiter.[94] The advantages of this are thought to be: (1) privacy; (2) speed; (3) cost; (4) informality of procedure; (5) expertise of the arbiter in the field of dispute; and (6) finality. In the author's experience of the arbitration of construction disputes in Scotland, whether these advantages are achieved depends very much on the procedures set down by the individual arbiter for the conduct of the dispute.[95] Otherwise, construction arbitrations can easily replicate the worst excesses of formal court procedure, and add a few of their own.

4.381   The legal basis of arbitration in Scotland is relatively easy to grasp from first principles, and, save for very minor statutory interference, is based on common law. Indeed the history of arbitration in Scotland is thought to predate the establishment of public courts.[96]

Put simply the fundamental principles are:

(1)   that as a matter of contract the disputants remit their disputes to the decision of another or others and provide the appropriate powers for a decision to be reached;

(2)   that the Scottish courts will not normally interfere with this process;

(3)   that once an award is made it is binding on the parties as a matter of contract, without the right of appeal, and the dispute will be treated by the courts as if decided by the courts themselves (*res judicata*);

(4)   that the full authority of the courts will be given to enforce the award, even where it might be argued that the award contains errors in law, or where a fair but unusual procedure has been adopted;

(5)   that the arbiter is entitled to be paid for his services and for any legal clerk that he may appoint to assist him;

(6)   that the arbiter will act to fulfil the submission to him, no more and no less.

4.382   To state these as principles is to over-simplify matters, but not greatly; indeed it has been the position in Scotland since the 25th Act of the Articles of Regulation 1695 that the court would not sustain the reduction of any decree arbitral "upon any cause or reason whatsoever unless that of corruption, bribery or falsehood, to be alleged against the judges-arbitrators who pronounced the same". This position has only been modified since 1972[97] in that now either of the parties to an arbitration before any decree arbitral is finally issued may require the arbiter to state a case for the opinion of the Court of Session on a point of law, unless they agree that the Act should not apply to their arbitration. The Scottish position can be contrasted with the English where arbitration is very largely governed by statute,[98]

---

[94]   In Scotland the expression "arbiter" is preferred to the English "arbitrator", except where there is an international commercial arbitration conducted in Scotland under the UNCITRAL Model Law, which is incorporated into Scots law for such arbitrations by s. 66 of the Law Reform (Miscellaneous Provisions) (Scotland) Act 1990.

[95]   See Ian Strathdee, *Scottish Construction Industry Arbitration Procedures* [1996] A.D.R.L.J. 25.

[96]   See J. M. Bell, *The History of Arbitration in Scotland* (2nd ed., 1877); particularly the Introduction.

[97]   Administration of Justice (Scotland) Act 1972, s. 3.

[98]   Arbitration Act 1996.

and, it may be said, by a different ethos, whereby the English courts have been reluctant to cede finality to an arbitrator's decision quite so much. The Scottish position was memorably put by Lord Dunedin in *Sanderson & Son v. Armour & Co. Ltd*[99] at page 126: "If the parties have contracted to arbitrate, to arbitration they must go."

Also in *Hamlyn & Co. v. Talisker Distillery*[1] at page 25, Lord Watson said: "It deprives the Court of jurisdiction to inquire into and decide the merits of the case, while it leaves the Court free to entertain the suit, and pronounce a decree in conformity with the award of the arbiter. Should the arbitration from any cause prove abortive, the full jurisdiction of the Court will revive, to the effect of enabling it to hear and determine the action upon its merits".

The scope of this work does not allow a detailed examination of the Scots law of arbitration,[2] but there are particular pitfalls[3] and peculiarities that are relevant in the construction context. Most notably, in Scotland an arbiter has no inherent power to award damages, and this is a power that must be expressly given to him in the submission to him.[4] An arbiter in Scotland would not normally have power to award interest before the date of his decree arbitral, but again he can be given this power.[5] Documents can be recovered from a party in Scotland before an arbitration has even commenced under the Administration of Justice (Scotland) Act 1972, s.1.[6] It is possible to raise a court action in order to arrest on the dependence of an action, and then to sist it for arbitration if there is a valid arbitration clause.[7] The Scottish Building Contract provides for multi-party arbitrations arising from the same set of facts.[8] In England there are specific rules for the conduct of a construction arbitration[9] which are not used in Scotland.[10]

4.383

---

[99] 1992 S.C. (H.L.) 117.

[1] (1894) 21 R. (H.L.) 21.

[2] For an excellent summary see *Stair Memorial Encyclopedia*, Vol. 2, Arbitration.

[3] Especially where the ICE 5th conditions are used where disputes have first to be referred to the engineer before going to arbitration: *Douglas Milne Ltd v. Borders Regional Council*, 1990 S.LT. 558.

[4] For example, SBC clause 41B.6.1.

[5] For example, SBC clause 41B.6.

[6] *Anderson v. Gibb*, 1992 G.W.D. 1–48.

[7] *Mendok B.V. v. Cumberland Maritime Corporation*, 1989 S.L.T. 192. English lawyers are normally amazed by the Scottish procedure for arrestment on the dependence which is of much wider application than the English *Maereva* injunction. For an introduction to Scottish court procedures for a practitioner from a different jurisdiction see Aird & Jameson, *The Scots Dimension to Cross Border Litigation* (1996).

[8] Provided for in clause 41B.2.

[9] Currently the Construction Industry Model Arbitration Rules, February 1998. These are for use under the Arbitration Act 1996 which does not apply in Scotland, and the rules are not used either. In the view of the author it would not take a lot to adapt these rules, particularly where an arbitration in Scotland is taking place under the UNCITRAL Model law which may be opted for in Scottish domestic arbitrations by Sched. 7 of the Law Reform (Miscellaneous Provisions) (Scotland) Act 1990. However, in the Scottish Building Contract clause 41 B is a lengthy clause with particular emphasis on the arbiter's powers. The SBCC publish a helpful "Guidance Note Upon Dispute Resolution in Scotland" dated April 28, 1998, including a model Adjudication Agreement between the parties and the adjudicator.

[10] For a useful *vade mecum* for English Construction Arbitrations see Powell-Smith, Sims and Dancaster, *Construction Arbitrations* (2nd ed.).

Judicial Review in arbitration

4.384   Judicial review is a long-standing remedy which the courts of supreme jurisdiction in Scotland and England have accepted as within their prerogative. The matter of judicial review should be distinguished from that of an appeal. A review is to establish that the judicial character of the inferior tribunal is supervised. The courts retain the power to review the powers of any inferior tribunals, such as planning authorities and other bodies that have been given decision-making powers by statute. The essence of the review relates to the question of how far the inferior tribunal can determine its own powers to decide an issue before it. In short, whether the inferior tribunal has jurisdiction to exercise its decision-making function.

4.385   The English position has focused on the distinction between judicial review of public law matters and private law matters; for example, the actings of a public authority exercising an administrative authority, *e.g.* a social security tribunal, are reviewable. However, private contractual matters such as a contract of employment, even one with a governmental body, is not. The question is to what extent an arbiter who is required to privately exercise his functions may be subject to judicial review.

4.386   Scots and English law differ on that matter in principle in relation to arbitration. The English courts have long-recognised all manner of appeal possibilities from arbitration proceedings, including instances where the arbiter has erred in law or fact, even whilst acting within his authority. To that extent English arbitration law remains out of step with most international arbitration, such as the UNCITRAL Model Law for Arbitration.

4.387   Scots law appears to be relatively well-decided that an arbiter may err in law or fact and his award will not be challengeable on those bases alone. However, there is academic uncertainty on whether the scope of the Court of Session's powers in Scotland to judicially review arbitration proceedings as to questions of fact or law has altered in recent years. Part of this may be due to a confusion between Scots and English law in relation to judicial review and appeals.

4.388   Scots law has recognised for a considerable time that the Court of Session may make orders in relation to an arbiter who exceeds his jurisdiction or fails to perform his role under a deed of submission (see *Forbes v. Underwood*[11]). Therefore, the Court of Session has not become bound up in the question of whether it has power of judicial review in private matters. This was authoratively reconfirmed in *West v. Secretary of State for Scotland*,[12] where it was held that any tripartite decision-making process was subject to judicial review, including arbitration.

4.389   The difficulty has long been in deciding what is a reviewable error relating to jurisdiction (or power to act), and an error that an arbiter or tribunal is quite entitled to make. For example, in a tribunal case in Scotland it was held that a National Insurance Commissioner who had decided that an

---

[11]   (1863) 13 R. 463.
[12]   1992 S.L.T. 636.

applicant was not entitled to benefits because he "had been directly involved with a trade dispute" had made an error of law in defining what "directly involved" meant, and thus misdefined its own powers to act *(Watt v. Lord Advocate*[13]). It is easy to see therefore that an arbiter's interpretation of his deed of submission could be attacked in the same way. But Scots law has tried to maintain its long-established principles of leaving arbiters to decide, by trying to define what is a jurisdiction question. In *Watt v. Lord Advocate* the Lord President referred to *Anisminic v. Foreign Compensation Commission*[14] in which Lord Reid (a Scot) said in the House of Lords:

> "It has sometimes been said that it is only where a tribunal acts without jurisdiction that its decision is a nullity. But in such cases the word jurisdiction has been used in a very wide sense, and I have come to the conclusion that it is better not to use the term except in the narrow and original sense of the tribunal being entitled to enter on the enquiry in question.
>
> But there are many cases where, although the tribunal had jurisdiction to enter on the enquiry, it had done or failed to do something in the course of the enquiry which is of such a nature that its decision is a nullity. It may have given its decision in bad faith. It may have made a decision which it had no power to make. It may have failed in the course of the enquiry to comply with the requirements of natural justice. It may in perfect good faith have misconstrued the provisions giving it power to act so that it failed to deal with the matter remitted to it and decided some question that was not remitted to it. It may have refused to take into account something which it was required to take into account. Or it may have based its decision on some matter which, under the provisions setting it up, it had no right to take into account. I do not intend this list to be exhaustive. But if it decides a question remitted to it for decision without committing any of these errors it is as much entitled to decide that question wrongly as it is rightly."

Lord Jauncey in *O'Neil v. Scottish Joint Committee for Teaching Staff*[15]   4.390
referred to *Anisminic* and *Watt* and said: "If the decision is based on a gross error of law it cannot be interfered with."

Lord Cullen in *Shanks and McEwan (Contractors) v. Mifflin Construction Ltd*[16] said he was "unable to agree with the contention that the finality of a decision of an Arbiter is dependent on whether it is sound in law or that the Lord President in West intended to countenance that proposition". However, in *West* the Lord President said: "there was no substantial difference between English law and Scots law as to the grounds on which the process of decision making may be open to review".

The problem is that the House of Lords have interpreted *Anisminic* quite   4.391
differently from judges in Scotland. In *O'Reilly v. Mackman*[17] at page 238 Lord Diplock said of *Anisminic* that it was:

---

13   1979 S.L.T. 137.
14   [1969] 2 A.C. 147.
15   1987 S.L.T. 648.
16   1993 S.L.T. 1124.
17   [1983] 2 A.C. 237.

"A landmark decision that liberated English public law from the fetters that the courts had... imposed on themselves so far as determinations by inferior courts and statutory tribunals were concerned, by drawing esoteric distinctions between errors of law committed by such tribunals that went to their jurisdiction, and errors of law committed by them within their jurisdiction".

4.392   The problem is that if *Anisminic* means that errors of law are in themselves an exceeding of jurisdiction (which is very close to the English concept of *certiorari*) and subject to judicial review, and in Scots law the grounds for judicial review cover arbitration and as such are even wider than those in England, then it may be that we have come full circle and that an arbiter's decision is now subject to reduction if it is incorrect in law. This is unfortunate as it creates uncertainty.

There has been no case law on the point so far in Scotland, and no case where the courts have said in recent times that errors in law by an arbiter within his powers can be reviewed. It is suggested that the courts in Scotland would not do this, as it would run counter to long-established principle.

4.393   In *Haden Young v. William McCrindle*[18] an interesting case of judicial review arose. Two contractors agreed on the identity of an arbiter who submitted his terms. The main contractor rejected these terms, and the arbiter simply withdrew them and replied with a simple acceptance of office. The main contractor said the arbiter had no jurisdiction to act as arbiter on principles of contract law, *i.e.* he had not made a clean acceptance the first time and it was now too late. Judicial review proceedings were raised. It was held that the arbiter had jurisdiction and had been validly appointed. His terms were a supplementary matter, however, and if these could not be agreed then the party who found them unacceptable would not be bound by the arbitration clause.

PART 5: PERFORMANCE SPECIFIED WORK

Clause 42

4.394   This Part of JCT 80 was added by Amendment 12 (July 1993). On a first reading of this clause the sneaking suspicion is that the provisions of the Contractor's Designed Portion conditions have been introduced by stealth. Under the Design Portion contracts the Contractor is to be given documents known as "The Employer's Requirements" which according to the Practice Note CD/2 should include in its brief function and performance requirements. Under these types of contracts the contractor is to give the Employer "The Contractor's Proposals". Under clause 42 the Contractor is to provide "The Contractor's statement". In both cases the Contractor is to provide an analysis of the portion of the Contract Sum which relates to that Work. Accordingly, it is difficult to distinguish whether there is any real difference between the Contractor designing part of the Works or meeting a performance specification.

4.395   Amendment 12 was issued with Practice Note 25 which attempts to explain what is meant by "Performance Specified Work". At Appendix B

---

[18] 1994 S.L.T. 221.

of the Practice Note an "Extract from the Code of Procedure for Project Specification issued by the Building Project Information Committee" is reproduced. It notes that the specification process can be considered as two stages:

> "(1) Ascertaining the performance required of the particular element, system, assembly, component or material.
> (2) Determining the products, materials and workmanship needed to meet the performance requirements, and stating any special conditions for carrying out the work.
>> The second of these stages is traditional prescriptive specification. If the project specification identifies only the performance requirements, leaving the manufacturer or contractor to determine the form and dimensions of the construction and/or the products, materials and workmanship, then this is known as performance specification. Specification by performance thus requires the manufacturer or contractor to complete the design process."

Clearly, therefore, the Contractor will be considered a designer too, and   4.396
one wonders why this option has been created rather than using the Contractor's Designed Portion, or by nominating specialist sub-contractors. The Contractor will have to appreciate that his existing insurance might need to be altered to meet such obligations. The allocation of liability is given in clause 42.17 which is that the Contractor shall exercise reasonable skill and care in the provision of Performance Specified Work but that does not affect any contractual obligation in regard to the supply of workmanship, materials or goods. Also in clause 42.17.2, "nothing in this contract shall operate as a guarantee of fitness for purpose of the Performance Specified Work". It is submitted therefore that many questions will remain if the Employer does not get what he wants, *i.e.* a part to perform as specified.

Practice Note 25 states at paragraph 2.8:   4.397

> "The provisions for Performance Specified Work should not be used for items which will materially affect the appearance of the building, or may result in changes in the design of other work (otherwise than at the interface with the Performance Specified Work), or will affect the use of the finished building, so that it would be essential to examine and accept the Contractor's proposals for the work before acceptance of the tender."

It is submitted that if nomination of sub-contractors has caused such   4.398
difficulties in interpretation in the courts of who is responsible for what, this is likely to be just as bad for Performance Specified Work, as the Architect may give notices under clauses 42.5 and 42.6 requiring the Contractor to give notices of deficiencies. But again, and as is similar to the disputes about the effect of a Final Certificate under clause 30.9, the Contractor is to be solely responsible. There are many questions as to how these provisions of clause 42 could be operated in any event for valuation purposes and for Variations.

CHAPTER 5

PRIVITY OF CONTRACT ISSUES

5.01   Privity of contract issues arise in the typical construction context because of the matrix of possibly numerous parties with distinct obligations to each other. An employer may owe certain obligations to a contractor, but, for example, will the contractor owe the same obligations to his sub-contractors? Such obligations may be expressly agreed or arise by implication. It is the "stepping down" of implied obligations that causes the most difficulty.

5.02   The *Stair Memorial Encyclopaedia,*[1] para. 119 states generally that implied obligations affecting the main contractor *vis-à-vis* the employer are applicable *mutatis mutandis* between the main contractor and the sub-contractor — but this is perhaps to put matters too widely. The authors refer to *J. & J. Fee Ltd v. Express Lift Co. Ltd,*[2] which provides that, for the DOM/2 form of sub-contract the main contractor has an implied obligation to provide the sub-contractor with correct information concerning the works in such a manner and at such a time as is reasonably necessary to enable the sub-contractor to fulfil his obligations under the form. It is not clear to the author why this particular implied term should be indicative of a general proposition. The authors then refer to *Ductform Ventilation (Fife) Ltd v. Andrews Weatherfoil*[3] which on inspection is a case concerning the relationship between sub-contractors and sub-sub-contractors.

5.03   In *Ductform* there was a non-standard form of sub-sub-contract to carry out works at a fixed price. The sub-sub-contractor as pursuer argued that there were two implied terms to the sub-sub-contract: (one) if for reasons outwith their control the contract works were carried out over a period materially longer than originally programmed for, the sub-sub-contractor was entitled to extra costs caused to them by such a delay; (two) the sub-contractor would see to it that all necessary steps were taken to provide the sub-sub-contractor with access to the site and to have the site ready to allow the sub-sub-contractor to carry out the works in good time so as to allow the sub-sub-contractor to complete their works within the period specified in the sub-sub-contract. Lord Sutherland held that in *Merton v. Leach*[4], the

---

[1] *Building Contracts* (Butterworths), Vol. 3.
[2] (1993) 34 Con. L.R. 147.
[3] 1995 S.L.T. 88.
[4] *Merton London Borough v. Leach* (Stanley Hugh) (1985) 32 B.L.R. 51.

terms which were implied in that case as between employer and main contractor did not impose any obligations on either party in respect of matters outwith the control of the party accepting the obligations. Lord Sutherland noted as for the second implied term that it sought to establish a duty on the defenders whether they had caused the delay or not; for example, the delay might have been caused by other sub-sub-contractors. His Lordship considered that the implied terms contended for were not necessary for business efficacy. He was assisted in this view as express terms to the same effect as the implied ones contended for had been superseded in the so-called "battle of the forms" during the negotiation of the sub-sub-contract.

The *Ductform* case did not confirm that the implied terms in *Merton v. Leach* are part of Scots law, but they were described as "helpful" in the *ratio* of Lord Sutherland. Perhaps the matter would benefit from clarification. On implied terms generally in construction contracts in Scotland in *McAlpine v. Lanarkshire and Ayrshire Railway*[5] it was held that for the construction of a railway there was an implied obligation upon the railway company and their engineer to supply drawings within a reasonable time, failure giving rise to a claim for damages.

There is another potential difficulty with building contracts related to privity of contract. For example, in the case of a nominated sub-contractor privity exists between the employer and the main contractor, and between the main contractor and the nominated sub-contractor. These "triangular relationships" are discussed in Chapter 4. For example, following *Borders Regional Council v. Smart*[6] the main contractor, after practical completion, may yet have the obligation of remedying of works carried out by a named sub-contractor where the named sub-contractor has gone into liquidation. **5.04**

Direct payment to a sub-contractor in the event of the main contractor's insolvency may run aground on the basis of privity of contract. In *Dunbarton County Council v. George Sellers and Sons*[7] there was a Regulations and General Conditions for Building Works in Scotland 1954 contract where the main contractor went into liquidation, but where there was a condition that the main contractor and his liquidator were not entitled to any further certificates until there was evidence that the sub-contractors had been paid previously certified sums. It was held that there was no privity of contract between the sub-contractors and the employer; neither was the main contractor the agent of the sub-contractor, nor was a trust established. Accordingly, the employers had to pay the liquidator for the painterwork sub-contract works, and not the sub-contractors directly. It is to get round such privity problems that the I.Mech E. form of contract provides that the main contractor acts as agent for the sub-contractor. **5.05**

---

[5] (1899) 17 R. 113.
[6] 1983 S.L.T. 164.
[7] 1973 S.L.T. (Sh. Ct.) 67.

5.06   The authors of the *Stair Memorial Encyclopaedia* chapter on building
contracts at paragraph 120 discuss mitigating the harshness of privity of
contract, an example of which was in *Smith and Montgomery v. Johnson Bros &
Co. Ltd*,[8] where the main contract permitted the employer to halt the works
but the sub-contract gave no equivalent power to the main contractor;
therefore the sub-contractor was entitled to claim against the main contractor.
The authors suggest that there are difficulties in avoiding such results. The
employer may impose a condition obliging the main contractor to include
certain conditions in any sub-contract, but that in itself will not import the
condition into the sub-contract. The employer may enter into a collateral
contract with the sub-contractor such as NSC/W/Scot, which brings about
confusing triangular relationships. There is also the question of whether an
effective *jus quaesitum tertio* could be created under Scots contract law.

JUS QUAESITUM TERTIO

5.07   This is an area of the law which has developed over recent years.[9] In relation
to construction issues the matter arose in *Scott Lithgow v. General Electric
Co.(Electrical Projects) Ltd*.[10] The case involved multiple pursuers and
defenders who were variously linked in contract concerning shipbuilding
works. Various alternative cases were pled in contract and delict, in respect
of defective wiring and design of the electrical surveillance and propulsion
system of the ship, *HMS Challenger*. Also the ultimate employer, the
Ministry of Defence, argued that a *jus quaesitum tertio* had been created in
their favour because they were referred to in sub-contracts. Lord Clyde
reviewed the authorities[11] and noted that in Gloag on *Contract* at page 239
the formulation of the principles of *jus quaesitum tertio* "may well have
been overtaken by later cases on that branch of the law" (at p. 260–F). Lord
Clyde then noted that the question of implying a *jus quaesitum tertio* for
losses incurred by a third party raised many of the same problems of recovery
of economic loss in delict on the basis of the proximate relationship of the
parties which might create a duty of care: "The problem begins to look like
the contractual equivalent of the issue which I have already discussed in
relation to the quasi delictual claims" (at p. 261–E). Lord Clyde was referred
to the case of *Blumer and Sons v. Scott & Sons*[12] which was similar. In the
Blumer case there was a contract between shipbuilders and an employer to

---

[8]   (1954) 1 D.L.R. 392.
[9]   In an entirely different context, see the comments of Lord Penrose in *Beta Computers
       (Europe) Ltd v. Adobe Systems (Europe) Ltd*, 1996 S.C.L.R. 587 at 597–F in relation to the
       rights of the copyright holder seeking to impose licensing conditions for proprietory software
       which is sold by a retailer.
[10]   1992 S.L.T. 244.
[11]   *ibid.* pp. 259–263.
[12]   (1874) 1 R. 379.

build and supply a ship to the satisfaction of the employer, with engines provided by one of two sub-contractors to the satisfaction of the shipbuilder. In that case the majority in the Inner House held that this did not create a right to sue as between the employer and the sub-contractor. Counsel in the *Scott Lithgow* case sought to distinguish *Blumer* as in that case the employer was not mentioned in the sub-contract. The question, as Lord Clyde saw it, was as set out in *Finnie v. Glasgow & South Western Railway Co*[13] (Lord Cranworth at p.88): "The *jus quaesitum* must be not merely a *jus* in which the *tertius* is interested, but it must be a *jus* that was intended to be beneficial in some way to a third person." Lord Clyde went on: "I am prepared to hold as a matter of law that they [the Ministry] could competently have a *jus quaesitum tertio* whereby they could claim damages from the first defenders, but whether in the circumstances they do have such a right is a matter which would be left to inquiry when the facts and in particular the whole terms of the relevant contracts can be explored" (p. 263–B). But Lord Clyde also stated that the intention of the parties to create a *jus quaesitum tertio* might be implied although it would be difficult to do so (p. 260–L).

In *Aberdeen Harbour Board v. Heating Enterprises*[14] counsel for the defenders appears to have raised an issue of whether a *jus quaesitum tertio* was created, but the matter was decided at first instance on different grounds, and upheld on appeal on different grounds again. The contractual chain in this case was landlord–tenant (or possibly sub-tenant; this factual issue was subject to denial), as employer–main contractor–nominated sub-contractor. On appeal Lord Dunpark was of the *obiter* view that no *jus quaesitum tertio* could be created where the sub-contractor, who sought the protection of an indemnity that applied to the main contractor under the main contract, was not named in the main contract, on top of which, the sub-contract was expressly stated not to create any privity of contract between the sub-contractor and the employer (pp. 422K–423A). Lord Cullen in the Extra Division expressly reserved his opinion on the *jus quaesitum tertio* issue (p. 425 –E).   5.08

More recently again in *Strathford East Kilbride v. HLM Design*[15] Lord MacLean in the Outer House rejected an argument that a *jus quaesitum tertio* had been created. The circumstances related to a fee proposal by a firm of architects in respect of a car dealership's premises. The car dealers were a distinct company affiliated to Ford Motor Co. Ltd. It was held on the facts that the fee proposal was agreed with the Ford Motor Co. Ltd as the "owner" as defined in the agreement. Whilst the agreement defined the "owner" as "Ford Motor Company, its affiliates and/or subsidiaries", the agreement had to be read as meaning whichever of these entities concluded   5.09

---

[13] (1857) 3 Macq. 75.
[14] 1988 S.L.T. 762 (OH); 1990 S.L.T. 416 (Ex Div).
[15] 1997 S.C.L.R. 877 (OH).

the contract, and not all or any affiliates, that might exist. However, Lord MacLean thought it quite possible to have made an agreement such as the pursuers contended for had the contracting parties wanted to. The architects argued that to create a *jus quaesitum tertio*, notice of such an arrangement would have to be intimated to the dealer before the works that were allegedly defectively built were completed. Lord MacLean said:

> "If Ford and the defenders had contracted to confer the benefit of [the indemnity against defects provision] upon whichever subsidiary took on the dealership, which, of course, I have held they did not, I do not see what difference it would make that the construction work was completed and, in that sense the contract had been completely performed. As I see it, the point is whether either of the contracted parties could lawfully revoke the contract conferring the benefit on a third party. In the circumstances figured, they would, in my opinion, be unable to revoke the contract and it cannot matter whether formal intimation had been made to the pursuers."

Concurrent liability in delict and contract

5.10   Where there are contractual connections between parties, there can also be a question of whether general duties of care co-exist, and perhaps fill any contractual gaps. The question is how far the existence of a contract — or the failure to enter into a contract which adequately covered the issue — negates duties in delict. The problem is more acute in the context of pure economic loss rather than damage to property.[16]

5.11   Although not a construction case,[17] being concerned with the duties of insurance agents, in *Henderson v. Merrett Syndicates Ltd*[18] it was held that a concurrent duty of care in contract and tort could co-exist although the scope of the duty in tort could not be wider than the scope of the duty in contract.

5.12   In Scotland there is judicial opinion in *Scott Lithgow v. GEC Electrical Products*[19] from Lord Clyde as follows:

> "I take the view as a matter of generality that while contractual relationships do not by themselves exclude the existence of a quasi delictual duty of care the existence of such relationships and of any restraints on liability are relevant considerations bearing on the decision whether such a duty can exist in any given case. The fact of the contractual chain in the present case seems to me to point away from any conclusion of a duty of care. A direct privity of contract will almost certainly do so except in cases where the quasi delictual duty is simply a different formulation of the existing duty under the contract, but in any such case the terms of the contract in question will probably require to be considered."

---

[16] See Headley, "Negligence — Pure Economic Loss — Goodbye Privity, Hello Contorts" [1995] C.L.J. 27.

[17] But see the comments of Lord Goff quoted in full at Chap. 6, para. 6.28.

[18] [1994] 3 All E.R. 506 (HL).

[19] 1992 S.L.T. 244 at 253.

In England judicial opinion generally seems much more orientated towards   5.13
a supremacy of contract analysis. In *Greater Nottingham Co-op v. Cementation*[20]
a piling sub-contractor had given a warranty as to design to the employer, but
not workmanship. This failure to cover all liabilities contractually was held to
exclude any duty in tort as regards workmanship. The circumstances here were
that a sub-contractor had allegedly carried out piling work negligently so that it
caused a nuisance to proprietors adjacent to the site. The employer had to
compensate adjacent proprietors, but the absence of a contractual warranty
from the sub-contractor to the employer, when it could have been obtained,
negatived any duty in tort for the employer's losses.[21]

Importing of terms into a sub-contract

Often there are attempts to incorporate similar terms in the sub-contract   5.14
as there are in the main contract, with varying degrees of success. In *Haskins
(Shutters) Ltd v. Ogilvie Builders*[22] the sub-contract stated that it "shall be in
the terms and conditions applicable to the main contract". There was an
arbitration clause in the main contract, and it was held by the sheriff that the
arbitration clause had not been incorporated into the sub-contract. This follows
a line of authority against the incorporation of arbitration clauses by reference
and without explicit agreement. However, for the incorporation of terms
mutatis mutandis where the sense allows, see also *Parklea v. Watson*.[23]

Sometimes there is a clause in a main contract to the effect that any sub-
contractor will be deemed to have knowledge of the main contract conditions.
This is not, of itself, enough to incorporate these conditions.[24] But, in *Nicol
Homeworld Contracts v. Charles Gray Builders Ltd*[25] there was a clause in
the nominated sub-contract document that the sub-contractor was deemed to
have knowledge of the main contract. Clause 27 of the main contract allowed
the architect to insist on the removal of defective work. The nominated sub-
contractor contended that there was nothing wrong with his work, but it was
held that he could not sue the main contractor until the value of the work had
been included under a certificate in the main contract. The certificate was
therefore a condition precedent to suing for payment. To dispute the quality
of workmanship issue with the employer, the sub-contractor should have
gone to arbitration borrowing the name of the main contractor.[26]

---

[20] [1988] 2 All E.R. 971.
[21] See also the discussion on the meaning of *Junior Books v. Veitchi* [1983] 1 A.C. 520 (HL) in
the light of *Henderson v. Merrett Syndicates Ltd* 3 W.L.R. 761 (HL) at Chap. 6, para. 6.28.
[22] 1978 S.L.T. (Sh. Ct.) 64.
[23] 1988 S.L.T. 605, discussed at Chap. 3, para. 3.22.
[24] For example see *Dawber Williamson Roofing v. Humberside County Council* [1979] 14
B.L.R. 70, discussed at Chap. 4, para. 4.110.
[25] 1986 S.L.T. 317.
[26] Name-borrowing arbitrations are a unique scheme under JCT Forms of Contract so that an
award of an arbitrator under the main contract directly affects the rights and liabilities of
the parties to the sub-contract: *Co-operative Wholesale Society Ltd v. Birse Construction
Ltd* [1997] 57 Con. L.R. 98 (AC).

Pay-when-paid-clauses

5.15   There is a mood that such clauses are intrinsically unfair and were a matter which the Latham Report criticised.[27] It led to their being outlawed by the Housing Grants, Construction and Regeneration Act 1996, s.113. It was probably not a matter of intrinsic unfairness that the sub-contractor should contractually be obliged to wait until the main contractor has been paid by the employer.[28] The standard form of sub-contract DOM/1 has no pay-when-paid clause. Under this form of contract the sub-contractor is to be paid interim payments each month (cl. 21), irrespective of whether the main contractor has been paid. However, under the standard form of sub-contract for engineering works (FCEC) a pay-when-paid provision existed.

5.16   In *Taymech Ltd v. Trafalgar House Construction (Regions)Ltd*[29] the sub-contractor sued for payment of sums not yet certified. The sub-contractor also arrested sums due by a third party to the main contractor. It was held that the arrestment was invalid as there was no proper cause of action for a debt under the sub-contract for sums which had not been certified or paid to the main contractor. (This contract was a non-standard form of contract.) The same decision was reached in *Costain v. Scottish Rugby Union.*[30]

5.17   The new provisions in section 113 of HGCRA may yet be interpreted as precluding "pay when certified" cases too; although an amendment at report stage covering "clauses having the effect of a pay-when-paid clause" was dropped because of the Government's opposition. Section 113 is not an absolute ban on pay-when-paid clauses as there is an exception where the third party is insolvent, although the clause has been drafted in such a way that an ambiguity may arise as to whether the third party has to have been insolvent at the time the contract is made.

Difficulties of co-ordination of works caused by privity

5.18   Clause 11.1 of DOM/1 provides that: "The Sub-Contractor shall carry out and complete the Sub-Contract Works ...in accordance with the progress of the Works." In *Piggot Foundations Ltd v. Shepherd Consrtuction Ltd*[31] it was held that in the absence of express provision the sub-contractor is under no obligation to comply with the main contractor's programme or to complete particular parts of the sub-contract works by a particular date to enable the main contractor to proceed with other parts of the works.

---

[27]   See discussion of the point in Chap. 8, paras 8.30–8.32.
[28]   See *Schindler Lifts (Hong Kong) v. Shui On Construction Co.* [1985] H.K.L.R. 118; *Brightside Mechanical & Electrical Services Group v. Hyundai Engineering & Construction Co.* [1988] 41 B.L.R. 110.
[29]   1994 G.W.D. 7–42.
[30]   1994 S.L.T. 573 (5 Judges).
[31]   (1994) C.I.L.L. 947.

Privity and warranties as to quality of materials

Gloucestershire County Council v. Richardson[32] involved the 1939 RIBA 5.19
contract, 1957 revision, where the architect nominated the supplier of
concrete columns and sent the contractor instructions to accept a quotation,
which they did. The supplier's quote contained clauses limiting liability for
defects. There were defects and the employer sued the main contractor. It
was held in the House of Lords that design, materials, specification of quality
and price were fixed between the employer and the supplier without
reference to the main contractor. This imposed severe restrictions on the
main contractor and the court held that neither a warranty as to fitness for
purpose nor quality should be implied as between the employer and main
contractor. The prior House of Lords decision in *Young and Marten Ltd v.
McManus Childs Ltd* (*infra*) was distinguished on the facts.

In *Young and Martin Ltd v. McManus Childs Ltd*[33] the contractors/ 5.20
developers on a housing estate sub-contracted roofing where the contract
required specific tiles made by one specific supplier. Tiles were obtained
that had defects due to faulty manufacture which could not be discovered
after reasonable inspection. After 12 months the tiles began to disintegrate.
The main contractor claimed the cost of re-roofing from the sub-
contractor.The sub-contractor argued that as he had not chosen the type of
tile and could not have discovered the defect he should not be liable. Also,
the limitation period had expired and the sub-contractor had no remedy left
against the supplier in any case. The House held the sub-contract was not a
contract for the sale of goods, where there would be an implied warranty as
to quality, but Lord Reid went on:

> "Moreover many contracts for work and materials closely resemble contracts
> of sale: where the employer contracts for the sale and installation of a machine
> or other article, the supply of the machine may be the main element and the
> work of installation be a comparatively small matter. If the employer had
> bought the article and installed it himself he would have had a warranty
> under section 14(2)[of the Sale of Goods Act], and it would be strange that
> the fact that the seller also agreed to install it should make all the difference."

The House held that there was good reason to imply a warranty of quality
against latent defects in the materials, *i.e.* it can be passed down the
contractual chain to the author of the defect, and without it the employer
(or contractor) would have no remedy if he could not recover from the
contractor (or sub-contractor). If the supplier becomes insolvent, or an action
has prescribed, these are matters that should be at the contractor's (sub-
contractor's) risk. It is quite a different thing if a contractor is obliged to
supply materials with the employer's full knowledge that the conditions of
supply exclude the usual warranties.

---

[32] [1969] 1 A.C. 480 (HL).
[33] [1969] 9 B.L.R. (HL).

5.21   The current JCT position is that suppliers to a sub-contractor are still unregulated by standard conditions. However if a supplier to a main contractor is nominated, then under clause 36 the Architect may only nominate a supplier who is prepared to enter into a contract with the main contractor on specified terms (cl. 36.4). The contract specifically provides that if the sale contract in any way limits or excludes the suppliers' liability to the Contractor and the Architect or Contract Administrator has approved the limitation or exclusion in writing, the Contractor's liability to the Employer is limited to the same extent (cl.36.5). The SBCC provides a Standard Form of Tender for use by a Nominated Supplier and a Warranty Agreement to be granted by the Supplier to the Employer (January 1992 revisions).

5.22   The chain of liability theory had been previously applied to domestic house builders. Where a house builder was contractually bound to a purchaser "in a proper and workmanlike manner to erect build and complete...a dwelling house" and materials were found to be defective, there is an important decision of the Court of Appeal in *Hancock v. B.W. Brazier (Anerley) Ltd.*[34] Here there was hardcore containing sodium sulphate used, which expanded on contact with water and also caused a chemical disintegration of the concrete foundations. Lord Denning specifically stated:

> "Let me say at once that all this trouble was in no way the fault of the builders. They had no reason to suspect the hardcore. They bought it in good faith. The defects were not apparent. No one could tell by looking at this hardcore that it had sodium sulphate mixed in with it. The builders used all reasonable skill and judgement."

However these comments related to workmanship and the problem was the performance of materials, on which the express terms of the contract were silent. Lord Denning went on:

> "The quality of the materials is left to be implied; and the necessary implication is that they should be good and suitable for the work. I am quite clear that it is implied in the contract that the hardcore must be good and proper hardcore, in the same way the bricks must be good and proper bricks. I know that the builders were not at fault themselves. Nevertheless this is a contract: it was their responsibility to see that good and proper hardcore was put in. As it was not put in they are in breach of their contract."

Lord Denning noted that the builders had the right to sue their own suppliers, presumably under the Sale of Goods Act.

5.23   Under the Supply of Goods and Services Act 1982, s.11D (effective in Scotland for contracts made on or after January 3, 1995), a contract for the transfer of goods (such as a building contract), "there is an implied term

---

[34] [1966] 2 All E.R. 901.

that the goods supplied under the contract are of satisfactory quality". Also under that Act, if the transferee expressly or by implication makes known any particular purpose for which the goods are being acquired, there is an implied term that the goods are reasonably fit for the purpose, whether or not that is a purpose for which such goods are commonly supplied (s. 11D (5) and (6)).

Design liability and privity

A warranty that materials will be of suitable quality and free of latent   5.24
defects on the chain of liability model is one thing for roof tiles and hardcore (*Young & Martin*; *Hancock*), but what if the contractor is installing a system where there is the implied warranty that due skill and care are used and a warranty that materials are free of latent defects? Will these, when taken together, amount to a warranty from the contractor that the system will work, *i.e.* be fit for its intended purpose?

In *Greater Glasgow Health Board v. Keppie Henderson and Partners*,[35]   5.25
this was considered by Lord Cullen in the Outer House. The case concerned the laying of underground pipes to carry hot water as part of a central heating system at the Western Infirmary, Glasgow. The pipes were of a specified type, protected by an outer pipe, galvanised and linked to an alarm system if there was a pressure drop. They were also coated with bitumen to provide a watertight exterior. Three parts of the system gave trouble and were required to be replaced. Lord Cullen held that a warranty as to the quality of materials and a warranty as to workmanship were distinct.

He went on:

> "As I have noted above the pursuer's submission was that it was enough for them to aver that in an elementary sense the system 'did not work'; and that this is what they had done. In my view a warranty that the system 'would work' goes far beyond a warranty as to materials and workmanship. Where there is no suggestion that the contractors were responsible for the design of the system or its integration into the design of the whole works or for the selection of the proprietary system which was installed there is no basis for the claim."

This case is also of interest as Lord Cullen discusses when a warranty   5.26
should be implied into a building contract. He states:

> "Whether and to what extent a warranty should be implied in a building contract depends, in my view, on the type of considerations which were discussed by the members of the House of Lords in the case of *Young and Martin*. At p. 465 Lord Reid observed that 'no warranty ought to be implied in a contract unless it is in all the circumstances reasonable'. The statements in that case were consistent with the tests for implication which were formulated in the cases of *Morton* [*infra*] and *McWhirter* [*infra*]."

---

35 1989 S.L.T. 387.

In *William Morton & Co. v. Muir Brothers & Co.*[36] in respect of implying terms Lord McLaren stated:

> "If the condition is such that every reasonable man, on the one part, would desire for his own protection to stipulate for the condition, and that no reasonable man, on the other part, would refuse to accede to it, then it is not immaterial that the condition should be taken for granted in all contracts of the class without the necessity of giving it formal expression."

In *McWhirter v. Longmuir*[37] Lord Jamieson said: "The court will only hold a term or condition to be implied in a written contract if its nature is such that it must necessarily be implied to give the contract business efficacy."

5.27   The key feature in the *Greater Glasgow* case was that there was no design aspect by the contractor of the system. In a design and build or package-deal type contract the fitness for purpose standard will readily be implied.[38] But design can be a question of degree at times, especially where a matter is left to the choice of the contractor: *e.g.* type or location of reinforcement in a concrete lintel, types of joint and many other matters that may not be specified. Although these are actually matters of choice and therefore design (*Hudson* at paragraph 4–064 has choice as the essential element of the function of design in the construction context) they are commonly regarded as "workmanship" matters. Although in a simple task, such as joining two bits of wood together, the contractor may choose the length of nail and where to put it, this will not normally be classed as design.

5.28   In *Independent Broadcasting Authority v. EMI Electronics and BICC Construction*[39] EMI tendered and IBA accepted the tender to carry out works involving the erection of a T.V. mast on the Yorkshire Moors. The description of the mast and the design of it were incorporated expressly into the main contract. The mast failed, through vortex shedding and asymmetric ice loading of the stays, and the sub-contractors, BICC, who had designed the mast were held at first instance to have been negligent in their design. In the Court of Appeal it was held that the main contractors had also accepted design responsibility for the quality of the mast, and also that it be reasonably fit for the purposes for which it was intended, both as a matter of contract. As a result it was unnecessary for the House to consider whether there is a general duty of fitness for purpose owed by a designer. However, important *obiter* points were made that follow the chain of responsibility idea where a sub-contractor carries out design. Lord Fraser stated:

---

[36] 1907 S.C. at p. 1224.
[37] 1948 S.L.T. at p. 499.
[38] *Viking Grain Storage v. T.H. White* [1985] 33 B.L.R. 10.
[39] [1980] 14 B.L.R. 1 (HL).

"In the present case, it is accepted by BICC that if EMI are liable in damages to IBA for the design of the mast, then BICC will be liable in turn to EMI. Accordingly the principle that was applied in *Young and Martin Ltd* in respect of materials ought in my opinion to be applied here in respect of the complete structure, including its design. Although EMI had no specialist knowledge of mast design, and although IBA knew that and did not rely on their skill to any extent for the design, I can see nothing unreasonable in holding that EMI are responsible to IBA for the design seeing that they can in turn recover from BICC who did the actual designing. On the other hand it would seem to be very improbable that IBA would have entered into a contract of this magnitude and this degree of risk without providing for some right of recourse against the principal contractor or the sub-contractors for defects of design."

Lord Scarman in the same case went on to compare design responsibility in the construction of a thing to the fitting of false teeth (*Samuels v. Davis*[39a]), in that the standard was not that of the reasonably competent professional designer, but that the design (like dentures) would be reasonably fit for its purpose. Lord Scarman stated:

"In the absence of any terms (express or implied) negativing the obligation, one who contracts to design an article for a purpose made known to him undertakes that the design is reasonably fit for the purpose. Such a design obligation is consistent with the statutory law regulating the sale of goods.... The critical question of fact is whether he for whom the mast was designed relied upon the skill of the supplier (*i.e.*, his or his sub-contractor's skill) to design and supply a mast fit for the known purpose for which it was required."

Keating[40] reads this decision as a warning to employers of the risks of design being carried out by a nominated sub-contractor (unless, presumably, a warranty is given to the employer):   5.29

"Where the employer has not relied on the contractor's skill and judgement in the selection for design purposes of a nominated sub-contractor or nominated supplier, or the works or materials they are to carry out or supply, a term that such work or materials will be reasonably fit for their purpose is not normally implied, unless the express terms or the surrounding circumstances of the contract show that the parties intended the contractor to accept such liability.[41] The practical significance of this principle is great and frequently does not seem to be appreciated. It means that under the ordinary procedures of nomination currently in use the employer has no remedy against the contractor if, for example, tiles, windows, mechanical plant, heating or air conditioning systems, or other specially designed parts of the works, the subject of nomination, are of good quality but unfit for their purpose....Partial reliance on the contractor's skill and judgement would give rise to the warranty of fitness for purpose on the part of the contractor so as to make him responsible for the sub-contractor, or at any rate in respect of that area where

---

[39a] (1943) 1 K.B. 526.
[40] May, *Keating on Building Contracts* (6th ed.), pp. 315–316.
[41] See *IBA v. EMI and BICC* [1980] 14 B.L.R. 1 (HL).

there has been such partial reliance.[42] But to be effective partial reliance must be such as to constitute a substantial and effective inducement to the employer to enter into the main contract.[43]"

5.30   It might be that Keating's view is too narrow, as a different emphasis might be put on Lord Fraser and Lord Scarman's speeches. Both of these, it is submitted, could be interpreted as meaning that where any part of the design process is carried out by a contractor or sub-contractor in a chain (whether the sub-contractor is nominated or not) that liability will transmit up and down the contractual chain. However, the question is undoubtedly a difficult one as the views of Lords Scarman and Fraser were *obiter*, and Lord Denning in *Greaves (Contractors) Ltd v. Baynham Meikle & Partners*[44] specifically said:

"What then is the position when an architect or an engineer is employed to design a house or a bridge? Is he under an implied warranty that, if the work is carried out to his design, it will be reasonably fit for the purpose or is he only under a duty to use reasonable skill and care? The question may require to be answered some day as a matter of law. But, in the present case I do not think we need answer it. For the evidence shows that both parties were of one mind on the matter. Their common intention was that the engineer should design a warehouse which would be fit for the purpose for which it was required. That common intention gives rise to a term implied in fact."

The *Greaves* case concerned a design and build contract for a warehouse to be used to store oil drums to be moved by fork-lift trucks, and where the floors had to take the weight. The contractor was liable to the employer when the floors cracked, and the contractor took action against the engineers whom they had brought in to design the floors. The engineers were found liable to the contractor because of an implied term in fact that the floors would be fit for their known purpose.

5.31   The Supreme Court of Ireland in *Norta Wallpapers (Ireland) v. Sisk & Sons (Dublin)*[45] considered the implication of a term as to fitness for purpose of a sub-contractor's design for a roof into a main contract, and said that such an implied term could not be read into a contract unless it was reasonable to do so and was within the presumed intention of the parties. This might seem inconsistent with *IBA v. EMI & BICC* but was considered and distinguished in the House as Norta's engineers had approved the sub-contractor's design; promised them the sub-contract and the price; and the main contractor was given no choice as to the identity of the sub-contractor, the design or the price.

5.32   In *Basildon District Council v. Lesser Ltd*[46] a specialist system builder contractor submitted design drawings and then entered into a contract to

---

[42] See *Cammell Laird v. Manganese Bronze* [1934] A.C. 402 (HL).
[43] *Medway Oil and Storage v. Silca Gel Corporation* (1928) 33 Com.Cas. 195 (HL).
[44] [1975] 1 W.L.R. 1095.
[45] (1978) 14 B.L.R. 49.
[46] [1985] 1 All E.R. 20.

carry them out for the employer, and expressly stated that the design drawings had been prepared under "the direction of the owner's engineer or architect". It was found that, as a matter of fact, all but a slight contribution had been designed by the contractor and there was an implied term that the buildings designed by the contractor would be fit for habitation and that their design was relied upon.

It is submitted that there still is no absolute answer on the issue of when 5.33 a fitness for purpose design warranty as opposed to the standard of the reasonably competent designer will be implied in the context of construction contracts where the contractor effects the design. The higher fitness for purpose standard will arise either from the express terms of the contract or by necessary implication. The JCT 81 With Contractor's Design contract (cl. 2.5.1) and the Contractor's Designed Portion Supplement to JCT 80 (cl. 2.6.1) both appear to provide for the lesser standard, although the matter is not beyond ambiguity. Both the above clauses are worded the same, as follows:

> "the Contractor shall have in respect of any defect or insufficiency in such design the like liability to the Employer, whether under statute or otherwise, as would an Architect, or as the case may be, other appropriate professional designer holding himself out as competent to take on work for such design, who acting independently under a separate contract with the Employer, had supplied such design for or in connection with works to be carried out and completed by a building contractor not being the supplier of the design."

Duty to warn of defects in design

Any analysis of whether a contractual relationship between a contractor 5.34 and an employer should give rise to any implied terms in Scotland may take as a recent starting point the comments made by Lord Cullen in *Greater Glasgow Health Board v. Keppie Henderson (supra)* on implying terms generally. As there are no standard forms of contract that expressly state that a contractor is bound to advise the employer that there may be deficiencies in the design given to the contractor, the question arises as to whether there should be an implied duty on the contractor to warn the employer of any such deficiencies, failing which the contractor will be in breach of contract. At first sight this might appear a remarkable term to imply, but as we shall see there is some case law to that effect, both in contract and in delict.

From a contractual point of view it is submitted that the provisions for 5.35 implying terms would have to be satisfied; but, as a first step, the legal effect of error in contract would require consideration. It is generally agreed that the Scots law relating to error in contract is in need of clarification.[47] It is not proposed to attempt that task in a rounded way in this work, but

---

[47] Scottish Law Commission, "Defective Consent and Consequential Matters", Memorandum 42, June 1978, Vol. 1, para. 1.10.

rather to raise a few questions on the topic. What would be the correct legal approach to the problem where (a) the architect has made a mistake that the design can be carried out; and (b) the contractor entered the agreement believing that the design could be built, based on his own experience, or reliance on the architect as a professional man, and the knowledge that variations might be issued?

Could it be said that there was never a contract at all in a real sense — there was no *consensus* — or there could never on the facts be *consensus?* Could it be said that there was a contract but when it became clear that the design could not be effected that the contract was a nullity from that point on — or would it depend on the nature of the design problem? Could it be said that failure to provide a design that could be effected would be a breach of contract for which the employer is liable? Could it be said that the contractor simply misunderstands how to effect the design and the cost to him? Could it be said that the architect simply misunderstands how to effect the design and the likely cost to his employer? Would any question of fraud or misrepresentation by either party be relevant for damages in inducing the contract?

5.36   A contract is void if at the time of contracting it involved a manifest impossibility, and it has been suggested by the authors of the *Stair Memorial Encyclopaedia* that the *Rutherglen Magistrates v. Cullen* case,[48] involving a contract to erect a bridge to a design that omitted foundations and where neither party envisaged foundations, might be an example of manifest impossibility at the beginning.

5.37   If the contractor is in "unilateral" error as to the quantity, quality or extent of work that is necessary to complete specified works the House of Lords have held that the contractor is still bound to complete and entitled to no extra payments. In *Tharsis Sulphur & Copper Company v. McElroy & Sons*[49] Lord Blackburn said:

> "When the Tharris Company, through their engineer, said in the specification 'We want this done', there can be no doubt that they thought and believed that a girder of this length and thickness could be made and they proposed it should be made .... They put it distinctly to the contractors to look at it for themselves; they called it to their attention in words, I think, in one part of the contract 'See if you can do this, and tell us what price you can do it for'; 'satisfy yourselves' (that is what it amounts to) 'whether you can do it before you enter into this contract".

Similarly in *Thorn v. The Mayor and Commonality of London*,[50] the specification for temporary works relating to the demolition and replacement of Blackfriars Bridge was found to be inadequate, and the contractor was

---

[48]   (1773) 2 Pat. 305 (HL); discussed in *Building Contracts*, Vol. 3, para. 18.
[49]   (1878) 3 App. Cas 1040, *per* Lord Blackburn, at 1054 and 1052.
[50]   [1876] 1 A.C. 120.

put to considerable extra expense in having to work when the tide permitted. The question was, did the specification come with an implied term that the works could be done according to it, failing which the contractor had a right in damages? The House found that no such warranty should be implied. The Lord Chancellor was of the opinion that the contractor could have said "I never intended to construct this work upon this new and unexpected footing." This would have opened up a claim for *quantum meruit*, but damages for breach of an implied warranty that was generally applicable in all construction cases was an entirely different matter.[51] Similarly, in Scotland in *Wilson v. Wallace and Connell*[52] a contractor was given a precise dimension for the design of tanks to be constructed to be watertight at a pressure of 60 feet of water. The contractor agreed to make these, but found that he had to use extra bolts so that they would be watertight. The Inner House held that was just what the contractor had bound himself to, to achieve the performance specified.

The Australian courts, when asked if there was a duty of care in the provision of pre-contract information in one case,[53] did not rule it out, but in another the employer was held not to have assumed responsibility for the completeness or accuracy of tender information about special site conditions.[54] **5.38**

Where there are bills of quantities incorporated into a contract for works at a lump sum then any varied work will give rise to an obligation to make further payment to the contractor at bill rates.[55] However, there can be a grey area[56] where the employer need not pay extra for "things that everybody must have understood are to be done but which happen to be omitted from the quantities." Also, in *Scott & Morris v. Hatton*[57] a builder who tendered to erect a house at the corner of a street in Edinburgh on a schedule of rates, and later having seen from the plans that the corner was to be rounded off, carried out the works anyway. It was held that he could not recover double the rates in the schedule on the basis that there was a custom that circular work was charged higher than corners. Again, the Lord Justice-Clerk was of the view that "they should at least have stopped when the plan was put in their hands before beginning to build, if they intended to contest the point". **5.39**

---

[51] Fraud would have been a different matter again; see *Sharpe v. San Paulo Railway Co.* (1872) L.R. 8 Ch. 597 at p. 607.

[52] (1859) 21 D. 306.

[53] *Morrison-Knudsen International v. Commonwealth of Australia* (1972) 13 B.L.R. 114 (High Court of Australia).

[54] *Dillingham Construction v. Downs* [1972] 13 B.L.R. 97 (Supreme Court of New South Wales). But compare this with the Court of Appeal decision in *Bacal Construction v. Northampton* [1975] 8 B.L.R. 89, where there was an express statement in tender documents that the site was a mixture of sand and clay, but tufa was discovered which required the foundations to be redesigned, that this was a breach of an implied term of warranty.

[55] *Thorn (supra)* at 127.

[56] *Patman and Fotheringham v. Pilditch* (1904), Hudson, *Building Contracts* (4th ed.), Vol. 2, p. 368.

[57] (1827) 6 S. 413.

5.40   It would appear therefore that if there is to be any duty to warn on design matters owed by the contractor where he has not produced the design, much will at least depend on the contractor's contractual obligations to complete (*i.e.* whether there is a bill of quantities or a lump sum contract with a specification of the works); an analysis of error which might render the contract void or voidable; and the question of impossibility, although the doctrine of severability may be applied to particular impossible terms. For example, in *Robertson v. Driver's Trustees*[58] a contractual period was found to be partly impossible and the court allowed deduction of liquidate damages only in part.

5.41   A contract, or a part of it, may also be unenforceable due to its uncertainty. In the context of a duty to warn this might be relevant if there is a "deeming" provision that the contractor's design is deemed to comply with local byelaws, even when in fact the design did not so comply, and the "deeming" provision was therefore incapable of being made sense of.[59] For a case like this would it be correct in law that the contractor owed a duty to warn that a particular contractual clause purporting to govern an important design matter might be so uncertain as to be unenforceable? If so, it is the author's submission that this would be moving into the area of a general duty to contract in the utmost good faith, which would not normally be the case for building contracts. However, in contract there is normally an implied obligation which may be stated positively or negatively, based on the principle that "no person can take advantage of the non-fulfillment of a condition the performance of which has been hindered by himself".[60] The positive expression of this has been put as follows:

> "Where in a written contract it appears that both parties have agreed that something should be done which cannot effectively be done unless both concur in doing it, the construction of the contract is that each agrees to do all that is necessary to be done on his part for the carrying out of that thing though there may be no express words to that effect."[61]

This co-operation can be enforced only to a "limited degree — to the extent that it is necessary to make the contract workable".[62] This co-operation is normally relevant as regards the implied duties of the employer,[63] and, in

---

[58] (1881) 8 R. 551. But see Gloag, p. 339.
[59] *London Borough of Newham v. Taylor Woodrow (Anglian) Ltd* [1982]19 B.L.R. 129, C.A.
[60] *Per* Blackburn J. in *Roberts v. Bury Commissioners* (1870) L.R. 5 C.P. 310 at 326.
[61] *MacKay v. Dick and Stevenson* (1881) 8 R. (H.L.) 37 at 40, *per* Lord Blackburn. As to the limits of this implied term, see W. M. Gloag, *The Law of Contract* (2nd ed., 1929), pp. 279, 280.
[62] *Per* Devlin J. in *Mona Oil Equipment & Supply Co. Ltd v. Rhodesia Railways Ltd* [1949] 2 All E.R. 1014 at 1018.
[63] *Luxor (Eastbourne) Ltd v. Cooper* [1941] A.C. 108 (HL); *London Borough of Merton v. Stanley Hugh Leach Ltd* [1985] 32 B.L.R. 51.

particular, in *Holland Hannen and Cubitts (Northern) Ltd v. Welsh Health Technical Services Organisation*,[64] the employer's architect to issue instructions.

It is commonplace for defects in design to also constitute breaches   5.42
of the Building Regulations, and, as such, for the question of illegality
of the contract to arise.[65] In Scotland the principal building regulations
are the Building Standards (Scotland) Regulations 1990[66] and the
Building Forms (Scotland) Regulations 1991[67] which are made under
the Building (Scotland) Act 1959. The 1990 Regulations consist of
statements of requirements supported by "Technical Standards" which
make much use of British Standards and of British Standard Codes of
Practice and make clear that any technical specification of a Member
State of the European Community that gives an equal standard of
protection or performance is "deemed to satisfy the requirements of the
regulations". This rule implements the provisions of the E.C. directive[68]
relating to construction products in so far as materials, fittings,
components and other manufactured products which comply with
European technical approval. Regulation 10, for example, covers
"suitability of materials, fittings and components" and regulation 11
covers "structural strength and stability". The Act does not impose
criminal liability and contains prospective provisions relating to civil
liability for damage, which have not yet been brought into effect.

A contractor's duty to warn of deficiencies of design arose in   5.43
*Equitable Debenture Assets Corporation Ltd v. William Moss Group
Ltd*[69] where it was held by the Official Referee that there was an implied
duty in contract and in tort on the contractor to warn of design defects
in the architect's design. The same judge in *Victoria University of
Manchester v. Hugh Wilson and Lewis Womersley and Pochin
(Contractors) Ltd*,[70] where a JCT 63 form obtained, held that there was
an implied duty in contract:

> "requiring the contractors to warn the architects as the University's agents,
> of defects in design, which they believed to exist. Belief that there were
> defects required more than mere doubt as to the correctness of the design,
> but less than actual knowledge of errors."

---

[64] [1981] 18 B.L.R. 80. The reasoning in this case as regards the liability of contractors for nominated sub-contractor designed work is criticised, in the author's view properly, in *Hudson's Building and Engineering Contracts* (11th ed.), I.N. Duncan Wallace at p. 539.

[65] See Chap. 4, para. 4.46.

[66] S.I. 1990 No. 2179.

[67] S.I. 1991 No. 160.

[68] EC Council Directive 89/106 (O.J. L40, II. 2.89, p. 12), Ch I, art. 4.2.

[69] (1984) C.I.L.L. 74; [1984] Con. L.R. 1; 1 Const. L.J. 131.

[70] (1984) C.I.L.L. 206; [1985] Con. L.R. 43.

5.44　　This duty has been reconsidered in *University of Glasgow v. W. Whitfield and John Laing Construction Ltd.*[71] A different Official Referee distinguished the above two cases and held that there was no room for the implication in contract in a JCT 63 form with Scottish Appendix of a duty on the contractor to warn the employer about possible defects in design, or to warn the architect in tort. But before leaving this area, the same judge in *Equitable Debenture* and *Victoria University of Manchester* has recently held again in *Lindenberg v. Joe Canning*[72] that a contractor who demolished walls, as he was required to do according to drawings he had been given, should have doubted that these were not load bearing and raised this with the employer's surveyor. The contractor was accordingly in breach of contract.

5.45　　In *Hudson* (11th ed.) at p. 543 it is suggested that duty to warn cases found in other jurisdictions are normally rationalised as a breach of an express or implied workmanship obligation, though it perhaps can also be explained as breach of an implied duty of co-operation.

---

[71]　(1988) 42 B.L.R. 66.
[72]　(1992) 62 B.L.R. 147.

CHAPTER 6

DELICTUAL LIABILITY FOR DEFECTIVE BUILDINGS

By way of introduction to the common law of delict in Scotland there are some 6.01
fundamental points to examine. A delict (perhaps a more modern expression
might be conveyed by the word delinquency) is a legal wrong, which may give
rise to certain obligations by operation of law (*ex lege*) to make reparation for
damage caused, whether or not contractual obligations also exist. In the Scots
law of delict the relevant party must have (i) owed the other a duty to take care of
their interest (duty of care); (ii) been at fault (*culpa*); and (iii) there must have
been a loss directly caused. Stair laid the basis for the general principles of delictual
liability when he recognised that to cause damage by delinquence gave rise to an
obediential obligation to make reparation for the damage caused: *damnum injuria
datum* (loss caused by wrongful conduct). This was a general innominate remedy,
based on defender's *culpa*, which includes deliberate as well as careless conduct.[1]
Stair identifies particular areas where damages and delinquences may occur: life
and health; liberty; fame, reputation and honour; and goods and possession.[2]
These may be summarised as damage to person or property.

In this field of the law relating to the construction industry, there have been 6.02
greatly significant developments in the U.K. courts and in the Commonwealth
— starting in 1972 with the case of *Dutton v. Bognor Regis United Building Co.*,[3]
leading to the seven-judge House of Lords decision in *Murphy v. Brentwood
Borough Council*[4] in 1991, and the five-judge House of Lords decision which
was issued on the same day, *Department of the Environment v. Thomas Bates
and Son Ltd.*[5] Perhaps surprisingly with such unusual judicial activity in this area,
it is still not entirely certain what the law in Scotland now is, and in New Zealand,[6]
Canada,[7] and Australia,[8] the *Murphy* case has not been followed. In order to

---

[1]   Generally, Stair I, ix.
[2]   Stair I, iv.
[3]   [1972] 1 All E.R. 462.
[4]   [1991] 1 A.C. 398.
[5]   [1991] 1 A.C. 499.
[6]   *Invercargill City Council v. Hamlin* [1994] 3 N.Z.L.R. 513 and 1995 Cons. L.J., Vol.11, No. 4, p. 284.
[7]   *Winnipeg Condominium Corporation No. 36 v. Bird Construction Co. Ltd*, 1995 Cons.
      L.J., Vol. 11, No.4, p. 305.
[8]   *Bryan v. Maloney*, 1995 Cons.L.J,.Vol. 11, No. 4, p. 273.

consider the relevant delictual issues there are two seminal decisions to consider before working through the other cases.

The neighbourhood principle

6.03   The first seminal case in Scots law is in the famous decision of the House of Lords in *Donoghue v. Stevenson*[9] concerning the rather prosaic circumstances of a lady who suffered nervous shock on discovering a decomposed snail in an opaque bottle of ginger beer which she had partly consumed and which a friend had bought her. The case concerned whether a manufacturer of an article was liable in delict to the ultimate user whoever that might be, and with whom there was no contract, for any personal injuries suffered. The judgment was more significant than the facts might suggest, as the House took the opportunity to discuss the wider implications of when a duty of care should be said to exist to one's neighbour. Lord Macmillan said:

> "In the daily contacts of social and business life, human beings are thrown into, or place themselves in, an infinite variety of relations with their fellows; and the law can refer only to the standards of the reasonable man in order to determine whether any particular relationship gives rise to a duty to take care as between those who stand in relation to each other...the categories of negligence are never closed."

Lord Atkin said:

> "The liability for negligence, whether you style it such or treat it as in other systems as a species of 'culpa', is no doubt based upon a general public sentiment of moral wrongdoing for which the offender must pay. But acts or omissions which any moral code would censure cannot, in a practical world, be treated so as to give a right to every person injured by them to demand relief. In this way rules of law arise which limit the range of complaints, and the extent of their remedy. The rule that you are to love your neighbour becomes in law, you must not injure your neighbour; and the lawyer's question, Who is my neighbour? receives a restricted reply. You must take reasonable care to avoid acts or omissions which you can reasonably foresee would be likely to injure your neighbour. Who, then, is in law my neighbour? The answer seems to be — persons who are so closely and directly affected by my act that I ought reasonably to have them in contemplation when I am directing my mind to the acts or omissions which are called in question."

If one step why not 50?

6.04   There was a dissenting judgment given in this case by Lord Buckmaster, who said:

> "There can be no special duty attaching to the manufacturer of food apart from that implied by contract or imposed by statute. If such a duty exists, it

---

[9]   1932 S.C. (H.L.) 31; 1932 S.L.T. 317.

seems to me that it must cover the manufacture of every article, and I cannot see any reason why it should not apply to the construction of a house. If one step, why not fifty? Yet if a house be, as it sometimes is, negligently built, and in consequence of that negligence the ceiling falls and injures the occupier or anyone else, no action against the builder exists according to English law, although I believe such a right did exist according to the laws of Babylon."[10]

Incidentally, as early as 1760 B.C., King Hammurabi of Babylon's First Dynasty, provided in Articles 229 and 233 of his code that:

> "229. If a builder builds a house for a man and does not make its construction firm and the house which he has built collapses and causes the death of the owner of the house that builder shall be put to death.
> 233. If a builder builds a house for a man and does not make its construction meet the requirements and a wall falls in, that builder shall strengthen the wall at his own expense."[11]

The words of Lord Atkin were said in a later case[12] by Lord Reid to express   6.05
a principle which ought to apply in general "unless there is some justification or valid explanation for its exclusion". Lord Pearson[13] said that the *Donoghue* principle was "a basic and general but not universal principle and does not in law apply to all the situations which are covered by the wide words of the passage. To some extent the decision in this case must be a matter of impression and instinctive judgement as to what is fair and just"; but Lord Diplock spoke differently, and said it was a guide but not a principle of universal application.[14] The precise formulation of the applicable general principles of the so-called "neighbourhood" test has defied formulation.. In particular, as we shall see, an attempt to restate a general formula for application in this area of the law in the previous House of Lords decision in *Anns v. Merton London Borough Council*[15] in 1978 given by Lord Wilberforce, which became known as the two-stage test, was considerably narrowed by Lord Keith in *Murphy*.

Two-stage test

Lord Wilberforce in *Anns* at 751–752 stated: 6.06

> "Through the trilogy of cases in this House — *Donoghue v. Stevenson* [1932] A.C. 562, *Hedley Byrne & Co. Ltd v. Heller and Partners Ltd* [1964] A.C. 465, and *Dorset Yacht Co. Ltd v. Home Office* [1970] A.C. 1004, the position has now been reached that in order to establish that a duty of care arises in a particular situation, it is not necessary to bring the facts of that situation

---

10 above citation at 577–578.
11 Code of Hammurabi, mentioned in N. G. Bunni, "Liability of Contractors for Design and Construction" [1993] I.C.L.R. 441.
12 *Home Office v. Dorset Yacht Co. Ltd* [1970] 2 All E.R. 294 at 297; [1970] A.C. 1004 at 1027.
13 *supra.* at 321, or 1054.
14 *supra.* at 325–326, or 1060.
15 [1978] A.C. 728.

within those of previous situations in which a duty of care has been held to exist. Rather the question has to be approached in two stages. First one has to ask whether, as between the alleged wrongdoer and the person who has suffered damage there is a sufficient relationship of neighbourhood such that, in the reasonable contemplation of the former, carelessness on his part may be likely to cause damage to the latter — in which case a prima facie duty of care arises. Secondly, if the first question is answered affirmatively, it is necessary to consider whether there are any considerations which ought to negative, or to reduce or limit the scope of the duty or the class of person to whom it is owed or the damages to which a breach of it may give rise."

Incrementally

6.07   Lord Keith in *Murphy* said about this test:

"Finally, in *Yuen Kun Yeu v. Attorney-General of Hong Kong* [1988] A.C. 175 at 193, and in *Hill v. Chief Constable of West Yorkshire* [1989] A.C. 53 at 63, I expressed the opinion, concurred in by the other members of the House who participated in the decisions, that the second stage of the test only came into play where some particular consideration of public policy excluded any duty of care. As regards the ingredients necessary to establish such a duty in novel situations, I consider that an incremental approach on the lines indicated by Brennan J. in *Council of the Shire of Sutherland v. Heyman* (1985) 157 C.L.R. 424 is to be preferred to the two stage test."

Brennan J., in the *Shire of Sutherland* case, said:

"It is preferable, in my view, that the law should develop novel categories of negligence incrementally and by analogy with established categories, rather than by a massive extension of a prima facie duty of care restrained only by indefinable considerations which ought to negative, or to reduce the or limit the scope of the duty or the class of person to whom it is owed."[16]

6.08   It has been construction cases that have perhaps caused the most difficulty in relation to the law of delict. What might be considered to be fundamental questions, such as to what extent should a builder owe a duty of care to anyone if his work has been negligent? what limits should be placed on that duty? and should any statutory bodies that administer building regulations have any similar duties? have led to complex decisions. *Murphy* should be taken as the highest recent authority, but unhappily not the clearest. The recurring questions of a builder's liability had previously been highlighted in the Outer House of the Court of Session by Lord McLuskey in *Norwich Union Life Insurance Society v. Covell Mathews Partnership.*[17] This case precedes *Murphy* by some four years,

---

[16] Interestingly, in the recent Australian case *Allan Bryan v. Judith Maloney*, Brennan J. gave the dissenting opinion where the other four judges allowed recovery by a second purchaser against the original builder for the cost of remedial works where foundations in clay soil were found to be inadequate.

[17] 1987 S.L.T. 452 at 454-455.

and may be questionable following *Murphy*, which although not a Scottish case, had opinions from Lord Keith, Lord Jauncey and Lord MacKay. Both *Anns* and *Murphy* were cases which involved defectively built foundations to properties, and the extent of the builder and the building authority's liability to third parties. In *Murphy* Lord MacKay is quite explicit that:

> "I have reached the clear conclusion that the proper exercise of the judicial function requires this House now to depart from *Anns* in so far as it affirmed a private law duty of care to avoid damage to property which causes present or imminent danger to the health and safety of owners, or occupiers, resting upon local authorities in relation to their function of supervising compliance with building byelaws or regulations, that *Dutton v. Bognor Regis Urban District Council* should be overruled and that all decisions subsequent to *Anns* which purported to follow it should be overruled. I accordingly reach the same conclusion as do my noble and learned friends."

However, Lord MacKay says nothing about the two-stage test in *Anns*, and seems to base his opinion on the fact that Parliament had passed the Defective Premises Act 1972 imposing duties on builders, which suggested to him that no wider duty owed by local authorities ought to be judicially created. Of significance is the fact that the Defective Premises Act 1972 does not apply in Scotland.[18] Also, Lord Mackay expressly reserved his opinion of what would be the position of a local authority which had been charged with the public law duty of supervising compliance with the relevant building byelaws or regulations and which had failed to do so and actual physical injury to persons was caused — not merely the possibility of damage occurring to the building itself. Indeed three of the four *Murphy* speeches expressly reserve this position. Another Scottish judge, Lord Jauncey, also says nothing about the *Anns* two-stage test and points to the relevance of the Defective Premises Act 1972. Accordingly, from a Scottish perspective substantial parts of the *ratios* of Lords Jauncey and MacKay in *Murphy* are irrelevant. However, Lord Keith makes no reference to the 1972 Act in his lengthier judgment. These judgments will be examined in detail below.

Leaving aside the general question of how delictual liability might occur; and leaving aside for the moment the question of specific delictual duties might affect a local authority; there is the fundamental question of the

6.09

---

[18] Section 1 reads: "1.—(1) A person taking on work for or in connection with the provision of a dwelling (whether the dwelling is provided by the erection or by the conversion or enlargement of a building) owes a duty —
  (a) if the dwelling is provided to the order of any person, to that person; and
  (b) without prejudice to paragraph (a) above, to every person who acquires an interest (whether legal or equitable) in the dwelling;
to see that the work which he takes on is done in a workman-like or, as the case may be, professional manner, with proper materials and so that as regards that work the dwelling will be fit for habitation when completed."

delictual liability of a builder or sub-contractor for a building erected by them which contains latent defects due to negligent workmanship that become progressively patent, creating a risk to personal safety, or the devaulation or loss of usefulness of the building, and how far such liability should stretch to any class of persons.

...an impossible distinction

6.10   In England the starting point for a discussion on these points is *Dutton v. Bognor Regis Building Co.*[19] in the Court of Appeal in 1972. The circumstances were that Mrs Dutton became the second purchaser of a recently-built domestic property that was sold to the first purchaser (who owned it for a matter of months) by the builder/developer. The property had been built on a landfill site which had been a rubbish dump, and it was found to have defective foundations which caused the walls and ceilings to crack, the staircase to slip, and the doors and windows not to close. Mrs Dutton sued for £2,240 being the cost of repair and £500 diminution of value. Without a hearing the case against the builder was settled at £625 on the basis that it was accepted that the builder/developer owed no duty standing the cases of *Bottomley v. Bannister*[20] and *Otto v. Bolton and Norris.*[21] Mrs Dutton continued her action against the planning authority alleging a breach of a duty of care in inspecting and ensuring that the foundations were adequate. In the Court of Appeal, Lord Denning indicated that the alleged duty owed by the local authority was entirely novel.[21a] As regards the builder, Lord Denning accepted that if he was not guilty of bad work then neither should the council be for passing it.[21b] Lord Denning noted that, historically, if one of the parties to a contract was negligent in carrying it out, no third party who was injured as a result of that negligence could sue for damages on that account. The reason given was that the only duty of care was that given by the contract and he referred to the speech of Alderson B. in *Winterbottom v. Wright*[22]: "If we were to hold that the plaintiff could sue in such a case, there is no point at which such actions would stop. The only safe rule is to confine the right to recover to those who enter into the contract: if we go one step beyond that, there is no reason why we should not go fifty."

6.11   Lord Denning claimed that *Donoghue v. Stevenson* did away with the old rule[22a] and noted that although *Donoghue* dealt with chattels, that case had considered *Bottomley v. Bannister*[23] (on builders) but did not expressly overrule it. Subsequent to *Donoghue* in 1936 a judge at first instance held

---

[19] [1972] 1 All E.R. 462.
[20] [1932] 1 K.B. 458.
[21] [1936] 1 All E.R. 960.
[21a] *op. cit.* 475b.
[21b] *op. cit.* 471b.
[22] (1842) 10 M.&W. 109 at 115.
[22a] *op. cit.* 471f.
[23] *supra.*

that a builder who builds a house for sale is under no duty to build it carefully. If a person was injured by his negligence, he could not recover *per Otto v. Bolton & Norris.*[24] Lord Denning found the distinction between a chattel and real property to be quite unsustainable. He also noted that there had been cases which recognised liability by a builder for negligent construction since *Donoghue, i.e. Gallagher v. McDowell Ltd*[25] and *Sharpe v. E.T. Sweeting & Son Ltd*[26]; but not explicitly where the builder was also the developer — and he held "that there was no sense in maintaining that distinction" and overruled *Bottomley* and *Otto*. He went on to look at the question of whether liability was restricted to those who suffered bodily harm only; and not for the mere diminishing of value of the building itself, or the cost of fixing the defect:

> "I cannot accept that submission. The damage done here was not solely economic loss. It was physical damage to the house. If counsel's submission were right, it would mean that, if the inspector negligently passes the house as properly built and it collapses and injures a person, the council are liable; but, if the owner discovers the defect in time to repair it — and he does repair it — the council are not liable. That is an impossible distinction. They are liable in either case. I would say the same about the manufacturer of an article. If he makes it negligently, with a latent defect (so that it breaks to pieces and injures someone), he is undoubtedly liable. Suppose that the defect is discovered in time to prevent the injury. Surely he is liable for the cost of the repair."

The *Dutton* decision was then followed in a number of important cases.[27] The case did not have a dissenting judgment, but Stamp L.J. did find difficulty with the idea of a house which was not a danger to person or property and which, due to a concealed defect, becomes valueless was opening up a new field of liability which could not be logically controlled. However without deciding the point, the court held that a local authority that was under a duty by Act of Parliament to perform the duty of making sure that the foundations of a house were secure for subsequent owners of the house, had a duty to avoid economic loss "at least as high as the defendant in the *Hedley Byrne* case". The *Hedley Byrne* case is discussed below, but depends on one of the parties specifically *relying* on the other. 6.12

In *Anns v. Merton London Borough Council* there was again a case of defective foundations where the only defendant was the local authority, so that the scope of the builder's duty of care and the measure of damages for 6.13

---

[24] [1936] 1 All E.R. 960.
[25] [1961] N.I. 26.
[26] [1963] 2 All E.R. 455.
[27] *Sparham-Souter v. Town and Country Developments (Essex) Ltd.* [1976] 2 W.L.R. 493; *Sutherland and Sutherland v. C.R. Maton & Son Ltd* [1976] 3 B.L.R. 87; *Anns v. Merton London Borough Council* [1978] A.C. 728; *Batty v. Metropolitan Property Realisations Ltd* [1978] Q.B. 554 (CA).

any breach of that duty was not directly in issue. Lord Wilberforce, with whose speech Lord Diplock, Lord Simon of Glaisdale and Lord Russell of Killowen agreed, dealt with the position of the builder and the damages recoverable (at pp. 758–760). Lord Wilberforce held that two alternative grounds of action may rest against the builder. First, on *Donoghue v. Stevenson* principles, in respect of all careless acts of a builder to subsequent purchasers, and he said that he agreed generally with the conclusions of Lord Denning in *Dutton*. Secondly: "since it is the duty of the builder (owner or not) to comply with the byelaw, I would be of the opinion that an action could be brought against him, in effect, for breach of statutory duty by any person for whose benefit or protection the byelaw was made."

The *Anns* case was brought on a preliminary issue and as such the full extent of the measure of damages that should be recoverable did not directly arise. However, Lord Wilberforce went on:

> "Subject always to adequate proof of causation, these damages may include damages for personal injury and damage to property. In my opinion they may also include damage to the dwelling house itself; for the whole purpose of the byelaws in requiring foundations to be of a certain standard is to prevent damage arising from weakness of the foundations which is certain to endanger the health or safety of the occupants. To allow recovery for such damage to the house follows, in my opinion, from normal principle. If classification is required, the relevant damage is in my opinion material, physical damage, and what is recoverable is the amount of expenditure necessary to restore the dwelling to a condition in which it is no longer a danger to the health or safety of persons occupying and possibly (depending on the circumstances) expenses arising from necessary displacement.... [The cause of action] can only arise when the state of the building is such that there is present or imminent danger to the health or safety of persons occupying it."

6.14   The existence of material physical damage resulting from the original defect and the presence or imminence of danger associated with that damage posed logical difficulties for Lord Jauncey in *Murphy*. It suggested to him that if a survey disclosed a defect before physical damage occurred then the question arises: "Why, it might be asked, should the householder in [this case] have no right of action if he takes steps to remove the danger before physical damage has occurred but have such a right if he waits until damage has occurred when remedial costs may very well be much higher?"

Lord MacKay also thought that such a distinction would be "capricious", and Lord Keith thought that there would be no logic in confining a remedy to cases where danger exists. Lord Bridge said that he could find no answer to this conundrum. Lord Jauncey also thought that there would be difficulties in establishing what "imminent" might mean in any given case. He also, as did Lord Bridge, went on with the, it is submitted unlikely, hypothesis, that if the house collapses without any warning and injures nobody, then the danger would have gone and there would be no right to recovery. Such a set of circumstances, it is submitted, would be odd in the extreme if the root problem was defective foundations.

As regards the central question of the liability of the builder, Lord Keith 6.15
in *Murphy* said:

"I see no reason to doubt that the principle of *Donoghue v. Stevenson* does
indeed apply so as to place the builder of premises under a duty to take
reasonable care to avoid injury through defects in the premises to the person
or property of those whom he should have had in his contemplation as likely
to suffer such injury if care is not taken. But it is against injury through latent
defects that the duty exists to guard....In the case of a building, it is right to
accept that a careless builder is liable, on the principle of *Donoghue v.
Stevenson*, where a latent defect results in physical injury to anyone, whether
owner, occupier, visitor or passer-by, or to the property of any such person.
But that principle is not apt to bring home liability towards an occupier who
knows the full extent of the defect yet continues to occupy the building."

Lord Bridge said:

"The House has already held in *D & F Estates*[27a] that a builder, in the absence
of any contractual duty or of a special relationship of proximity introducing
the *Hedley Byrne* principle of reliance, owes no duty of care in tort in respect
of the quality of his work. As I pointed out in *D &F Estates*, to hold that the
builder owed such a duty of care to any person acquiring an interest in the
product of the builder's work would be to impose upon him the obligations
of an indefinitely transmissable warranty of quality."

Lord Bridge at page 207 simply held that:

"the cost of replacing defective plaster [in *D. & F. Estates*]...was not an item of
damage for which the builder...could possibly be made liable under the principle
of *Donoghue v. Stevenson* or any legitimate development of that principle. To
make him so would be to impose upon him for the benefit of those to whom he
has no contractual relationship the obligation of one who warranted the quality
of the plaster as regards materials, workmanship and fitness for purpose."

In *D. & F. Estates* the case for the plaintiffs was that the builder, with
whom they never had a contract, owed them a duty to supervise the work of
their plastering sub-contractors against applying defective plaster to the interior
of a dwelling, and that the cost of replacing the plaster was recoverable.

The court had to consider *Dutton* and *Anns* amongst others, to decide 6.16
what the extent of a builder's duty to avoid defects was since *Dutton* and
Anns: did this extend to defects caused by the work of their sub-contractors,
and what measure of damages should be recoverable? Lord Bridge reserved
his view as to the extent of an *Anns* liability for defects; held that replacement
of defective plaster was irrecoverable under *Donoghue* principles as it was
not properly damage to person or property but pure economic loss; and held
that there was no principle that a main contractor should be liable to third
parties in negligence for defective work carried out by his sub-contractor.

[27a] *D. & F. Estates v. Church Commissioners* [1989] A.C. 177.

6.17   The House of Lords in *D. & F. Estates* considered that, apart from *Dutton* and *Anns,* the position in English law was that the supplier of a defective product was only liable for damage to property or personal injury caused by the defective product, but not for the loss of the product itself. In order to understand the position in *Anns* and *Dutton* where there were defective foundations, both Lord Bridge and Lord Oliver who delivered judgments, with which Lord Templeman, Lord Ackner, and Lord Jauncey agreed, mooted the theory that a building may be a "complex structure" such that failure by one part may cause recoverable property damage to another part of the same structure. Lord Oliver stated:

> "On that footing, damage caused to other parts of the building from, for instance, defective foundations or defective steel work would ground an action but not damage to the defective part itself except in so far as that part caused other damage, when the damages would include the cost of repair to that part so far as necessary to remedy damage caused to other parts. Thus to remedy cracking in walls and ceilings caused by defective foundations necessarily involves repairing or replacing the foundations themselves."

D. & F. Estates was in some way removed from *Anns* on the facts as the defect was not the foundations but decorative interior plaster, which was discovered to have been carelessly applied some 15 years later, when redecoration was being carried out. The House was also concerned with venturing too far into the field of consumer protection when the Defective Premises Act 1972 only applied to builders, and defects arising within six years.

6.18   *Murphy* was another foundations case, where the obligation of the local authority was at first sight on a stronger footing than in *Anns,* because there was a clear statutory duty to withhold approval of the defective design, not simply to inspect. Again, the builder was not a defendant but the scope of the builder's negligence and the duty of care which he owed had a direct bearing on whether the local authority could be liable. Lord Keith took the view that *Anns* was wrongly decided because the loss caused by discovering defective foundations was pure economic loss. He drew the analogy to the position held for chattels by the unanimous decision of the United States Supreme Court in *East River Steamship Corporation v. Transamerica Delaval Inc.*[28] In that case charterers of a super-tanker were denied recovery in tort against the manufacturers of turbines which had suffered damage through a design or manufacturing defect and which had to be replaced as being pure economic loss. Lord Bridge referred to part of the judgment of Blackmun J. as follows:

> "We realize that the damage may be qualitative, occurring through gradual deterioration or internal breakage. Or it may be calamitous.... But either way, since by definition no person or other property is damaged, the resulting loss is purely economic. Even when the harm to the product itself occurs through an abrupt, accident-like event, the resulting loss due to repair costs, decreased value, and lost profits is essentially the failure of the purchaser to receive the benefit of its bargain — traditionally the core of contract law."

---

[28] (1986) 106 S.Ct. 2295.

However Lord Keith further said: "If in the *East River* case the defective turbine had caused the loss of the ship the manufacturer of it could consistently with normal principles, I would think, properly be held liable for that loss."

This would appear to leave the door open, at least partially, to the "complex structure" theory, and he states with regard to *D. & F. Estates*:   6.19

> "Lord Bridge at p. 206 suggested that in the case of a complex structure such as a building one element of the structure might be regarded for *Donoghue v. Stevenson* purposes as distinct from another element, so that damage to one part of the structure caused by the hidden defect in another part might qualify to be treated as 'other property'. I think that it would be unrealistic to take this view as regards a building the whole of which had been erected and equipped by *the same contractor* [emphasis added]. In that situation the whole package provided by the contractor would, in my opinion, fall to be regarded as one unit rendered unsound as such by a defect in a particular part. On the other hand where, for example, the electric wiring had been installed by a sub-contractor and due to a defect caused by a lack of care a fire occurred which destroyed the building, it might not be stretching ordinary principles too far to hold the electrical sub-contractor liable for the damage. ...But even if Lord Bridge's theory were to be held to be acceptable, it would not seem to extend to the founding of liability on a local authority, considering that the purposes of the [Public Health] Act of 1936 are concerned with averting danger to health and safety, not danger of damage to property. Further it would not cover the situation which might arise through discovery, before any damage had occurred, of a defect likely to give rise to damage in the future."

Although the point is not expressly dealt with by Lord Keith, the question must arise as to what the position would be if defective foundations are laid by a sub-contractor, which is by far the most common way.

The author of the "complex structure" theory in *D. & F. Estates*, viz.   6.20
Lord Bridge, and Lord Oliver who accepted it as applying *Donoghue v. Stevenson* principles (albeit subject to anomalies concerning imminent danger), revised their opinions in *Murphy*. Lord Bridge made the most spectacular turn around, and, ignoring any question of sub-contractors raised by Lord Keith, said simply:

> "The reality is that the structural elements in any building form a single indivisible unit of which the different parts are essentially interdependent. To the extent that there is any defect in one part of the structure it must to a greater or lesser degree necessarily affect all other parts of the structure. Therefore any defect in the structure is a defect in the quality of the whole and it is quite artificial, in order to impose a legal liability which the law would otherwise not impose, to treat a defect in an integral structure, so far as it weakens the structure, as a dangerous defect liable to cause damage to 'other property'."

Lord Bridge drew the distinction between something that "positively   6.21
malfunctions", such as a defective central heating boiler that explodes or a fire caused by a defective electrical installation, and defective foundations that lead to settlement which is apparent. This time, Lord Bridge drew the,

not particularly convincing, in the author's view, analogy with a car owner who discovers that he has defective brakes, *i.e.* it may be unfit once the defect is discovered but is not then a danger. It makes no difference in tort that a defect is discovered which prevents a car from starting or stopping; in each case it is a qualitative defect and the cost of fixing it is pure economic loss. In Lord Bridge's view the "fallacy... which vitiates the judgments of Lord Denning M.R. and Sachs L.J. in *Dutton*...[is] once a chattel is known to be dangerous it is simply unusable".

Lord Oliver in *Murphy*, in reference to the "complex structure" theory, says that Lord Bridge has now "amply demonstrated the artificiality of the theory and, for the reasons which he has given, it must be rejected as a viable explanation of the underlying basis for the decision in *Anns*."

As regards the "complex structure" theory, Lord Jauncey seems also to leave the door open if part of the works is done by another contractor, and uses the peculiar analogy of a steel frame which was erected by a specialist contractor which failed to give adequate support to floors and walls. This would be recoverable but foundations built into a house by a single builder would not. This seems to be a peculiar departure, and, it is submitted, leaves all sorts of arguments open in future given the reality of modern procurement systems.

6.22   Lord Oliver in *Murphy* provides the most sophisticated analysis of the problem with economic loss. The House had allowed recovery of economic loss in *Hedley Byrne & Co. v. Heller & Partners*[28a] and Lord Devlin had "convincingly demonstrated the illogicality of the distinction between financial loss caused directly and financial loss resulting from physical injury to personal property at p.517".

Lord Oliver went on:

> "The critical question ...is not the nature of the damage in itself, whether physical or pecuniary, but whether the scope of the duty of care in the circumstances of the case is such as to embrace damage of the kind which the plaintiff claims to be sustained. The essential question which has to be asked in every case, given that damage which is the essential ingredient of the action has occurred, is whether the relationship between the plaintiff and the defendant is such — or, to use the favoured expression, whether it is of sufficient " proximity" — that it imposes upon the latter a duty to take care to avoid or prevent that loss which has in fact been sustained. That the requisite degree of proximity may be established in circumstances in which the plaintiff's injury results from his reliance upon a statement or advice upon which he was entitled to rely and upon which it was contemplated that he would be likely to rely is clear from *Hedley Byrne* and subsequent cases, but *Anns* was not such a case, and neither is the instant case. It is not, however, necessarily to be assumed that the reliance cases form the only possible category of cases in which a duty to take reasonable care to avoid or prevent pecuniary loss can arise....Nor is it self-evident logically where the line is to

---

[28a] [1964] A.C. 465.

be drawn.…The solution to such borderline cases has so far to be achieved pragmatically…not by the application of logic but by the perceived necessity as a matter of policy to place some limits — perhaps arbitrary limits — to what would otherwise be an endless, cumulative causative chain bounded only by theoretical foreseeability."

Here Lord Oliver is very close to a restatement of the second-stage test of Lord Wilberforce in *Anns*.

On the question of economic loss he goes on:

"I frankly doubt whether, in searching for such limits, the categorisation of the damage as 'material', 'physical', 'pecuniary' or 'economic' provides a particularly useful contribution. Where it does, I think, serve a useful purpose is in identifying those cases in which it is necessary to search for and find something more than the mere reasonable forseeability of damage which has occurred as providing the degree of 'proximity' necessary to support the action."

Lord Oliver thought that it was this which was lost sight of in *Anns*, but that proximity was "that elusive element…which persistently defies definition". It was the imminent danger to health or safety to the occupant aspect of *Anns* which was novel and which he did not accept. Nor did he accept that statutory provisions themselves should give rise to a private right against a local authority or a builder on the basis of proximity.   6.23

What then can be concluded from *Murphy?* It is undoubtedly a matter of regret that the matter is not clear-cut. It appears that the following may safely be said: 6.24

1. *Anns* and *Dutton* have been overruled.
2. The basis of this overruling is that a builder has no duty of care generally to third parties for any complete structure that he erects as this would be going further than the legislature did in the Defective Premises Act 1972 (which does not apply to Scotland), and would amount to a transferable warranty of quality.
3. Even if a defect in quality is one as to create danger to the safety of occupiers, the cost of putting it right is still economic loss and irrecoverable.
4. If a defect in quality causes further and progressive damage to the building this will not amount to damage to other property, unless (perhaps) the defect was caused by the design or workmanship of a specialist sub-contractor.
5. At common law the enforcement of regulations or byelaws, or the requirement to build to them, does not create sufficient proximity as to give rise to a duty of care and not one which permits the recovery of economic loss.

What remains in doubt is: 6.25

1. If *Anns* and *Dutton* have been overruled, in what respects have other cases that followed them been overruled, particularly as regards the two-stage test?
2. What is the position in Scotland where the 1972 Act does not apply?
3. What is the position where there is a sudden and unexpected collapse of a building where the fault can be traced to an independent sub-contractor and the rest of the property is damaged or destroyed?

4. What is the position where the defective work was as a result of an extension or remedial work to existing property?[29]
5. To what extent will proximity and reliance in the typical relationships under a building contract give rise to a duty to avoid negligent workmanship?

6.26　　In Scotland, the question has arisen as to the position of defective refurbishment works. In *McLeod v. Scottish Special Housing Association*[30] Lord Coulsfield in an Outer House decision dealt with the situation where internal insulation in public sector rental property was replaced in 1980. In 1984 the tenant exercised his option to buy and in 1987 it became apparent that the steel cladding of the house was deteriorating because of condensation building up behind the insulation. It was argued that the cladding was "other property", and although the action was dismissed on other grounds, Lord Coulsfield held that it was plausible to distinguish between the outer skin of a building and an insulation system which was subsequently installed and not part of the original design.

Also, in *Parkhead Housing Association v. Phoenix Preservation Ltd*[31] Lord Prosser said that he: "was not satisfied that what was said in *D & F Estates* upon the matter can be applied very easily to the situation where a contractor, or a sub-contractor, does work on an existing building, of a kind not readily described as adding a new and distinguishable part to that building." The case concerned a defective damp-proof course, the result of which, it was averred, was damp and mould growth in the property. Lord Prosser followed the decision of the House in the Scottish case of *Junior Books v. The Veitchi Co. Ltd*[32] — which was specifically left in *Murphy* and not overruled, being described as a case decided on reliance principles. It was also said in that case to be understandable on the basis of proximity; whereas in *D. & F. Estates* the decision in *Junior Books* was said to depend on a unique non-contractual relationship between an employer and a named sub-contractor which did not lay down any principle of general application. Since then, most commentators have queried what was thought to be unique about a commonplace relationship in the typical construction project. Lord Prosser in *Parkhead* held that penetration by damp and rot was physical damage rather than economic loss.

The case of *Batty v. Metropolitan Realisations Ltd*[33] can presumably, since *D. & F. Estates* and *Murphy* be taken as overruled. Lord Bridge in *D. & F. Estates*

---

[29]　Section 3 of the Defective Premises Act 1972 provides: "3.—(1) Where work of construction, repair, maintenance or demolition or any other work is done on or in relation to premises, any duty of care owed, because of the doing of the work, to persons who might reasonably be expected to be affected by the defects in the state of the premises created by the doing of the work shall not be abated by the subsequent disposal of the premises by the person who owed the duty." The section does not apply to premises which are let: s. 3(2)(a).
[30]　1990 S.L.T. 749.
[31]　1990 S.L.T. 812.
[32]　1982 S.L.T. 492.
[33]　[1978] Q.B. 554 (CA).

said that his short judgment in that case, which depended on the speech of Lord Wilberforce in *Anns*, was unsound. In *Batty* a house was built on a plateau above a steep slope, and some three years after the house was built there was a severe landslip below the house, damaging the garden but not the house. The court treated the house as doomed and as falling within the present or imminent danger test of *Anns*.

The second seminal case, after *Donoghue v. Stevenson*, in this area to expand the common law position concerned the existence of a duty of care by the maker of a statement which he ought reasonably to have known would be relied on by another to their financial detriment. This took matters further than mere acts or omissions, and also allowed recovery where what was lost was money — not goods as identified by Stair. The case was *Hedley Byrne & Co. Ltd v. Heller & Partners Ltd.*[34]   6.27

The most significant development in the area of construction law was in *Junior Books v. Veitchi.*[34a] The circumstances were that the work of laying flooring in a factory at Grangemouth was sub-contracted to the defenders and carried out in 1969–70. It was averred that in 1972 the flooring showed signs of bad workmanship or materials or both. A sum of over £200,000 was claimed in respect of replacing the floor surface; storing goods elsewhere; paying wages to employees unable to work; fixed overheads; and loss of profit. There was no averment of a contractual relationship or actual threat of danger. In the House it was held that proof should be allowed on the basis that this economic loss was recoverable on *Hedley Byrne* principles. In particular, Lord Roskill listed the following facts as being of crucial importance:

1. The appellants were nominated sub-contractors (actually they were named).
2. The appellants were specialists in flooring.
3. The appellants knew what products were required by the respondents and their main contractors and specialised in the production of these products.
4. The appellants alone were responsible for the composition and construction of the flooring.
5. The respondents relied upon the appellant's skill and experience.
6. The appellants as nominated sub-contractors must have known that the respondents relied upon their skill and experience.
7. The relationship between the parties was as close as it could be short of actual privity of contract.
8. The appellants must be taken to have known that if they did the work negligently (as it must be assumed that they did) the resulting defects would at some time require remedying by the respondents expending money upon the remedial measures as a consequence of which the respondents would suffer financial or economic loss.

---

[34] [1964] A.C. 465.
[34a] *op. cit.*

6.28   Exactly what is to be made of *Junior Books* is unclear, because in reality there was very little that was exceptional about the contractual arrangements. Indeed, Lord Roskill did not appear to notice any distinction between a named and a nominated sub-contractor. Again in the Lords in the context of whether duties of care in tort were co-existant with a contractual arrangement, in *Henderson v. Merrett Syndicates Ltd*, Lord Goff said[35]:

> " in many cases in which a contractual chain comparable to that in the present case is constructed it may well prove to be inconsistent with an assumption of responsibility which has the effect of, so to speak short circuiting the contractual structure so put in place by the parties.... Let me take the analogy of the common case of an ordinary building contract, under which main contractors contract with the building owner for the construction of the relevant building, and the main contractor sub-contracts with sub-contractors or suppliers (often nominated by the building owner) for the performance of the work or the supply of materials in accordance with standards and subject to terms established in the sub-contract. I put on one side cases in which the sub-contractor causes physical damage to property of the building owner, where the claim does not depend on an assumption of responsibility by the sub-contractor to the building owner; though the sub-contractor may be protected from liability by a contractual exemption clause authorised by the building owner. But if the sub-contracted work or materials do not in the result conform to the required standard, it will not ordinarily be open to the building owner to sue the sub-contractor or supplier direct under the *Hedley Byrne* principle, claiming damages from him on the basis that he has been negligent in relation to the performance of his functions. For there is generally no assumption of responsibility by the sub-contractor or supplier direct to the building owner, the parties having so structured their relationship that it is inconsistent with any such assumption of responsibility. This was the conclusion of the Court of Appeal in *Simaan General Contracting Co. v. Pilkington Glass Ltd (No. 2)* [1988] Q.B. 758. As Bingham L.J. put it, at p. 781:
>
>> 'I do not, however, see any basis on which [the nominated suppliers] could be said to have assumed a direct responsibility for the quality of the goods to [the building owners]: such a responsibility is, I think, inconsistent with the structure of the contract the parties have chosen to make.'
>
> It is true that, in this connection, some difficulty has been created by the decision of your Lordship's House in *Junior Books Ltd. v. Veitchi Co. Ltd*. In my opinion, however, it is unnecessary for your Lordships to reconsider that decision for the purposes of the present appeal."

6.29   It might fairly be said that the question of the delictual liability for defective buildings under Scots law seems far from settled.

---

[35] [1994] 3 W.L.R. 761 at 790.

CHAPTER 7

ARCHITECTS AND THE PROFESSIONAL TEAM

There are a number of recurring questions that arise in relation to the role   7.01
of the architect under a building contract. These arise in relation to his
position of not being a party to the building contract, but with certain duties
that are expressly provided for *vis-à-vis* the contractor, nominated sub-
contractor, nominated supplier, and other contractual and delictual duties
to his own client as an independent professional. He normally also has a
special role as certifier.

In the first place the architect is not normally in any direct contractual   7.02
relationship with the contractor, therefore any duties which he might owe
to the contractor could only arise in delict or in relation to the *jus quaesitum
tertio*. In an old Scots case, *Beattie v. Gilroy*,[1] the contractor was required
to carry out variations and the surveyor/architect was required to re-measure
them. The surveyor/architect sued the contractor for payment of his fees on
the basis that the re-measurement work was done for the benefit of the
contractor. It was held that there was no contract between the architect and
the contractor and hence no title to sue.

Nor does the *jus quaesitum tertio* normally help the contractor. It has been   7.03
held not to exist in relation to a contract between a client and his architect in
McKnight & Sons v. District Committee of the Middle Ward of Lanarkshire.[2]
The contractor unsuccessfully argued that he had a right of action against the
architect in contract under the *jus quaesitum tertio* in relation to his failure to
certify. This was rejected in the Outer House who appeared to indicate that
an action could lie in delict where there had been fraud by the architect and
collusion with the employer. The normal way to raise an action for a certificate,
in the absence of a binding arbitration clause, would now be to sue the
employer in respect of a contractual failure by the architect as his agent. The
new statutory regime under the Housing Grants, Construction and
Regeneration Act 1996 will also be relevant (s.108 — Right to refer disputes
to adjudication; s.109 — Entitlement to stage payments; s.110 — Dates for
payment; s. 112 — Right to suspend performance for non-payment; and s. 114
— The Scheme for Construction Contracts).

---

[1] (1882) 10 R. 226.
[2] *McKnight & Sons v. District Committee of the Middle Ward of Lanarkshire*, 1899 7 S.L.T. 47, OH.

7.04   What is clear is that the architect will normally be the general agent of the employer. In *Black v. Cornelius*[3] it was stated authoritatively by Lord Gifford: "I think that the architect is a general agent of the employer for all purposes necessary for carrying out the works", a view with which the remainder of the Second Division concurred. This case involved a surveyor's fees and Lord Ormidale went on: "I have no doubt that an architect employed in the ordinary way has authority to employ a surveyor, and that the surveyor, if not otherwise paid, has a good claim against the person who employs the architect."

7.05   However, privity of contract issues can arise in relation to employer and architect. In *Simpson v. Ross and Morton*,[4] Mr and Mrs Simpson, as employer, entered a building contract where the amount "nil" had been entered for the amount of liquidate damages. The building was late, and the Simpsons then sued the architect for breach of an implied term of contract that he would act with the degree of skill and care to be expected of competent members of his profession. It is not explicitly clear from the judgment if counsel for the defender conceded that the "nil" damages entry would preclude recovery of damages (an arguable matter in the opinion of the author — see chapter 5). In any event the action was dismissed on the basis that a separate company, entirely owned by the Simpsons, had been set up to operate from the building. Any losses arising from delays in commencement of trading for the separate company did not flow from the alleged breach of contract to the Simpsons.

    In similar circumstances recently in *Strathford East Kilbride Ltd v. HLM Design Ltd*[5] where a car dealership facility was built but the operators of this were not the employers under the building contract, it was held that on a proper construction of the contract there was no intention to create a *jus quaesitum tertio,* and that any interest that the dealers acquired was not sufficient to enable them to sue under the building contract.

7.06   As the general agent of the employer the familiar issues of agency law arise as to when the actings of the agent will be binding on the employer as principal. For example, an agent who contracts for an undisclosed principal will be personally liable for any contract made: see particularly *Sika Contractors Ltd v. Gill*[6] where an engineer accepted a contractor's quotation on his own notepaper, with no mention of the principal, and when the employer became insolvent the engineer was held personally liable to the contractor.

7.07   The question of the implied authority of the architect to issue variations to the contractor has been the subject of a Scottish House of Lords case in *Forrest v. Scottish County Investments Ltd.*[7] Here the architect approved

---

3   (1879) 6 R. 581.
4   1992 S.L.T. (Sh. Ct.) 33.
5   1997 S.C.L.R. 877.
6   (1978) 9 B.L.R. 11.
7   1916 S.C. (H.L.) 28.

variations in the sizes of rybats and the question between the employer and the architect was whether the architect had the power to do so. The House of Lords held that the architect had such power as this was a matter of "constructional arrangement" and therefore distinct from the substitution of materials which the Inner House in *Steel v. Young*[8] had said the architect did not have power to do.

Clearly, much will depend on the contractual provisions which describe   7.08
what the architect's role is under the main contract, such as JCT 80, with regard to issuing variations. Lord McLaren in *Robertson v. Jarvie*[9] states:

> "I think there can be no doubt that within the scope of his employment an architect is the proprietor's agent, and if the building contract provides that the work is to be done to the satisfaction of the architect, then any order within the scope of the contract which the architect may give is a sufficient authority to the tradesman to execute the work, because he is entitled to take the order of the agent as equivalent to the order of the principal. Of course there might be a different question if the order given by the architect was so opposed to the terms of the contract that the tradesman was not entitled to assume that he had authority; but where as in this case, the contract itself contemplates variations upon the specification, then such variations when ordered by the architect, if they fairly fall within the scope of the contract, are just as binding on the principal as if they had been ordered by himself."

A singular area of difficulty in the role of the architect is in relation to   7.09
certification of works as having been done to his satisfaction, as we have seen in relation to JCT 80, clause 30, and the amendments that have been made following the decision in *Crown Estates Commissioners v. Mowlem*.[10] The matter was also looked at in the Inner House in *Robertson v. Jarvie*[11] where the Lord President made rather far-reaching remarks at page 706:

> "In the first place, upon the contract, I think it is clear enough that the architect, having been put forward by the proprietor as acting for him, is entitled to be the judge of whether the work is executed in a satisfactory manner or not. It would not be possible, I think, for the defender, who has got his house built, to have said to the pursuer 'I won't take such and such a piece of work, because it does not satisfy my architect'; and, on the other hand, I think it follows equally upon the other side that, as to the quality of the work, if the defender allows his architect, as he naturally would, really to represent him in this matter, and be the medium of communication between him and the tradesmen, and if the architect is satisfied with the work that is put in, the defender cannot turn round and say: 'I am going to have another opinion about this, and I will get somebody else and put him in the witness-box to say that this work has not been executed in a satisfactory manner'."

---

[8]   1907 S.C. 360.
[9]   1908 S.L.T. at pp. 707–708.
[10] 10 Court L.J. 311 (CA).
[11] *op. cit.*

The Lord President then goes on to say at page 707: "if the architect says, as indeed I suppose he must say, that he did authorise these additions, for which he afterwards granted a certificate, there can be no enquiry as to whether these things were disconform to contract or not, the architect being the proper judge of such matters."

7.10   This would appear to overrule, or at the very least draw a fine distinction between, the earlier case of *Ramsay v. Brand*[12] as it involved the same judges, and as *Ramsay v. Brand* was cited in *Robertson v. Jarvie* as still leaving open room for enquiry on work alleged to be a departure from the contract. In *Ramsay v. Brand* the Lord President said at page 1215:

> "On some of the items the architect says, or is deemed by the pursuer to say, at one and the same time, that the work is disconform to contract, but that it would meet with his approval. Now, the architect to whose satisfaction the work is to be done according to specification cannot approve of work disconform to specification, for without special permission he has no authority to dispense with performance of the express terms of the contract. His approval only applies to the mode of fulfilling the express provisions of the contract. Of course, in many cases departures from the contract are agreed upon by the parties as the work proceeds, and very often the architect represents the employer in such arrangements. But this is a totally different matter, and does not affect the principle now stated."

If *Ramsay* has not been overruled, and nothing was expressly said in *Robertson* to that effect, then the distinction might be that an architect's certificate that works have been done conform to contract would normally be unchallengable, except if it can be shown that the architect knew that they were not, but that he accepted them anyway. On this point in relation to the ICE 5th contract in *Shanks & McEwan (Contractors) v. Strathclyde Regional Council*,[13] a case stated by an arbiter was answered to the effect that an engineer's acceptance of cracked tunnel segments which were disconform to specification, but which he ordered to be made watertight, was a variation for which the contractors were entitled to be reimbursed. Regrettably the older Scots cases were not apparently considered in the most recent Scottish case *Belcher Food Products Ltd v. Miller & Black.*[14]

7.11   In relation to valuation certificates there has been a long history of cases which culminated in *Sutcliffe v. Thackrah.*[15] There had been a line of authority that in performing the certification process, the architect was immune from suit as he was acting in the capacity of arbitrator. The matter was commented upon by Lord Reid in *Sutcliffe*, who said that the architect was not acting as an arbiter: "The reason must, I think, be derived at least in part from the peculiar nature of the duties of a judicial character. In this country judicial duties do not involve investigation. They do not arise until there is a dispute."

---

[12]   (1898) 25 R. 1212.
[13]   1995 S.L.T. 172.
[14]   1999 S.L.T. 142. See Chap. 4, para. 4.18.
[15]   [1974] 1 All E.R. 859 (HL).

Lord Reid continued:

> "the building owner and the contractor make their contract on the understanding that in all such matters the architect will act in a fair and unbiased manner and it must therefore be implicit in the owner's contract with the architect that he shall not only exercise due care and skill but also reach such decisions fairly, holding the balance between the client and the contractor."

Once the immunity from suit issue was disposed of, the decision reached 7.12
was similar to *Ramsay v. Brand*[16] as the employer had the right to sue his architect who negligently certified work for payment when it was defective. The *Sutcliffe* case is particularly significant in that the certificates which were issued were interim ones, and the main problem was that the contractor's employment had been determined under JCT 63, and the contractor had then become insolvent. This then raises the question of the extent and scope of the architect's certification role at interim stages. Before *Sutcliffe* reached the Lords it was considered at first instance under the name *Sutcliffe v. Chippendale and Edmondson*,[17] and in relation to matters which were not relevant to the appeal it was held:

> "If and when something occurs which should indicate to [the architect] a lack of competence in the contractor, then, in the interest of the employer, the standard of his supervision should be higher. No-one suggests that the architect is required to tell a contractor how his work is to be done, nor is the architect responsible for the manner in which the contractor does the work. What his supervisory duty does require of him is to follow the progress of the work and to take steps to see that those works comply with the general requirements of the contract in specification and quality. If he should fail to exercise his professional care and skill in this respect, he should be liable to his employer for any damage attributed to that failure."

Architect's duties in administering the contract

An architect is normally an independent professional who has a role in 7.13
designing the works and administering them. In administration, certification that works have been done to his satisfaction is not the only problem. He may be employed as part of a professional team. Recently, in *Chesham Properties Ltd v. Bucknall Austin Management Services*[18] it was held in the Official Referee's Court that in a case where there were 33 professional advisers, the architect was found to have no duty to report to the employer any actual or potential deficiencies in the performance of the project manager; but he did have a duty to report deficiencies in the performance

---

[16] (1898) 25 R. 1212.
[17] [1971] 18 B.L.R. 149.
[18] [1996] 82 B.L.R. 92; 53 Con. L.R. 22.

of the structural engineer and the quantity surveyor which could be read from the express terms of the contract but in addition would be necessarily implied.

7.14 The JCT 80 contract has various administrative roles for the Architect in relation to the Contractor. The Contractor has an obligation to proceed regularly and diligently with the works under clause 25. In *West Faulkner Associates v. Newham London Borough Council*[19] the architects refused to certify that the contractors were failing to proceed regularly and diligently, on the basis that they were proceeding regularly, if not diligently, because sufficient men were regularly in attendance although the works were behind schedule. The architects were held liable to the employers for this failure.

7.15 The Architect also has an obligation to grant extensions of time under JCT 80, clause 25. In *John Barker Construction Ltd v. London Portman Hotel Ltd*[20] it was held that the Architect's decision in relation to applications for extensions of time was fundamentally flawed, was not a fair determination, was impressionistic, and that he had so misapplied the contractual machinery for granting extensions that it had become frustrated. As the arbitration clause had been removed, the court held that it would not be practicable to remit the matter to the Architect for re-determination, and that the court could determine a fair and reasonable extension of time.

Duties to the contractor

7.16 The extent to which an architect may owe any duties in delict to the contractor raises interesting questions. In *Michael Salliss & Co. v. ECA Calil*[21] the contractors sued the employers and also the architects. Negligence was alleged against the architects on several points. In this case the opportunity was taken to review several "duty to contractor" cases, such as *Arenson v. Casson, Beckman, Rutley & Co.*[22] which, although it was a case about negligent valuation of shares by chartered accountants, contained the following comments by Lord Salmon in the Lords in relation to the *Sutcliffe*[23] case:

> "The architect owed a duty to his client, the building owner, arising out of the contract between them to use reasonable care in issuing his certificates. He also, however, owed a similar duty of care to the contractor arising out of their proximity: see *Hedley Byrne Co Ltd v. Heller & Partners Ltd*. In *Sutcliffe v. Thackrah* the architect negligently certified that more money was due than was in fact due, and he was successfully sued for the damage which this had caused his client. He might, however, have negligently certified that less money was payable than was in fact

---

[19] (1995) 71 B.L.R. 1 (CA).
[20] (1996) 83 B.L.R. 31; 50 Con.L.R. 43; 12 Const. L.J. 277.
[21] (1988) 4 Const. L.J.
[22] [1975] 3 All E.R. 901.
[23] *op. cit.*

due and thereby starved the contractor of money. In a trade in which cash flow is especially important, this might have caused the contractor serious damage for which the architect could have been successfully sued."

In *Michael Sallis* it was argued that under JCT 63 the architect had a 7.17 duty to the contractors to use all proper professional skill and care in authorising extensions to the contract period under clause 23, and this was upheld. This meant to act with reasonable expedition, and also that a 29-week extension of time rather than a 12-week extension ought to have been given. It was also held that to the extent that the contractors were able to establish damage resulting from the architect's unfairness in respect of matters which, under the contract, the architect was required to act impartially, damages were recoverable; even if pure economic loss. But it was also held that no duty was owed to the contractor in respect of the preparation of plans and specifications, or in deciding matters such as whether or not he should cause a survey to be carried out. He owed no duty of care to the contractor in considering whether he should order a variation. This was because in these situations the architect had no duty to act fairly; his role being that of agent of the employer in these respects.

In relation to an engineer's certificate under ICE 5th contract, Lord 7.18 McCluskey has recently stated *obiter* in *Costain Building and Civil Engineering Ltd v. Scottish Rugby Union plc*[24]: "If the engineer failed altogether to issue a certificate, whether in bad faith or through negligence or idleness, the contractor (and probably the employer as well) would no doubt have a remedy against the engineer." [25]

At least as regards the employer it has been held in England that where 7.19 there is a contractual relationship between the employer and the architect there may be a concurrent duty to take reasonable care to avoid economic loss so long as the duty is fair and reasonable.[26]

Sallis has however been doubted, if not expressly overruled, in relation 7.20 to an engineer's role under the FIDIC form of contract in *Pacific Associates v. Baxter.*[27] Whilst this case had some exceptional features ((1) the contractor had settled a claim against the employers and then sought to sue the engineer for a large sum on top of the settled figure; (2) there was a clause in the contract that expressly stated that the engineer would not be personally liable for any default on the part of the employer), the Court of Appeal held that there could be no duty owed to the contractor by the engineer. The

---

[24] 1994 S.L.T. 573.
[25] Lord Jauncey had said in *G. Percy Trentham Ltd v. Beattie Watkinson & Partners*, 1987 S.L.T. 449 that the relationship between a contractor and engineer was sufficiently proximate to give rise to a duty of care, but not necessarily based on what a reasonably competent engineer would have done.
[26] *Wessex Regional Health Authority v. HLM Design Ltd* (1994) 10 Const. L.J. 165.
[27] [1989] 2 All E.R. 159.

basis of the decision was that there was an arbitration clause as between the contractor and the employer, and that there was a disclaimer. The problem is that there was also an arbitration clause in the *Sallis* case, if not a disclaimer. The fact of the arbitration clause was considered in *Sallis,* but the view was taken there that the comments by Hunter J. in *Shui On Construction Company Ltd v. Shui Kay Co. Ltd*[28] were preferable: "I do not see why the fact that two parties, the contractor and the building owner have entered into a private arrangement which might curb the powers of the court in certain respects can operate as a policy defence to an architect. It seems to me ... a non-sequitur."

7.21	However in the Hong Kong case *Leon Engineering and Construction Co. v. Ka Duk Investment Co.*[29] a standard form of building contract, private with quantities, for Hong Kong was considered. The contractors alleged that the architect as certifier owed them a duty of care to give proper, timely and impartial consideration to its claims and to issue all certificates in strict accordance with the terms of the contract. The High Court of Hong Kong held that the duty that was alleged was co-terminous with the main contractor's rights against the employer under the contract. There was adequate machinery under the contract between the employer and the contractor to enforce the contractor's rights and there was no good reason at tender stage to suppose that such rights and machinery would not together provide the contractor with an adequate remedy. It was held that in these circumstances the certifying architect or engineer does not owe to the contractor a duty in tort co-terminous with the obligation in contract owed to the contractor by the employer. In this respect *Pacific Associates v. Baxter*[30] was followed. In the author's view this matter is far from beyond doubt and it only awaits a case where the circumstances are that the employer has become insolvent and the contractor seeks to sue the architect.

7.22	In an interesting recent case *John Mowlem & Co. plc v. Eagle Star Insurance Co. Ltd (No.1)*[31] the contractor had been awarded upwards of £12 million at an arbitration for wrongful determination of their contract by the employer. The employer then became insolvent and the contractor sued the main shareholders of the employer for wrongful interference with the contract. This claim was allowed to proceed against several of the shareholders but not the architect shareholder as the allegation that the architect had procured a breach by the employers was described as too artificial.

Supervision

7.23	The courts have been reluctant to exclude the liability of the contractor for defective work on the basis that the architect should have been more

[28]	(1985) 4 Const. L.J. 305.
[29]	(1989) 5 Const. L.J. 288.
[30]	[1989] C.L.Y. 2543.
[31]	(1992) 62 B.L.R. 126.

thorough in his inspection. In *East Ham Borough Council v. Bernard Sunley Ltd*[32] Lord Pearson observed:

> "it seems to be unreasonable...to let [the contractor] shelter behind the architect's failure to detect faults in the course of his visits during the progress of the work. The architect's duty is to the employer and not to the contractor, and the extent of his obligation to make inspections and tests depend upon his contract with the employers and the arrangements made and in the circumstances of the case. Prima facie the contractors should be and remain liable for their own breaches of contract, and should not have a general release from liability in respect of all breaches which the architect should have detected but failed to detect throughout the currency of the contract."

In relation to variations the matter has been put more strongly in *AMF International Ltd v. Magnet Bowling*[33]:   7.24

> "in general the architect owes no duty to the builder to tell him promptly during the course of construction, even as regards permanent work when he is going wrong; he may, if he wishes, leave that to the final stages notwithstanding that the correction of the fault then may be much more costly to the builder than had his error been pointed out earlier."

The architect and design matters

The question of the standard that the architect's design is to reach has already been discussed. An interesting additional question arose in *Wagner Associates v. Joseph Dunn (Bottlers)*.[34] Here the architects sued for fees and were met with a counterclaim that a wall had been designed negligently. The Lord Ordinary held that it had and in addition that the architects should have warned their clients of the risk of using such a design, and if they had, the clients would probably have opted for a safer design; in which case the client did not have to prove that no architect exercising reasonable care and skill would have submitted a design of that type. Lord Davidson said: "In my opinion the relationship of architect and client in connection with the design need not be restricted to an assessment of the plans which the architect proposes. In my opinion the pursuers duty to explain the position to the client introduces an additional dimension."   7.25

Limits of knowledge

In *Richard Roberts Holdings Ltd v. Douglas Smith Stimson Partnership*[35] architects were retained in relation to alterations to a dyeworks. The lining   7.26

---

[32]   [1966] A.C. 406.
[33]   [1968] 1 W.L.R. 1028 at 1053.
[34]   1986 S.L.T. 267 (OH).
[35]   [1988] 46 B.L.R. 50.

to a tank which they had chosen was thought to be too expensive. A specialist sub-contractor installed a different lining and contracted directly with the employer. The materials were inadequate. An action against the architect for breach of contract in recommending or permitting the alternative method of lining was successful.

7.26a   Also in *Holland Hannen & Cubitts v. Welsh Health Technical Services Organisation*,[36] the architects were held to be under a duty to ask probing questions of a sub-contractor about the design of specialist windows provided by that sub-contractor.

Revision of design

7.27   In so far as the architect designs, there is the question of whether the obligation to design includes making necessary revisions as the works progress. There may even be a question of impossibility arising. In *Norwest Holst Construction Ltd v. Renfrewshire Council*[37] it was held, in relation to ICE 5th contract, that the engineer was required to devise a solution to resolve the issue of impossibility. Otherwise, it has been said in *Brickfield Properties v. Newton*[38]: "It savours of the ridiculous for the architect to be able to say, as it was here suggested that he could say, 'true my design was faulty, but of course I saw to it that the contractor followed it faithfully' and be enabled on that ground to succeed in the action."

7.28   Is there a duty to reappraise a design, even after practical completion, or indeed after the issue of a final certificate? *London Borough of Merton v. Lowe and Pickford*[39] would suggest that any such design obligation would extend after practical completion but before the issue of a final certificate. It is a moot point as to whether any design responsibility would continue after the issue of the final certificate. In *T.E. Eckersley v. Binnie & Partners*[40] where there was an explosion of methane at a pumping station it was suggested at first instance that the engineer had an obligation to keep his client appraised of developing knowledge concerning risks with methane years after completion. This suggestion was criticised *obiter dicta* in the Court of Appeal but not entirely dismissed, especially by Bingham L.J.

Recommending a builder

7.29   In *Pratt v. George J. Hill* [41] the architects described builders as very reliable in the construction of a bungalow. In fact, they turned out not to be and the architects were held negligent.

---

[36] (1981) 18 B.L.R. 80.
[37] 1996 G.W.D. 40–2261 (1st Div.).
[38] [1971] 1 W.L.R. 862.
[39] (1982) 18 B.L.R. 130.
[40] (1988) Con L.R. 1.
[41] (1987) 38 B.L.R. 25.

Delegation to specialist sub-contractors

In *Moresk v. Hicks*[42] it was held that it was not the ordinary practice of   7.30
the profession for an architect to delegate his work for design to an engineer
and to then seek to disown responsibility for it. Here there was a defective
reinforced concrete frame. The architect had nominated sub-contractors
with structural engineering partners to design the frame, and the architect
approved the drawings. It was held that the architect had no implied duty to
delegate design, and especially to a sub-contractor. However in *Merton
London Borough Council v. Lowe*[43] an architect selected a specialist
contractor for plastering ceilings for a swimming pool. The finishing coating
used was a trade secret (Pyrok) that had worked successfully before.
Cracking appeared at the time of practical completion and tests showed the
undercoat was too weak for the finish. The architect said that he would
monitor the matter. Five years on the architect issued a final certificate
with no re-inspection. One year on the pool ceiling had to be taken down.
The architect had not been negligent in specifying the Pyrok, but had been
negligent in not calling for a full inspection and issuing the final certificate.

This certification-unseen issue has had a long history and in the old
Scots case of *Jamieson v. Simon*[44] an architect failed to see that the bottoming
of a cement floor was composed of proper materials and dry rot broke out
in the woodwork. This was held to be negligence.

Normally current RIBA conditions of contract for engagement of an   7.31
architect provide that the architect will not be responsible for the detailed
design or performance of specialist sub-contract work, but only for the
direction and integration of their work and for the general inspection of
their work. Similar clauses exist for consultants.

Architects and others who give practical financial advice have to be on   7.32
guard. In *Nye Saunders & Partners v. Bristow*[45] an estimate of the cost of
works that did not take inflation into account meant that the architects could
not recover their fees. Similarly in *Gable House Estates Ltd v. Halpern
Partnership*[46] an architect had prepared several plans for the refurbishment
of a listed building. The one that was chosen was based on net lettable area,
and the architects had noted that "all areas are approximate". This was held
to have been inadequate notice, and if the true position had been explained,
the employers would have been unlikely to have proceeded.

---

[42]   [1966] 2 Lloyds Rep. 338.
[43]   (1981) 18 B.L.R. 130.
[44]   (1899) 1 F. 1211.
[45]   39 B.L.R. 92 (CA).
[46]   48 Con. L.R. 1.

CHAPTER 8

RECENT CHANGES

8.01   It has taken from July 5, 1993, with the Joint Review of Procurement and Contractual Arrangements in the United Kingdom Construction Industry being announced in the House of Commons; to the Final Report of the Government/Industry Review of Procurement and Contractual Arrangements in the U.K. Construction Industry, *Constructing the Team* by Sir Michael Latham in July 1994; to May 1, 1998 for the commencement order for the relevant sections of the Housing Grants, Construction and Regeneration Act 1996 (HGCRA) to become law. In between we have had the election of a new Government and a renewed impetus behind the Private Finance Initiative. This chapter examines the Latham Report[1] and the HGCRA.

8.02   The Latham Report begins by explaining that it is the product of extensive consultation and that clients had been major participants in the discussions (Chap.1.5), but also that this report was not a government review of the industry, but one commissioned jointly by the then Government and the industry with the participation of clients. "It is a personal report of an independent, but friendly, observer."[2] The Report states that clients will have a wish-list for projects that will normally include:

1. value for money;
2. pleasing to look at;
3. free from defects on completion;
4. delivery on time;
5. fit for the purpose;
6. supported by worthwhile guarantees;
7. reasonable running costs;
8. satisfactory durability.[3]

However, it was pointed out that often the client does not know his own mind.[4] The Report recommends at item 1.1 that the Department of the

---

[1] For the fullest criticism of the Latham Report, in typically cogent style, see I.N. Duncan Wallace, "An Emperor without Clothes — Latham and the DOE " in *Contemporary Issues in Construction Law Volume II — Construction Contract Reform* (J. Uff, ed., 1997), chap. 9.
[2] Foreword p.(v).
[3] para. 3.2.
[4] para. 3.4.

Environment (now the Department of the Environment, Transport and the Regions) be the lead department for implementing the Report; at 1.2, that the Government should establish itself as a best-practice client; and, at 1.3, that a Construction Clients' Forum be set up to represent private sector clients.

The Report suggested that clients would be well advised to retain an external expert, but not initially with the title of project manager, to help decide if the project is necessary. The consultancy service offered by the RIAS which gives clients practical and objective advice about their procurement strategies before any decisions are made was noted, apparently favourably. There follows under the heading of Contract Strategy and Risk Assessment a comparison of objectives against contract options; such as the traditional JCT 80 type, construction management, management contracting, design and manage, and design and build. The analysis is acknowledged as being for guidance only, but in any event leads to Latham's recommendations 2, 3 and 4: that there should be a guide to clients on briefing drawn up by the Construction Industry Council with a checklist that should be signed off; and that the DOE should publish a Construction Strategy Code of Practice. Procurement of large process/power plant projects appears to have been treated separately from other types of construction by the DOE, and Latham draws comparisons with the recommendations that had been made in this sector for the oil and gas industry by the 1993 Report *Cost Reduction In the New Era* (CRINE), with the recommendations that he goes on to make. He recommends (no. 5) that process plant industry clients and contractors should be consulted by the DOE for their perspectives on construction.

8.03

In Chapter 4 Sir Michael went on to illustrate the problems of design procurement; especially as between the architect, structural engineer, manufacturers, the services engineer and specialist sub-contractors. One submission to the review described the process as impossible to co-ordinate before construction starts, and criticism of the SFA/92 "Standard Form of Agreement for the Appointment of an Architect" was noted. Recommendation 6 is that a reconstituted JCT should prepare a checklist such as that in the British Property Federation's Manual at Appendix 1, or the Building Services Research and Information Association (BSRIA) 1994 Report by C. J. Parsloe, and each stage of design should be ticked off by a lead manager or project manager. A perceived problem was that the client may only rarely understand design proposals from conceptual drawings. Computer-aided design (CAD) is recommended as a new development for construction which follows similar technological developments in the manufacturing industry known as "knowledge-based engineering" (KBE). The Co-ordinating Committee for Project Information published its Codes of Procedure for Production Drawings, Project Specification and a Common Arrangement of Work sections for Building Works in 1987. This technique was highlighted as something that should have been normal practice years ago, especially to keep clients aware of potential delay risks with incomplete

8.04

designs, and recommendation 7 advocated the use of CPI (co-ordinated project information).

8.05   The recurring problems of the role of the specialist contractor were considered; and also that they can comprise a disparate group. These specialist areas might include piling; structural steelwork; lifts and escalators; curtain walling and other cladding; flooring and suspended ceiling systems; I.T. networks; heating and ventilation systems; air conditioning systems; hot and cold water services; fire engineering; public health engineering; lighting and power; and building automation, security and energy management systems. Recommendation 8 was that a separate design agreement for the specialist engineering contractor involving the same standard of liability as the design consultant be used, with a checklist, as for recommendation 6. The existing procurement routes for specialist engineering contractors was considered. Nomination under JCT 80 was noted as used in only 11 per cent of cases, and the Chartered Institute of Purchasing and Supply described it as "a contradiction in terms", and recommended that it be dropped. Sir Michael did not endorse that, merely stating that it should not be followed as a normal procedure. Other choices such as joint venture companies, separate contracts, and appointing the specialist as the main contractor were discussed; but the advantages of construction management as a system that allows for separate contracts with specialist contractors, to be balanced against financial risk and high managerial involvement, were viewed favourably. It was noted that there was no current JCT Construction Management form, but that the New Engineering Contract produced by the Institution of Civil Engineers allowed this option.

8.06   Reference was made in Chapter 5 of the Report to various surveys of the industry's perception of the available standard forms and the role of the JCT, which produced generally lukewarm findings. Bonds were seen as currently subject to on-going DOE work but Sir Michael noted that he believed that bonds should be comprehensible, not drafted to be "on demand" but to make prompt payment possible without recourse to litigation, and to have a clear end date. It is in Chapter 5 that Sir Michael, after noting the problems associated with pay-when-paid contracts, stood back and criticised the basic assumptions of current standard forms when compared to the situation on the ground. At paragraph 5.17 he notes:

> "2. Contracts which are drafted on the basis that:
> (a)   design and construction are totally separated, in that the main contractor and sub-contractors have no design responsibilities or involvement in the design;
> (b)   all design work will be fully planned by consultants retained by the client and not subject to change once tender information has been sent out;
> (c)   the actual construction work will mainly be carried out by the contractor rather than by domestic sub-contractors;
> (d)   the architect or engineer acting as contract administrator will also be accepted by the parties to the main contract as impartial adjudicator between client and contractor, especially over matters relating to

measurement and certification of work done and related payment or time issues;

do not seem to me to relate easily to reality on modern construction sites and may require revision or replacement by other contractual approaches."

It is in the next step that Sir Michael caused eyebrows to be raised with his use of what he had described in the Foreword as what " management jargon calls 'seeking win-win solutions.'" At paragraph 5.18 he writes: 8.07

"The most effective form of contract in modern conditions should include:-

1. A specific duty for all parties to deal fairly with each other, and with their sub-contractors, specialists and suppliers, in an atmosphere of mutual co-operation.

2. Firm duties of teamwork, with shared financial motivation to pursue those objectives. These should involve a general presumption to achieve "win-win" solutions to those problems that arise in the course of a project.

3. A wholly interrelated package of documents which clearly defines the roles and duties of all involved, and which is suitable for all types of project and for any procurement route.

4. Easily comprehensible language with guidance notes attached.

5. Separation of the roles of contract administrator, project or lead manager and adjudicator. The project or lead manager should be clearly defined as the client's representative.

6. A choice of allocation of risks, to be decided as appropriate to each project but then allocated to the party best able to manage, estimate and carry the risk.

7. Taking all reasonable steps to avoid changes to pre-planned works information. But, where variations occur, they should be priced in advance, with provision for independent adjudication if agreement cannot be reached.

8. Express provision for assessing interim payments by methods other than monthly valuation *i.e.* milestones, activity schedules or payment schedules. Such arrangements must also be reflected in the related sub-contract documentation. The eventual aim should be to phase out the traditional system of monthly measurement or remeasurement but meanwhile provision should be still made for it.

9. Clearly setting out the period within which interim payments must be made to all participants in the process, failing which they will have an automatic right to compensation, involving the payment of interest at a sufficiently heavy rate to deter slow payment.

10. Providing for secure trust fund routes for payment.

11. While taking all possible steps to avoid conflict on site, providing for speedy dispute resolution if any conflict arises, by a pre-determined impartial adjudicator/referee/expert.

12. Providing for incentives for exceptional performance.

13. Making provision where appropriate for advance mobilisation payments (if necessary, bonded) to contractors and sub-contractors, including in respect of off site prefabricated materials provided by part of the construction team."

8.08   The Report notes that most of these principles are to be found in the
            New Engineering Contract,[5] but that it would still require amendment,
            especially on the spirit of co-operation and "win-win" points. Latham
            did not recommend legislation to achieve these aims. Instead he
            recommended (no. 9) that the JCT be restructured and that a "family"
            of contracts be developed on the NEC model, taking account of the
            amendments he suggests, as should the CCSJC (Conditions of Contract
            Joint Standing Committee) in respect of the ICE conditions, and that
            this should be done under the auspices of a Joint Liaison Committee
            (recommendation 11).

8.09   In Chapter 6 the Report notes that professional fee scales are no longer
            viewed as appropriate and that the construction industry favours fees to be
            negotiated. This raises questions of value for money as against cost,
            especially in the context of competitive tendering by consultants.
            Recommendation 13.5 was that a task-force be set up by the DOE and the
            Construction Industry Council to chose and endorse a specific quality and
            price assessment for the engagement of professional consultants and to
            consider detailed issues of maintenance of a Consultants' Register and
            prequalification.

8.10   At paragraph 6.12 the complexity of modern construction techniques
            was seen to cause clients difficulties in finding designers who would be
            responsible for all aspects of design and the administration of a contract.
            The developing discipline of project management was considered and it
            was recommended that clients should consider at an early stage if they
            need one (14.3), and if so, what clear contractual responsibilities should
            exist.[6]

8.11   Recommendation 15 deals with a rationalisation of prequalification for
            contractors and sub-contractors which was perceived as inconsistent, and
            recommendation 16 reaffirmed that the National Joint Consultative
            Committee's Codes of Procedure for Single Stage Selective Tendering/Two
            Stage Selective Tendering be followed, subject to clearer guidance in the
            Construction Strategy Code of Practice (CSCP)[7] as to the applicability of
            E.U. procurement legislation. Recommendation 17 was for interim
            arrangements.

8.12   The selection of sub-contractors was recommended to follow a joint
            Code of Practice prepared by the Construction Industry Employers Council
            and the Constructors Liaison Group (CLG). The Code of Practice should
            contain commitments to short-tender lists; selection on quality and price;

---

[5]   Itself since the subject of detailed criticisim by Donald Valentine in The New Engineering
      Contract: Major Drafting Defects in *Contemporary Issues in Construction Law Volume II
      — Construction Contract Reform* (J. Uff, ed., 1997), chap. 8.
[6]   In relation to implied duties of project managers see *Chesham Properties Ltd v. Bucknall
      Austin Project Management Services Ltd* (1996) 82 B.L.R. 92.
[7]   See recommendation 3.

that the contract should comply with the recommendations of Chapters 5 and 8, as should sub-sub-contract documentation; clients should be given the opportunity to object to sub-contractors; Dutch auctioning should be ruled out; and sub-contractors should undertake to co-ordinate their work effectively with each other and the main contractor.

Chapter 6 ends with comments on "Partnering", which is described as a contractual arrangement for a specific length of time or for an indefinite period (6.43). Advantages in maximising expertise, especially in large projects such as process plant and power station construction, were noted; with disadvantages of "cosiness". Again the E.U. procurement provisions would have to be considered, so that recommendation 19 is that specific advice be given to public authorities so that they can experiment with the idea. "Partners" should initially be sought by competitive tendering, and should include measurable targets for productivity improvements.   8.13

Chapter 7 concerns issues of training of operatives, consultants, and research and development within the industry. Certain areas were highlighted as suitable for review, leading to the controversial recommendation 24 that a target of 30 per cent real cost reduction should be accepted and striven for by the year 2000.   8.14

Under the heading "Teamwork on Site" the role and motivation of sub-contractors was considered in Chapter 8. This led to recommendation 25 concerning the legislative underpinning of certain "pay-when-paid" clauses as unfair, the right to immediate adjudication, and the setting up of secure trust funds. These are discussed further in the context of the HGCRA. However, it should be noted at this stage that recommendation 27 on secure trust funds and research into the applicability of a scheme similar to that under the German Civil Code (s. 648) or the Ontario Construction Lien Act 1983 were not legislated for in HGCRA.   8.15

The last substantial area of the Report in Chapter 11 is headed "Liability Post Completion". The existing system of contractual retentions during the defects liability period; possible alternatives such as retention bonds; the current development of collateral warranties to fill gaps that the law of negligence leaves in doubt; and exposure to potentially uninsured risks, were considered. Sir Michael described the current arrangements as "inadequate" (para. 11.3). Four recent reports were considered.[8] Sir Michael noted that a working party at the DOE were looking at several options along with clients, contractors and the Constructors Liaison Group (CLG — comprising the National Specialist Contractors Council, the Specialist Engineering Contractors' Group and the Building Structures Group).   8.16

---

[8] *Building Users Insurance Against Latent Defects* (known as the BUILD Report, NEDC, 1988); *Professional Liability — Report of the Study Teams* (known as the Likierman Report, HMSO, 1989); the GAIPEC Report (*Report of the Work of the Group of European Inter Professional and Trade Associations for the Building Industry*, September 1992) and the European Commission's "Staff Discussion Paper... with Regard to Liabilities and Guarantees in the Construction Sector", June 1993.

The first issue was joint liability. It is unclear from the Report if this refers to joint liability for delictual/tortious acts but seems to relate to joint and several liability provisions in commonly drafted collateral warranties. It was proposed that liability should be apportioned fairly rather than jointly and severally. The second issue was prescription and limitation periods. The majority favoured a single 10-year period from practical completion or "effective occupation". The CLG rejected this on the basis that sub-contract works may have been completed long before practical completion. They suggested the 10-year period run from completion of the sub-contract works, or alternatively that the period be shortened to five years. The third issue was transfer of clients' rights. The majority favoured a loophole-free assignation system to future transferees of a property in respect of repair and reinstatement of the building to its intended condition, with exceptions for consequential losses and economic losses. The CLG thought that the recommendations went too far, and that any tenants' rights of action should be via the current owner; and that specialist contractors should have equivalent rights against clients and their advisers. In recommendation 28 Sir Michael called for legislative changes to implement the majority conclusions of the CLG with possibly a compulsory BUILD insurance (building users insurance against latent defects). He also noted that there was concern about suppliers and their ability to contract out of liability by exclusion clauses, but that introduced wider sale of goods issues which could be considered further by the Implementation Forum. Recommendation 29 saw the culmination of the questions of liability being underwritten by compulsory latent defects insurance for 10 years (para. 11.18(2)). Neither recommendation 28 or 29 were enacted into HGCRA.

HOUSING GRANTS, CONSTRUCTION AND REGENERATION ACT 1996 (HGCRA)

8.17   Following the Latham Report there was a DOE consultation exercise in mid-1995 and on the basis of the consultation the reform of liability law for construction and compulsory latent defects insurance was dropped. This seemed to be partly due to a reluctance to "ring fence" construction on questions of limitation periods, the issue of joint and several liability, and because the question of third party rights in contract were all the subject of separate Law Commission papers and review.[9]

Similarly, the Government was not convinced that trust funds were consistent with well-established practice in respect of insolvency. "Trust funds would ... ring-fence payments owed on construction contracts from the main assets of the insolvent company."[10] The Government spokesman

---

[9]   See The Law Commission http://www.gtnet.gov.uk/lawcomm/homepage.htm

[10]   *per* Earl Ferrers, Government spokesman, H.L. Committee Stage: *Hansard,* H.C. Vol. 570, col. 1921 1–2.

also said the prospect for contractors or their clients of sums being set aside was unattractive.[11] This would appear to ignore the fact that current JCT standard forms of contract ostensibly require the employer to do precisely that.[12]

The first relevant section for construction law is in Part II of HGCRA at   8.18
section 104. This section defines a construction contract as one for the carrying out of, the arranging for the carrying out of, or the provision of, labour for construction operations, which are defined in section 105. Section 104(2) includes an agreement to do architectural, design or surveying work, or to provide advice on building, engineering, interior or exterior decoration or the laying out of landscape. A distinction is drawn between a contract of employment which is not covered, as opposed to contracts for services. The HGCRA therefore does not cover contracts for the supply of materials unless installed or designed (s. 105(2)(d)) or perhaps which involve advice. There does appear to be room for confusion though as s. 104(5) provides that for an agreement which relates to construction operations and "other matters", the Act applies only in so far as the agreement relates to construction operations. It is the author's view that it may be difficult to tease out which part of a contract the Act may apply to. Section 104(4) enables the Secretary of State to make orders as to what is and what is not a construction contract. Such an Exclusion Order was made on March 6, 1988 to come into force on the same day as HGCRA, *i.e.* May 1, 1998.[13] Under article 3 of the Exclusion Order agreements made under specified statutory provisions dealing with works relating to roads, planning obligations, sewerage works and externally financed NHS Trust agreements are excluded. Article 4 excludes agreements entered into by specified public bodies under the private finance initiative (or a project applying similar principles). Article 5 excludes agreements which primarily relate to the financing of works. Article 6 excludes development agreements, which contain provision for the disposal of an interest in land.

Section 105 defines "construction operations" in a broad sense, but uses   8.19
slightly different criteria from the CDM regulations.[14] It may be open to question whether the installation of I.T. services is included unless these become fixtures; but the position with respect to offshore construction is even more unclear as parts of the processes, *e.g.* drilling; extraction; tunnelling or boring; construction of underground works; assembly, installation or demolition of plant or machinery, are excluded. It will be a moot point if sub-sea works are excluded. Purely artistic works, *e.g.* murals, are excluded (s.105(2)(d)).

---

[11] *ibid.*
[12] See clauses 30.4 and 30.5 of JCT 80, discussed at Chap. 4.
[13] The Construction Contracts (Scotland) Exclusion Order 1988 No. 686 (S.33).
[14] See Chap. 1, para. 1–05 *ante.*

8.20   Section 106 expressly excludes construction contracts with a residential occupier or on a dwelling which is intended principally for occupation as a residence, but whether this section will apply to sub-contractors who are not in contract with the occupier will be a matter for interpretation.

8.21   Section 107 provides that the Act will only apply to agreements in writing, which are broadly defined to include evidenced in writing, or subject to a written arbitration agreement, or written submissions in adjudication proceedings or legal proceedings where the other party does not deny that the Act applies. The familiar questions of whether letters of intent will be construed as contractual has not been dealt with by the Act. Writing means recorded by any means (s.107(6)) and will presumably include e-mail and suchlike. It is not clear whether drawings on their own would suffice.

8.22   Section 108 introduces one of the most substantial changes in the law relating to construction contracts. It introduces a right to refer a dispute or difference to adjudication. The basic idea is that this will introduce a quick-fix method of handling disputes in the course of almost all construction contracts, and is developed further in relation to payment issues by sections 109–113. However there are many substantial issues that raise problems and significant loopholes exist with regard to payment issues.

8.23   The first question might be what exactly is adjudication. This is not a matter that is defined in the Act, but would appear to be something distinct from arbitration, as the adjudicator's decision is to be binding "until the dispute is finally determined ... by arbitration" (s.108(3)). In any event a closer analysis of the provisions of section 108 and the Scheme for Construction Contracts (Scotland) Regulations[15] made under HGCRA would indicate that adjudication is not merely arbitration by another name. There are similarities but significant differences. For example, the timetable for adjudication set under section 108 does not make the adjudicator the master of procedure as an arbiter would be. The adjudicator is required by section 108(2)(c) to reach a decision within 28 days of referral. This extremely short time can only be extended by the adjudicator with the consent of the party referring, and then for up to 14 days; or if both parties agree. Procedure, at least as regards the timetable, is therefore in the hands of the parties.

8.24   What exactly the adjudicator has the power to do in such a short timescale, or must do, is open to interpretation. Section 108(1)(e) requires the adjudication procedure to impose a duty on the adjudicator to act impartially; and section 108(1)(f) enables the adjudicator to take the initiative in ascertaining the facts and the law. Whilst the impartiality provision is unsurprising, it is not made clear that the adjudicator cannot be the traditional architect or engineer as the Latham Report encouraged. Further, will the matter of taking initiative require this of the adjudicator, and to what extent will the corpus of arbitration law on the arbiter acting in accord with natural justice be swept away? Indeed one comentator has written that:

---

[15]   S.I. 1998 No. 687 (S.34).

"Adjudication is designed to produce a temporary decision only based upon the minimum of submissions and evidence and either party is free to seek to overturn that decision by other means at a later time. The primary objective is a quick decision, not necessarily the right decision, and the Adjudicator is not necessarily required to observe 'natural justice' in the procedure he adopts. Provided there is no manifest unfairness to one of the parties, his decision will be binding unless it is wholly unsupportable on the face of the submissions or unless he has acted in 'bad faith'."[16]

The Scheme, section 108(5) tells us, will apply to all relevant construction contracts if they have not been drafted to comply with subsections (1) to (4) of section 108. The Scheme at paragraph 12 on the Powers of the Adjudicator adds to the "impartiality" issue by adding that he should so act in accordance with the contract, the applicable law, and to avoid unnecessary expense. This is hardly a restatement of the general law of natural justice in arbitration, but seems nearer the statement of principle found in section 1(a) of the English (not applicable in Scotland) Arbitration Act 1996: "the object of arbitration is to obtain the fair resolution of disputes by an impartial tribunal without unnecessary delay or expense." Close inspection of the Act and the Scheme disclose no obligation on the adjudicator to act fairly. But section 108(3) requires that contractual adjudication must be stated as binding until the dispute is finally determined by legal proceedings, arbitration or by agreement; and that the adjudicator shall not be liable for the discharge of his function unless in bad faith (s.108(4)). This could mean that the adjudicator makes a decision that is unjust and unfair that stands irrespective of bad faith until set aside; although the adjudicator could then be liable to one or other of the parties for his "bad faith", which is not quite the same as lack of impartiality. One imagines that in the course of a contract where a rogue adjudicator's decision could have substantial effects for a long time or affect a chain of relationships, judicial review might be brought in the Court of Session under Chapter 58 of the Rules of the Court of Session. Far from easing relations and team-building we might have two additional layers of procedure, the latter for the purpose of clarifying the former: what might be described as a "lose-lose" situation and Latham's nightmare. 8.25

The Scheme sets out in paragraphs 1–26 extensive provisions for adjudication which the Act does not, and it remains to be seen whether these paragraphs will be adopted as standard for adjudications that take place under section 108. These include reaching decisions in absence, and opening up, reviewing and revising certificates, and adjudicating on several disputes under different contracts. There is even in Scotland under paragraph 24 of the Scheme a provision that parties must consent to the registration of a 8.26

---

[16] Sims, "Adjudication under the HGCR Act 1996 — A Construction Viewpoint" in *Contemporary Issues in Construction Law Volume II — Construction Contract Reform* (J. Uff, ed., 1997), p. 31.

decision of the adjudicator in the Books of Council and Session. There is ample scope for interpretation on all these issues.

Adjudication is however not something that is entirely novel in the construction context. Provisions for adjudication could be found in DOM/ 1 and DOM/2; JCT 81; ICE 5th and related sub-contracts; GC/Wks/1 ed. 3; PSA/1 Form of Main Contract; and the ACA Form of Building Agreement. The Official Referees Solicitors Association published adjudication rules in 1996, and the Centre for Dispute Resolution has published model rules for adjudication; all of these are different. There have also been decided cases on related issues in England. In *Cape Durasteel Ltd v. Rosser and Russell Building Services*[17] the Official Referee stated:

> "It is clear on the authorities that ... the test to be applied is the customary one of ascertaining the presumed intention of the parties from their contract and its circumstances. It is plain that 'adjudication' taken by itself means a process by which a dispute is resolved in a judicial manner. It is equally clear that 'adjudication' has yet no settled special meaning in the construction industry (which is not surprising since it is a creature of contract and contractual procedures utilising an 'adjudicator' vary as do forms of contract). Even if it were to have the special meaning accorded to it in some sections of the construction industry where it describes the initial determination of certain classes of dispute in a summary manner, the force of which is tempered by its ephemeral status as there are concomitant provisions for the decision to be reviewed and if necessary reversed by an arbitrator, I would see no reason why it should have that meaning in this contract."

8.27   In *Channel Tunnel Group v. Balfour Beatty*[18] the contract set out a dispute resolution procedure, by which differences were first to be referred to and settled by a panel of three, acting as experts and not arbitrators. In the event of dissatisfaction with the panel's decision, either party had a right to refer the dispute further to arbitration in accordance with the Rules of Conciliation and Arbitration of the International Chamber of Commerce. A dispute arose concerning valuation of variations and the contractor threatened to walk off. The employer sought an injunction to stop the contractor walking off and the contractor applied for the injunction proceedings to be stayed for arbitration. The House of Lords held that it had the power to stay proceedings even if the dispute resolution mechanism fell short of an immediately effective agreement to arbitrate. This may be authority for the proposition that no interim orders would be granted by a Scottish court in relation to a contract with an adjudication clause which could be subject to later arbitration. On the other hand in *Costain Building and Civil Engineering Ltd v. Scottish Rugby Union plc*[19] a court of five judges in the Inner House considered the employer's motion to recall arrestments on the dependence of an action by the contractor in respect of payment of sums claimed but

[17] (1995) 46 Con. L.R. 75.
[18] [1993] 2 W.L.R. 262.
[19] 1994 S.C.L.R. 257.

uncertified under ICE 5th contract. Consideration was given *inter alia* to whether the contractual mechanism of clause 66(2) prevented the court's intervention. Clause 66(2) provided: "that the Contractor and the Employer shall both give effect forthwith to every decision of the Engineer unless and until the same shall be revised by an arbitrator as hereinafter provided. Such decisions shall be final and binding upon the Contractor and the Employer unless and until the dispute or difference has been referred to arbitration as hereinafter provided and an award made and published". The wording of clause 66(2) is very similar to section 108(3). Lord Hope in the Inner House in *Costain* gave the leading judgment and referred to the Court of Appeal decision in *Northern Regional Health Authority v. Derek Crouch Construction Co. Ltd*[20] as consistent with the law of Scotland that the parties are free to "set up a method for the adjudication of their rights and obligations which will exclude the jurisdiction of the court on the merits of any dispute".[21] However in the Lords in *Beaufort Developments*[22] Lord Hope said that "the Court of Appeal in *Crouch* having started from the correct principle, fell into error in its application to the facts". He went on:

> "If the contract provides that the sole means of establishing the facts is the expression of opinion in an architect's certificate, that provision must be given effect to by the court. But in all other respects, where a party comes to the court in the search of an ordinary remedy in respect of an alleged breach of it, the court is entitled to examine the facts and to form its own opinion upon them in the light of the evidence. The fact that the architect has formed an opinion on the matter will be part of the evidence. But, as it will not be conclusive evidence, the court can disregard his opinion if it does not agree with it."

The problem with adjudication is that it has now become a statutory matter and it will be questionable how far adjudication can be equated in the same way as a private agreement for resolving disputes between parties.

It may be that the decision of an adjudicator will be considered on the same bases as cases concerning expert determination, or it may be that the two are mutually exclusive.[23] In *Conoco (U.K.) Ltd v. Phillips Petroleum Co.*[24] there was contractual provision for an expert determination where the expert was the master of procedure, gave reasons in writing, and specifically that the expert was not an arbitrator, and that his decision would be final and binding. The question arose as to whether the expert's decision should be set aside on the basis of manifest error. Reference was made to *Jones v. Sherwood Computer Services plc*[25] where Dillon L.J. said the following:

8.28

[20] [1984] 2 All E.R. 175.
[21] 1994 S.C.L.R. at 266–B.
[22] *Beaufort Developments (N.I.) Ltd. v. Gilbert-Ash (N.I.) Ltd* [1999] A.C. 266.
[23] See John Kendall, *Expert Determination* (2nd ed., FT Law & Tax, London, 1977).
[24] (1996) BLISS 19.08.96.
[25] [1992] 2 All E.R. 170 at 179.

"On principle, the first step must be to see what the parties have agreed to remit to the expert, this being ... a matter of contract. The next step must be to see what the nature of the mistake was, if there is evidence to show that. If the mistake made was that the expert departed from his instructions in a material respect, *e.g.* if he valued the wrong number of shares or valued shares in the wrong company, or ... the expert had valued machinery himself whereas his instructions were to employ an expert valuer of his choice to do that, either party would be able to say that the certificate was not binding because the expert had not done what he was appointed to do."

There will therefore be the question of the materiality of any breach of the adjudication provisions. However, in *Conoco* it was held that where the contract read "the decision of the expert shall be final and binding ... save in the event of fraud or manifest error", this restricted the right to challenge "whether on procedural or substantive grounds to those two events".[26] Conversely, highly legalistic challenges to an adjudicator's decision under HGCRA and the Scheme would appear to be possible if such decisions are not final and binding. In the recent House of Lords decision in *Beaufort Developments (N.I.) Ltd v. Gilbert-Ash N.I. Ltd*[27] their Lordships overruled as wrong the Court of Appeal decision in *Northern Regional Health Authority v. Derek Crouch Construction Co. Ltd.*[28] The *Crouch* decision had been that the courts did not have the power to open up and revise interim certificates of an architect if that power had been specifically given under contract to an arbitrator. In so far as an adjudicator's decision under section 108(3) is to be binding until the dispute is finally determined by legal proceedings, by arbitration (if the contract provides for arbitration or the parties otherwise agree to arbitration) or by agreement, it would appear from the section and the decision in *Beaufort* that adjudicators' decisions are as ephemeral as interim certificates, unless agreed to be final determinations of the dispute. If they are not conclusive then it is difficult to see how the courts would enforce an adjudicator's award at all on an interim basis. This raises the question of why registration in the Books of Council and Session under the Scheme in Scotland for diligence purposes is appropriate, unless adjudicators' decisions under the scheme are to be seen as enforceable as interim orders of a court. By comparison with arbitration there is authority in Scotland that interim awards can be issued by an arbiter if there is consent to registration.[29]

8.29   At the time of writing there has been one decided case with respect to the adjudication provisions issued by the Hon. Mr Justice Dyson in the Technology and Construction Court.[30] This was the first serious challenge

---

[26] See also *Nikko Hotels v. MEPC* [1991] 2 E.G.L.R. 103; and *Dixon Group plc v. Jan Andrews Murray-Oboynski* (1997) ORB No. 152 at http://www.open.gov.uk/courts/court/orb_152.htm
[27] *op. cit.*
[28] [1984] Q.B. 644.
[29] *Lyle v. Falconer* (1842) 5 D. 236.
[30] *Macob Civil Engineering v. Morrison Construction* TCC February 12, 1999 (published on http://tap.ccta.gov.uk/courtser/judgments.nsf/Technology+and+Construction+Court/By+Case+Reference); [1999] 89 B.L.R. 93.

to an adjudicator's decision on the basis that there were failures to comply with natural justice; and also whether an English court could make an interim order to enforce an adjudicator's award. This latter issue concerned section 42 of the Arbitration Act 1996, as modified by paragraph 24 of the Scheme, for either party to apply to the court for an order requiring compliance with an adjudicator's award. To that extent the decision proceeds on matters which are not part of the law of Scotland. However the general thrust of the decision is instructive. The timetable for decision making was referred to as:

> "very tight....Many would say unreasonably tight, and likely to result in injustice. Parliament must be taken to have been aware of this.... It is clear that Parliament intended that the adjudication should be conducted in a manner which those familiar with the grinding detail of the traditional approach to the resolution of construction disputes apparently find difficult to accept."[31]

The judge held that an adjudicator's award could be enforced by proceedings for summary judgment, rather than a mandatory injunction (which would equate with specific implement in Scotland). The judge said:

> "I do not consider that the mere fact that the decision may later be revised is a good reason for saying that summary judgment is inappropriate. The grant of summary judgment does not pre-empt any later decision that an arbitrator may make. It merely reflects the fact that there is no defence to a claim to enforce the decision of the adjudicator at the time of judgment."

Nor did the judge think that it would be appropriate to stay (or sist, in Scotland) the court proceedings on the basis that the effect of the adjudicator's decision had purportedly been referred to arbitration.

The legal arguments that underpinned these findings were made on English law matters, but the overall impression of the purpose and effect of the adjudication provisions has been signalled.

The Latham Report stated that it should be the eventual aim "to phase out the traditional system of monthly measurement or remeasurement". Instead it recommended: "Express provision for assessing interim payments by methods other than by monthly valuation *i.e.* milestones, activity schedules or payment schedules." HGCRA does not specifically do that, but rather at section 109 gives a party to a construction contract an entitlement to payment by instalments, stage payments or other periodic payments unless the duration of the work is specified to be less than 45 days, or there is an agreed estimate that the work will be less than 45 days. The Act goes on, at section 109(2), to leave the parties free to agree the amounts of the payments and the intervals at which, or circumstances in which, they become due, failing which, by section 109(3), the Scheme will apply. Part II of the Scheme provides in paragraphs 2 to 4 what happens if the amount or intervals or both cannot be agreed. Paragraphs 2 and 3 provide that an aggregated amount shall be payable, "equal to the value of any work

8.30

---

[31] *ibid.* at para. 14.

performed" from the commencement of the contract to the end of the relevant period; and where the contract provides for the payment of materials, an amount "equal to the value of any materials manufactured on site or brought onto site for the purposes of the works during the period from commencement of the contract to the end of the relevant period"; and any other sum specified; less any amounts which have been paid or are due; shall be payable.

8.31 Section 109 effectively resolves the question of construction contracts being entire contracts,[32] and any issues of implied rights to interim payments.[33] Section 109 does not create a statutory implied term, but leaves the parties free to agree amounts, intervals and circumstances, failing which the Scheme applies. There are a number of criticisms that can be made. First, we have seen the difficulty in valuing construction works as against bills of quantities, and the ways in which profit is marked up and variations anticipated. It was this problem which Latham sought to move away from but which the Act leaves unresolved. The interpretation paragraph (12) of the scheme defines "value of work" on the fall-back basis of cost plus overhead or profit included in the contract price which is the familiar recipe for dispute. Secondly, all of the problems concerning materials such as reservation of title clauses, direct purchase of materials off-site, materials being brought on site ahead of schedule or need, the difference between certification and transfer of title and the different contractual chain of suppliers, which have been discussed in relation to clause 16 of JCT 80, have simply not been addressed.

8.32 Just as for the adjudication provisions, there is significant scope for the exploitation of ambiguity in the scheme, for example, as to when the amounts of any payment become due. Paragraph 4 provides that payment shall become due on the later of seven days from the "relevant period" (which paragraph 12 tells us is a fall-back period of 28 days) or the making of a claim by the payee. Can the payer simply delay payment and wait for a claim? How relevant must the claim be?

On top of this section 110 provides that every construction contract shall provide an "adequate mechanism for determining what payments become due under the contract, and when". Does the phrase "adequate mechanism" mean interim certificates, which as we have seen are not binding on an employer,[34] and can be made a condition precedent on a right to payment?[35] In the absence of an adequate mechanism paragraph 4 of the scheme provides a system whereby payment becomes due, on the later of seven days from

---

[32] See Chap. 4, paras 4.04–4.12.

[33] *D.R. Bradley (Cable Jointing) v. Jefco Mechanical Services* (1989) 6 Construction Law Digest 7–21.

[34] See Chap. 3, para. 3.60 *ante* and *Redpath Dorman Long Ltd v. Cummins Engine Co. Ltd*, 1982 S.L.T. 489.

[35] See *Costain Building & Civil Engineering Ltd v. Scottish Rugby Union plc*, 1994 S.C.L.R. 257; *Lubenham Fidelities and Investments Co. Ltd v. South Pembrokeshire District Council* [1986] 33 B.L.R. 39.

the relevant 28-day period or on the date when claimed by the payee. The scheme is therefore quite unconcerned with the quality of work done, so long as a mechanism exists. However, HGCRA does not preclude set-off or abatement (the Scottish terminology of retention or compensation is not used), indeed section 110(2) (a) and (b) envisage it, by the giving of notice specifying the amount of payment proposed to be made not later than five days after payment becomes due, subject to set-off. Section 111 requires an effective notice of intention to withold payment procedure, detailing grounds and amounts, which has to be made before the final date for payment. The practical effect of this is that set-off can be exercised against interim payments, although an effective notice is not required until a period before the final date for payment, which probably could be drafted to emasculate the effect of the notice provisions.

Section 112 of HGCRA introduces a novel right to all construction 8.33 contracts for a party who is not paid in full by the final date for payment to suspend performance of his obligations to the other party. Suspension is different from recission of contract, or determination under JCT contracts, but it is not clear whether this clause can be contracted out of. There is scope for confusion as to when any such right to suspend can be exercised as it is predicated on the "final date for payment", and where there has been "no effective notice to withold payment". Both of these terms allow for ambiguity. In the case of a "final date for payment" the Scheme, at paragraph 8, provides a fall-back position where no final date is specified. The fall-back is difficult to understand as a distinction is drawn between the "final date for making payment" which is 17 days later than the date the "payment becomes due". The problem is that "payment becomes due" in respect of instalments seven days after the making of a relevant claim or the expiry of the 28-day period; but paragraph 5 refers to a "final payment" which is due 30 days following the completion of the work or the making of a relevant claim. Therefore, the scheme would appear to create ambiguity by the use of the word final in different senses: *i.e.* both in relation to instalments, and on completion of the work (which is not defined). It is possible that section 112 will be interpreted to permit suspension only after the completion of the work, and therefore only relate to obligations in a defects liability period. This may never have been the intention, but the wording of the scheme is confusing, and suspension has been described as possibly a kind of "blackmail" by Duncan Wallace,[36] which leaves the contractor open to a claim for damages that he has wrongfully repudiated the contract.

Section 112 (2) requires that seven days' notice be given stating the grounds for the intention to suspend performance: section 112(3) states that the right to suspend performance ceases when the party in default makes

---

[36] I. Duncan Wallace in " An Emperor without Clothes — Latham and the DOE" *ante* at p.175.

payment in full of the amount due. This may be difficult to interpret in relation to bona fide set-off questions. Section 112(4) appears to entitle the suspendor, or a party who is affected by another's suspension, to an extension of time to complete, which disregards the period of suspension. Experience shows that this will be a ripe area for disputes given the problems of computing extensions of time at the best of times,[37] and the section makes no reference to loss and expense issues relating to the period of suspension.

8.34   Section 113 is the response to the Latham recommendation (25) to outlaw pay-when-paid clauses. This is another statutory intervention into the free negotiation of contracts peculiarly for the construction industry. Quite why this provision was thought so necessary for the construction industry on its own, when it had featured in standard forms of contract (FCEC) in the U.K. and widely in other jurisdictions, has been described as "overkill".[38] Section 113 (1) is another curious piece of draftsmanship. It states:

> "s. 113. — (1) A provision making payment under a construction contract conditional on the payer receiving payment from a third person is ineffective, unless that third person, or any other person payment by whom is under the contract (directly or indirectly) a condition of payment by that third person, is insolvent."

The initial curiosity is in relation to insolvency being put into the present tense. Does this mean insolvent at the time the contract is made (implausible), or should it be interpreted as "becomes insolvent". The next question that is likely to come up is what is meant by receiving payment. Payment may never be made, for bona fide reasons of set-off or insolvency. Payment may be forthcoming on the occasion of certain events in relation to the timing of instalments or the determination of a dispute by adjudication, arbitration or litigation. Is it the intention of Parliament that parties are not to be free to draft back-to-back contracts based on the satisfaction of conditions related to payment, but not specifically around receipt of payment? For example, would a clause in a sub-contract still be effective if it states that payment will be due to the sub-contractor if a certificate is issued, or if no set-off is claimed by the employer in respect of the sub-contractor's works, or some such piece of draftsmanship which distinguishes an entitlement to payment from actually having received the cash from the employer. The critical question will be whether an adequate mechanism for section 110 purposes is created, and the Scheme falls back on the previous payment mechanisms if a clause is ineffective under section 113.

8.35   It is the author's view that the lasting problems of construction law are unlikely to be wafted away by this single piece of legislation and the Report which preceded it, however challenging and visionary it was. There has

---

[37] See Chapter 4; and for a fuller analysis Pickavance, *Delay and Disruption in Construction Contracts* (1997).
[38] I. Duncan Wallace, *op. cit.* at p. 186.

been further. visionary thinking since Latham, although not this time suggesting legislative reform but concentrating on management techniques based around four key elements: product development, project implementation, partnering the supply chain and production of components.[39] The Egan Report even went as far as to suggest that construction contracts be abandoned altogether:

"Contracts can add significantly to the cost of a project and often add no value for the client. If the relationship between a constructor and employer is soundly based and the parties recognise their mutual interdependence, then formal contract documents should gradually become obsolete. The Construction industry may find this revolutionary. So did the motor industry, but we have seen non-contractually based relationships between Nissan and its 130 principal suppliers and we know that they work."

Without wanting to sound sardonic, perhaps this optimistic prophesying might be tempered by reflecting on the words of the poet Kipling:

"I tell this tale, which is strictly true,
Just by way of convincing you
How very little, since things were made,
Things have altered in the building trade.
...

Your glazing is new and your plumbing's strange,
But otherwise I perceive no change;
And in less than a month, if you do as I bid,
I'll learn you to build me a Pyramid!"
A Truthful Song.

---

[39] *Rethinking Construction* (1998), the report of the DETR's Construction Task Force chaired by Sir John Egan; www.construction.detr.gov.uk/cis/rethink/index.htm.

APPENDIX 1

STANDARD FORM OF BUILDING CONTRACT: PRIVATE WITH QUANTITIES (1998 EDITION)

APPENDIX 1

Articles of Agreement

Standard Form of Building Contract:
Private with Quantities.
(1998 edition)

made the _____ day of _____ 19 _____

BETWEEN _____

of (or whose registered office is situated at) _____

(hereinafter called 'the Employer') of the one part

AND _____

of (or whose registered office is situated at) _____

(hereinafter called 'the Contractor') [a] of the other part.

Appendix 1

Whereas

Recitals First   the Employer is desirous of [b] _____

_____

at _____

_____

and has caused Drawings and Bills of Quantities to be prepared which show and describe the work to be done;

Second   the Contractor has supplied the Employer with a fully priced copy of the said Bills of Quantities (which copy is hereinafter referred to as 'the Contract Bills');

[e] and has provided the Employer with a priced Activity Schedule;

Third   the said Drawings numbered _____

(hereinafter referred to as 'the Contract Drawings') and the Contract Bills have been signed by or on behalf of the parties hereto;

Fourth   the status of the Employer, for the purposes of the statutory tax deduction scheme under the Income and Corporation Taxes Act 1988, as at the Base Date is stated in the Appendix;

[f] Fifth   the extent of the application of the Construction (Design and Management) Regulations 1994 (the 'CDM Regulations') to the work referred to in the First recital is stated in the Appendix;

[e] Sixth   the Employer has provided the Contractor with a schedule ('Information Release Schedule') which states what information the Architect will release and the time of that release;

Seventh   if the Employer requires any bond to be on terms other than those agreed between the JCT and the British Bankers' Association, the Contractor has been given copies of these terms;

Footnotes

[b] State nature of intended works.

[c] [d] Not used.

[e] Delete if not provided.

[f] See the notes on the JCT 80 Fifth recital in Practice Note 27 'The application of the Construction (Design and Management) Regulations 1994 to Contracts on JCT Standard Forms of Contract' for the statutory obligations which must have been fulfilled before the Contractor can begin carrying out the Works.

Appendix 1

Now it is hereby agreed as follows

Contractor's
obligations

Article 1
For the consideration hereinafter mentioned the Contractor will upon and subject to the Contract Documents carry out and complete the Works shown upon, described by or referred to in those Documents.

Contract Sum

Article 2
The Employer will pay to the Contractor the sum of _____

_____(£_____ · _____)
(hereinafter referred to as 'the Contract Sum') or such other sum as shall become payable hereunder at the times and in the manner specified in the Conditions.

Architect

Article 3
The term 'the Architect' in the Conditions shall mean

_____

of _____

_____

or, in the event of his death or ceasing to be the Architect for the purpose of this Contract, such other person as the Employer shall nominate within a reasonable time but in any case no later than 21 days after such death or cessation for that purpose, not being a person to whom the Contractor no later than 7 days after such nomination shall object for reasons considered to be sufficient by a person appointed pursuant to the procedures under this Contract relevant to the resolution of disputes or differences. Provided always that no person subsequently appointed to be the Architect under this Contract shall be entitled to disregard or overrule any certificate or opinion or decision or approval or instruction given or expressed by the Architect for the time being.

Footnotes   [g] [h] [i] Not used.

311

Appendix 1

Article 4

Quantity
Surveyor

The term 'the Quantity Surveyor' in the Conditions shall mean

_____

of _____

_____

or, in the event of his death or ceasing to be the Quantity Surveyor for the purpose of this
Contract, such other person as the Employer shall nominate within a reasonable time but in
any case no later than 21 days after such death or cessation for that purpose, not being a
person to whom the Contractor no later than 7 days after such nomination shall object for
reasons considered to be sufficient by a person appointed pursuant to the procedures under
this Contract relevant to the resolution of disputes or differences.

Article 5

Dispute or difference –
adjudication

If any dispute or difference arises under this Contract either Party may refer it to adjudication
in accordance with clause 41A.

Article 6·1 [k]

Planning
Supervisor

The term 'the Planning Supervisor' in the Conditions shall mean the Architect

or _____

of _____

_____

or in the event of the death of the Planning Supervisor or his ceasing to be the Planning
Supervisor such other person as the Employer shall appoint as the Planning Supervisor
pursuant to regulation 6(5) of the CDM Regulations.

Article 6·2 [k]

Principal
Contractor

The term 'the Principal Contractor' in the Conditions shall mean the Contractor, or, in the
event of his ceasing to be the Principal Contractor, such other contractor as the Employer
shall appoint as the Principal Contractor pursuant to regulation 6(5) of the CDM Regulations.

Footnotes

[j] Not used.

[k] Delete articles 6·1 and 6·2 when only regulations 7
and 13 of the CDM Regulations apply; see Appendix
under the reference to the Fifth recital.

312

Appendix 1

Article 7A

Dispute or difference –
arbitration

Where the entry in the Appendix stating that "Clause 41B applies" has not been deleted then, subject to article 5, if any dispute or difference as to any matter or thing of whatsoever nature arising under this Contract or in connection therewith, except in connection with the enforcement of any decision of an Adjudicator appointed to determine a dispute or difference arising thereunder, shall arise between the Parties either during the progress or after the completion or abandonment of the Works or after the determination of the employment of the Contractor, except under clause 31 *(statutory tax deduction scheme)* to the extent provided in clause 31·9 or under clause 3 of the VAT Agreement, it shall be referred to arbitration in accordance with clause 41B and the JCT 1998 edition of the Construction Industry Model Arbitration Rules (CIMAR). [l]

Article 7B

Dispute or difference –
legal proceedings

Where the entry in the Appendix stating that "Clause 41B applies" has been deleted then, subject to article 5, if any dispute or difference as to any matter or thing of whatsoever nature arising under this Contract or in connection therewith shall arise between the Parties either during the progress or after the completion or abandonment of the Works or after the determination of the employment of the Contractor it shall be determined by legal proceedings.

Footnotes

[l] The JCT 1998 edition of the Construction Industry Model Arbitration Rules (CIMAR) contains procedures for beginning an arbitration and the appointment of an arbitrator, the consolidation or joinder of disputes including related disputes between different parties engaged under different contracts on the same project, and for the conduct of arbitral proceedings. The objective of CIMAR is the fair, impartial, speedy, cost-effective and binding resolution of construction disputes. The JCT 1998 edition of the Construction Industry Model Arbitration Rules (CIMAR) includes additional rules concerning the calling of preliminary meetings and supplemental and advisory procedures which may, with the agreement of the parties, be used with Rule 7 (short hearing), 8 (documents only) or 9 (full procedure).

[m] Not used.

313

Appendix 1

[A1] **AS WITNESS THE HANDS OF THE PARTIES HERETO**

[A1] For Agreement executed under hand and NOT as a deed.

[A1] Signed by or on behalf of the Employer _____

      in the presence of:

[A1] Signed by or on behalf of the Contractor _____

      in the presence of:

[A2] For Agreement executed as a deed under the law of England and Wales by a company or other body corporate: insert the name of the party mentioned and identified on page 1 and then use *either* [A3] and [A4] *or* [A5]. If the party is an *individual* see note [A6].

[A3] For use if the party is using its common seal, which should be affixed under the party's name.

[A4] For use of the party's officers authorised to affix its common seal.

[A5] For use if the party is a company registered under the Companies Acts which is not using a common seal: insert the names of the two officers by whom the company is acting *who MUST be either a director and the company secretary or two directors*, and insert their signatures with 'Director' or 'Secretary' as appropriate. *This method of execution is NOT valid for local authorities or certain other bodies incorporated by Act of Parliament or by charter if exempted under s. 718(2) of the Companies Act 1985.*

[A2] **EXECUTED AS A DEED BY THE EMPLOYER**
      hereinbefore mentioned namely _____

[A3]   by affixing hereto its common seal

[A4]   in the presence of:

* OR —

[A5]   acting by a director and its secretary*/two directors* whose signatures are here
      subscribed:
      namely _____

      [Signature] _____ *DIRECTOR*

      and _____

      [Signature] _____ *SECRETARY*/DIRECTOR**

[A2] **AND AS A DEED BY THE CONTRACTOR**
      hereinbefore mentioned namely _____

[A3]   by affixing hereto its common seal

[A4]   in the presence of:

[A6] If executed as a deed by an *individual*: insert the name at [A2], delete the words at [A3], substitute 'whose signature is here subscribed' and insert the individual's signature. The individual MUST sign in the presence of a witness who attests the signature. Insert at [A4] the signature and name of the witness. Sealing by an individual is not required.

Other attestation clauses are required under the law of Scotland.

* OR —

[A5]   acting by a director and its secretary*/two directors* whose signatures are here
      subscribed:
      namely _____

      [Signature] _____ *DIRECTOR*

      and _____

      [Signature] _____ *SECRETARY*/DIRECTOR**

Appendix 1

The Conditions

Part 1: General

1   **Interpretation, definitions etc.**

<table>
<tr><td>Method of reference to clauses</td><td>1·1</td><td>Unless otherwise specifically stated a reference in the Articles of Agreement, the Conditions or the Appendix to any clause means that clause of the Conditions.</td></tr>
<tr><td>Articles etc. to be read as a whole</td><td>1·2</td><td>The Articles of Agreement, the Conditions and the Appendix are to be read as a whole and the effect or operation of any article or clause in the Conditions or item in or entry in the Appendix must therefore unless otherwise specifically stated be read subject to any relevant qualification or modification in any other article or any of the clauses in the Conditions or item in or entry in the Appendix.</td></tr>
<tr><td>Definitions</td><td>1·3</td><td>Unless the context otherwise requires or the Articles or the Conditions or an item in or entry in the Appendix specifically otherwise provides, the following words and phrases in the Articles of Agreement, the Conditions and the Appendix shall have the meanings given below or as ascribed in the article, clause or Appendix item to which reference is made:</td></tr>
</table>

Word or phrase	Meaning
3·3A Quotation:	a Quotation by a Nominated Sub-Contractor pursuant to **clause 3·3A** of Conditions NSC/C *(Conditions of Nominated Sub-Contract)*.
13A Quotation:	see **clause 13A·1·1**.
Activity Schedule:	the schedule of activities as attached to the Appendix with each activity priced and with the sum of those prices being the Contract Sum excluding provisional sums, prime cost sums and any Contractor's profit thereon and the value of work for which Approximate Quantities are included in the Contract Bills: see **clause 30·2·1**.
Adjudication Agreement:	see **clause 41A·2·1**.
Adjudicator:	any individual appointed pursuant to **clause 41A** as the Adjudicator.
All Risks Insurance:	see **clause 22·2**.
Analysis:	see **clause 42·13**.
Appendix:	the Appendix to the Conditions as completed by the parties.
Approximate Quantity:	a quantity in the Contract Bills identified therein as an approximate quantity. [n]
Arbitrator:	the person appointed under **clause 41B** to be the Arbitrator.
Architect:	the person entitled to the use of the name 'Architect' and named in **article 3** or any successor duly appointed under **article 3** or otherwise agreed as the person to be the Architect.
Articles or Articles of Agreement:	the Articles of Agreement to which the Conditions are annexed, and references to any recital are to the recitals set out before the Articles.
Base Date:	the date stated in the **Appendix**.

See next page for footnote [n].

Appendix 1

Word or phrase	Meaning
CDM Regulations:	the Construction (Design and Management) Regulations 1994 or any remaking thereof or any amendment to a regulation therein.
Certificate of Completion of Making Good Defects:	see **clause 17·4**.
Completion Date:	the Date for Completion as fixed and stated in the **Appendix** or any date fixed either under **clause 25** or in a confirmed acceptance of a 13A Quotation.
Conditions:	the clauses 1 to 37, either clause 38 or 39 or 40, clauses 41A, 41B, 41C and 42 and the Supplemental Provisions ('the VAT Agreement') annexed to the Articles of Agreement.
confirmed acceptance:	see **clause 13A·3·2**.
Contract Bills:	the Bills of Quantities referred to in the **First recital** which have been priced by the Contractor and signed by or on behalf of the Parties to this Contract.
Contract Documents:	the Contract Drawings, the Contract Bills, the Articles of Agreement, the Conditions and the Appendix.
Contract Drawings:	the Drawings referred to in the **First recital** which have been signed by or on behalf of the Parties to this Contract.
Contract Sum:	the sum named in **article 2** but subject to **clause 15·2**.
Contractor:	the person named as Contractor in the Articles of Agreement.
Contractor's Statement:	see **clause 42**.
Date for Completion:	the date fixed and stated in the **Appendix**.
Date of Possession:	the date stated in the **Appendix** under the reference to **clause 23·1**.
Defects Liability Period:	the period named in the **Appendix** under the reference to **clause 17·2**.
Domestic Sub-Contractor:	see **clause 19·2**.
Employer:	the person named as Employer in the Articles of Agreement.

Footnote

[n] General Rules 10.1 to 10.6 of the Standard Method of Measurement 7th Edition provide:

10.1
Where work can be described and given in items in accordance with these rules but the quantity of work required cannot be accurately determined, an estimate of the quantity shall be given and identified as an approximate quantity.

10.2
Where work cannot be described and given in items in accordance with these rules it shall be given as a Provisional Sum and identified as for either defined or undefined work as appropriate.

10.3
A Provisional Sum for defined work is a sum provided for work which is not completely designed but for which the following information shall be provided:
(a) The nature and construction of the work.
(b) A statement of how and where the work is fixed to the building and what other work is to be fixed thereto.
(c) A quantity or quantities which indicate the scope and extent of the work.
(d) Any specific limitations and the like identified in Section A35.

10.4
Where Provisional Sums are given for defined work the Contractor will be deemed to have made due allowance in programming, planning and pricing Preliminaries. Any such allowance will only be subject to adjustment in those circumstances where a variation in respect of other work measured in detail in accordance with the rules would give rise to adjustment.

10.5
A Provisional Sum for undefined work is a sum provided for work where the information required in accordance with rule 10.3 cannot be given.

10.6
Where Provisional Sums are given for undefined work the Contractor will be deemed not to have made any allowance in programming, planning and pricing Preliminaries.

Appendix 1

Word or phrase	Meaning
Excepted Risks:	ionising radiations or contamination by radioactivity from any nuclear fuel or from any nuclear waste from the combustion of nuclear fuel, radioactive toxic explosive or other hazardous properties of any explosive nuclear assembly or nuclear component thereof, pressure waves caused by aircraft or other aerial devices travelling at sonic or supersonic speeds.
Final Certificate:	the certificate to which **clause 30·8** refers.
Health and Safety Plan:	where it is stated in the Appendix that all the CDM Regulations apply, the plan provided to the Principal Contractor and developed by him to comply with regulation 15(4) of the CDM Regulations and, for the purpose of regulation 10 of the CDM Regulations, received by the Employer before any construction work under this Contract has started; and any further development of that plan by the Principal Contractor during the progress of the Works.
Information Release Schedule:	the schedule referred to in the **Sixth recital** or as varied pursuant to **clause 5·4·1**.
Interim Certificate:	any one of the certificates to which **clauses 30·1** and **30·7** and the entry in the **Appendix** under the reference to **clause 30·1·3** refer.
Joint Fire Code:	the Joint Code of Practice on the Protection from Fire of Construction Sites and Buildings Undergoing Renovation which is published by the Building Employers Confederation (now Construction Confederation), the Loss Prevention Council and the National Contractors' Group with the support of the Association of British Insurers, the Chief and Assistant Chief Fire Officers Association and the London Fire Brigade which is current at the Base Date.
Joint Names Policy:	see **clause 22·2**.
Nominated Sub-Contract:	an Agreement NSC/A *(Articles of Nominated Sub-Contract Agreement)*, the Conditions NSC/C *(Conditions of Nominated Sub-Contract)* incorporated therein and the documents annexed thereto.
Nominated Sub-Contractor:	see **clause 35·1**.
Nominated Supplier:	see **clause 36·1·1**.
Numbered Documents:	the Numbered Documents annexed to Agreement NSC/A *(Articles of Nominated Sub-Contract Agreement)*.
Parties:	the Employer and the Contractor named as the Employer and the Contractor in the Articles of Agreement.
Party:	the Employer or the Contractor named as the Employer or the Contractor in the Articles of Agreement.
Performance Specified Work:	see **clause 42·1**.
Period of Interim Certificates:	the period named in the **Appendix** under the reference to **clause 30·1·3**.
person:	an individual, firm (partnership) or body corporate.
Planning Supervisor:	the Architect or the other person named in **article 6·1** or any successor duly appointed by the Employer as the Planning Supervisor pursuant to regulation 6(5) of the CDM Regulations.

317

Appendix 1

Word or phrase	Meaning
Practical Completion:	see **clause 17·1**.
Price Statement:	see **clause 13·4·1·2 Alternative A**.
Principal Contractor:	the Contractor or any other contractor duly appointed by the Employer as the Principal Contractor pursuant to regulation 6(5) of the CDM Regulations.
provisional sum:	includes a sum provided for work whether or not identified as being for defined or undefined work* and a provisional sum for Performance Specified Work: see **clause 42·7**.
Public Holiday:	Christmas Day, Good Friday or a day which under the Banking and Financial Dealings Act 1971 is a bank holiday. [o]
Quantity Surveyor:	the person named in **article 4** or any successor duly appointed under **article 4** or otherwise agreed as the person to be the Quantity Surveyor.
Relevant Event:	any one of the events set out in **clause 25·4**.
Retention:	see **clause 30·2**.
Retention Percentage:	see **clause 30·4·1·1** and any entry in the **Appendix** under the reference to **clause 30·4·1·1**.
Site Materials:	all unfixed materials and goods delivered to, placed on or adjacent to the Works and intended for incorporation therein.
Specified Perils:	fire, lightning, explosion, storm, tempest, flood, bursting or overflowing of water tanks, apparatus or pipes, earthquake, aircraft and other aerial devices or articles dropped therefrom, riot and civil commotion, but excluding Excepted Risks.
Statutory Requirements:	see **clause 6·1·1**.
Valuation:	a valuation by the Quantity Surveyor pursuant to **clause 13·4·1·2 Alternative B** or the amount of any Price Statement or any part thereof accepted pursuant to **clause 13·4·1·2 paragraph A2** or amended Price Statement or any part thereof accepted pursuant to **clause 13·4·1·2 paragraph A4·2**.
Variation:	see **clause 13·1**.
VAT Agreement:	see **clause 15·1**.
Works:	the works briefly described in the **First recital** and shown upon, described by or referred to in the Contract Documents and including any changes made to these works in accordance with this Contract.

1·4 [Number not used]

Contractor's responsibility

1·5 Notwithstanding any obligation of the Architect to the Employer and whether or not the Employer appoints a clerk of works, the Contractor shall remain wholly responsible for carrying out and completing the Works in all respects in accordance with the Conditions, whether or not the Architect or the clerk of works, if appointed, at any time goes on to the Works or to any workshop or other place where work is being prepared to inspect the same or otherwise, or the Architect includes the value of any work, materials or goods in a certificate for payment or issues the certificate of Practical Completion or the Certificate of Completion of Making Good Defects.

Footnotes

*See footnote [n] to clause 1·3 *(Definitions)*.

[o] Amend as necessary if different Public Holidays are applicable.

318

Appendix 1

<table>
<tr>
<td>Reappointment of Planning Supervisor or Principal Contractor – notification to Contractor</td>
<td>1·6</td>
<td>If the Employer pursuant to article 6·1 or to article 6·2 by a further appointment replaces the Planning Supervisor referred to in, or appointed pursuant to, article 6·1 or replaces the Contractor or any other contractor appointed as the Principal Contractor, the Employer shall immediately upon such further appointment notify the Contractor in writing of the name and address of the new appointee.</td>
</tr>
<tr>
<td>Giving or service of notices or other documents</td>
<td>1·7</td>
<td>Where the Contract does not specifically state the manner of giving or service of any notice or other document required or authorised in pursuance of this Contract such notice or other document shall be given or served by any effective means to any agreed address. If no address has been agreed then if given or served by being addressed, pre-paid and delivered by post to the addressee's last known principal business address or, where the addressee is a body corporate, to the body's registered or principal office it shall be treated as having been effectively given or served.</td>
</tr>
<tr>
<td>Reckoning periods of days</td>
<td>1·8</td>
<td>Where under this Contract an act is required to be done within a specified period of days after or from a specified date, the period shall begin immediately after that date. Where the period would include a day which is a Public Holiday that day shall be excluded.</td>
</tr>
<tr>
<td>Employer's Representative</td>
<td>1·9</td>
<td>The Employer may give written notice to the Contractor that from the date stated in the notice the individual identified in the notice will exercise all the functions ascribed to the Employer in the Conditions subject to any exceptions stated in the notice. [p]</td>
</tr>
<tr>
<td>Applicable law</td>
<td>1·10</td>
<td>Whatever the nationality, residence or domicile of the Employer, the Contractor or any sub-contractor or supplier and wherever the Works are situated the law of England shall be the law applicable to this Contract. [q]</td>
</tr>
<tr>
<td>Electronic data interchange</td>
<td>1·11</td>
<td>Where the Appendix so states, the 'Supplemental Provisions for EDI' annexed to the Conditions shall apply.</td>
</tr>
</table>

2   Contractor's obligations

<table>
<tr>
<td>Contract Documents</td>
<td>2·1</td>
<td></td>
<td>The Contractor shall upon and subject to the Conditions carry out and complete the Works in compliance with the Contract Documents, using materials and workmanship of the quality and standards therein specified, provided that where and to the extent that approval of the quality of materials or of the standards of workmanship is a matter for the opinion of the Architect such quality and standards shall be to the reasonable satisfaction of the Architect.</td>
</tr>
<tr>
<td>Contract Bills – relation to Articles, Conditions and Appendix</td>
<td>2·2</td>
<td>·1</td>
<td>Nothing contained in the Contract Bills shall override or modify the application or interpretation of that which is contained in the Articles of Agreement, the Conditions or the Appendix.</td>
</tr>
<tr>
<td></td>
<td>2·2</td>
<td>·2</td>
<td>Subject always to clause 2·2·1:</td>
</tr>
<tr>
<td>Preparation of Contract Bills – errors in preparation etc.</td>
<td></td>
<td>·2   ·1</td>
<td>the Contract Bills (or any addendum bill issued as part of the information referred to in clause 13A·1·1 for the purpose of obtaining a 13A Quotation), unless otherwise specifically stated therein in respect of any specified item or items, are to have been prepared in accordance with the Standard Method of Measurement of Building Works, 7th Edition, published by the Royal Institution of Chartered Surveyors and the Building Employers Confederation (now Construction Confederation);</td>
</tr>
<tr>
<td></td>
<td></td>
<td>·2   ·2</td>
<td>if in the Contract Bills (or in any addendum bill issued as part of the information referred to in clause 13A·1·1 for the purpose of obtaining a 13A Quotation which Quotation has been accepted by the Employer) there is any departure from the method of preparation referred to in clause 2·2·2·1 or any error in description or in quantity or omission of items (including any error in or omission of information in any item which is the subject of a provisional sum for defined work*) then such departure or error or omission shall not vitiate this Contract but the departure or error or omission shall be corrected; where the description of a provisional sum for defined work* does not provide the information required by General Rule 10.3 in the Standard Method of Measurement the correction shall be made by correcting the description so that it does provide such information; any such correction under</td>
</tr>
</table>

2·2 ·2 ·2 *continued*

this clause 2·2·2·2 shall be treated as if it were a Variation required by an instruction of the Architect under clause 13·2.

Discrepancies in or divergences between documents

2·3 If the Contractor shall find any discrepancy in or divergence between any two or more of the following documents, including a divergence between parts of any one of them or between documents of the same description, namely:

2·3 ·1 the Contract Drawings,

2·3 ·2 the Contract Bills,

2·3 ·3 any instruction issued by the Architect under the Conditions (save insofar as any such instruction requires a Variation in accordance with the provisions of clause 13·2),

2·3 ·4 any drawings or documents issued by the Architect under clause 5·3·1·1, 5·4·1, 5·4·2 or 7, and

2·3 ·5 the Numbered Documents,

he shall immediately give to the Architect a written notice specifying the discrepancy or divergence, and the Architect shall issue instructions in regard thereto.

2·4 ·1 If the Contractor shall find any discrepancy or divergence between his Statement in respect of Performance Specified Work and any instruction of the Architect issued after receipt by the Architect of the Contractor's Statement, he shall immediately give to the Architect a written notice specifying the discrepancy or divergence, and the Architect shall issue instructions in regard thereto.

2·4 ·2 If the Contractor or the Architect shall find any discrepancy in the Contractor's Statement, the Contractor shall correct the Statement to remove the discrepancy and inform the Architect in writing of the correction made. Such correction shall be at no cost to the Employer.

3 Contract Sum – additions or deductions – adjustment – Interim Certificates

Where in the Conditions it is provided that an amount is to be added to or deducted from the Contract Sum or dealt with by adjustment of the Contract Sum then as soon as such amount is ascertained in whole or in part such amount shall be taken into account in the computation of the next Interim Certificate following such whole or partial ascertainment.

4 Architect's instructions

Compliance with Architect's instructions

4·1 ·1 The Contractor shall forthwith comply with all instructions issued to him by the Architect in regard to any matter in respect of which the Architect is expressly empowered by the Conditions to issue instructions; save that:

·1 ·1 where such instruction is one requiring a Variation within the meaning of clause 13·1·2 the Contractor need not comply to the extent that he makes reasonable objection in writing to the Architect to such compliance;

·1 ·2 where pursuant to clause 13·2·3 clause 13A applies to an instruction, the Variation to which that instruction refers shall not be carried out until

– the Architect has issued to the Contractor a confirmed acceptance of the 13A Quotation

or

– an instruction in respect of the Variation has been issued under clause 13A·4·1.

4·1 ·2 If within 7 days after receipt of a written notice from the Architect requiring compliance with an instruction the Contractor does not comply therewith, then the Employer may employ and pay other persons to execute any work whatsoever which may be necessary to give effect to such instruction; and all costs incurred in connection with

Appendix 1

4·1 **·2** *continued*

such employment may be deducted by him from any monies due or to become due to the Contractor under this Contract or may be recoverable from the Contractor by the Employer as a debt.

Provisions empowering instructions

4·2 Upon receipt of what purports to be an instruction issued to him by the Architect the Contractor may request the Architect to specify in writing the provision of the Conditions which empowers the issue of the said instruction. The Architect shall forthwith comply with any such request, and if the Contractor shall thereafter comply with the said instruction (neither Party before such compliance having invoked the procedures under this Contract relevant to the resolution of disputes or differences in order that it may be decided whether the provision specified by the Architect empowers the issue of the said instruction), then the issue of the same shall be deemed for all the purposes of this Contract to have been empowered by the provision of the Conditions specified by the Architect in answer to the Contractor's request.

Instructions to be in writing

4·3 **·1** All instructions issued by the Architect shall be issued in writing.

Procedure if instructions given otherwise than in writing

4·3 **·2** If the Architect purports to issue an instruction otherwise than in writing it shall be of no immediate effect, but shall be confirmed in writing by the Contractor to the Architect within 7 days, and if not dissented from in writing by the Architect to the Contractor within 7 days from receipt of the Contractor's confirmation shall take effect as from the expiration of the latter said 7 days. Provided always:

·2 **·1** that if the Architect within 7 days of giving such an instruction otherwise than in writing shall himself confirm the same in writing, then the Contractor shall not be obliged to confirm as aforesaid, and the said instruction shall take effect as from the date of the Architect's confirmation; and

·2 **·2** that if neither the Contractor nor the Architect shall confirm such an instruction in the manner and at the time aforesaid but the Contractor shall nevertheless comply with the same, then the Architect may confirm the same in writing at any time prior to the issue of the Final Certificate, and the said instruction shall thereupon be deemed to have taken effect on the date on which it was issued otherwise than in writing by the Architect.

5 **Contract Documents – other documents – issue of certificates**

Custody of Contract Bills and Contract Drawings

5·1 The Contract Drawings and the Contract Bills shall remain in the custody of the Architect or the Quantity Surveyor so as to be available at all reasonable times for the inspection of the Employer and of the Contractor.

Copies of documents

5·2 Immediately after the execution of this Contract the Architect without charge to the Contractor shall provide him (unless he shall have been previously so provided) with:

5·2 **·1** one copy certified on behalf of the Employer of the Contract Documents;

5·2 **·2** two further copies of the Contract Drawings; and

5·2 **·3** two copies of the unpriced Bills of Quantities.

Descriptive schedules etc. – master programme of Contractor

5·3 **·1** So soon as is possible after the execution of this Contract:

·1 **·1** the Architect without charge to the Contractor shall provide him (unless he shall have been previously so provided) with 2 copies of any descriptive schedules or other like documents necessary for use in carrying out the Works; and

·1 **·2** the Contractor without charge to the Employer shall provide the Architect (unless he shall have been previously so provided) with 2 copies of his master programme for the execution of the Works and within 14 days of any decision by the Architect under clause 25·3·1 or of the date of issue of a confirmed acceptance of a 13A Quotation with 2 copies of any amendments and revisions to take account of that decision or of that confirmed acceptance. [r]

Footnote [r] To be deleted if no master programme is required.

321

5·3 ·2   Nothing contained in the descriptive schedules or other like documents referred to in clause 5·3·1·1 (nor in the master programme for the execution of the Works or any amendment to that programme or revision therein referred to in clause 5·3·1·2) shall impose any obligation beyond those imposed by the Contract Documents. [s]

Information Release Schedule   **5·4** ·1   Except to the extent that the Architect is prevented by the act or default of the Contractor or of any person for whom the Contractor is responsible, the Architect shall ensure that 2 copies of the information referred to in the Information Release Schedule are released at the time stated in the Schedule provided that the Employer and Contractor may agree, which agreement shall not be unreasonably withheld or delayed, to vary any such time.

Provision of further drawings or details   **5·4** ·2   Except to the extent included in the Information Release Schedule the Architect as and when from time to time may be necessary without charge to the Contractor shall provide him with 2 copies of such further drawings or details which are reasonably necessary to explain and amplify the Contract Drawings and shall issue such instructions (including those for or in regard to the expenditure of provisional sums) to enable the Contractor to carry out and complete the Works in accordance with the Conditions. Such provision shall be made or instructions given at a time when, having regard to the progress of the Works, or, where in the opinion of the Architect Practical Completion of the Works is likely to be achieved before the Completion Date, having regard to such Completion Date, it was reasonably necessary for the Contractor to receive such further drawings or details or instructions. Where the Contractor is aware and has reasonable grounds for believing that the Architect is not so aware of the time when it is necessary for the Contractor to receive such further drawings or details or instructions the Contractor shall, if and to the extent that it is reasonably practicable to do so, advise the Architect of the time sufficiently in advance of when the Contractor needs such further drawings or details or instructions to enable the Architect to fulfill his obligations under clause 5·4·2.

Availability of certain documents   **5·5**   The Contractor shall keep one copy of the Contract Drawings, one copy of the unpriced Bills of Quantities, one copy of the descriptive schedules or other like documents referred to in clause 5·3·1·1, one copy of the master programme referred to in clause 5·3·1·2 (unless clause 5·3·1·2 has been deleted) and one copy of the drawings and details referred to in clause 5·4·2 upon the site so as to be available to the Architect or his representative at all reasonable times.

Return of drawings etc.   **5·6**   Upon final payment under clause 30·8 the Contractor shall if so requested by the Architect forthwith return to him all drawings, details, descriptive schedules and other documents of a like nature which bear the name of the Architect.

Limits to use of documents   **5·7**   None of the documents provided in accordance with the Information Release Schedule or mentioned in clause 5 shall be used by the Contractor for any purpose other than this Contract, and neither the Employer, the Architect nor the Quantity Surveyor shall divulge or use except for the purposes of this Contract any of the rates or prices in the Contract Bills.

Issue of Architect's certificates   **5·8**   Except where otherwise specifically so provided any certificate to be issued by the Architect under the Conditions shall be issued to the Employer, and immediately upon the issue of any such certificate the Architect shall send a duplicate copy thereof to the Contractor.

Supply of as-built drawings etc. – Performance Specified Work   **5·9**   Before the date of Practical Completion the Contractor shall without further charge to the Employer supply to the Employer such drawings and information showing or describing any Performance Specified Work as built, and concerning the maintenance and operation of any Performance Specified Work including any installations forming a part thereof, as may be specified in the Contract Bills or in an instruction on the expenditure of the provisional sum for the Performance Specified Work.

6   **Statutory obligations, notices, fees and charges**

Statutory Requirements   **6·1** ·1   Subject to clause 6·1·5 the Contractor shall comply with, and give all notices required by, any Act of Parliament, any instrument, rule or order made under any Act of Parliament, or any regulation or byelaw of any local authority or of any statutory undertaker which has any jurisdiction with regard to the Works or with whose systems the same are or will be connected (all requirements to be so complied with being referred to in the Conditions as 'the Statutory Requirements').

Footnote   [s] Words in parentheses to be deleted if no master programme is required.

322

Appendix 1

6·1   ·2   If the Contractor shall find any divergence between the Statutory Requirements and all or any of the documents referred to in clause 2·3 or between the Statutory Requirements and any instruction of the Architect requiring a Variation issued in accordance with clause 13·2, he shall immediately give to the Architect a written notice specifying the divergence.

6·1   ·3   If the Contractor gives notice under clause 6·1·2 or if the Architect shall otherwise discover or receive notice of a divergence between the Statutory Requirements and all or any of the documents referred to in clause 2·3 or between the Statutory Requirements and any instruction requiring a Variation issued in accordance with clause 13·2, the Architect shall within 7 days of the discovery or receipt of a notice issue instructions in relation to the divergence. If and insofar as the instructions require the Works to be varied, they shall be treated as if they were Architect's instructions requiring a Variation issued in accordance with clause 13·2.

6·1   ·4   ·1   If in any emergency compliance with clause 6·1·1 requires the Contractor to supply materials or execute work before receiving instructions under clause 6·1·3 the Contractor shall supply such limited materials and execute such limited work as are reasonably necessary to secure immediate compliance with the Statutory Requirements.

　　　　·4   ·2   The Contractor shall forthwith inform the Architect of the emergency and of the steps that he is taking under clause 6·1·4·1.

　　　　·4   ·3   Work executed and materials supplied by the Contractor under clause 6·1·4·1 shall be treated as if they had been executed and supplied pursuant to an Architect's instruction requiring a Variation issued in accordance with clause 13·2 provided that the emergency arose because of a divergence between the Statutory Requirements and all or any of the documents referred to in clause 2·3 or between the Statutory Requirements and any instruction requiring a Variation issued in accordance with clause 13·2, and the Contractor has complied with clause 6·1·4·2.

6·1   ·5   Provided that the Contractor complies with clause 6·1·2, the Contractor shall not be liable to the Employer under this Contract if the Works do not comply with the Statutory Requirements where and to the extent that such non-compliance of the Works results from the Contractor having carried out work in accordance with the documents referred to in clause 2·3 or with any instruction requiring a Variation issued by the Architect in accordance with clause 13·2.

Divergence –
Statutory
Requirements and
the Contractor's
Statement

6·1   ·6   If the Contractor or the Architect shall find any divergence between the Statutory Requirements and any Contractor's Statement he shall immediately give the other a written notice specifying the divergence. The Contractor shall inform the Architect in writing of his proposed amendment for removing the divergence; and the Architect shall issue instructions in regard thereto. The Contractor's compliance with such instructions shall be subject to clause 42·15 and at no cost to the Employer save as provided in clause 6·1·7.

Change in
Statutory
Requirements
after Base Date

6·1   ·7   If after the Base Date there is a change in the Statutory Requirements which necessitates some alteration or modification to any Performance Specified Work such alteration or modification shall be treated as if it were an instruction of the Architect under clause 13·2 requiring a Variation.

Fees or charges

6·2   The Contractor shall pay and indemnify the Employer against liability in respect of any fees or charges (including any rates or taxes) legally demandable under any Act of Parliament, any instrument, rule or order made under any Act of Parliament, or any regulation or byelaw of any local authority or of any statutory undertaker in respect of the Works. The amount of any such fees or charges (including any rates or taxes other than value added tax) shall be added to the Contract Sum unless they:

6·2   ·1   arise in respect of work executed or materials or goods supplied by a local authority or statutory undertaker as a Nominated Sub-Contractor or as a Nominated Supplier; or

6·2   ·2   are priced in the Contract Bills; or

6·2   ·3   are stated by way of a provisional sum in the Contract Bills.

Exclusion of
provisions on
Domestic Sub-
Contractors and
Nominated Sub-
Contractors

6·3   The provisions of clauses 19 and 35 shall not apply to the execution of part of the Works by a local authority or a statutory undertaker executing such work solely in pursuance of its statutory obligations and such bodies shall not be sub-contractors within the terms of this Contract.

Appendix 1

6A   **Provisions for use where the Appendix states that all the CDM Regulations apply**

Employer's
obligation –
Planning
Supervisor –
Principal
Contractor

6A·1   The Employer shall ensure:

that the Planning Supervisor carries out all the duties of a planning supervisor under the CDM Regulations; and

where the Contractor is not the Principal Contractor, that the Principal Contractor carries out all the duties of a principal contractor under the CDM Regulations.

Contractor –
compliance with
duties of a
principal
contractor

6A·2   Where the Contractor is and while he remains the Principal Contractor, the Contractor shall comply with all the duties of a principal contractor set out in the CDM Regulations; and in particular shall ensure that the Health and Safety Plan has the features required by regulation 15(4) of the CDM Regulations. Any amendment by the Contractor to the Health and Safety Plan shall be notified to the Employer, who shall where relevant thereupon notify the Planning Supervisor and the Architect.

Successor
appointed to the
Contractor as
Principal
Contractor

6A·3   Clause 6A·3 applies from the time the Employer pursuant to article 6·2 appoints a successor to the Contractor as the Principal Contractor. The Contractor shall comply at no cost to the Employer with all the reasonable requirements of the Principal Contractor to the extent that such requirements are necessary for compliance with the CDM Regulations; and, notwithstanding clause 25, no extension of time shall be given in respect of such compliance.

Health and safety
file

6A·4   Within the time reasonably required in writing by the Planning Supervisor to the Contractor, the Contractor shall provide, and shall ensure that any sub-contractor, through the Contractor, provides, such information to the Planning Supervisor or, if the Contractor is not the Principal Contractor, to the Principal Contractor as the Planning Supervisor reasonably requires for the preparation, pursuant to regulations 14(d), 14(e) and 14(f) of the CDM Regulations, of the health and safety file required by the CDM Regulations.

7   Levels and setting out of the Works

The Architect shall determine any levels which may be required for the execution of the Works, and shall provide the Contractor by way of accurately dimensioned drawings with such information as shall enable the Contractor to set out the Works at ground level. The Contractor shall be responsible for and shall, at no cost to the Employer, amend any errors arising from his own inaccurate setting out. With the consent of the Employer the Architect may instruct that such errors shall not be amended and an appropriate deduction for such errors not required to be amended shall be made from the Contract Sum.

8   Work, materials and goods

Kinds and
standards etc.

8·1   ·1   All materials and goods shall, so far as procurable, be of the kinds and standards described in the Contract Bills, and also, in regard to any Performance Specified Work, in the Contractor's Statement, provided that materials and goods shall be to the reasonable satisfaction of the Architect where and to the extent that this is required in accordance with clause 2·1.

8·1   ·2   All workmanship shall be of the standards described in the Contract Bills, and also, in regard to any Performance Specified Work, in the Contractor's Statement, or, to the extent that no such standards are described in the Contract Bills, or, in regard to any Performance Specified Work, in the Contractor's Statement, shall be of a standard appropriate to the Works, provided that workmanship shall be to the reasonable satisfaction of the Architect where and to the extent that this is required in accordance with clause 2·1.

8·1   ·3   All work shall be carried out in a proper and workmanlike manner and in accordance with the Health and Safety Plan.

Substitution of
materials or
goods –
Performance
Specified Work

8·1   ·4   The Contractor shall not substitute any materials or goods described in any Contractor's Statement for Performance Specified Work without the Architect's consent in writing which consent shall not be unreasonably withheld or delayed. No such consent shall relieve the Contractor of any other obligation under this Contract.

Vouchers – materials and goods	8·2	·1	The Contractor shall upon the request of the Architect provide him with vouchers to prove that the materials and goods comply with clause 8·1.
Executed work	8·2	·2	In respect of any materials, goods or workmanship, as comprised in executed work, which are to be to the reasonable satisfaction of the Architect in accordance with clause 2·1, the Architect shall express any dissatisfaction within a reasonable time from the execution of the unsatisfactory work.
Inspection – tests	8·3		The Architect may issue instructions requiring the Contractor to open up for inspection any work covered up or to arrange for or carry out any test of any materials or goods (whether or not already incorporated in the Works) or of any executed work, and the cost of such opening up or testing (together with the cost of making good in consequence thereof) shall be added to the Contract Sum unless provided for in the Contract Bills or unless the inspection or test shows that the materials, goods or work are not in accordance with this Contract.
Powers of Architect – work not in accordance with the Contract	8·4		If any work, materials or goods are not in accordance with this Contract the Architect, without prejudice to the generality of his powers, may:
	8·4	·1	notwithstanding the power of the Architect under clause 8·4·2, issue instructions in regard to the removal from the site of all or any of such work, materials or goods; and/or
	8·4	·2	after consultation with the Contractor (who shall immediately consult with any relevant Nominated Sub-Contractor) and with the agreement of the Employer, allow all or any of such work, materials or goods to remain and confirm this in writing to the Contractor (which shall not be construed as a Variation) and where so allowed and confirmed an appropriate deduction shall be made in the adjustment of the Contract Sum; and/or
	8·4	·3	after consultation with the Contractor (who shall immediately consult with any relevant Nominated Sub-Contractor) issue such instructions requiring a Variation as are reasonably necessary as a consequence of such an instruction under clause 8·4·1 or such confirmation under clause 8·4·2 and to the extent that such instructions are so necessary and notwithstanding clauses 13·4, 25 and 26 no addition to the Contract Sum shall be made and no extension of time shall be given; and/or
	8·4	·4	having had due regard to the Code of Practice appended to these Conditions *(following clause 42)*, issue such instructions under clause 8·3 to open up for inspection or to test as are reasonable in all the circumstances to establish to the reasonable satisfaction of the Architect the likelihood or extent, as appropriate to the circumstances, of any further similar non-compliance. To the extent that such instructions are so reasonable, whatever the results of the opening up for inspection or test, and notwithstanding clauses 8·3 and 26 no addition to the Contract Sum shall be made. Clause 25·4·5·2 shall apply unless as stated therein the inspection or test showed that the work, materials or goods were not in accordance with this Contract.
Powers of Architect – non-compliance with clause 8·1·3	8·5		Where there is any failure to comply with clause 8·1·3 in regard to the carrying out of the work in a proper and workmanlike manner the Architect, without prejudice to the generality of his powers, may, after consultation with the Contractor (who shall immediately consult with any relevant Nominated Sub-Contractor), issue such instructions whether requiring a Variation or otherwise as are reasonably necessary as a consequence thereof. To the extent that such instructions are so necessary and notwithstanding clauses 13·4 and 25 and 26 no addition to the Contract Sum shall be made and no extension of time shall be given in respect of compliance by the Contractor with such instruction.
Exclusion from the Works of persons employed thereon	8·6		The Architect may (but not unreasonably or vexatiously) issue instructions requiring the exclusion from the site of any person employed thereon.

9 Royalties and patent rights

Treatment of royalties etc. – indemnity to Employer	9·1		All royalties or other sums payable in respect of the supply and use in carrying out the Works as described by or referred to in the Contract Bills of any patented articles, processes or inventions shall be deemed to have been included in the Contract Sum, and the Contractor shall indemnify the Employer from and against all claims, proceedings, damage, costs and expense which may be brought or made against the Employer or to which he may be put by reason of the Contractor infringing or being held to have infringed any patent rights in relation to any such articles, processes or inventions.

Architect's
instructions –
treatment of
royalties etc.
9·2 Provided that where in compliance with Architect's instructions the Contractor shall supply and use in carrying out the Works any patented articles, processes or inventions, the Contractor shall not be liable in respect of any infringement or alleged infringement of any patent rights in relation to any such articles, processes or inventions and all royalties damages or other monies which the Contractor may be liable to pay to the persons entitled to such patent rights shall be added to the Contract Sum.

10 Person-in-charge

The Contractor shall constantly keep upon the site a competent person-in-charge and any instructions given to him by the Architect or directions given to him by the clerk of works in accordance with clause 12 shall be deemed to have been issued to the Contractor.

11 Access for Architect to the Works

The Architect and his representatives shall at all reasonable times have access to the Works and to the workshops or other places of the Contractor where work is being prepared for this Contract, and when work is to be so prepared in workshops or other places of a Domestic Sub-Contractor or a Nominated Sub-Contractor the Contractor shall by a term in the sub-contract so far as possible secure a similar right of access to those workshops or places for the Architect and his representatives and shall do all things reasonably necessary to make such right effective. Access in accordance with clause 11 may be subject to such reasonable restrictions of the Contractor or any Domestic Sub-Contractor or any Nominated Sub-Contractor as are necessary to protect any proprietary right of the Contractor or of any Domestic or Nominated Sub-Contractor in the work referred to in clause 11.

12 Clerk of works

The Employer shall be entitled to appoint a clerk of works whose duty shall be to act solely as inspector on behalf of the Employer under the directions of the Architect and the Contractor shall afford every reasonable facility for the performance of that duty. If any direction is given to the Contractor by the clerk of works the same shall be of no effect unless given in regard to a matter in respect of which the Architect is expressly empowered by the Conditions to issue instructions and unless confirmed in writing by the Architect within 2 working days of such direction being given. If any such direction is so given and confirmed then as from the date of issue of that confirmation it shall be deemed to be an Architect's instruction.

13 Variations and provisional sums

Definition of
Variation
13·1 The term 'Variation' as used in the Conditions means:

13·1 ·1 the alteration or modification of the design, quality or quantity of the Works including

 ·1 ·1 the addition, omission or substitution of any work,

 ·1 ·2 the alteration of the kind or standard of any of the materials or goods to be used in the Works,

 ·1 ·3 the removal from the site of any work executed or materials or goods brought thereon by the Contractor for the purposes of the Works other than work materials or goods which are not in accordance with this Contract;

13·1 ·2 the imposition by the Employer of any obligations or restrictions in regard to the matters set out in clauses 13·1·2·1 to 13·1·2·4 or the addition to or alteration or omission of any such obligations or restrictions so imposed or imposed by the Employer in the Contract Bills in regard to:

 ·2 ·1 access to the site or use of any specific parts of the site;

 ·2 ·2 limitations of working space;

 ·2 ·3 limitations of working hours;

326

Appendix 1

13·1 *continued*

·2   ·4   the execution or completion of the work in any specific order;

but excludes

13·1 ·3 nomination of a sub-contractor to supply and fix materials or goods or to execute work of which the measured quantities have been set out and priced by the Contractor in the Contract Bills for supply and fixing or execution by the Contractor.

13·2 ·1 The Architect may issue instructions requiring a Variation.

13·2 ·2 Any instruction under clause 13·2·1 shall be subject to the Contractor's right of reasonable objection set out in clause 4·1·1.

13·2 ·3 The valuation of a Variation instructed under clause 13·2·1 shall be in accordance with clause 13·4·1·1 unless the instruction states that the treatment and valuation of the Variation are to be in accordance with clause 13A or unless the Variation is one to which clause 13A·8 applies. Where the instruction so states, clause 13A shall apply unless the Contractor within 7 days (or such other period as may be agreed) of receipt of the instruction states in writing that he disagrees with the application of clause 13A to such instruction. If the Contractor so disagrees, clause 13A shall not apply to such instruction and the Variation shall not be carried out unless and until the Architect instructs that the Variation is to be carried out and is to be valued pursuant to clause 13·4·1. [t]

13·2 ·4 The Architect may sanction in writing any Variation made by the Contractor otherwise than pursuant to an instruction of the Architect.

13·2 ·5 No Variation required by the Architect or subsequently sanctioned by him shall vitiate this Contract.

Instructions on
provisional sums
13·3 The Architect shall issue instructions in regard to:

13·3 ·1 the expenditure of provisional sums included in the Contract Bills; [u] and

13·3 ·2 the expenditure of provisional sums included in a Nominated Sub-Contract.

Valuation of
Variations and
provisional sum
work and work
covered by an
Approximate
Quantity
13·4 ·1 ·1 Subject to clause 13·4·1·3

– all Variations required by an instruction of the Architect or subsequently sanctioned by him in writing, and

– all work which under the Conditions is to be treated as if it were a Variation required by an instruction of the Architect under clause 13·2, and

– all work executed by the Contractor in accordance with instructions by the Architect as to the expenditure of provisional sums which are included in the Contract Bills, and

– all work executed by the Contractor for which an Approximate Quantity has been included in the Contract Bills

shall, unless otherwise agreed by the Employer and the Contractor, be valued (in the Conditions called 'the Valuation'), under Alternative A in clause 13·4·1·2 or, to the extent that Alternative A is not implemented by the Contractor or, if implemented, to the extent that the Price Statement or amended Price Statement is not accepted, under Alternative B in clause 13·4·1·2. Clause 13·4·1·1 shall not apply in respect of a Variation for which the Architect has issued a confirmed acceptance of a 13A Quotation or is a Variation to which clause 13A·8 applies.

Footnotes

[t] A longer period than 7 days may need to be agreed where the Variation involves a major input from sub-contractors.

[u] If the Architect nominates a sub-contractor or supplier by any instructions under clause 13·3·1, then the provisions of Part 2 of the Conditions apply to such nominations.

Appendix 1

13·4 ·1 ·2   *Alternative A: Contractor's Price Statement*

Paragraph:

A1 Without prejudice to his obligation to comply with any instruction or to execute any work to which clause 13·4·1·1 refers, the Contractor may within 21 days from receipt of the instruction or from commencement of work for which an Approximate Quantity is included in the Contract documents or, if later, from receipt of sufficient information to enable the Contractor to prepare his Price Statement, submit to the Quantity Surveyor his price ('Price Statement') for such compliance or for such work.

The Price Statement shall state the Contractor's price for the work which shall be based on the provisions of clause 13·5 *(valuation rules)* and may also separately attach the Contractor's requirements for:

·1 any amount to be paid in lieu of any ascertainment under clause 26·1 of direct loss and/or expense not included in any accepted 13A Quotation or in any previous ascertainment under clause 26;

·2 any adjustment to the time for the completion of the Works to the extent that such adjustment is not included in any revision of the Completion Date that has been made by the Architect under clause 25·3 or in his confirmed acceptance of any 13A Quotation. *(See paragraph A7)*

A2 Within 21 days of receipt of a Price Statement the Quantity Surveyor, after consultation with the Architect, shall notify the Contractor in writing

either

·1 that the Price Statement is accepted

or

·2 that the Price Statement, or a part thereof, is not accepted.

A3 Where the Price Statement or a part thereof has been accepted the price in that accepted Price Statement or in that part which has been accepted shall in accordance with clause 13·7 be added to or deducted from the Contract Sum.

A4 Where the Price Statement or a part thereof has not been accepted:

·1 the Quantity Surveyor shall include in his notification to the Contractor the reasons for not having accepted the Price Statement or a part thereof and set out those reasons in similar detail to that given by the Contractor in his Price Statement and supply an amended Price Statement which is acceptable to the Quantity Surveyor after consultation with the Architect;

·2 within 14 days from receipt of the amended Price Statement the Contractor shall state whether or not he accepts the amended Price Statement or part thereof and if accepted paragraph A3 shall apply to that amended Price Statement or part thereof; if no statement within the 14 day period is made the Contractor shall be deemed not to have accepted, in whole or in part, the amended Price Statement;

·3 to the extent that the amended Price Statement is not accepted by the Contractor, the Contractor's Price Statement and the amended Price Statement may be referred either by the Employer or by the Contractor as a dispute or difference to the Adjudicator in accordance with the provisions of clause 41A.

A5 Where no notification has been given pursuant to paragraph A2 the Price Statement is deemed not to have been accepted, and the Contractor may, on or after the expiry of the 21 day period to which paragraph A2 refers, refer his Price Statement as a dispute or difference to the Adjudicator in accordance with the provisions of clause 41A.

13·4 ·1 ·2 *continued*

A6 Where a Price Statement is not accepted by the Quantity Surveyor after consultation with the Architect or an amended Price Statement has not been accepted by the Contractor and no reference to the Adjudicator under paragraph A4·3 or paragraph A5 has been made, Alternative B shall apply.

A7 ·1 Where the Contractor pursuant to paragraph A1 has attached his requirements to his Price Statement the Quantity Surveyor after consultation with the Architect shall within 21 days of receipt thereof notify the Contractor

·1 ·1 either that the requirement in paragraph A1·1 in respect of the amount to be paid in lieu of any ascertainment under clause 26·1 is accepted or that the requirement is not accepted and clause 26·1 shall apply in respect of the ascertainment of any direct loss and/or expense; and

·1 ·2 either that the requirement in paragraph A1·2 in respect of an adjustment to the time for the completion of the Works is accepted or that the requirement is not accepted and clause 25 shall apply in respect of any such adjustment.

A7 ·2 If the Quantity Surveyor has not notified the Contractor within the 21 days specified in paragraph A7·1, clause 25 and clause 26 shall apply as if no requirements had been attached to the Price Statement.

·1 ·2 **Alternative B**

The Valuation shall be made by the Quantity Surveyor in accordance with the provisions of clauses 13·5·1 to 13·5·7.

·1 ·3 The valuation of Variations to the sub-contract works executed by a Nominated Sub-Contractor in accordance with instructions of the Architect and of all instructions issued under clause 13·3·2 and all work executed by a Nominated Sub-Contractor for which an Approximate Quantity is included in any bills of quantities included in the Numbered Documents shall (unless otherwise agreed by the Contractor and the Nominated Sub-Contractor concerned with the approval of the Employer) be made in accordance with the relevant provisions of Conditions NSC/C.

13·4 ·2 Where under the instruction of the Architect as to the expenditure of a provisional sum a prime cost sum arises and the Contractor under clause 35·2 tenders for the work covered by that prime cost sum and that tender is accepted by or on behalf of the Employer, that work shall be valued in accordance with the accepted tender of the Contractor and shall not be included in the Valuation of the instruction of the Architect in regard to the expenditure of the provisional sum.

Valuation rules **13·5** ·1 To the extent that the Valuation relates to the execution of additional or substituted work which can properly be valued by measurement or to the execution of work for which an Approximate Quantity is included in the Contract Bills such work shall be measured and shall be valued in accordance with the following rules:

·1 ·1 where the additional or substituted work is of similar character to, is executed under similar conditions as, and does not significantly change the quantity of, work set out in the Contract Bills the rates and prices for the work so set out shall determine the Valuation;

·1 ·2 where the additional or substituted work is of similar character to work set out in the Contract Bills but is not executed under similar conditions thereto and/or significantly changes the quantity thereof, the rates and prices for the work so set out shall be the basis for determining the valuation and the valuation shall include a fair allowance for such difference in conditions and/or quantity;

·1 ·3 where the additional or substituted work is not of similar character to work set out in the Contract Bills the work shall be valued at fair rates and prices;

·1 ·4 where the Approximate Quantity is a reasonably accurate forecast of the quantity of work required the rate or price for the Approximate Quantity shall determine the Valuation;

13·5 *continued*

·1 ·5 where the Approximate Quantity is not a reasonably accurate forecast of the quantity of work required the rate or price for that Approximate Quantity shall be the basis for determining the Valuation and the Valuation shall include a fair allowance for such difference in quantity.

Provided that clause 13·5·1·4 and clause 13·5·1·5 shall only apply to the extent that the work has not been altered or modified other than in quantity.

13·5 ·2 To the extent that the Valuation relates to the omission of work set out in the Contract Bills the rates and prices for such work therein set out shall determine the valuation of the work omitted.

13·5 ·3 In any valuation of work under clauses 13·5·1 and 13·5·2:

·3 ·1 measurement shall be in accordance with the same principles as those governing the preparation of the Contract Bills as referred to in clause 2·2·2·1;

·3 ·2 allowance shall be made for any percentage or lump sum adjustments in the Contract Bills; and

·3 ·3 allowance, where appropriate, shall be made for any addition to or reduction of preliminary items of the type referred to in the Standard Method of Measurement, 7th Edition, Section A (Preliminaries/General Conditions); provided that no such allowance shall be made in respect of compliance with an Architect's instruction for the expenditure of a provisional sum for defined work.*

13·5 ·4 To the extent that the Valuation relates to the execution of additional or substituted work which cannot properly be valued by measurement the Valuation shall comprise:

·4 ·1 the prime cost of such work (calculated in accordance with the 'Definition of Prime Cost of Daywork carried out under a Building Contract' issued by the Royal Institution of Chartered Surveyors and the Building Employers Confederation (now Construction Confederation) which was current at the Base Date) together with percentage additions to each section of the prime cost at the rates set out by the Contractor in the Contract Bills; or

·4 ·2 where the work is within the province of any specialist trade and the said Institution and the appropriate [v] body representing the employers in that trade have agreed and issued a definition of prime cost of daywork, the prime cost of such work calculated in accordance with that definition which was current at the Base Date together with percentage additions on the prime cost at the rates set out by the Contractor in the Contract Bills.

Provided that in any case vouchers specifying the time daily spent upon the work, the workmen's names, the plant and the materials employed shall be delivered for verification to the Architect or his authorised representative not later than the end of the week following that in which the work has been executed.

13·5 ·5 If

compliance with any instruction requiring a Variation or

compliance with any instruction as to the expenditure of a provisional sum for undefined work* or

compliance with any instruction as to the expenditure of a provisional sum for defined work* to the extent that the instruction for that work differs from the description given for such work in the Contract Bills or

the execution of work for which an Approximate Quantity is included in the Contract Bills to such extent as the quantity is more or less than the quantity ascribed to that work in the Contract Bills

substantially changes the conditions under which any other work is executed, then such

---

Footnotes

* See footnote [n] to clause 1·3 *(Definitions).*

[v] There are three Definitions to which clause 13·5·4·2 refers namely those agreed between the Royal

Institution and the Electrical Contractors Association, the Royal Institution and the Electrical Contractors Association of Scotland and the Royal Institution and the Heating and Ventilating Contractors Association.

Appendix 1

13·5   **·5**   *continued*

other work shall be treated as if it had been the subject of an instruction of the Architect requiring a Variation under clause 13·2 which shall be valued in accordance with the provisions of clause 13.

13·5   **·6**   **·1**   The Valuation of Performance Specified Work shall include allowance for the addition or omission of any relevant work involved in the preparation and production of drawings, schedules or other documents;

·6   **·2**   the Valuation of additional or substituted work related to Performance Specified Work shall be consistent with the rates and prices of work of a similar character set out in the Contract Bills or the Analysis making due allowance for any changes in the conditions under which the work is carried out and/or any significant change in the quantity of the work set out in the Contract Bills or in the Contractor's Statement. Where there is no work of a similar character set out in the Contract Bills or the Contractor's Statement a fair valuation shall be made;

·6   **·3**   the Valuation of the omission of work relating to Performance Specified Work shall be in accordance with the rates and prices for such work set out in the Contract Bills or the Analysis;

·6   **·4**   any valuation of work under clauses 13·5·6·2 and 13·5·6·3 shall include allowance for any necessary addition to or reduction of preliminary items of the type referred to in the Standard Method of Measurement, 7th Edition, Section A (Preliminaries/General Conditions);

·6   **·5**   where an appropriate basis of a fair valuation of additional or substituted work relating to Performance Specified Work is daywork the Valuation shall be in accordance with clauses 13·5·4·1 or 13·5·4·2 and the proviso to clause 13·5·4 shall apply;

·6   **·6**   if

compliance with any instruction under clause 42·11 requiring a Variation to Performance Specified Work or

compliance with any instruction as to the expenditure of a provisional sum for Performance Specified Work to the extent that the instruction for that Work differs from the information provided in the Contract Bills pursuant to clause 42·7·2 and/or 42·7·3 for such Performance Specified Work

substantially changes the conditions under which any other work is executed (including any other Performance Specified Work) then such other work (including any other Performance Specified Work) shall be treated as if it had been the subject of an instruction of the Architect requiring a Variation under clause 13·2 or, if relevant, under clause 42·11 which shall be valued in accordance with the provisions of clause 13·5.

13·5   **·7**   To the extent that the Valuation does not relate to the execution of additional or substituted work or the omission of work or to the extent that the valuation of any work or liabilities directly associated with a Variation cannot reasonably be effected in the Valuation by the application of clauses 13·5·1 to ·6 a fair valuation thereof shall be made.

Provided that no allowance shall be made under clause 13·5 for any effect upon the regular progress of the Works or for any other direct loss and/or expense for which the Contractor would be reimbursed by payment under any other provision in the Conditions.

Contractor's right to be present at measurement

13·6   Where it is necessary to measure work for the purpose of the Valuation the Quantity Surveyor shall give to the Contractor an opportunity of being present at the time of such measurement and of taking such notes and measurements as the Contractor may require.

Valuations – Employer/ Contractor agreement – 13A Quotation for a Variation and Variations thereto – addition to or deduction from Contract Sum

13·7   Effect shall be given to the Valuation under clause 13·4·1·1, to an agreement by the Employer and the Contractor to which clause 13·4·1·1 refers, to a 13A Quotation for which the Architect has issued a confirmed acceptance and to a valuation pursuant to clause 13A·8 by addition to or deduction from the Contract Sum.

331

Appendix 1

13A **Variation instruction – Contractor's quotation in compliance with the instruction**

Contractor to
submit his
quotation
('13A Quotation')

13A Clause 13A shall only apply to an instruction where pursuant to clause 13·2·3 the Contractor has not disagreed with the application of clause 13A to such instruction.

13A·1 ·1 The instruction to which clause 13A is to apply shall have provided sufficient information [w] to enable the Contractor to provide a quotation, which shall comprise the matters set out in clause 13A·2 (a '13A Quotation'), in compliance with the instruction; and in respect of any part of the Variation which relates to the work of any Nominated Sub-Contractor sufficient information to enable the Contractor to obtain a 3·3A Quotation from the Nominated Sub-Contractor in accordance with clause 3·3A·1·2 of the Conditions NSC/C. If the Contractor reasonably considers that the information provided is not sufficient, then, not later than 7 days from the receipt of the instruction, he shall request the Architect to supply sufficient further information.

13A·1 ·2 The Contractor shall submit to the Quantity Surveyor his 13A Quotation in compliance with the instruction and shall include therein 3·3A Quotations in respect of any parts of the Variation which relate to the work of Nominated Sub-Contractors not later than 21 days from

the date of receipt of the instruction

or if applicable, the date of receipt by the Contractor of the sufficient further information to which clause 13A·1·1 refers

whichever date is the later and the 13A Quotation shall remain open for acceptance by the Employer for 7 days from its receipt by the Quantity Surveyor.

13A·1 ·3 The Variation for which the Contractor has submitted his 13A Quotation shall not be carried out by the Contractor or as relevant by any Nominated Sub-Contractor until receipt by the Contractor of the confirmed acceptance issued by the Architect pursuant to clause 13A·3·2.

Content of the
Contractor's
13A Quotation

13A·2 The 13A Quotation shall separately comprise:

13A·2 ·1 the value of the adjustment to the Contract Sum (other than any amount to which clause 13A·2·3 refers) including therein the effect of the instruction on any other work including that of Nominated Sub-Contractors supported by all necessary calculations by reference, where relevant, to the rates and prices in the Contract Bills and including, where appropriate, allowances for any adjustment of preliminary items;

13A·2 ·2 any adjustment to the time required for completion of the Works (including where relevant stating an earlier Completion Date than the Date for Completion given in the Appendix) to the extent that such adjustment is not included in any revision of the Completion Date that has been made by the Architect under clause 25·3 or in his confirmed acceptance of any other 13A Quotation;

13A·2 ·3 the amount to be paid in lieu of any ascertainment under clause 26·1 of direct loss and/or expense not included in any other accepted 13A Quotation or in any previous ascertainment under clause 26;

13A·2 ·4 a fair and reasonable amount in respect of the cost of preparing the 13A Quotation;

and, where specifically required by the instruction, shall provide indicative information in statements on

13A·2 ·5 the additional resources (if any) required to carry out the Variation; and

13A·2 ·6 the method of carrying out the Variation.

Each part of the 13A Quotation shall contain reasonably sufficient supporting information to enable that part to be evaluated by or on behalf of the Employer.

Acceptance of
13A Quotation –
Architect's
confirmed
acceptance

13A·3 ·1 If the Employer wishes to accept a 13A Quotation the Employer shall so notify the Contractor in writing not later than the last day of the period for acceptance stated in clause 13A·1·2.

Footnote

[w] The information provided to the Contractor should normally be in a similar format to that provided at the tender stage; and may be in the form of drawings and/or in an addendum bill of quantities and/or in a specification or otherwise. If an addendum bill is provided see the relevant provisions in clause 2·2·2.

332

13A·3 ·2 If the Employer accepts a 13A Quotation the Architect shall, immediately upon that acceptance, confirm such acceptance by stating in writing to the Contractor (in clause 13A and elsewhere in the Conditions called a 'confirmed acceptance'):

    ·2 ·1 that the Contractor is to carry out the Variation;

    ·2 ·2 the adjustment of the Contract Sum, including therein any amounts to which clause 13A·2·3 and clause 13A·2·4 refer, to be made for complying with the instruction requiring the Variation;

    ·2 ·3 any adjustment to the time required by the Contractor for completion of the Works and the revised Completion Date arising therefrom (which, where relevant, may be a date earlier than the Date for Completion given in the Appendix) and, where relevant, any revised period or periods for the completion of the Nominated Sub-Contract work of each Nominated Sub-Contractor; and

    ·2 ·4 that the Contractor, pursuant to clause 3·3A·3 of the Conditions NSC/C, shall accept any 3·3A Quotation included in the 13A Quotation for which the confirmed acceptance has been issued.

Contractor's 13A Quotation not accepted

13A·4 If the Employer does not accept the 13A Quotation by the expiry of the period for acceptance stated in clause 13A·1·2, the Architect shall, on the expiry of that period,

either

13A·4 ·1 instruct that the Variation is to be carried out and is to be valued pursuant to clause 13·4·1;

or

13A·4 ·2 instruct that the Variation is not to be carried out.

Payment for a 13A Quotation

13A·5 If a 13A Quotation is not accepted a fair and reasonable amount shall be added to the Contract Sum in respect of the cost of preparation of the 13A Quotation provided that the 13A Quotation has been prepared on a fair and reasonable basis. The non-acceptance by the Employer of a 13A Quotation shall not of itself be evidence that the Quotation was not prepared on a fair and reasonable basis.

Restriction on use of a 13A Quotation

13A·6 If the Architect has not, under clause 13A·3·2, issued a confirmed acceptance of a 13A Quotation neither the Employer nor the Contractor may use that 13A Quotation for any purpose whatsoever.

Number of days – clauses 13A·1·1 and/or 13A·1·2

13A·7 The Employer and the Contractor may agree to increase or reduce the number of days stated in clause 13A·1·1 and/or in clause 13A·1·2 and any such agreement shall be confirmed in writing by the Employer to the Contractor. Where relevant the Contractor shall notify each Nominated Sub-Contractor of any agreed increase or reduction pursuant to this clause 13A·7.

Variations to work for which a confirmed acceptance of a 13A Quotation has been issued – valuation

13A·8 If the Architect issues an instruction requiring a Variation to work for which a 13A Quotation has been given and in respect of which the Architect has issued a confirmed acceptance to the Contractor such Variation shall not be valued under clause 13·5; but the Quantity Surveyor shall make a valuation of such Variation on a fair and reasonable basis having regard to the content of such 13A Quotation and shall include in that valuation the direct loss and/or expense, if any, incurred by the Contractor because the regular progress of the Works or any part thereof has been materially affected by compliance with the instruction requiring the Variation.

14   Contract Sum

Quality and quantity of work included in Contract Sum

14·1 The quality and quantity of the work included in the Contract Sum shall be deemed to be that which is set out in the Contract Bills.

Contract Sum – only adjusted under the Conditions – errors in computation

14·2 The Contract Sum shall not be adjusted or altered in any way whatsoever otherwise than in accordance with the express provisions of the Conditions, and subject to clause 2·2·2·2 any error whether of arithmetic or not in the computation of the Contract Sum shall be deemed to have been accepted by the parties hereto.

Appendix 1

15 Value added tax – supplemental provisions

Definitions – VAT Agreement

15·1 In clause 15 and in the supplemental provisions pursuant hereto (hereinafter called the 'VAT Agreement') 'tax' means the value added tax introduced by the Finance Act 1972 which is under the care and management of the Commissioners of Customs and Excise (hereinafter and in the VAT Agreement called 'the Commissioners').

Contract Sum – exclusive of VAT

15·2 Any reference in the Conditions to 'Contract Sum' shall be regarded as such Sum exclusive of any tax and recovery by the Contractor from the Employer of tax properly chargeable by the Commissioners on the Contractor under or by virtue of the Finance Act 1972 or any amendment or re-enactment thereof on the supply of goods and services under this Contract shall be under the provisions of clause 15 and of the VAT Agreement. Clause 1A of the VAT Agreement shall only apply where so stated in the Appendix. [x]

Possible exemption from VAT

15·3 To the extent that after the Base Date the supply of goods and services to the Employer becomes exempt from the tax there shall be paid to the Contractor an amount equal to the loss of credit (input tax) on the supply to the Contractor of goods and services which contribute exclusively to the Works.

16 Materials and goods unfixed or off-site

Unfixed materials and goods – on site

16·1 Unfixed materials and goods delivered to, placed on or adjacent to the Works and intended therefor shall not be removed except for use upon the Works unless the Architect has consented in writing to such removal which consent shall not be unreasonably delayed or withheld. Where the value of any such materials or goods has in accordance with clause 30·2 been included in any Interim Certificate under which the amount properly due to the Contractor has been paid by the Employer, such materials and goods shall become the property of the Employer, but, subject to clause 22B or 22C (if applicable), the Contractor shall remain responsible for loss or damage to the same.

Unfixed materials and goods – off-site

16·2 Where the value of any 'listed items' has in accordance with clause 30·3 been included in any Interim Certificate under which the amount properly due to the Contractor has been paid by the Employer, such listed items shall become the property of the Employer and thereafter the Contractor shall not, except for use upon the Works, remove or cause or permit the same to be moved or removed from the premises where they are, but the Contractor shall nevertheless be responsible for any loss thereof or damage thereto and for the cost of storage, handling and insurance of the same until such time as they are delivered to and placed on or adjacent to the Works whereupon the provisions of clause 16·1 (except the words "Where the value" to the words "the property of the Employer, but,") shall apply thereto.

17 Practical Completion and defects liability

Certificate of Practical Completion

17·1 When in the opinion of the Architect Practical Completion of the Works is achieved and the Contractor has complied sufficiently with clause 6A·4, and, if relevant, the Contractor has complied with clause 5·9 *(Supply of as-built drawings etc. – Performance Specified Work)*, he shall forthwith issue a certificate to that effect and Practical Completion of the Works shall be deemed for all the purposes of this Contract to have taken place on the day named in such certificate.

Defects, shrinkages or other faults

17·2 Any defects, shrinkages or other faults which shall appear within the Defects Liability Period and which are due to materials or workmanship not in accordance with this Contract or to frost occurring before Practical Completion of the Works, shall be specified by the Architect in a schedule of defects which he shall deliver to the Contractor as an instruction of the Architect not later than 14 days after the expiration of the said Defects Liability Period, and within a reasonable time after receipt of such schedule the defects, shrinkages and other faults therein specified shall be made good by the Contractor at no cost to the Employer unless the Architect with the consent of the Employer shall otherwise instruct; and if the

---

Footnote

[x] Clause 1A can only apply where the Contractor is satisfied at the date the Contract is entered into that his output tax on all supplies to the Employer under the Contract will be at either a positive or a zero rate of tax.

On and from 1 April 1989 the supply in respect of a building designed for a 'relevant residential purpose' or for a 'relevant charitable purpose' (as defined in the legislation which gives statutory effect to the VAT changes operative from 1 April 1989) is only zero rated if the person to whom the supply is made has given to the Contractor a certificate in statutory form: see the VAT leaflet 708 revised 1989. Where a contract supply is zero rated by certificate only the person holding the certificate (usually the Contractor) may zero rate his supply.

17·2 *continued*

Architect does so otherwise instruct then an appropriate deduction in respect of any such defects, shrinkages or other faults not made good shall be made from the Contract Sum.

Defects etc. – Architect's instructions

17·3 Notwithstanding clause 17·2 the Architect may whenever he considers it necessary so to do issue instructions requiring any defect, shrinkage or other fault which shall appear within the Defects Liability Period and which is due to materials or workmanship not in accordance with this Contract or to frost occurring before Practical Completion of the Works, to be made good, and the Contractor shall within a reasonable time after receipt of such instructions comply with the same at no cost to the Employer unless the Architect with the consent of the Employer shall otherwise instruct; and if the Architect does so otherwise instruct then an appropriate deduction in respect of any such defects, shrinkages or other faults not made good shall be made from the Contract Sum. Provided that no such instructions shall be issued after delivery of a schedule of defects or after 14 days from the expiration of the Defects Liability Period.

Certificate of Completion of Making Good Defects

17·4 When in the opinion of the Architect any defects, shrinkages or other faults which he may have required to be made good under clauses 17·2 and 17·3 shall have been made good he shall issue a certificate to that effect, and completion of making good defects shall be deemed for all the purposes of this Contract to have taken place on the day named in such certificate (the 'Certificate of Completion of Making Good Defects').

Damage by frost

17·5 In no case shall the Contractor be required to make good at his own cost any damage by frost which may appear after Practical Completion, unless the Architect shall certify that such damage is due to injury which took place before Practical Completion.

18   Partial possession by Employer

Employer's wish – Contractor's consent

18·1 If at any time or times before the date of issue by the Architect of the certificate of Practical Completion the Employer wishes to take possession of any part or parts of the Works and the consent of the Contractor *(which consent shall not be unreasonably delayed or withheld)* has been obtained, then, notwithstanding anything expressed or implied elsewhere in this Contract, the Employer may take possession thereof. The Architect shall thereupon issue to the Contractor on behalf of the Employer a written statement identifying the part or parts of the Works taken into possession and giving the date when the Employer took possession (in clauses 18, 20·3, 22·3·1 and 22C·1 referred to as 'the relevant part' and 'the relevant date' respectively).

Practical Completion – relevant part

18·1   ·1 For the purposes of clauses 17·2, 17·3, 17·5 and 30·4·1·2 Practical Completion of the relevant part shall be deemed to have occurred and the Defects Liability Period in respect of the relevant part shall be deemed to have commenced on the relevant date.

Defects etc. – relevant part

18·1   ·2 When in the opinion of the Architect any defects, shrinkages or other faults in the relevant part which he may have required to be made good under clause 17·2 or clause 17·3 shall have been made good he shall issue a certificate to that effect.

Insurance – relevant part

18·1   ·3 As from the relevant date the obligation of the Contractor under clause 22A or of the Employer under clause 22B·1 or clause 22C·2 whichever is applicable to insure shall terminate in respect of the relevant part but not further or otherwise; and where clause 22C applies the obligation of the Employer to insure under clause 22C·1 shall from the relevant date include the relevant part.

Liquidated damages – relevant part

18·1   ·4 In lieu of any sum to be paid by the Contractor or withheld or deducted by the Employer under clause 24 in respect of any period during which the Works may remain incomplete occurring after the relevant date there shall be paid such sum as bears the same ratio to the sum which would be paid apart from the provisions of clause 18 as the Contract Sum less the amount contained therein in respect of the relevant part bears to the Contract Sum; or the Employer may give a notice pursuant to clause 30·1·1·4 that he will deduct such sum from the monies due to the Contractor.

19   Assignment and sub-contracts

Assignment

19·1   ·1 Neither the Employer nor the Contractor shall, without the written consent of the other, assign this Contract.

Appendix 1

19·1 ·2 Where clause 19·1·2 is stated in the Appendix to apply then, in the event of transfer by the Employer of his freehold or leasehold interest in, or of a grant by the Employer of a leasehold interest in, the whole of the premises comprising the Works, the Employer may at any time after Practical Completion of the Works assign to any such transferee or lessee the right to bring proceedings in the name of the Employer (whether by arbitration or litigation) to enforce any of the terms of this Contract made for the benefit of the Employer hereunder. The assignee shall be estopped from disputing any enforceable agreements reached between the Employer and the Contractor and which arise out of and relate to this Contract (whether or not they are or appear to be a derogation from the right assigned) and made prior to the date of any assignment.

Sub-letting –
Domestic Sub-
Contractors –
Architect's
consent

19·2 ·1 A person to whom the Contractor sub-lets any portion of the Works other than a Nominated Sub-Contractor is in this Contract referred to as a 'Domestic Sub-Contractor'.

19·2 ·2 The Contractor shall not without the written consent of the Architect (which consent shall not be unreasonably delayed or withheld) sub-let any portion of the Works. The Contractor shall remain wholly responsible for carrying out and completing the Works in all respects in accordance with clause 2·1 notwithstanding the sub-letting of any portion of the Works.

Sub-letting – list
in Contract Bills

19·3 ·1 Where the Contract Bills provide that certain work measured or otherwise described in those Bills and priced by the Contractor must be carried out by persons named in a list in or annexed to the Contract Bills and selected therefrom by and at the sole discretion of the Contractor the provisions of clause 19·3 shall apply in respect of that list.

19·3 ·2 ·1 The list referred to in clause 19·3·1 must comprise not less than three persons. Either the Employer (or the Architect on his behalf) or the Contractor shall be entitled with the consent of the other, which consent shall not be unreasonably delayed or withheld, to add [y] additional persons to the list at any time prior to the execution of a binding sub-contract agreement.

·2 ·2 If at any time prior to the execution of a binding sub-contract agreement and for whatever reason less than three persons named in the list are able and willing to carry out the relevant work then

either the Employer and the Contractor shall by agreement (which agreement shall not be unreasonably delayed or withheld) add [y] the names of other persons so that the list comprises not less than three such persons

or the work shall be carried out by the Contractor who may sub-let to a Domestic Sub-Contractor in accordance with clause 19·2.

19·3 ·3 A person selected by the Contractor under clause 19·3 from the aforesaid list shall be a Domestic Sub-Contractor.

Sub-letting –
conditions of any
sub-letting

19·4 It shall be a condition in any sub-letting to which clause 19·2 or 19·3 refers that:

19·4 ·1 the employment of the Domestic Sub-Contractor under the sub-contract shall determine immediately upon the determination (for any reason) of the Contractor's employment under this Contract; and

19·4 ·2 the sub-contract shall provide that:

·2 ·1 subject to clause 16·1 of these Conditions (in clauses 19·4·2·2 to ·4 called 'the Main Contract Conditions'), unfixed materials and goods delivered to, placed on or adjacent to the Works by the sub-contractor and intended therefor shall not be removed except for use on the Works unless the Contractor has consented in writing to such removal, which consent shall not be unreasonably delayed or withheld;

·2 ·2 where, in accordance with clause 30·2 of the Main Contract Conditions, the value of any such materials or goods shall have been included in any Interim Certificate under which the amount properly due to the Contractor shall have been paid by the Employer to the Contractor, such materials or goods shall be and become the property of the Employer and the sub-contractor shall not deny that such materials or goods are and have become the property of the Employer;

Footnote   [y] Any such addition must be initialled by or on behalf of
the parties.

336

Appendix 1

Injury or damage
to property –
exclusion of the
Works and Site
Materials

20·3 **·1** Subject to clause 20·3·2 the reference in clause 20·2 to 'property real or personal' does not include the Works, work executed and/or Site Materials up to and including the date of issue of the certificate of Practical Completion or up to and including the date of determination of the employment of the Contractor (whether or not the validity of that determination is disputed) under clause 27 or clause 28 or clause 28A or, where clause 22C applies, under clause 27 or clause 28 or clause 28A or clause 22C·4·3, whichever is the earlier.

20·3 **·2** If clause 18 has been operated then, in respect of the relevant part and as from the relevant date, such relevant part shall not be regarded as 'the Works' or 'work executed' for the purpose of clause 20·3·1.

21 Insurance against injury to persons or property

Contractor's
insurance –
personal injury or
death – injury or
damage to
property

21·1 **·1** **·1** Without prejudice to his obligation to indemnify the Employer under clause 20 the Contractor shall take out and maintain insurance which shall comply with clause 21·1·1·2 in respect of claims arising out of his liability referred to in clauses 20·1 and 20·2.

·1 **·2** The insurance in respect of claims for personal injury to or the death of any person under a contract of service or apprenticeship with the Contractor, and arising out of and in the course of such person's employment, shall comply with all relevant legislation. For all other claims to which clause 21·1·1·1 applies the insurance cover [z]:

– shall indemnify the Employer in like manner to the Contractor but only to the extent that the Contractor may be liable to indemnify the Employer under the terms of this Contract; and

– shall be not less than the sum stated in the Appendix [aa] for any one occurrence or series of occurrences arising out of one event.

21·1 **·2** As and when he is reasonably required to do so by the Employer the Contractor shall send to the Architect for inspection by the Employer documentary evidence that the insurances required by clause 21·1·1·1 have been taken out and are being maintained, but at any time the Employer may (but not unreasonably or vexatiously) require to have sent to the Architect for inspection by the Employer the relevant policy or policies and the premium receipts therefor.

21·1 **·3** If the Contractor defaults in taking out or in maintaining insurance as provided in clause 21·1·1·1 the Employer may himself insure against any liability or expense which he may incur arising out of such default and a sum or sums equivalent to the amount paid or payable by him in respect of premiums therefor may be deducted by him from any monies due or to become due to the Contractor under this Contract or such amount may be recoverable by the Employer from the Contractor as a debt.

21·2 **·1** Where it is stated in the Appendix that the insurance to which clause 21·2·1 refers may be required by the Employer the Contractor shall, if so instructed by the Architect, take out a policy of insurance in the names of the Employer and the Contractor [bb] for such amount of indemnity as is stated in the Appendix in respect of any expense, liability, loss, claim or proceedings which the Employer may incur or sustain by reason of injury or damage to any property caused by collapse, subsidence, heave, vibration, weakening or removal of support or lowering of ground water arising out of or in the course of or by reason of the carrying out of the Works excepting injury or damage:

·1 **·1** for which the Contractor is liable under clause 20·2;

·1 **·2** attributable to errors or omissions in the designing of the Works;

·1 **·3** which can reasonably be foreseen to be inevitable having regard to the nature of the work to be executed and the manner of its execution;

---

[z] It should be noted that the cover granted under public liability policies taken out pursuant to clause 21·1·1 may not be co-extensive with the indemnity given to the Employer in clauses 20·1 and 20·2: for example each claim may be subject to the excess in the policy and cover may not be available in respect of loss or damage due to gradual pollution.

[aa] The Contractor may, if he so wishes, insure for a sum greater than that stated in the Appendix.

[bb] A policy of insurance taken out for the purposes of clause 21·2 should not have an expiry date earlier than the end of the Defects Liability Period.

Injury or damage to property – exclusion of the Works and Site Materials

20·3 ·1 Subject to clause 20·3·2 the reference in clause 20·2 to 'property real or personal' does not include the Works, work executed and/or Site Materials up to and including the date of issue of the certificate of Practical Completion or up to and including the date of determination of the employment of the Contractor (whether or not the validity of that determination is disputed) under clause 27 or clause 28 or clause 28A or, where clause 22C applies, under clause 27 or clause 28 or clause 28A or clause 22C·4·3, whichever is the earlier.

20·3 ·2 If clause 18 has been operated then, in respect of the relevant part and as from the relevant date, such relevant part shall not be regarded as 'the Works' or 'work executed' for the purpose of clause 20·3·1.

21 Insurance against injury to persons or property

Contractor's insurance – personal injury or death – injury or damage to property

21·1 ·1 ·1 Without prejudice to his obligation to indemnify the Employer under clause 20 the Contractor shall take out and maintain insurance which shall comply with clause 21·1·1·2 in respect of claims arising out of his liability referred to in clauses 20·1 and 20·2.

·1 ·2 The insurance in respect of claims for personal injury to or the death of any person under a contract of service or apprenticeship with the Contractor, and arising out of and in the course of such person's employment, shall comply with all relevant legislation. For all other claims to which clause 21·1·1·1 applies the insurance cover [z]:

– shall indemnify the Employer in like manner to the Contractor but only to the extent that the Contractor may be liable to indemnify the Employer under the terms of this Contract; and

– shall be not less than the sum stated in the Appendix [aa] for any one occurrence or series of occurrences arising out of one event.

21·1 ·2 As and when he is reasonably required to do so by the Employer the Contractor shall send to the Architect for inspection by the Employer documentary evidence that the insurances required by clause 21·1·1·1 have been taken out and are being maintained, but at any time the Employer may (but not unreasonably or vexatiously) require to have sent to the Architect for inspection by the Employer the relevant policy or policies and the premium receipts therefor.

21·1 ·3 If the Contractor defaults in taking out or in maintaining insurance as provided in clause 21·1·1·1 the Employer may himself insure against any liability or expense which he may incur arising out of such default and a sum or sums equivalent to the amount paid or payable by him in respect of premiums therefor may be deducted by him from any monies due or to become due to the Contractor under this Contract or such amount may be recoverable by the Employer from the Contractor as a debt.

Insurance – liability etc. of Employer

21·2 ·1 Where it is stated in the Appendix that the insurance to which clause 21·2·1 refers may be required by the Employer the Contractor shall, if so instructed by the Architect, take out a policy of insurance in the names of the Employer and the Contractor [bb] for such amount of indemnity as is stated in the Appendix in respect of any expense, liability, loss, claim or proceedings which the Employer may incur or sustain by reason of injury or damage to any property caused by collapse, subsidence, heave, vibration, weakening or removal of support or lowering of ground water arising out of or in the course of or by reason of the carrying out of the Works excepting injury or damage:

·1 ·1 for which the Contractor is liable under clause 20·2;

·1 ·2 attributable to errors or omissions in the designing of the Works;

·1 ·3 which can reasonably be foreseen to be inevitable having regard to the nature of the work to be executed and the manner of its execution;

Footnotes

[z] It should be noted that the cover granted under public liability policies taken out pursuant to clause 21·1·1 may not be co-extensive with the indemnity given to the Employer in clauses 20·1 and 20·2: for example each claim may be subject to the excess in the policy and cover may not be available in respect of loss or damage due to gradual pollution.

[aa] The Contractor may, if he so wishes, insure for a sum greater than that stated in the Appendix.

[bb] A policy of insurance taken out for the purposes of clause 21·2 should not have an expiry date earlier than the end of the Defects Liability Period.

Appendix 1

21·2   *continued*

·1   ·4   which it is the responsibility of the Employer to insure under clause 22C·1 (if applicable);

·1   ·5   to the Works and Site Materials brought on to the site of the Contract for the purpose of its execution except in so far as any part or parts thereof are the subject of a certificate of Practical Completion;

·1   ·6   arising from any consequence of war, invasion, act of foreign enemy, hostilities (whether war be declared or not), civil war, rebellion or revolution, insurrection or military or usurped power;

·1   ·7   directly or indirectly caused by or contributed to by or arising from the Excepted Risks;

·1   ·8   directly or indirectly caused by or arising out of pollution or contamination of buildings or other structure or of water or land or the atmosphere happening during the period of insurance; save that this exception shall not apply in respect of pollution or contamination caused by a sudden identifiable, unintended and unexpected incident which takes place in its entirety at a specific moment in time and place during the period of insurance provided that all pollution or contamination which arises out of one incident shall be considered for the purpose of this insurance to have occurred at the time such incident takes place;

·1   ·9   which results in any costs or expenses being incurred by the Employer or in any other sums being payable by the Employer in respect of damages for breach of contract except to the extent that such costs or expenses or damages would have attached in the absence of any contract.

21·2   ·2   Any such insurance as is referred to in clause 21·2·1 shall be placed with insurers to be approved by the Employer, and the Contractor shall send to the Architect for deposit with the Employer the policy or policies and the premium receipts therefor.

21·2   ·3   The amounts expended by the Contractor to take out and maintain the insurance referred to in clause 21·2·1 shall be added to the Contract Sum.

21·2   ·4   If the Contractor defaults in taking out or in maintaining the Joint Names Policy as provided in clause 21·2·1 the Employer may himself insure against any risk in respect of which the default shall have occurred.

Excepted Risks   **21·3**   Notwithstanding the provisions of clauses 20·1, 20·2 and 21·1·1, the Contractor shall not be liable either to indemnify the Employer or to insure against any personal injury to or the death of any person or any damage, loss or injury caused to the Works or Site Materials, work executed, the site, or any property, by the effect of an Excepted Risk.

22   **Insurance of the Works** [cc]

Insurance of the Works – alternative clauses   **22·1**   Clause 22A or clause 22B or clause 22C shall apply whichever clause is stated to apply in the Appendix.

Footnote

[cc] **Clause 22A** is applicable to the erection of new buildings where the **Contractor** is required to take out a Joint Names Policy for All Risks Insurance for the Works and **clause 22B** is applicable where the **Employer** has elected to take out such Joint Names Policy. **Clause 22C** is to be used for alterations of or extensions to existing structures under which the **Employer** is required to take out a Joint Names Policy for All Risks Insurance for the Works and also a Joint Names Policy to insure the existing structures and their contents owned by him or for which he is responsible against loss or damage thereto by the Specified Perils.

339

Appendix 1

22·2 In clauses 22A, 22B, 22C and, so far as relevant, in other clauses of the Conditions the following phrases shall have the meanings given below:

All Risks Insurance: [dd]

insurance which provides cover against any physical loss or damage to work executed and Site Materials and against the reasonable cost of the removal and disposal of debris and of any shoring and propping of the Works which results from such physical loss or damage but excluding the cost necessary to repair, replace or rectify

1 property which is defective due to

·1 wear and tear,

·2 obsolescence,

·3 deterioration, rust or mildew;

[ee] 2 any work executed or any Site Materials lost or damaged as a result of its own defect in design, plan, specification, material or workmanship or any other work executed which is lost or damaged in consequence thereof where such work relied for its support or stability on such work which was defective;

3 loss or damage caused by or arising from

·1 any consequence of war, invasion, act of foreign enemy, hostilities (whether war be declared or not), civil war, rebellion, revolution, insurrection, military or usurped power, confiscation, commandeering, nationalisation or requisition or loss or destruction of or damage to any property by or under the order of any government *de jure* or *de facto* or public, municipal or local authority;

·2 disappearance or shortage if such disappearance or shortage is only revealed when an inventory is made or is not traceable to an identifiable event;

·3 an Excepted Risk (as defined in clause 1·3);

and if the Contract is carried out in Northern Ireland

·4 civil commotion;

·5 any unlawful, wanton or malicious act committed maliciously by a person or persons acting on behalf of or in connection with an unlawful association; 'unlawful association' shall mean any organisation which is engaged in terrorism and includes an organisation which at any relevant time is a proscribed organisation within the meaning of the Northern Ireland (Emergency Provisions) Act 1973; 'terrorism' means the use of violence for political ends and includes any use of violence for the purpose of putting the public or any section of the public in fear.

Footnotes

[dd] The definition of 'All Risks Insurance' in clause 22·2 defines the risks for which insurance is required. Policies issued by insurers are not standardised and there will be some variation in the way the insurance for those risks is expressed. See also Practice Note 22 and Guide, Part A.

[ee] In any policy for 'All Risks Insurance' taken out under clauses 22A, 22B or 22C·2 cover should not be reduced by the terms of any exclusion written in the policy beyond the terms of paragraph 2; thus an exclusion in terms "This Policy excludes all loss of or damage to the property insured due to defective design, plan, specification, materials or workmanship" would not be in accordance with the terms of those clauses and of the definition of 'All Risks Insurance'. Cover which goes beyond the terms of the exclusion in paragraph 2 may be available though not standard in all policies taken out to meet the obligation in clauses 22A, 22B or 22C·2: and leading insurers who underwrite 'All Risks' cover for the Works have confirmed that where such improved cover is being given it will not be withdrawn as a consequence of the publication of the terms of the definition in clause 22·2 of 'All Risks Insurance'.

340

Appendix 1

22·2 *continued*

Joint Names Policy: a policy of insurance which includes the Employer and the Contractor as the insured and under which the insurers have no right of recourse against any person named as an insured, or, pursuant to clause 22·3, recognised as an insured thereunder.

Nominated and Domestic Sub-Contractors – benefit of Joint Names Policies – Specified Perils

22·3 ·1   The Contractor where clause 22A applies, and the Employer where either clause 22B or clause 22C applies, shall ensure that the Joint Names Policy referred to in clause 22A·1 or clause 22A·3 or the Joint Names Policies referred to in clause 22B·1 or in clauses 22C·1 and 22C·2 shall

     either   provide for recognition of each sub-contractor nominated by the Architect as an insured under the relevant Joint Names Policy

     or   include a waiver by the relevant insurers of any right of subrogation which they may have against any such Nominated Sub-Contractor

in respect of loss or damage by the Specified Perils to the Works and Site Materials and where clause 22A or clause 22B or clause 22C·2 applies and, where clause 22C·1 applies, in respect of loss or damage by the Specified Perils to the existing structures (which shall include from the relevant date any relevant part to which clause 18·1·3 refers) together with the contents thereof owned by the Employer or for which he is responsible; and that this recognition or waiver shall continue up to and including the date of issue of the certificate of practical completion of the sub-contract works (as referred to in clause 2·11 of Conditions NSC/C or the date of determination of the employment of the Contractor (whether or not the validity of that determination is contested) under clause 27 or clause 28 or clause 28A or, where clause 22C applies, under clause 27 or clause 28 or clause 28A or clause 22C·4·3, whichever is the earlier. The provisions of clause 22·3·1 shall apply also in respect of any Joint Names Policy taken out by the Employer under clause 22A·2 or by the Contractor under clause 22B·2 or under clause 22C·3 in respect of a default by the Employer under clause 22C·2.

22·3 ·2   Except in respect of the Joint Names Policy referred to in clause 22C·1 (or the Joint Names Policy referred to in clause 22C·3 in respect of a default by the Employer under clause 22C·1) the provisions of clause 22·3·1 in regard to recognition or waiver shall apply to Domestic Sub-Contractors. Such recognition or waiver for Domestic Sub-Contractors shall continue up to and including the date of issue of any certificate or other document which states that the domestic sub-contract works are practically complete or the date of determination of the employment of the Contractor as referred to in clause 22·3·1, whichever is the earlier.

22A   Erection of new buildings – All Risks Insurance of the Works by the Contractor [cc]

New buildings – Contractor to take out and maintain a Joint Names Policy for All Risks Insurance

22A·1   The Contractor shall take out and maintain a Joint Names Policy for All Risks Insurance for cover no less than that defined in clause 22·2 [dd] [ff] for the full reinstatement value of the Works (plus the percentage, if any, to cover professional fees stated in the Appendix) and shall (subject to clause 18·1·3) maintain such Joint Names Policy up to and including the date of issue of the certificate of Practical Completion or up to and including the date of determination of the employment of the Contractor under clause 27 or clause 28 or clause 28A (whether or not the validity of that determination is contested), whichever is the earlier.

Where the Employer's status for VAT purposes is exempt or partially exempt the full reinstatement value to which this clause refers shall be inclusive of any VAT on the supply of the work and materials referred to in clause 22A·4·3 for which the Contractor is chargeable by the Commissioners.

Footnote   [ff] In some cases it may not be possible for insurance to be taken out against certain of the risks covered by the definition of 'All Risks Insurance'. This matter should be arranged between the parties prior to entering into the Contract and either the definition of 'All Risks Insurance' given in clause 22·2 amended or the risks actually covered should replace this definition; in the latter case clause 22A·1, clause 22A·3 or clause 22B·1, whichever is applicable, and other relevant clauses in which the definition 'All Risks Insurance' is used should be amended to include the words used to replace this definition.

Appendix 1

Single policy –
insurers approved
by Employer –
failure by
Contractor to
insure

22A·2 The Joint Names Policy referred to in clause 22A·1 shall be taken out with insurers approved by the Employer, and the Contractor shall send to the Architect for deposit with the Employer that Policy and the premium receipt therefor and also any relevant endorsement or endorsements thereof as may be required to comply with the obligation to maintain that Policy set out in clause 22A·1 and the premium receipts therefor. If the Contractor defaults in taking out or in maintaining the Joint Names Policy as required by clauses 22A·1 and 22A·2 the Employer may himself take out and maintain a Joint Names Policy against any risk in respect of which the default shall have occurred and a sum or sums equivalent to the amount paid or payable by him in respect of premiums therefor may be deducted by him from any monies due or to become due to the Contractor under this Contract or such amount may be recoverable by the Employer from the Contractor as a debt.

Use of annual
policy maintained
by Contractor –
alternative to use
of clause 22A·2

22A·3 ·1 If the Contractor independently of his obligations under this Contract maintains a policy of insurance which provides (*inter alia*) All Risks Insurance for cover no less than that defined in clause 22·2 for the full reinstatement value of the Works (plus the percentage, if any, to cover professional fees stated in the Appendix) then the maintenance by the Contractor of such policy shall, if the policy is a Joint Names Policy in respect of the aforesaid Works, be a discharge of the Contractor's obligation to take out and maintain a Joint Names Policy under clause 22A·1. If and so long as the Contractor is able to send to the Architect for inspection by the Employer as and when he is reasonably required to do so by the Employer documentary evidence that such a policy is being maintained then the Contractor shall be discharged from his obligation under clause 22A·2 to deposit the policy and the premium receipt with the Employer but on any occasion the Employer may (but not unreasonably or vexatiously) require to have sent to the Architect for inspection by the Employer the policy to which clause 22A·3·1 refers and the premium receipts therefor. The annual renewal date, as supplied by the Contractor, of the insurance referred to in clause 22A·3·1 is stated in the Appendix.

22A·3 ·2 The provisions of clause 22A·2 shall apply in regard to any default in taking out or in maintaining insurance under clause 22A·3·1.

Loss or damage to
Works – insurance
claims –
Contractor's
obligations – use
of insurance
monies

22A·4 ·1 If any loss or damage affecting work executed or any part thereof or any Site Materials is occasioned by any one or more of the risks covered by the Joint Names Policy referred to in clause 22A·1 or clause 22A·2 or clause 22A·3 then, upon discovering the said loss or damage, the Contractor shall forthwith give notice in writing both to the Architect and to the Employer of the extent, nature and location thereof.

22A·4 ·2 The occurrence of such loss or damage shall be disregarded in computing any amounts payable to the Contractor under or by virtue of this Contract.

22A·4 ·3 After any inspection required by the insurers in respect of a claim under the Joint Names Policy referred to in clause 22A·1 or clause 22A·2 or clause 22A·3 has been completed the Contractor with due diligence shall restore such work damaged, replace or repair any such Site Materials which have been lost or damaged, remove and dispose of any debris and proceed with the carrying out and completion of the Works.

22A·4 ·4 The Contractor, for himself and for all Nominated and Domestic Sub-Contractors who are, pursuant to clause 22·3, recognised as an insured under the Joint Names Policy referred to in clause 22A·1 or clause 22A·2 or clause 22A·3, shall authorise the insurers to pay all monies from such insurance in respect of the loss or damage referred to in clause 22A·4·1 to the Employer. The Employer shall pay all such monies (less only the amount properly incurred by the Employer in respect of professional fees but not exceeding the amount arrived at by applying the percentage to cover professional fees stated in the Appendix to the amount of the monies so paid excluding any amount included therein for professional fees) to the Contractor by instalments under certificates of the Architect issued at the Period of Interim Certificates.

22A·4 ·5 The Contractor shall not be entitled to any payment in respect of the restoration, replacement or repair of such loss or damage and (when required) the removal and disposal of debris other than the monies received under the aforesaid insurance.

Appendix 1

22B **Erection of new buildings – All Risks Insurance of the Works by the Employer** [cc]

New buildings –
Employer to take
out and maintain a
Joint Names
Policy for All Risks
Insurance

22B·1 The Employer shall take out and maintain a Joint Names Policy for All Risks Insurance for cover no less than that defined in clause 22·2 [dd] [ff] for the full reinstatement value of the Works (plus the percentage, if any, to cover professional fees stated in the Appendix) and shall (subject to clause 18·1·3) maintain such Joint Names Policy up to and including the date of issue of the certificate of Practical Completion or up to and including the date of determination of the employment of the Contractor under clause 27 or clause 28 or clause 28A (whether or not the validity of that determination is contested), whichever is the earlier.

Where the Employer's status for VAT purposes is exempt or partially exempt the full reinstatement value to which this clause refers shall be inclusive of any VAT on the supply of the work and materials referred to in clause 22B·3·3 for which the Contractor is chargeable by the Commissioners.

Failure of
Employer to
insure – rights of
Contractor

22B·2 The Employer shall, as and when reasonably required to do so by the Contractor, produce documentary evidence and receipts showing that the Joint Names Policy required under clause 22B·1 has been taken out and is being maintained. If the Employer defaults in taking out or in maintaining the Joint Names Policy required under clause 22B·1 then the Contractor may himself take out and maintain a Joint Names Policy against any risk in respect of which a default shall have occurred and a sum or sums equivalent to the amount paid or payable by him in respect of the premiums therefor shall be added to the Contract Sum.

Loss or damage to
Works – insurance
claims –
Contractor's
obligations –
payment by
Employer

22B·3 ·1 If any loss or damage affecting work executed or any part thereof or any Site Materials is occasioned by any one or more of the risks covered by the Joint Names Policy referred to in clause 22B·1 or clause 22B·2 then, upon discovering the said loss or damage, the Contractor shall forthwith give notice in writing both to the Architect and to the Employer of the extent, nature and location thereof.

22B·3 ·2 The occurrence of such loss or damage shall be disregarded in computing any amounts payable to the Contractor under or by virtue of this Contract.

22B·3 ·3 After any inspection required by the insurers in respect of a claim under the Joint Names Policy referred to in clause 22B·1 or clause 22B·2 has been completed the Contractor with due diligence shall restore such work damaged, replace or repair any such Site Materials which have been lost or damaged, remove and dispose of any debris and proceed with the carrying out and completion of the Works.

22B·3 ·4 The Contractor, for himself and for all Nominated and Domestic Sub-Contractors who are, pursuant to clause 22·3, recognised as an insured under the Joint Names Policy referred to in clause 22B·1 or clause 22B·2, shall authorise the insurers to pay all monies from such insurance in respect of the loss or damage referred to in clause 22B·3·1 to the Employer.

22B·3 ·5 The restoration, replacement or repair of such loss or damage and (when required) the removal and disposal of debris shall be treated as if they were a Variation required by an instruction of the Architect under clause 13·2.

22C **Insurance of existing structures – insurance of Works in or extensions to existing structures** [cc]

Existing
structures and
contents –
Specified Perils –
Employer to take
out and maintain
Joint Names
Policy

22C·1 The Employer shall take out and maintain a Joint Names Policy in respect of the existing structures (which shall include from the relevant date any relevant part to which clause 18·1·3 refers) together with the contents thereof owned by him or for which he is responsible, for the full cost of reinstatement, repair or replacement of loss or damage due to one or more of the Specified Perils [gg] up to and including the date of issue of the certificate of Practical Completion or up to and including the date of determination of the employment of the Contractor under clause 22C·4·3 or clause 27 or clause 28 or clause 28A (whether or not the validity of that determination is contested), whichever is the earlier. The Contractor, for himself and for all Nominated Sub-Contractors who are, pursuant to clause 22·3·1, recognised as an insured under the Joint Names Policy referred to in clause 22C·1 or clause 22C·3, shall authorise the insurers to pay all monies from such insurance in respect of loss or damage to the Employer. [hh]

See next page for footnotes [gg] and [hh].

343

Appendix 1

22C·1 *continued*

Where the Employer's status for VAT purposes is exempt or partially exempt the full cost of reinstatement, repair or replacement of loss or damage to which this clause refers shall be inclusive of any VAT chargeable on the supply of such reinstatement, repair or replacement.

Works in or extensions to existing structures – All Risks Insurance – Employer to take out and maintain Joint Names Policy

22C·2 The Employer shall take out and maintain a Joint Names Policy for All Risks Insurance for cover no less than that defined in clause 22·2 [dd] [gg] for the full reinstatement value of the Works (plus the percentage, if any, to cover professional fees stated in the Appendix) and shall (subject to clause 18·1·3) maintain such Joint Names Policy up to and including the date of issue of the certificate of Practical Completion or up to and including the date of determination of the employment of the Contractor under clause 22C·4·3 or clause 27 or clause 28 or clause 28A (whether or not the validity of that determination is contested), whichever is the earlier.

Where the Employer's status for VAT purposes is exempt or partially exempt the full reinstatement value to which this clause refers shall be inclusive of any VAT on the supply of the work and materials referred to in clause 22C·4·4·1 for which the Contractor is chargeable by the Commissioners.

Failure of Employer to insure – rights of Contractor

22C·3 The Employer shall, as and when reasonably required to do so by the Contractor, produce documentary evidence and receipts showing that the Joint Names Policy required under clause 22C·1 or clause 22C·2 has been taken out and is being maintained. If the Employer defaults in taking out or in maintaining the Joint Names Policy required under clause 22C·1 the Contractor may himself take out and maintain a Joint Names Policy against any risk in respect of which the default shall have occurred and for that purpose shall have such right of entry and inspection as may be required to make a survey and inventory of the existing structures and the relevant contents. If the Employer defaults in taking out or in maintaining the Joint Names Policy required under clause 22C·2 the Contractor may take out and maintain a Joint Names Policy against any risk in respect of which the default shall have occurred. A sum or sums equivalent to the premiums paid or payable by the Contractor pursuant to clause 22C·3 shall be added to the Contract Sum.

Loss or damage to Works – insurance claims – Contractor's obligations – payment by Employer

22C·4 If any loss or damage affecting work executed or any part thereof or any Site Materials is occasioned by any one or more of the risks covered by the Joint Names Policy referred to in clause 22C·2 or clause 22C·3 then, upon discovering the said loss or damage, the Contractor shall forthwith give notice in writing both to the Architect and to the Employer of the extent, nature and location thereof and

22C·4 ·1 the occurrence of such loss or damage shall be disregarded in computing any amounts payable to the Contractor under or by virtue of this Contract;

22C·4 ·2 the Contractor, for himself and for all Nominated and Domestic Sub-Contractors who are, pursuant to clause 22·3, recognised as an insured under the Joint Names Policy referred to in clause 22C·2 or clause 22C·3, shall authorise the insurers to pay all monies from such insurance in respect of the loss or damage referred to in clause 22C·4 to the Employer;

22C·4 ·3 ·1 if it is just and equitable so to do the employment of the Contractor under this Contract may within 28 days of the occurrence of such loss or damage be determined at the option of either Party by notice by registered post or recorded delivery from either Party to the other. Within 7 days of receiving such a notice (but not thereafter) either Party may invoke the relevant procedures applicable under the Contract to the resolution of disputes or differences in order that it may be decided whether such determination is just and equitable;

·3 ·2 upon the giving or receiving by the Employer of a notice of determination, or where the relevant procedures referred to in clause 22C·4·3·1 have been invoked and the notice of determination has been upheld, the provisions of clauses 28A·4 and 28A·5 (except clause 28A·5·5) shall apply.

Footnotes

[gg] In some cases it may not be possible for insurance to be taken out against certain of the Specified Perils or the risks covered by the definition of 'All Risks Insurance'. This matter should be arranged between the parties prior to entering into the Contract and either the definitions of Specified Perils and/or All Risks Insurance given in clauses 1·3 and 22·2 amended or the risks actually covered should replace the definitions; in the latter case clause 22C·1 and/or clause 22C·2 and other relevant clauses in which the definitions 'All Risks Insurance' and/or 'Specified Perils' are used should be amended to include the words used to replace those definitions.

[hh] Some Employers e.g. tenants may not be able to fulfil the obligations in clause 22C·1. If so clause 22C·1 should be amended accordingly.

344

Appendix 1

22C·4 **·4** If no notice of determination is served under clause 22C·4·3·1, or where the relevant procedures referred to in clause 22C·4·3·1 have been invoked and the notice of determination has not been upheld, then

  ·4 **·1** after any inspection required by the insurers in respect of a claim under the Joint Names Policy referred to in clause 22C·2 or clause 22C·3 has been completed, the Contractor with due diligence shall restore such work damaged, replace or repair any such Site Materials which have been lost or damaged, remove and dispose of any debris and proceed with the carrying out and completion of the Works; and

  ·4 **·2** the restoration, replacement or repair of such loss or damage and (when required) the removal and disposal of debris shall be treated as if they were a Variation required by an instruction of the Architect under clause 13·2.

22D   Insurance for Employer's loss of liquidated damages – clause 25·4·3

22D·1 Where it is stated in the Appendix that the insurance to which clause 22D refers may be required by the Employer then forthwith after the Contract has been entered into the Architect shall either inform the Contractor that no such insurance is required or instruct the Contractor to obtain a quotation for such insurance. This quotation shall be for an insurance on an agreed value basis [ii] to be taken out and maintained by the Contractor until the date of Practical Completion and which will provide for payment to the Employer of a sum calculated by reference to clause 22D·3 in the event of loss or damage to the Works, work executed, Site Materials, temporary buildings, plant and equipment for use in connection with and on or adjacent to the Works by any one or more of the Specified Perils and which loss or damage results in the Architect giving an extension of time under clause 25·3 in respect of the Relevant Event in clause 25·4·3. The Architect shall obtain from the Employer any information which the Contractor reasonably requires to obtain such quotation. The Contractor shall send to the Architect as soon as practicable the quotation which he has obtained and the Architect shall thereafter instruct the Contractor whether or not the Employer wishes the Contractor to accept that quotation and such instruction shall not be unreasonably withheld or delayed. If the Contractor is instructed to accept the quotation the Contractor shall forthwith take out and maintain the relevant policy and send it to the Architect for deposit with the Employer, together with the premium receipt therefor and also any relevant endorsement or endorsements thereof and the premium receipts therefor.

22D·2 The sum insured by the relevant policy shall be a sum calculated at the rate stated in the Appendix as liquidated and ascertained damages for the period of time stated in the Appendix.

22D·3 Payment in respect of this insurance shall be calculated at the rate referred to in clause 22D·2 (or any revised rate produced by the application of clause 18·1·4) for the period of any extension of time finally given by the Architect as referred to in clause 22D·1 or for the period of time stated in the Appendix, whichever is the less.

22D·4 The amounts expended by the Contractor to take out and maintain the insurance referred to in clause 22D·1 shall be added to the Contract Sum. If the Contractor defaults in taking out or in maintaining the insurance referred to in clause 22D·1 the Employer may himself insure against any risk in respect of which the default shall have occurred.

22FC   Joint Fire Code – compliance

Application of clause

22FC **·1** Clause 22FC applies where it is stated in the Appendix that the Joint Fire Code applies.

Compliance with Joint Fire Code

22FC **·2** **·1** The Employer shall comply with the Joint Fire Code and ensure such compliance by his servants or agents and by any person employed, engaged or authorised by him upon or in connection with the Works or any part thereof other than the Contractor and the persons for whom the Contractor is responsible pursuant to clause 22FC·2·2.

Footnote

[ii] The adoption of an agreed value is to avoid any dispute over the amount of the payment due under the insurance once the policy is issued. Insurers on receiving a proposal for the insurance to which clause 22D refers will normally reserve the right to be satisfied that the sum referred to in clause 22D·2 is not more than a genuine pre-estimate of the damages which the Employer considers, at the time he enters into the Contract, he will suffer as a result of any delay.

22FC *continued*

·2 ·2 The Contractor shall comply with the Joint Fire Code and ensure such compliance by his servants or agents or by any person employed or engaged by him upon or in connection with the Works or any part thereof their servants or agents or by any other person who may properly be on the site upon or in connection with the Works or any part thereof other than the Employer or any person employed, engaged or authorised by him or by any local authority or statutory undertaker executing work solely in pursuance of its statutory rights or obligations.

Breach of Joint Fire Code – Remedial Measures

22FC ·3 ·1 If a breach of the Joint Fire Code occurs and the insurer under the Joint Names Policy in respect of the Works specifies by notice the remedial measures he requires ('the Remedial Measures') and the time by which such Remedial Measures are to be completed ('the Remedial Measures Completion Date') the Contractor shall ensure that the Remedial Measures are carried out, where relevant in accordance with the instructions of the Architect, by the Remedial Measures Completion Date.

·3 ·2 If the Contractor, within 7 days of receipt of a notice specifying the Remedial Measures, does not begin to carry out or thereafter fails without reasonable cause regularly and diligently to proceed with the Remedial Measures then the Employer may employ and pay other persons to carry out the Remedial Measures; and, subject to clause 22FC·4, all costs incurred in connection with such employment may be withheld and/or deducted by him from any monies due or to become due to the Contractor or may be recoverable from the Contractor by the Employer as a debt.

Indemnity

22FC ·4 The Contractor shall indemnify the Employer and the Employer shall indemnify the Contractor in respect of the consequences of a breach of the Joint Fire Code to the extent that these consequences result from a breach by the Contractor or by the Employer of their respective obligations under clause 22FC.

Joint Fire Code – amendments

22FC ·5 If after the Base Date the Joint Fire Code is amended and the Joint Fire Code as amended is, under the Joint Names Policy, applicable to the Works, the net extra cost, if any, of compliance by the Contractor with the amended Joint Fire Code shall be added to the Contract Sum.

23 Date of Possession, completion and postponement

Date of Possession – progress to Completion Date

23·1 ·1 On the Date of Possession possession of the site shall be given to the Contractor who shall thereupon begin the Works and regularly and diligently proceed with the same and shall complete the same on or before the Completion Date.

23·1 ·2 Where clause 23·1·2 is stated in the Appendix to apply the Employer may defer the giving of possession for a period not exceeding six weeks or such lesser period stated in the Appendix calculated from the Date of Possession.

Architect's instructions – postponement

23·2 The Architect may issue instructions in regard to the postponement of any work to be executed under the provisions of this Contract.

Possession by Contractor – use or occupation by Employer

23·3 ·1 For the purposes of the Works insurances the Contractor shall retain possession of the site and the Works up to and including the date of issue of the certificate of Practical Completion, and, subject to clause 18, the Employer shall not be entitled to take possession of any part or parts of the Works until that date.

23·3 ·2 Notwithstanding the provisions of clause 23·3·1 the Employer may, with the consent in writing of the Contractor, use or occupy the site or the Works or part thereof whether for the purposes of storage of his goods or otherwise before the date of issue of the certificate of Practical Completion by the Architect. Before the Contractor shall give his consent to such use or occupation the Contractor or the Employer shall notify the insurers under clause 22A or clause 22B or clause 22C·2 to ·4 whichever may be applicable and obtain confirmation that such use or occupation will not prejudice the insurance. Subject to such confirmation the consent of the Contractor shall not be unreasonably delayed or withheld.

Appendix 1

23·3 ·3   Where clause 22A·2 or clause 22A·3 applies and the insurers in giving the confirmation referred to in clause 23·3·2 have made it a condition of such confirmation that an additional premium is required the Contractor shall notify the Employer of the amount of the additional premium. If the Employer continues to require use or occupation under clause 23·3·2 the additional premium required shall be added to the Contract Sum and the Contractor shall provide the Employer, if so requested, with the additional premium receipt therefor.

24   **Damages for non-completion**

Certificate of Architect

24·1   If the Contractor fails to complete the Works by the Completion Date then the Architect shall issue a certificate to that effect. In the event of a new Completion Date being fixed after the issue of such a certificate such fixing shall cancel that certificate and the Architect shall issue such further certificate under clause 24·1 as may be necessary.

Payment or allowance of liquidated damages

24·2 ·1   Provided:
- –   the Architect has issued a certificate under clause 24·1; and
- –   the Employer has informed the Contractor in writing before the date of the Final Certificate that he may require payment of, or may withhold or deduct, liquidated and ascertained damages,

the Employer may, not later than 5 days before the final date for payment of the debt due under the Final Certificate:

either

 ·1 ·1   require in writing the Contractor to pay to the Employer liquidated and ascertained damages at the rate stated in the Appendix (or at such lesser rate as may be specified in writing by the Employer) for the period between the Completion Date and the date of Practical Completion and the Employer may recover the same as a debt;

or

 ·1 ·2   give a notice pursuant to clause 30·1·1·4 or clause 30·8·3 to the Contractor that he will deduct from monies due to the Contractor liquidated and ascertained damages at the rate stated in the Appendix (or at such lesser rate as may be specified in the notice) for the period between the Completion Date and the date of Practical Completion.

24·2 ·2   If, under clause 25·3·3, the Architect fixes a later Completion Date or a later Completion Date is stated in a confirmed acceptance of a 13A Quotation, the Employer shall pay or repay to the Contractor any amounts recovered, allowed or paid under clause 24·2·1 for the period up to such later Completion Date.

24·2 ·3   Notwithstanding the issue of any further certificate of the Architect under clause 24·1 any requirement of the Employer which has been previously stated in writing in accordance with clause 24·2·1 shall remain effective unless withdrawn by the Employer.

25   **Extension of time [ij]**

Interpretation of delay

25·1   In clause 25 any reference to delay, notice or extension of time includes further delay, further notice or further extension of time.

Notice by Contractor of delay to progress

25·2 ·1 ·1   If and whenever it becomes reasonably apparent that the progress of the Works is being or is likely to be delayed the Contractor shall forthwith give written notice to the Architect of the material circumstances including the cause or causes of the delay and identify in such notice any event which in his opinion is a Relevant Event.

 ·1 ·2   Where the material circumstances of which written notice has been given under clause 25·2·1·1 include reference to a Nominated Sub-Contractor, the Contractor shall forthwith send a copy of such written notice to the Nominated Sub-Contractor concerned.

Footnote   [ij] See clauses 38·4·7, 39·5·7 and 40·7 (restriction of fluctuations or price adjustment during period where Contractor is in default over completion).

25·2 ·2 In respect of each and every Relevant Event identified in the notice given in accordance with clause 25·2·1·1 the Contractor shall, if practicable in such notice, or otherwise in writing as soon as possible after such notice:

    ·2 ·1 give particulars of the expected effects thereof; and

    ·2 ·2 estimate the extent, if any, of the expected delay in the completion of the Works beyond the Completion Date resulting therefrom whether or not concurrently with delay resulting from any other Relevant Event

    and shall give such particulars and estimate to any Nominated Sub-Contractor to whom a copy of any written notice has been given under clause 25·2·1·2.

25·2 ·3 The Contractor shall give such further written notices to the Architect, and send a copy to any Nominated Sub-Contractor to whom a copy of any written notice has been given under clause 25·2·1·2, as may be reasonably necessary or as the Architect may reasonably require for keeping up-to-date the particulars and estimate referred to in clauses 25·2·2·1 and 25·2·2·2 including any material change in such particulars or estimate.

Fixing Completion Date   **25·3** ·1 If, in the opinion of the Architect, upon receipt of any notice, particulars and estimate under clauses 25·2·1·1, 25·2·2 and 25·2·3.

    ·1 ·1 any of the events which are stated by the Contractor to be the cause of the delay is a Relevant Event and

    ·1 ·2 the completion of the Works is likely to be delayed thereby beyond the Completion Date

    the Architect shall in writing to the Contractor give an extension of time by fixing such later date as the Completion Date as he then estimates to be fair and reasonable. The Architect shall, in fixing such new Completion Date, state:

    ·1 ·3 which of the Relevant Events he has taken into account and

    ·1 ·4 the extent, if any, to which he has had regard to any instructions issued under clause 13·2 which require as a Variation the omission of any work or obligation and/or under clause 13·3 in regard to the expenditure of a provisional sum for defined work or for Performance Specified Work which results in the omission of any such work,

    and shall, if reasonably practicable having regard to the sufficiency of the aforesaid notice, particulars and estimate, fix such new Completion Date not later than 12 weeks from receipt of the notice and of reasonably sufficient particulars and estimate, or, where the period between receipt thereof and the Completion Date is less than 12 weeks, not later than the Completion Date.

    If, in the opinion of the Architect, upon receipt of any such notice, particulars and estimate, it is not fair and reasonable to fix a later date as a new Completion Date, the Architect shall if reasonably practicable having regard to the sufficiency of the aforesaid notice, particulars and estimate so notify the Contractor in writing not later than 12 weeks from receipt of the notice, particulars and estimate, or, where the period between receipt thereof and the Completion Date is less than 12 weeks, not later than the Completion Date.

25·3 ·2 After the first exercise by the Architect of his duty under clause 25·3·1 or after any revision to the Completion Date stated by the Architect in a confirmed acceptance of a 13A Quotation in respect of a Variation the Architect may in writing fix a Completion Date earlier than that previously fixed under clause 25 or than that stated by the Architect in a confirmed acceptance of a 13A Quotation if in his opinion the fixing of such earlier Completion Date is fair and reasonable having regard to any instructions issued after the last occasion on which the Architect fixed a new Completion Date

    – under clause 13·2 which require or sanction as a Variation the omission of any work or obligation; and/or

    – under clause 13·3 in regard to the expenditure of a provisional sum for defined work or for Performance Specified Work which result in the omission of any such work.

Appendix 1

25·3   ·2   *continued*

Provided that no decision under clause 25·3·2 shall alter the length of any adjustment to the time required by the Contractor for the completion of the Works in respect of a Variation for which a 13A Quotation has been given and which has been stated in a confirmed acceptance of a 13A Quotation or in respect of a Variation or work for which an adjustment to the time for completion of the Works has been accepted pursuant to clause 13·4·1·2 paragraph A7.

25·3   ·3   After the Completion Date, if this occurs before the date of Practical Completion, the Architect may, and not later than the expiry of 12 weeks after the date of Practical Completion shall, in writing to the Contractor either

    ·3   ·1   fix a Completion Date later than that previously fixed if in his opinion the fixing of such later Completion Date is fair and reasonable having regard to any of the Relevant Events, whether upon reviewing a previous decision or otherwise and whether or not the Relevant Event has been specifically notified by the Contractor under clause 25·2·1·1; or

    ·3   ·2   fix a Completion Date earlier than that previously fixed under clause 25 or stated in a confirmed acceptance of a 13A Quotation if in his opinion the fixing of such earlier Completion Date is fair and reasonable having regard to any instructions issued after the last occasion on which the Architect fixed a new Completion Date

        –   under clause 13·2 which require or sanction as a Variation the omission of any work or obligation; and/or

        –   under clause 13·3 in regard to the expenditure of a provisional sum for defined work or for Performance Specified Work which result in the omission of any such work; or

    ·3   ·3   confirm to the Contractor the Completion Date previously fixed or stated in a confirmed acceptance of a 13A Quotation.

Provided that no decision under clause 25·3·3·1 or clause 25·3·3·2 shall alter the length of any adjustment to the time required by the Contractor for the completion of the Works in respect of a Variation for which a 13A Quotation has been given and which has been stated in a confirmed acceptance of a 13A Quotation.

25·3   ·4   Provided always that:

    ·4   ·1   the Contractor shall use constantly his best endeavours to prevent delay in the progress of the Works, howsoever caused, and to prevent the completion of the Works being delayed or further delayed beyond the Completion Date;

    ·4   ·2   the Contractor shall do all that may reasonably be required to the satisfaction of the Architect to proceed with the Works.

25·3   ·5   The Architect shall notify in writing to every Nominated Sub-Contractor each decision of the Architect under clause 25·3 fixing a Completion Date and each revised Completion Date stated in the confirmed acceptance of a 13A Quotation together with, where relevant, any revised period or periods for the completion of the work of each Nominated Sub-Contractor stated in such confirmed acceptance.

25·3   ·6   No decision of the Architect under clause 25·3·2 or clause 25·3·3·2 shall fix a Completion Date earlier than the Date for Completion stated in the Appendix.

Relevant Events   **25·4**   The following are the Relevant Events referred to in clause 25:

25·4   ·1   force majeure;

25·4   ·2   exceptionally adverse weather conditions;

25·4   ·3   loss or damage occasioned by any one or more of the Specified Perils;

25·4   ·4   civil commotion, local combination of workmen, strike or lock-out affecting any of the trades employed upon the Works or any of the trades engaged in the preparation, manufacture or transportation of any of the goods or materials required for the Works;

349

Appendix 1

25·4   ·5   compliance with the Architect's instructions

     ·5   ·1   under clauses 2·3, 2·4·1, 13·2 (except for a confirmed acceptance of a 13A Quotation), 13·3 (except compliance with an Architect's instruction for the expenditure of a provisional sum for defined work* or of a provisional sum for Performance Specified Work), 13A·4·1, 23·2, 34, 35 or 36; or

     ·5   ·2   in regard to the opening up for inspection of any work covered up or the testing of any of the work, materials or goods in accordance with clause 8·3 (including making good in consequence of such opening up or testing) unless the inspection or test showed that the work, materials or goods were not in accordance with this Contract;

25·4   ·6   ·1   where an Information Release Schedule has been provided, failure of the Architect to comply with clause 5·4·1;

     ·6   ·2   failure of the Architect to comply with clause 5·4·2;

25·4   ·7   delay on the part of Nominated Sub-Contractors or Nominated Suppliers which the Contractor has taken all practicable steps to avoid or reduce;

25·4   ·8   ·1   the execution of work not forming part of this Contract by the Employer himself or by persons employed or otherwise engaged by the Employer as referred to in clause 29 or the failure to execute such work;

     ·8   ·2   the supply by the Employer of materials and goods which the Employer has agreed to provide for the Works or the failure so to supply;

25·4   ·9   the exercise after the Base Date by the United Kingdom Government of any statutory power which directly affects the execution of the Works by restricting the availability or use of labour which is essential to the proper carrying out of the Works or preventing the Contractor from, or delaying the Contractor in, securing such goods or materials or such fuel or energy as are essential to the proper carrying out of the Works;

25·4   ·10 ·1   the Contractor's inability for reasons beyond his control and which he could not reasonably have foreseen at the Base Date to secure such labour as is essential to the proper carrying out of the Works; or

     ·10 ·2   the Contractor's inability for reasons beyond his control and which he could not reasonably have foreseen at the Base Date to secure such goods or materials as are essential to the proper carrying out of the Works;

25·4   ·11 the carrying out by a local authority or statutory undertaker of work in pursuance of its statutory obligations in relation to the Works, or the failure to carry out such work;

25·4   ·12 failure of the Employer to give in due time ingress to or egress from the site of the Works or any part thereof through or over any land, buildings, way or passage adjoining or connected with the site and in the possession and control of the Employer, in accordance with the Contract Bills and/or the Contract Drawings, after receipt by the Architect of such notice, if any, as the Contractor is required to give, or failure of the Employer to give such ingress or egress as otherwise agreed between the Architect and the Contractor;

25·4   ·13 where clause 23·1·2 is stated in the Appendix to apply, the deferment by the Employer of giving possession of the site under clause 23·1·2;

25·4   ·14 by reason of the execution of work for which an Approximate Quantity is included in the Contract Bills which is not a reasonably accurate forecast of the quantity of work required;

25·4   ·15 delay which the Contractor has taken all practicable steps to avoid or reduce consequent upon a change in the Statutory Requirements after the Base Date which necessitates some alteration or modification to any Performance Specified Work;

25·4   ·16 the use or threat of terrorism and/or the activity of the relevant authorities in dealing with such use or threat;

Footnote   *See footnote [n] to clause 1·3 *(Definitions)*.

25·4 ·17 compliance or non-compliance by the Employer with clause 6A·1;

25·4 ·18 delay arising from a suspension by the Contractor of the performance of his obligations under the Contract to the Employer pursuant to clause 30·1·4.

26 **Loss and expense caused by matters materially affecting regular progress of the Works**

Matters materially affecting regular progress of the Works – direct loss and/or expense

26·1 If the Contractor makes written application to the Architect stating that he has incurred or is likely to incur direct loss and/or expense (of which the Contractor may give his quantification) in the execution of this Contract for which he would not be reimbursed by a payment under any other provision in this Contract due to deferment of giving possession of the site under clause 23·1·2 where clause 23·1·2 is stated in the Appendix to be applicable or because the regular progress of the Works or of any part thereof has been or is likely to be materially affected by any one or more of the matters referred to in clause 26·2; and if and as soon as the Architect is of the opinion that the direct loss and/or expense has been incurred or is likely to be incurred due to any such deferment of giving possession or that the regular progress of the Works or of any part thereof has been or is likely to be so materially affected as set out in the application of the Contractor then the Architect from time to time thereafter shall ascertain, or shall instruct the Quantity Surveyor to ascertain, the amount of such loss and/or expense which has been or is being incurred by the Contractor; provided always that:

26·1 ·1 the Contractor's application shall be made as soon as it has become, or should reasonably have become, apparent to him that the regular progress of the Works or of any part thereof has been or was likely to be affected as aforesaid; and

26·1 ·2 the Contractor shall in support of his application submit to the Architect upon request such information as should reasonably enable the Architect to form an opinion as aforesaid; and

26·1 ·3 the Contractor shall submit to the Architect or to the Quantity Surveyor upon request such details of such loss and/or expense as are reasonably necessary for such ascertainment as aforesaid.

List of matters

26·2 The following are the matters referred to in clause 26·1:

26·2 ·1 ·1 where an Information Release Schedule has been provided, failure of the Architect to comply with clause 5·4·1;

·1 ·2 failure of the Architect to comply with clause 5·4·2;

26·2 ·2 the opening up for inspection of any work covered up or the testing of any of the work, materials or goods in accordance with clause 8·3 (including making good in consequence of such opening up or testing), unless the inspection or test showed that the work, materials or goods were not in accordance with this Contract;

26·2 ·3 any discrepancy in or divergence between the Contract Drawings and/or the Contract Bills and/or the Numbered Documents;

26·2 ·4 ·1 the execution of work not forming part of this Contract by the Employer himself or by persons employed or otherwise engaged by the Employer as referred to in clause 29 or the failure to execute such work;

·4 ·2 the supply by the Employer of materials and goods which the Employer has agreed to provide for the Works or the failure so to supply;

26·2 ·5 Architect's instructions under clause 23·2 issued in regard to the postponement of any work to be executed under the provisions of this Contract;

26·2 ·6 failure of the Employer to give in due time ingress to or egress from the site of the Works or any part thereof through or over any land, buildings, way or passage adjoining or connected with the site and in the possession and control of the Employer, in accordance with the Contract Bills and/or the Contract Drawings, after receipt by the Architect of such notice, if any, as the Contractor is required to give, or failure of the Employer to give such ingress or egress as otherwise agreed between the Architect and the Contractor;

26·2 ·7 Architect's instructions issued

under clause 13·2 or clause 13A·4·1 requiring a Variation (except for a Variation for which the Architect has given a confirmed acceptance of a 13A Quotation or for a Variation thereto) or

under clause 13·3 in regard to the expenditure of provisional sums (other than instructions to which clause 13·4·2 refers or an instruction for the expenditure of a provisional sum for defined work* or of a provisional sum for Performance Specified Work);

26·2 ·8 the execution of work for which an Approximate Quantity is included in the Contract Bills which is not a reasonably accurate forecast of the quantity of work required;

26·2 ·9 compliance or non-compliance by the Employer with clause 6A·1;

26·2 ·10 suspension by the Contractor of the performance of his obligations under the Contract to the Employer pursuant to clause 30·1·4 provided the suspension was not frivolous or vexatious.

Relevance of certain extensions of Completion Date

26·3 If and to the extent that it is necessary for ascertainment under clause 26·1 of loss and/or expense the Architect shall state in writing to the Contractor what extension of time, if any, has been made under clause 25 in respect of the Relevant Event or Events referred to in clause 25·4·5·1 (so far as that clause refers to clauses 2·3, 13·2, 13·3 and 23·2) and in clauses 25·4·5·2, 25·4·6, 25·4·8 and 25·4·12.

Nominated Sub-Contractors – matters materially affecting regular progress of the sub-contract works – direct loss and/or expense

26·4 ·1 The Contractor upon receipt of a written application properly made by a Nominated Sub-Contractor under clause 4·38·1 of Conditions NSC/C shall pass to the Architect a copy of that written application. If and as soon as the Architect is of the opinion that the loss and/or expense to which the said clause 4·38·1 refers has been incurred or is likely to be incurred due to any deferment of the giving of possession where clause 23·1·2 is stated in the Appendix to apply or that the regular progress of the sub-contract works or of any part thereof has been or is likely to be materially affected as referred to in clause 4·38·1 of Conditions NSC/C and as set out in the application of the Nominated Sub-Contractor then the Architect shall himself ascertain, or shall instruct the Quantity Surveyor to ascertain, the amount of loss and/or expense to which the said clause 4·38·1 refers.

26·4 ·2 If and to the extent that it is necessary for the ascertainment of such loss and/or expense the Architect shall state in writing to the Contractor with a copy to the Nominated Sub-Contractor concerned what was the length of the revision of the period or periods for completion of the sub-contract works or of any part thereof to which he gave consent in respect of the Relevant Event or Events set out in clause 2·6·5·1 (so far as that clause refers to clauses 2·3, 13·2, 13·3 and 23·2 of the Main Contract Conditions), 2·6·5·2, 2·6·6, 2·6·8, 2·6·12 and 2·6·15 of Conditions NSC/C.

Amounts ascertained – added to Contract Sum

26·5 Any amount from time to time ascertained under clause 26 shall be added to the Contract Sum.

Reservation of rights and remedies of Contractor

26·6 The provisions of clause 26 are without prejudice to any other rights and remedies which the Contractor may possess.

27 Determination by Employer

Notices under clause 27

27·1 Any notice or further notice to which clauses 27·2·1, 27·2·2, 27·2·3 and 27·3·4 refer shall be in writing and given by actual delivery, or by special delivery or by recorded delivery. If sent by special delivery or recorded delivery the notice or further notice shall, subject to proof to the contrary, be deemed to have been received 48 hours after the date of posting (excluding Saturday and Sunday and Public Holidays).

Footnote

*See footnote (n) to clause 1·3 *(Definitions)*.

Appendix 1

27·2 ·1   If, before the date of Practical Completion, the Contractor shall make a default in any one or more of the following respects:

    ·1 ·1   without reasonable cause he wholly or substantially suspends the carrying out of the Works; or

    ·1 ·2   he fails to proceed regularly and diligently with the Works; or

    ·1 ·3   he refuses or neglects to comply with a written notice or instruction from the Architect requiring him to remove any work, materials or goods not in accordance with this Contract and by such refusal or neglect the Works are materially affected; or

    ·1 ·4   he fails to comply with the provisions of clause 19·1·1 or clause 19·2·2; or

    ·1 ·5   he fails pursuant to the Conditions to comply with the requirements of the CDM Regulations,

the Architect may give to the Contractor a notice specifying the default or defaults (the 'specified default or defaults').

27·2 ·2   If the Contractor continues a specified default for 14 days from receipt of the notice under clause 27·2·1 then the Employer may on, or within 10 days from, the expiry of that 14 days by a further notice to the Contractor determine the employment of the Contractor under this Contract. Such determination shall take effect on the date of receipt of such further notice.

27·2 ·3   If

the Contractor ends the specified default or defaults, or

the Employer does not give the further notice referred to in clause 27·2·2

and the Contractor repeats a specified default (whether previously repeated or not) then, upon or within a reasonable time after such repetition, the Employer may by notice to the Contractor determine the employment of the Contractor under this Contract. Such determination shall take effect on the date of receipt of such notice.

27·2 ·4   A notice of determination under clause 27·2·2 or clause 27·2·3 shall not be given unreasonably or vexatiously.

27·3 ·1   If the Contractor

makes a composition or arrangement with his creditors, or becomes bankrupt, or,

being a company,

makes a proposal for a voluntary arrangement for a composition of debts or scheme of arrangement to be approved in accordance with the Companies Act 1985 or the Insolvency Act 1986 as the case may be or any amendment or re-enactment thereof, or

has a provisional liquidator appointed, or

has a winding-up order made, or

passes a resolution for voluntary winding-up (except for the purposes of amalgamation or reconstruction), or

under the Insolvency Act 1986 or any amendment or re-enactment thereof has an administrator or an administrative receiver appointed

then:

27·3 ·2   the Contractor shall immediately inform the Employer in writing if he has made a composition or arrangement with his creditors, or, being a company, has made a proposal for a voluntary arrangement for a composition of debts or scheme of arrangement to be approved in accordance with the Companies Act 1985 or the Insolvency Act 1986 as the case may be or any amendment or re-enactment thereof;

27·3 ·3 where a provisional liquidator or trustee in bankruptcy is appointed or a winding-up order is made or the Contractor passes a resolution for voluntary winding-up (except for the purposes of amalgamation or reconstruction) the employment of the Contractor under this Contract shall be forthwith automatically determined but the said employment may be reinstated if the Employer and the Contractor [kk] shall so agree;

27·3 ·4 where clause 27·3·3 does not apply the Employer may at any time, unless an agreement to which clause 27·5·2·1 refers has been made, by notice to the Contractor determine the employment of the Contractor under this Contract and such determination shall take effect on the date of receipt of such notice.

Corruption

27·4 The Employer shall be entitled to determine the employment of the Contractor, under this or any other contract, if the Contractor shall have offered or given or agreed to give to any person any gift or consideration of any kind as an inducement or reward for doing or forbearing to do or for having done or forborne to do any action in relation to the obtaining or execution of this or any other contract with the Employer, or for showing or forbearing to show favour or disfavour to any person in relation to this or any other contract with the Employer, or if the like acts shall have been done by any person employed by the Contractor or acting on his behalf (whether with or without the knowledge of the Contractor), or if in relation to this or any other contract with the Employer the Contractor or any person employed by him or acting on his behalf shall have committed an offence under the Prevention of Corruption Acts 1889 to 1916.

Insolvency of
Contractor –
option to
Employer

27·5 Clauses 27·5·1 to 27·5·4 are only applicable where clause 27·3·4 applies.

27·5 ·1 From the date when, under clause 27·3·4, the Employer could first give notice to determine the employment of the Contractor, the Employer, subject to clause 27·5·3, shall not be bound by any provisions of this Contract to make any further payment thereunder and the Contractor shall not be bound to continue to carry out and complete the Works in compliance with clause 2·1.

27·5 ·2 Clause 27·5·1 shall apply until

either

·2 ·1 the Employer makes an agreement (a '27·5·2·1 agreement') with the Contractor on the continuation or novation or conditional novation of this Contract, in which case this Contract shall be subject to the terms set out in the 27·5·2·1 agreement

or

·2 ·2 the Employer determines the employment of the Contractor under this Contract in accordance with clause 27·3·4, in which case the provisions of clause 27·6 or clause 27·7 shall apply.

27·5 ·3 Notwithstanding clause 27·5·1, in the period before either a 27·5·2·1 agreement is made or the Employer under clause 27·3·4 determines the employment of the Contractor, the Employer and the Contractor may make an interim arrangement for work to be carried out. Subject to clause 27·5·4 any right of set-off which the Employer may have shall not be exercisable in respect of any payment due from the Employer to the Contractor under such interim arrangement.

27·5 ·4 From the date when, under clause 27·3·4, the Employer may first determine the employment of the Contractor (but subject to any agreement made pursuant to clause 27·5·2·1 or arrangement made pursuant to clause 27·5·3) the Employer may take reasonable measures to ensure that Site Materials, the site and the Works are adequately protected and that Site Materials are retained in, on the site of or adjacent to the Works as the case may be. The Contractor shall allow and shall in no way hinder or delay the taking of the aforesaid measures. The Employer may deduct the reasonable cost of taking such measures from any monies due or to become due to the Contractor under this Contract (including any amount due under an agreement to which clause 27·5·2·1, or under an interim arrangement to which clause 27·5·3, refers) or may recover the same from the Contractor as a debt.

Footnote   [kk] See JCT Practice Note 24: after certain insolvency events an Insolvency Practitioner acts for the Contractor.

Appendix 1

27·6 In the event of the determination of the employment of the Contractor under clause 27·2·2, 27·2·3, 27·3·3, 27·3·4 or 27·4 and so long as that employment has not been reinstated then:

27·6 ·1 the Employer may employ and pay other persons to carry out and complete the Works and to make good defects of the kind referred to in clause 17 and he or they may enter upon the site and the Works and use all temporary buildings, plant, tools, equipment and Site Materials, and may purchase all materials and goods necessary for the carrying out and completion of the Works and for the making good of defects as aforesaid; provided that where the aforesaid temporary buildings, plant, tools, equipment and Site Materials are not owned by the Contractor the consent of the owner thereof to such use is obtained by the Employer;

27·6 ·2 ·1 except where an insolvency event listed in clause 27·3·1 (other than the Contractor being a company making a proposal for a voluntary arrangement for a composition of debts or scheme of arrangement to be approved in accordance with the Companies Act 1985 or the insolvency Act 1986 as the case may be or any amendment or re-enactment) has occurred the Contractor shall, if so required by the Employer or by the Architect on behalf of the Employer within 14 days of the date of determination, assign to the Employer without payment the benefit of any agreement for the supply of materials or goods and/or for the execution of any work for the purposes of this Contract to the extent that the same is assignable;

 ·2 ·2 except where the Contractor has a trustee in bankruptcy appointed or being a company has a provisional liquidator appointed or has a petition alleging insolvency filed against it which is subsisting or passes a resolution for voluntary winding-up (other than for the purposes of amalgamation or reconstruction) which takes effect as a creditors' voluntary liquidation, the Employer may pay any supplier or sub-contractor for any materials or goods delivered or works executed for the purposes of this Contract before or after the date of determination in so far as the price thereof has not already been discharged by the Contractor. Payments made under clause 27·6·2·2 may be deducted from any sum due or to become due to the Contractor or may be recoverable from the Contractor by the Employer as a debt;

27·6 ·3 the Contractor shall, when required in writing by the Architect so to do (but not before), remove from the Works any temporary buildings, plant, tools, equipment, goods and materials belonging to him and the Contractor shall have removed by their owner any temporary buildings, plant, tools, equipment, goods and materials not owned by him. If within a reasonable time after such requirement has been made the Contractor has not complied therewith in respect of temporary buildings, plant, tools, equipment, goods and materials belonging to him, then the Employer may (but without being responsible for any loss or damage) remove and sell any such property of the Contractor, holding the proceeds less all costs incurred to the credit of the Contractor.

27·6 ·4 ·1 Subject to clauses 27·5·3 and 27·6·4·2 the provisions of this Contract which require any further payment or any release or further release of Retention to the Contractor shall not apply; provided that clause 27·6·4·1 shall not be construed so as to prevent the enforcement by the Contractor of any rights under this Contract in respect of amounts properly due to be discharged by the Employer to the Contractor which the Employer has unreasonably not discharged and which, where clause 27·3·4 applies, have accrued 28 days or more before the date when under clause 27·3·4 the Employer could first give notice to determine the employment of the Contractor or, where clause 27·3·4 does not apply, which have accrued 28 days or more before the date of determination of the employment of the Contractor.

 ·4 ·2 Upon the completion of the Works and the making good of defects as referred to in clause 27·6·1 (but subject, where relevant, to the exercise of the right under clause 17·2 and/or clause 17·3 of the Architect, with the consent of the Employer, not to require defects of the kind referred to in clause 17 to be made good) then within a reasonable time thereafter an account in respect of the matters referred to in clause 27·6·5 shall be set out either in a statement prepared by the Employer or in a certificate issued by the Architect.

27·6 ·5 ·1 The amount of expenses properly incurred by the Employer including those incurred pursuant to clause 27·6·1 and of any direct loss and/or damage caused to the Employer as a result of the determination;

 ·5 ·2 the amount of any payment made to the Contractor;

355

Appendix 1

27·6	*continued*

·5 ·3 the total amount which would have been payable for the Works in accordance with this Contract.

27·6 ·6 If the sum of the amounts stated under clauses 27·6·5·1 and 27·6·5·2 exceeds or is less than the amount stated under clause 27·6·5·3 the difference shall be a debt payable by the Contractor to the Employer or by the Employer to the Contractor as the case may be.

Employer decides not to complete the Works

27·7 ·1 If the Employer decides after the determination of the employment of the Contractor not to have the Works carried out and completed, he shall so notify the Contractor in writing within 6 months from the date of such determination. Within a reasonable time from the date of such written notification the Employer shall send to the Contractor a statement of account setting out:

·1 ·1 the total value of work properly executed at the date of determination of the employment of the Contractor, such value to be ascertained in accordance with the Conditions as if the employment of the Contractor had not been determined, together with any amounts due to the Contractor under the Conditions not included in such total value;

·1 ·2 the amount of any expenses properly incurred by the Employer and of any direct loss and/or damage caused to the Employer as a result of the determination.

After taking into account amounts previously paid to the Contractor under this Contract, if the amount stated under clause 27·7·1·2 exceeds or is less than the amount stated under clause 27·7·1·1 the difference shall be a debt payable by the Contractor to the Employer or by the Employer to the Contractor as the case may be.

27·7 ·2 If after the expiry of the 6 month period referred to in clause 27·7·1 the Employer has not begun to operate the provisions of clause 27·6·1 and has not given a written notification pursuant to clause 27·7·1 the Contractor may require by notice in writing to the Employer that he states whether clauses 27·6·1 to 27·6·6 are to apply and, if not to apply, require that a statement of account pursuant to clause 27·7·1 be prepared by the Employer for submission to the Contractor.

Other rights and remedies

27·8 The provisions of clauses 27·2 to 27·7 are without prejudice to any other rights and remedies which the Employer may possess.

28 Determination by Contractor

Notices under clause 28

28·1 Any notice or further notice to which clauses 28·2·1, 28·2·2, 28·2·3, 28·2·4 and 28·3 refer shall be in writing and given by actual delivery, or by special delivery or by recorded delivery. If sent by special delivery or recorded delivery the notice or further notice shall, subject to proof to the contrary, be deemed to have been received 48 hours after the date of posting (excluding Saturday and Sunday and Public Holidays).

Default by Employer – suspension of uncompleted works

28·2 ·1 If the Employer shall make default in any one or more of the following respects:

·1 ·1 he does not pay by the final date for payment the amount properly due to the Contractor in respect of any certificate and/or any VAT on that amount pursuant to the VAT Agreement; or

·1 ·2 he interferes with or obstructs the issue of any certificate due under this Contract; or

·1 ·3 he fails to comply with the provisions of clause 19·1·1; or

·1 ·4 he fails pursuant to the Conditions to comply with the requirements of the CDM Regulations,

the Contractor may give to the Employer a notice specifying the default or defaults (the 'specified default or defaults').

356

Appendix 1

28·2 ·2 If, before the date of Practical Completion, the carrying out of the whole or substantially the whole of the uncompleted Works is suspended for the continuous period of the length stated in the Appendix by reason of one or more of the following events:

    ·1 ·1 where an Information Release Schedule has been provided, failure of the Architect to comply with clause 5·4·1, or

    ·1 ·2 failure of the Architect to comply with clause 5·4·2, or

    ·2 ·2 Architect's instructions issued under clause 2·3, 13·2 or 23·2 unless caused by reason of some negligence or default of the Contractor, his servants or agents or of any person employed or engaged upon or in connection with the Works or any part thereof, his servants or agents other than a Nominated Sub-Contractor, the Employer or any person employed or engaged by the Employer; or

    ·2 ·3 delay in the execution of work not forming part of this Contract by the Employer himself or by persons employed or otherwise engaged by the Employer as referred to in clause 29 or the failure to execute such work or delay in the supply by the Employer of materials and goods which the Employer has agreed to supply for the Works or the failure so to supply; or

    ·2 ·4 failure of the Employer to give in due time ingress to or egress from the site of the Works or any part thereof through or over any land, buildings, way or passage adjoining or connected with the site and in the possession and control of the Employer, in accordance with the relevant Contract Documents, after receipt by the Architect of such notice, if any, as the Contractor is required to give, or failure of the Employer to give such ingress or egress as otherwise agreed between the Architect and the Contractor,

the Contractor may give to the Employer a notice specifying the event or events ('the specified suspension event or events').

28·2 ·3 If

    – the Employer continues a specified default, or

    – a specified suspension event is continued

for 14 days from receipt of the notice under clause 28·2·1 or clause 28·2·2 then the Contractor may on, or within 10 days from, the expiry of that 14 days by a further notice to the Employer determine the employment of the Contractor under this Contract. Such determination shall take effect on the date of receipt of such further notice.

28·2 ·4 If

    – the Employer ends the specified default or defaults, or

    – the specified suspension event or events cease, or

    – the Contractor does not give the further notice referred to in clause 28·2·3

and

    – the Employer repeats (whether previously repeated or not) a specified default, or

    – a specified suspension event is repeated for whatever period (whether previously repeated or not), whereby the regular progress of the Works is or is likely to be materially affected

then, upon or within a reasonable time after such repetition, the Contractor may by notice to the Employer determine the employment of the Contractor under this Contract. Such determination shall take effect on the date of receipt of such notice.

28·2 ·5 A notice of determination under clause 28·2·3 or clause 28·2·4 shall not be given unreasonably or vexatiously.

357

Appendix 1

28·3 ·1 If the Employer [II]

makes a composition or arrangement with his creditors, or becomes bankrupt, or,

being a company,

makes a proposal for a voluntary arrangement for a composition of debts or scheme of arrangement to be approved in accordance with the Companies Act 1985 or the Insolvency Act 1986 as the case may be or any amendment or re-enactment thereof, or

has a provisional liquidator appointed, or

has a winding-up order made, or

passes a resolution for voluntary winding-up (except for the purposes of amalgamation or reconstruction), or

under the Insolvency Act 1986 or any amendment or re-enactment thereof has an administrator or an administrative receiver appointed

then:

28·3 ·2 the Employer shall immediately inform the Contractor in writing if he has made a composition or arrangement with his creditors, or, being a company, has made a proposal for a voluntary arrangement for a composition of debts or scheme of arrangement to be approved in accordance with the Companies Act 1985 or the Insolvency Act 1986 or any amendment or re-enactment thereof as the case may be;

28·3 ·3 the Contractor may by notice to the Employer determine the employment of the Contractor under this Contract. Such determination shall take effect on the date of receipt of such notice. Provided that after the occurrence of any of the events set out in clause 28·3·1 and before the taking effect of any notice of determination of his employment issued by the Contractor pursuant to clause 28·3·3 the obligation of the Contractor to carry out and complete the Works in compliance with clause 2·1 shall be suspended.

28·4 In the event of the determination of the employment of the Contractor under clause 28·2·3, 28·2·4 or 28·3·3 and so long as that employment has not been reinstated the provisions of clauses 28·4·1, 28·4·2 and 28·4·3 shall apply; such application shall be without prejudice to the accrued rights or remedies of either party or to any liability of the classes mentioned in clause 20 which may accrue either before the Contractor or any sub-contractors, their servants or agents or others employed on or engaged upon or in connection with the Works or any part thereof other than the Employer or any person employed or engaged by the Employer shall have removed his or their temporary buildings, plant, tools, equipment, goods or materials (including Site Materials) or by reason of his or their so removing the same. Subject to clauses 28·4·2 and 28·4·3 the provisions of this Contract which require any payment or release or further release of Retention to the Contractor shall not apply.

28·4 ·1 The Contractor shall, with all reasonable dispatch and in such manner and with such precautions as will prevent injury, death or damage of the classes in respect of which before the date of determination he was liable to indemnify the Employer under clause 20, remove from the site all his temporary buildings, plant, tools, equipment, goods and materials (including Site Materials) and shall ensure that his sub-contractors do the same, but subject always to the provisions of clause 28·4·3·5.

28·4 ·2 Within 28 days of the determination of the employment of the Contractor the Employer shall pay to the Contractor the Retention deducted by the Employer prior to the determination of the employment of the Contractor but subject to any right of the Employer of deduction therefrom which has accrued before the date of determination of the Contractor's employment.

28·4 ·3 The Contractor shall with reasonable dispatch prepare an account setting out the sum of the amounts referred to in clauses 28·4·3·1 to 28·4·3·5 which shall include as relevant amounts in respect of all Nominated Sub-Contractors:

Appendix 1

28·4 *continued*

· 3 ·1 the total value of work properly executed at the date of determination of the employment of the Contractor, such value to be ascertained in accordance with the Conditions as if the employment of the Contractor had not been determined, together with any amounts due to the Contractor under the Conditions not included in such total value; and

· 3 ·2 any sum ascertained in respect of direct loss and/or expense under clauses 26 and 34·3 (whether ascertained before or after the date of determination); and

· 3 ·3 the reasonable cost of removal pursuant to clause 28·4·1; and

· 3 ·4 any direct loss and/or damage caused to the Contractor by the determination; and

· 3 ·5 the cost of materials or goods (including Site Materials) properly ordered for the Works for which the Contractor shall have paid or for which the Contractor is legally bound to pay, and on such payment in full by the Employer such materials or goods shall become the property of the Employer.

After taking into account amounts previously paid to the Contractor under this Contract the Employer shall pay to the Contractor the amount properly due in respect of this account within 28 days of its submission by the Contractor to the Employer but without any deduction of Retention.

Other rights and remedies

28·5 The provisions of clauses 28·2 to 28·4 are without prejudice to any other rights and remedies which the Contractor may possess.

28A Determination by Employer or Contractor

Grounds for determination of the employment of the Contractor

28A·1 ·1 If, before the date of Practical Completion, the carrying out of the whole or substantially the whole of the uncompleted Works is suspended for the relevant continuous period of the length stated in the Appendix by reason of one or more of the following events:

·1 ·1 force majeure; or

·1 ·2 loss or damage to the Works occasioned by any one or more of the Specified Perils; or

·1 ·3 civil commotion; or

·1 ·4 Architect's instructions issued under clause 2·3, 13·2 or 23·2 which have been issued as a result of the negligence or default of any local authority or statutory undertaker executing work solely in pursuance of its statutory obligations; or

·1 ·5 hostilities involving the United Kingdom (whether war be declared or not); or

·1 ·6 terrorist activity

then the Employer or the Contractor may upon the expiry of the aforesaid relevant period of suspension give notice in writing to the other by actual delivery or by special delivery or recorded delivery that unless the suspension is terminated within 7 days after the date of receipt of that notice the employment of the Contractor under this Contract will determine 7 days after the date of receipt of the aforesaid notice; and the employment of the Contractor shall so determine 7 days after receipt of such notice. If sent by special delivery or recorded delivery the notice shall, subject to proof to the contrary, be deemed to have been received 48 hours after the date of posting (excluding Saturday and Sunday and Public Holidays).

28A·1 ·2 The Contractor shall not be entitled to give notice under clause 28A·1·1 in respect of the matter referred to in clause 28A·1·1·2 where the loss or damage to the Works occasioned by any one or more of the Specified Perils was caused by some negligence or default of the Contractor, his servants or agents or of any person employed or engaged upon or in connection with the Works or any part thereof, his servants or agents other than the Employer or any person employed or engaged by the Employer or by any local authority or statutory undertaker executing work solely in pursuance of its statutory obligations.

359

28A·1 ·3   A notice of determination under clause 28A·1·1 shall not be given unreasonably or vexatiously.

28A·2   Upon determination of the employment of the Contractor under clause 28A·1·1 the provisions of this Contract which require any further payment or any release or further release of Retention to the Contractor shall not apply; and the provisions of clauses 28A·3 to 28A·6 shall apply.

28A·3   The Contractor shall, with all reasonable dispatch and in such manner and with such precautions as will prevent injury, death or damage of the classes in respect of which before the date of determination of his employment he was liable to indemnify the Employer under clause 20, remove from the site all his temporary buildings, plant, tools, equipment, goods and materials (including Site Materials) and shall ensure that his sub-contractors do the same, but subject always to the provisions of clause 28A·5·4.

28A·4   The Employer shall pay to the Contractor one half of the Retention deducted by the Employer prior to the determination of the employment of the Contractor within 28 days of the date of determination of the Contractor's employment and the other half as part of the account to which clause 28A·5 refers but subject to any right of deduction therefrom which has accrued before the date of such determination.

28A·5   The Contractor shall, not later than 2 months after the date of the determination of the Contractor's employment, provide the Employer with all documents (including those relating to Nominated Sub-Contractors and Nominated Suppliers) necessary for the preparation of the account to which this clause refers. Subject to due discharge by the Contractor of this obligation the Employer shall with reasonable dispatch prepare an account setting out the sum of the amounts referred to in clauses 28A·5·1 to 28A·5·4 and, if clause 28A·6 applies, clause 28A·5·5, which shall include as relevant amounts in respect of all Nominated Sub-Contractors:

28A·5 ·1   the total value of work properly executed at the date of determination of the employment of the Contractor, such value to be ascertained in accordance with the Conditions as if the employment of the Contractor had not been determined, together with any amounts due to the Contractor under the Conditions not included in such total value; and

28A·5 ·2   any sum ascertained in respect of direct loss and/or expense under clauses 26 and 34·3 (whether ascertained before or after the date of determination); and

28A·5 ·3   the reasonable cost of removal under clause 28A·3; and

28A·5 ·4   the cost of materials or goods (including Site Materials) properly ordered for the Works for which the Contractor shall have paid or for which the Contractor is legally bound to pay, and on such payment in full by the Employer such materials or goods shall become the property of the Employer; and

28A·5 ·5   any direct loss and/or damage caused to the Contractor by the determination.

After taking into account amounts previously paid to the Contractor under this Contract the Employer shall pay to the Contractor the amount properly due in respect of this account within 28 days of its submission by the Employer to the Contractor but without deduction of any Retention.

28A·6   Where determination of the employment of the Contractor has occurred in respect of the matter referred to in clause 28A·1·1·2 and the loss or damage to the Works occasioned by any one or more of the Specified Perils was caused by some negligence or default of the Employer or of any person for whom the Employer is responsible, then upon such determination of the employment of the Contractor the account prepared under clause 28A·5 shall include the amount, if any, to which clause 28A·5·5 refers.

28A·7   The Employer shall inform the Contractor in writing which part or parts of the amounts paid or payable under clause 28A·5 is or are fairly and reasonably attributable to any Nominated Sub-Contractor and shall so inform each Nominated Sub-Contractor in writing.

Appendix 1

29 **Works by Employer or persons employed or engaged by Employer**

Information in
Contract Bills

29·1 Where the Contract Bills, in regard to any work not forming part of this Contract and which is to be carried out by the Employer himself or by persons employed or otherwise engaged by him, provide such information as is necessary to enable the Contractor to carry out and complete the Works in accordance with the Conditions, the Contractor shall permit the execution of such work.

Information not in
Contract Bills

29·2 Where the Contract Bills do not provide the information referred to in clause 29·1 and the Employer requires the execution of work not forming part of this Contract by the Employer himself or by persons employed or otherwise engaged by the Employer, then the Employer may, with the consent of the Contractor (which consent shall not be unreasonably delayed or withheld), arrange for the execution of such work.

29·3 Every person employed or otherwise engaged by the Employer as referred to in clauses 29·1 and 29·2 shall for the purpose of clause 20 be deemed to be a person for whom the Employer is responsible and not to be a sub-contractor.

30 **Certificates and payments**

Interim
Certificates and
valuations –
final date for
payment –
interest

30·1 ·1 ·1 The Architect shall from time to time as provided in clause 30 issue Interim Certificates stating the amount due to the Contractor from the Employer specifying to what the amount relates and the basis on which that amount was calculated; and the final date for payment pursuant to an Interim Certificate shall be 14 days from the date of issue of each Interim Certificate.

If the Employer fails properly to pay the amount, or any part thereof, due to the Contractor under the Conditions by the final date for its payment the Employer shall pay to the Contractor in addition to the amount not properly paid simple interest thereon for the period until such payment is made. Payment of such simple interest shall be treated as a debt due to the Contractor by the Employer. The rate of interest payable shall be five per cent (5%) over the Base Rate of the Bank of England which is current at the date the payment by the Employer became overdue. Any payment of simple interest under this clause 30·1·1·1 shall not in any circumstances be construed as a waiver by the Contractor of his right to proper payment of the principal amount due from the Employer to the Contractor in accordance with, and within the time stated in, the Conditions or of the rights of the Contractor in regard to suspension of the performance of his obligations under this Contract to the Employer pursuant to clause 30·1·4 or to determination of his employment pursuant to the default referred to in clause 28·2·1·1.

·1 ·2 Notwithstanding the fiduciary interest of the Employer in the Retention as stated in clause 30·5·1 the Employer is entitled to exercise any right under this Contract of withholding and/or deduction from monies due or to become due to the Contractor against any amount so due under an Interim Certificate whether or not any Retention is included in that Interim Certificate by the operation of clause 30·4. Such withholding and/or deduction is subject to the restriction in clause 35·13·5·3·2.

·1 ·3 Not later than 5 days after the date of issue of an Interim Certificate the Employer shall give a written notice to the Contractor which shall, in respect of the amount stated as due in that Interim Certificate, specify the amount of the payment proposed to be made, to what the amount of the payment relates and the basis on which that amount is calculated.

·1 ·4 Not later than 5 days before the final date for payment of the amount due pursuant to clause 30·1·1·1 the Employer may give a written notice to the Contractor which shall specify any amount proposed to be withheld and/or deducted from that due amount, the ground or grounds for such withholding and/or deduction and the amount of withholding and/or deduction attributable to each ground.

·1 ·5 Where the Employer does not give any written notice pursuant to clause 30·1·1·3 and/or to clause 30·1·1·4 the Employer shall pay the Contractor the amount due pursuant to clause 30·1·1·1.

361

Advance payment	30·1	·1	·6	Where it is stated in the Appendix that clause 30·1·1·6 applies, the advance payment identified in the Appendix shall be paid to the Contractor on the date stated in the Appendix and such advance payment shall be reimbursed to the Employer by the Contractor on the terms stated in the Appendix. Provided that where the Appendix states that an advance payment bond is required such payment shall only be made if the Contractor has provided to the Employer such bond from a surety approved by the Employer on the terms agreed between the British Bankers' Association and the JCT and annexed to the Appendix unless pursuant to the Seventh Recital a bond on other terms is required by the Employer.

| Interim valuations | 30·1 | ·2 | ·1 | Interim valuations shall be made by the Quantity Surveyor whenever the Architect considers them to be necessary for the purpose of ascertaining the amount to be stated as due in an Interim Certificate. [mm] |

| Application by Contractor – amount of gross valuation | | ·2 | ·2 | Without prejudice to the obligation of the Architect to issue Interim Certificates as stated in clause 30·1·1·1, the Contractor, not later than 7 days before the date of an Interim Certificate, may submit to the Quantity Surveyor an application which sets out what the Contractor considers to be the amount of the gross valuation pursuant to clause 30·2. The Contractor shall include with his application any application made to the Contractor by a Nominated Sub-Contractor which sets out what the Nominated Sub-Contractor considers to be the amount of the gross valuation pursuant to clause 4·17 of Conditions NSC/C. If the Contractor submits such an application the Quantity Surveyor shall make an interim valuation. To the extent that the Quantity Surveyor disagrees with the gross valuation in the Contractor's application and/or in a Nominated Sub-Contractor's application the Quantity Surveyor at the same time as making the valuation shall submit to the Contractor a statement, which shall be in similar detail to that given in the application, which identifies such disagreement. |

| Issue of Interim Certificates | 30·1 | ·3 | | Interim Certificates shall be issued at the Period of Interim Certificates specified in the Appendix up to and including the end of the period during which the certificate of Practical Completion is issued. Thereafter Interim Certificates shall be issued as and when further amounts are ascertained as payable to the Contractor from the Employer and after the expiration of the Defects Liability Period named in the Appendix or upon the issue of the Certificate of Completion of Making Good Defects (whichever is the later) provided always that the Architect shall not be required to issue an Interim Certificate within one calendar month of having issued a previous Interim Certificate. |

| Right of suspension of obligations by Contractor | 30·1 | ·4 | | Without prejudice to any other rights and remedies which the Contractor may possess, if the Employer shall, subject to any notice issued pursuant to clause 30·1·1·4, fail to pay the Contractor in full (including any VAT due pursuant to the VAT Agreement) by the final date for payment as required by the Conditions and such failure shall continue for 7 days after the Contractor has given to the Employer, with a copy to the Architect, written notice of his intention to suspend the performance of his obligations under this Contract to the Employer and the ground or grounds on which it is intended to suspend performance then the Contractor may suspend such performance of his obligations under this Contract to the Employer until payment in full occurs. Such suspension shall not be treated as a suspension to which clause 27·2·1·1 refers or a failure to proceed regularly and diligently with the Works to which clause 27·2·1·2 refers. |

| Ascertainment of amounts due in Interim Certificates | 30·2 | | | The amount stated as due in an Interim Certificate, subject to any agreement between the parties as to stage payments, shall be the gross valuation as referred to in clause 30·2 less |

any amount which may be deducted and retained by the Employer as provided in clause 30·4 (in the Conditions called 'the Retention') and

the amount of any advance payment or part thereof due for reimbursement to the Employer in accordance with the terms for such reimbursement stated in the Appendix pursuant to clause 30·1·1·6 and

the total amount stated as due in Interim Certificates previously issued under the Conditions.

The gross valuation shall be the total of the amounts referred to in clauses 30·2·1 and 30·2·2 less the total of the amounts referred to in clause 30·2·3 and applied up to and including a date not more than 7 days before the date of the Interim Certificate.

Footnote

[mm] Where formula adjustment under clause 40 applies, clause 40·2·1 provides: "Interim valuations shall be made before the issue of each Interim Certificate and accordingly the words "whenever the Architect considers them to be necessary" shall be deemed to have been deleted in clause 30·1·2·1".

Appendix 1

30·2 **·1** There shall be included the following which are subject to Retention:

·1 **·1** the total value of the work properly executed by the Contractor including any work so executed to which Alternative B in clause 13·4·1·2 applies or to which a Price Statement or any part thereof accepted pursuant to clause 13·4·1·2 paragraph A2 or amended Price Statement or any part thereof accepted pursuant to clause 13·4·1·2 paragraph A4·2 applies but excluding any restoration, replacement or repair of loss or damage and removal and disposal of debris which in clauses 22B·3·5 and 22C·4·4·2 are treated as if they were a Variation, together with, where applicable, any adjustment of that value under clause 40. Where it is stated in the Appendix that a priced Activity Schedule is attached thereto the value of the work to which the Activity Schedule relates shall be the total of the various sums which result from the application of the proportion of the work in an activity listed in the Activity Schedule properly executed to the price for that work as stated in the Activity Schedule;

·1 **·2** the total value of the materials and goods delivered to or adjacent to the Works for incorporation therein by the Contractor but not so incorporated, provided that the value of such materials and goods shall only be included as and from such times as they are reasonably, properly and not prematurely so delivered and are adequately protected against weather and other casualties;

·1 **·3** the total value of any materials or goods or items pre-fabricated which are 'listed items' the value of which is required pursuant to clause 30·3 to be included in the amount stated as due in the Interim Certificate;

·1 **·4** the amounts referred to in clause 4·17·1 of Conditions NSC/C in respect of each Nominated Sub-Contractor;

·1 **·5** the profit of the Contractor upon the total of the amounts referred to in clauses 30·2·1·4 and 30·2·2·5 less the total of the amount referred to in clause 30·2·3·2 at the rates included in the Contract Bills, or, in the case where the nomination arises from an instruction as to the expenditure of a provisional sum, at rates related thereto, or, if none, at reasonable rates.

30·2 **·2** There shall be included the following which are not subject to Retention:

·2 **·1** any amounts to be included in Interim Certificates in accordance with clause 3 as a result of payments made or costs incurred by the Contractor under clauses 6·2, 8·3, 9·2, 21·2·3, 22B·2 and 22C·3;

·2 **·2** any amounts ascertained under clause 26·1 or 34·3 or in respect of any restoration, replacement or repair of loss or damage and removal and disposal of debris which in clauses 22B·3·5 and 22C·4·4·2 are treated as if they were a Variation;

·2 **·3** any amount to which clause 35·17 refers;

·2 **·4** any amount payable to the Contractor under clause 38 or 39, if applicable;

·2 **·5** the amounts referred to in clause 4·17·2 of Conditions NSC/C in respect of each Nominated Sub-Contractor.

30·2 **·3** There shall be deducted the following which are not subject to Retention:

·3 **·1** any amount deductible under clause 7 or 8·4·2 or 17·2 or 17·3 or any amount allowable by the Contractor to the Employer under clause 38 or 39, if applicable;

·3 **·2** any amount referred to in clause 4·17·3 of Conditions NSC/C in respect of each Nominated Sub-Contractor.

Off-site materials or goods – 'the listed items' **30·3** The materials or goods or items pre-fabricated for inclusion in the Works to which this clause refers ('the listed items') shall have been listed by the Employer in a list supplied to the Contractor and annexed to the Contract Bills . The amount stated as due in an Interim Certificate shall include the value of any listed items before delivery thereof to or adjacent to the Works provided that the following conditions have been fulfilled:

30·3 **·1** the Contractor has provided the Architect with reasonable proof that the property in uniquely identified listed items is vested in the Contractor so that, pursuant to clause 16·2, after the amount in respect thereof included in an Interim Certificate as properly due to the Contractor has been paid by the Employer, the uniquely identified listed items shall become the property of the Employer; and, if so stated in the Appendix, has also

363

30·3 ·1 *continued*

provided from a surety approved by the Employer a bond in favour of the Employer on the terms agreed between the JCT and the British Bankers' Association and annexed to the Appendix unless pursuant to the Seventh recital a bond on other terms is required by the Employer;

30·3 ·2 the Contractor in respect of listed items which are not uniquely identified has provided the Architect

with reasonable proof that the property in such listed items is vested in the Contractor so that, pursuant to clause 16·2, after the amount in respect thereof included in an Interim Certificate as properly due to the Contractor has been paid by the Employer, such listed items shall become the property of the Employer; and

the Contractor has provided from a surety approved by the Employer a bond in favour of the Employer on the terms agreed between the JCT and the British Bankers' Association and annexed to the Appendix unless pursuant to the Seventh recital a bond on other terms is required by the Employer;

30·3 ·3 the listed items are in accordance with the Contract;

30·3 ·4 the listed items at the premises where they have been manufactured or assembled or stored

either

are set apart

or

have been clearly and visibly marked individually or in sets by letters or figures or by reference to a pre-determined code

and identify

·4 ·1 the Employer and to whose order they are held; and

·4 ·2 their destination as the Works;

30·3 ·5 the Contractor has provided the Employer with reasonable proof that the listed items are insured against loss or damage for their full value under a policy of insurance protecting the interests of the Employer and the Contractor in respect of the Specified Perils, during the period commencing with the transfer of property in the listed items to the Contractor until they are delivered to, or adjacent to, the Works.

Retention – rules for ascertainment

30·4 ·1 The Retention which the Employer may deduct and retain as referred to in clause 30·2 shall be such percentage of the total amount included under clause 30·2·1 in any Interim Certificate as arises from the operation of the following rules:

·1 ·1 the percentage (in the Conditions and Appendix called 'the Retention Percentage') deductible under clause 30·4·1·2 shall be 5 per cent (unless a lower rate shall have been agreed between the parties and specified in the Appendix as the Retention Percentage); and the percentage deductible under clause 30·4·1·3 shall be one half of the Retention Percentage; [nn]

·1 ·2 [oo] the Retention Percentage may be deducted from so much of the said total amount as relates to:

work which has not reached Practical Completion (as referred to in clauses 17·1, 18·1·1 or 35·16); and

Footnotes

[nn] Where the Employer at the tender stage estimates the Contract Sum to be £500,000 or over, the Retention Percentage should not be more than 3 per cent.

[oo] By the operation of clauses 30·4·1·2 and 30·4·1·3 the Contractor will have released to him by the Employer upon payment of the next Interim Certificate after Practical Completion of the whole or part of the Works approximately one half of the Retention on the whole or the appropriate part; and upon payment of the next

Interim Certificate after the expiration of the Defects Liability Period named in the Appendix, or after the issue of the Certificate of Completion of Making Good Defects, whichever is the later, the balance of the Retention on the whole or the appropriate part. When Retention is so included in Interim Certificates it becomes a 'sum due' to the Contractor and therefore subject to the rights of the Employer to deduct therefrom in accordance with the rights of the Employer so to deduct as set out in the Conditions.

Appendix 1

30·4 ·1 ·2 *continued*

amounts in respect of the value of materials and goods included under clauses 30·2·1·2, 30·2·1·3 and 30·2·1·4 (so far as that clause relates to materials and goods as referred to in clause 4·17·1 of Conditions NSC/C);

·1 ·3 [oo] half the Retention Percentage may be deducted from so much of the said total amount as relates to work which has reached Practical Completion (as referred to in clauses 17·1, 18·1·1 or 35·16) but in respect of which a Certificate of Completion of Making Good Defects under clause 17·4 or a certificate under clause 18·1·2 or an Interim Certificate under clause 35·17 has not been issued.

30·4 ·2 The Retention deducted from the value of work executed by the Contractor or any Nominated Sub-Contractor, and from the value of materials and goods intended for incorporation in the Works but not so incorporated, and specified in the statements issued under clause 30·5·2·1, is hereinafter referred to as the 'Contractor's retention' and the 'Nominated Sub-Contract retention' respectively.

Rules on treatment of Retention

30·5 The Retention shall be subject to the following rules:

30·5 ·1 the Employer's interest in the Retention is fiduciary as trustee for the Contractor and for any Nominated Sub-Contractor (but without obligation to invest);

30·5 ·2 ·1 at the date of each Interim Certificate the Architect shall prepare, or instruct the Quantity Surveyor to prepare, a statement specifying the Contractor's retention and the Nominated Sub-Contract retention for each Nominated Sub-Contractor deducted in arriving at the amount stated as due in such Interim Certificate;

·2 ·2 such statement shall be issued by the Architect to the Employer, to the Contractor and to each Nominated Sub-Contractor whose work is referred to in the statement.

30·5 ·3 The Employer shall, to the extent that the Employer exercises his right under clause 30·4, if the Contractor or any Nominated Sub-Contractor so requests, at the date of payment under each Interim Certificate place the Retention in a separate banking account (so designated as to identify the amount as the Retention held by the Employer on trust as provided in clause 30·5·1) and certify to the Architect with a copy to the Contractor that such amount has been so placed. The Employer shall be entitled to the full beneficial interest in any interest accruing in the separate banking account and shall be under no duty to account for any such interest to the Contractor or any sub-contractor.

30·5 ·4 Where the Employer exercises the right to withhold and/or deduct referred to in clause 30·1·1·2 against any Retention he shall inform the Contractor of the amount of that withholding and/or deduction from either the Contractor's retention or the Nominated Sub-Contract retention of any Nominated Sub-Contractor by reference to the latest statement issued under clause 30·5·2·1.

Final adjustment of Contract Sum – documents from Contractor

30·6 ·1 ·1 Not later than 6 months after Practical Completion of the Works the Contractor shall provide the Architect, or, if so instructed by the Architect, the Quantity Surveyor, with all documents necessary for the purposes of the adjustment of the Contract Sum including all documents relating to the accounts of Nominated Sub-Contractors and Nominated Suppliers.

·1 ·2 Not later than 3 months after receipt by the Architect or by the Quantity Surveyor of the documents referred to in clause 30·6·1·1

·2 ·1 the Architect, or, if the Architect has so instructed, the Quantity Surveyor, shall ascertain (unless previously ascertained) any loss and/or expense under clauses 26·1, 26·4·1 and 34·3, and

·2 ·2 the Quantity Surveyor shall prepare a statement of all adjustments to be made to the Contract Sum as referred to in clause 30·6·2 other than any to which clause 30·6·1·2·1 applies

and the Architect shall forthwith send a copy of any ascertainment to which clause 30·6·1·2·1 refers and of the statement prepared in compliance with clause 30·6·1·2·2 to the Contractor and the relevant extract therefrom to each Nominated Sub-Contractor.

Appendix 1

30·6 ·2 The Contract Sum shall be adjusted by:

– the amount of any Valuations agreed by the Employer and the Contractor to which clause 13·4·1·1 refers, and

– the amounts stated in any 13A Quotations for which the Architect has issued to the Contractor a confirmed acceptance pursuant to clause 13A·3·2 and for the amount of any Variations thereto as valued pursuant to clause 13A·8, and

– the amount of any Price Statement or any part thereof accepted pursuant to clause 13·4·1·2 paragraph A2 or amended Price Statement or any part thereof accepted pursuant to clause 13·4·1·2 paragraph A4·2

and as follows:

there shall be deducted:

·2 ·1 all prime cost sums, all amounts in respect of sub-contractors named as referred to in clause 35·1, the certified value of any work by a Nominated Sub-Contractor, whose employment has been determined in accordance with clause 35·24, which was not in accordance with the relevant Sub-Contract but which has been paid or otherwise discharged by the Employer, and any Contractor's profit thereon included in the Contract Bills;

·2 ·2 all provisional sums and the value of all work for which an Approximate Quantity is included in the Contract Bills;

·2 ·3 the amount of the valuation under clause 13·5·2 of items omitted in accordance with a Variation required by the Architect under clause 13·2, or subsequently sanctioned by him in writing, together with the amount included in the Contract Bills for any other work as referred to in clause 13·5·5 which is to be valued under clause 13·5;

·2 ·4 any amount deducted or deductible under clause 7 or 8·4·2 or 17·2 or 17·3 or any amount allowed or allowable to the Employer under clause 38, 39 or 40, whichever is applicable;

·2 ·5 any other amount which is required by this Contract to be deducted from the Contract Sum;

there shall be added:

·2 ·6 the amounts of the nominated sub-contract sums or tender sums for all Nominated Sub-Contractors as finally adjusted or ascertained under all relevant provisions of Conditions NSC/C;

·2 ·7 the tender sum (or such other sum as is appropriate in accordance with the terms of the tender as accepted by or on behalf of the Employer) for any work for which a tender made under clause 35·2 has been accepted;

·2 ·8 any amounts properly chargeable to the Employer in accordance with the nomination instruction of the Architect in respect of materials or goods supplied by Nominated Suppliers; such amounts shall include the discount for cash of 5 per cent referred to in clause 36 but shall exclude any value added tax which is treated, or is capable of being treated, as input tax (as referred to in the Finance Act 1972) by the Contractor;

·2 ·9 the profit of the Contractor upon the amounts referred to in clauses 30·6·2·6, 30·6·2·7 and 30·6·2·8 at the rates included in the Contract Bills or in the cases where the nomination arises from an instruction as to the expenditure of a provisional sum at rates related thereto or if none at reasonable rates;

·2 ·10 any amounts paid or payable by the Employer to the Contractor as a result of payments made or costs incurred by the Contractor under clauses 6·2, 8·3, 9·2 and 21·2·3;

·2 ·11 the amount of the Valuation under clause 13·5 of any Variation, including the valuation of other work as referred to in clause 13·5·5, other than the amount of the valuation of any omission under clause 13·5·2;

Appendix 1

30·6 *continued*

·2 ·12 the amount of the Valuation of work executed by, or the amount of any disbursements by, the Contractor in accordance with instructions of the Architect as to the expenditure of provisional sums included in the Contract Bills and of all work for which an Approximate Quantity is included in the Contract Bills;

·2 ·13 any amount ascertained under clause 26·1 or 34·3;

·2 ·14 any amount paid by the Contractor under clause 22B or clause 22C which the Contractor is entitled to have added to the Contract Sum;

·2 ·15 any amount paid or payable to the Contractor under clause 38, 39 or 40, whichever is applicable;

·2 ·16 any other amount which is required by this Contract to be added to the Contract Sum;

·2 ·17 any amount to be paid in lieu of any ascertainment under clause 26·1 accepted pursuant to clause 13·4·1·2 paragraph A7.

Interim Certificate – final adjustment or ascertainment of nominated sub-contract sums

30·7 So soon as is practicable but not less than 28 days before the date of issue of the Final Certificate referred to in clause 30·8 and notwithstanding that a period of one month may not have elapsed since the issue of the previous Interim Certificate, the Architect shall issue an Interim Certificate the gross valuation for which shall include the amounts of the sub-contract sums for all Nominated Sub-Contracts as finally adjusted or ascertained under all relevant provisions of Conditions NSC/C.

Issue of Final Certificate

30·8 ·1 The Architect shall issue the Final Certificate (and inform each Nominated Sub-Contractor of the date of its issue) not later than 2 months after whichever of the following occurs last:

the end of the Defects Liability Period;

the date of issue of the Certificate of Completion of Making Good Defects under clause 17·4;

the date on which the Architect sent a copy to the Contractor of any ascertainment to which clause 30·6·1·2·1 refers and of the statement prepared in compliance with clause 30·6·1·2·2.

The Final Certificate shall state:

·1 ·1 the sum of the amounts already stated as due in Interim Certificates plus the amount of any advance payment paid pursuant to clause 30·1·1·6, and

·1 ·2 the Contract Sum adjusted as necessary in accordance with clause 30·6·2, and

·1 ·3 to what the amount relates and the basis on which the statement in the Final Certificate has been calculated

and the difference (if any) between the two sums shall (without prejudice to the rights of the Contractor in respect of any Interim Certificates which have subject to any notice issued pursuant to clause 30·1·1·4 not been paid in full by the Employer by the final date for payment of such Certificate) be expressed in the said Certificate as a balance due to the Contractor from the Employer or to the Employer from the Contractor as the case may be.

30·8 ·2 Not later than 5 days after the date of issue of the Final Certificate the Employer shall give a written notice to the Contractor which shall, in respect of any balance stated as due to the Contractor from the Employer in the Final Certificate, specify the amount of the payment proposed to be made, to what the amount of the payment relates and the basis on which that amount is calculated.

Appendix 1

30·8 · **3** The final date for payment of the said balance payable by the Employer to the Contractor or by the Contractor to the Employer as the case may be shall be 28 days from the date of issue of the said Certificate. Not later than 5 days before the final date for payment of the balance the Employer may give a written notice to the Contractor which shall specify any amount proposed to be withheld and/or deducted from any balance due to the Contractor, the ground or grounds for such withholding and/or deduction and the amount of withholding and/or deduction attributable to each ground.

30·8 · **4** Where the Employer does not give a written notice pursuant to clause 30·8·2 and/or clause 30·8·3 the Employer shall pay the Contractor the balance stated as due to the Contractor in the Final Certificate.

30·8 · **5** If the Employer or the Contractor fails properly to pay the said balance, or any part thereof, by the final date for its payment the Employer or the Contractor as the case may be shall pay to the other, in addition to the balance not properly paid, simple interest thereon for the period until such payment is made. The rate of interest payable shall be five per cent (5%) over the Base Rate of the Bank of England which is current at the date the payment by the Employer or by the Contractor as the case may be became overdue. Any payment of simple interest under this clause 30·8 shall not in any circumstances be construed as a waiver by the Contractor or by the Employer as the case may be of his right to proper payment of the aforesaid balance due from the Employer to the Contractor or from the Contractor to the Employer in accordance with this clause 30·8.

30·8 · **6** Liability for payment of the balance pursuant to clause 30·8·3 and of any interest pursuant to clause 30·8·5 shall be treated as a debt due to the Contractor by the Employer or to the Employer by the Contractor as the case may be.

Effect of Final Certificate

30·9 · **1** Except as provided in clauses 30·9·2 and 30·9·3 (and save in respect of fraud), the Final Certificate shall have effect in any proceedings under or arising out of or in connection with this Contract (whether by adjudication under article 5 or by arbitration under article 7A or by legal proceedings under article 7B) as

· **1** · **1** conclusive evidence that where and to the extent that any of the particular qualities of any materials or goods or any particular standard of an item of workmanship was described expressly in the Contract Drawings or the Contract Bills, or in any of the Numbered Documents, or in any instruction issued by the Architect under the Conditions, or in any drawings or documents issued by the Architect under clause 5·3·1·1 or 5·4 or 7, to be for the approval of the Architect, the particular quality or standard was to the reasonable satisfaction of the Architect, but such Certificate shall not be conclusive evidence that such or any other materials or goods or workmanship comply or complies with any other requirement or term of this Contract, and

· **1** · **2** conclusive evidence that any necessary effect has been given to all the terms of this Contract which require that an amount is to be added to or deducted from the Contract Sum or an adjustment is to be made of the Contract Sum save where there has been any accidental inclusion or exclusion of any work, materials, goods or figure in any computation or any arithmetical error in any computation, in which event the Final Certificate shall have effect as conclusive evidence as to all other computations, and

· **1** · **3** conclusive evidence that all and only such extensions of time, if any, as are due under clause 25 have been given, and

· **1** · **4** conclusive evidence that the reimbursement of direct loss and/or expense, if any, to the Contractor pursuant to clause 26·1 is in final settlement of all and any claims which the Contractor has or may have arising out of the occurrence of any of the matters referred to in clause 26·2 whether such claim be for breach of contract, duty of care, statutory duty or otherwise.

30·9 · **2** If any adjudication, arbitration or other proceedings have been commenced by either Party before the Final Certificate has been issued the Final Certificate shall have effect as conclusive evidence as provided in clause 30·9·1 after either

· **2** · **1** such proceedings have been concluded, whereupon the Final Certificate shall be subject to the terms of any decision, award or judgment in or settlement of such proceedings, or

368

Appendix 1

30·9 *continued*

·2 ·2 a period of 12 months after the issue of the Final Certificate during which neither Party has taken any further step in such proceedings, whereupon the Final Certificate shall be subject to any terms agreed in partial settlement,

whichever shall be the earlier.

30·9 ·3 If any adjudication, arbitration or other proceedings have been commenced by either Party within 28 days after the Final Certificate has been issued, the Final Certificate shall have effect as conclusive evidence as provided in clause 30·9·1 save only in respect of all matters to which those proceedings relate.

30·9 ·4 Where pursuant to clause 41A·7·1 either Party wishes to have a dispute or difference on which an Adjudicator has given his decision on a date which is after the date of issue of the Final Certificate finally determined by arbitration or legal proceedings, either Party may commence arbitration or legal proceedings within 28 days of the date on which the Adjudicator gave his decision.

Effect of certificates other than Final Certificate

30·10 Save as aforesaid no certificate of the Architect shall of itself be conclusive evidence that

30·10 ·1 any works, materials or goods

or

30·10 ·2 any Performance Specified Work

to which it relates are in accordance with this Contract.

31 Statutory tax deduction scheme

Definitions

31·1 In this Condition 'the Act' means the Income and Corporation Taxes Act 1988; 'the Regulations' means the Income Tax (Sub-Contractors in the Construction Industry) Regulations 1993 S.I. No. 743; "'contractor'" means a person who is a contractor for the purposes of the Act and the Regulations; 'evidence' means such evidence as is required by the Regulations to be produced to a 'contractor' for the verification of a 'sub-contractor's' tax certificate; 'statutory deduction' means the deduction referred to in S.559(4) of the Act or such other deduction as may be in force at the relevant time; "'sub-contractor'" means a person who is a sub-contractor for the purposes of the Act and the Regulations; 'tax certificate' is a certificate issuable under S.561 of the Act.

Whether Employer a 'contractor'

31·2 ·1 Clauses 31·3 to ·9 shall not apply if, in the Appendix, the Employer is stated not to be a 'contractor'.

31·2 ·2 If in the Appendix the words "is a 'contractor'" are deleted, nevertheless if, at any time up to the issue and payment of the Final Certificate, the Employer becomes such a 'contractor', the Employer shall so inform the Contractor and the provisions of clause 31 shall immediately thereupon become operative.

Provision of evidence – tax certificate

31·3 ·1 Not later than 21 days before the first payment under this Contract is due to the Contractor or after clause 31·2·2 has become operative the Contractor shall:

either

·1 ·1 provide the Employer with the evidence that the Contractor is entitled to be paid without the statutory deduction;

or

·1 ·2 inform the Employer in writing, and send a duplicate copy to the Architect, that he is not entitled to be paid without the statutory deduction.

31·3 ·2 If the Employer is not satisfied with the validity of the evidence submitted in accordance with clause 31·3·1·1, he shall within 14 days of the Contractor submitting such evidence notify the Contractor in writing that he intends to make the statutory deduction from payments due under this Contract to the Contractor who is a 'sub-contractor' and give his reasons for that decision. The Employer shall at the same time comply with clause 31·6·1.

Uncertificated Contractor obtains tax certificate	**31·4** ·1	Where clause 31·3·1·2 applies, the Contractor shall immediately inform the Employer if he obtains a tax certificate and thereupon clause 31·3·1·1 shall apply.

Expiry of tax certificate

31·4 ·2 If the period for which the tax certificate has been issued to the Contractor expires before the final payment is made to the Contractor under this Contract the Contractor shall not later than 28 days before the date of expiry:

either

·2 ·1 provide the Employer with evidence that the Contractor from the said date of expiry is entitled to be paid for a further period without the statutory deduction in which case the provisions of clause 31·3·2 shall apply if the Employer is not satisfied with the evidence;

or

·2 ·2 inform the Employer in writing that he will not be entitled to be paid without the statutory deduction after the said date of expiry.

Cancellation of tax certificate

31·4 ·3 The Contractor shall immediately inform the Employer in writing if his current tax certificate is cancelled and give the date of such cancellation.

Vouchers

31·5 The Employer shall, as a 'contractor' in accordance with the Regulations, send promptly to the Inland Revenue any voucher which, in compliance with the Contractor's obligations as a 'sub-contractor' under the Regulations, the Contractor gives to the Employer.

Statutory deduction – direct cost of materials

31·6 ·1 If at any time the Employer is of the opinion (whether because of the information given under clause 31·3·1·2 or of the expiry or cancellation of the Contractor's tax certificate or otherwise) that he will be required by the Act to make a statutory deduction from any payment due to be made the Employer shall immediately so notify the Contractor in writing and require the Contractor to state not later than 7 days before each future payment becomes due (or within 10 days of such notification if that is later) the amount to be included in such payment which represents the direct cost to the Contractor and any other person of materials used or to be used in carrying out the Works.

31·6 ·2 Where the Contractor complies with clause 31·6·1 he shall indemnify the Employer against loss or expense caused to the Employer by any incorrect statement of the amount of direct cost referred to in clause 31·6·1.

31·6 ·3 Where the Contractor does not comply with clause 31·6·1 the Employer shall be entitled to make a fair estimate of the amount of direct cost referred to in clause 31·6·1.

Correction of errors

31·7 Where any error or omission has occurred in calculating or making the statutory deduction the Employer shall correct that error or omission by repayment to, or by deduction from payments to, the Contractor as the case may be subject only to any statutory obligation on the Employer not to make such correction.

Relation to other clauses

31·8 If compliance with clause 31 involves the Employer or the Contractor in not complying with any other of the Conditions, then the provisions of clause 31 shall prevail.

Disputes or differences – application of relevant procedures

31·9 The relevant procedures applicable under the Contract to the resolution of disputes or differences shall apply to any dispute or difference between the Employer and the Contractor as to the operation of clause 31 except where the Act or the Regulations or any other Act of Parliament or statutory instrument, rule or order made under an Act of Parliament provide for some other method of resolving such dispute or difference.

32 [Number not used]

33 [Number not used]

Appendix 1

34   Antiquities

34·1 All fossils, antiquities and other objects of interest or value which may be found on the site or in excavating the same during the progress of the Works shall become the property of the Employer and upon discovery of such an object the Contractor shall forthwith:

34·1 ·1 use his best endeavours not to disturb the object and shall cease work if and insofar as the continuance of work would endanger the object or prevent or impede its excavation or its removal;

34·1 ·2 take all steps which may be necessary to preserve the object in the exact position and condition in which it was found; and

34·1 ·3 inform the Architect or the clerk of works of the discovery and precise location of the object.

34·2 The Architect shall issue instructions in regard to what is to be done concerning an object reported by the Contractor under clause 34·1, and (without prejudice to the generality of his power) such instructions may require the Contractor to permit the examination, excavation or removal of the object by a third party. Any such third party shall for the purposes of clause 20 be deemed to be a person for whom the Employer is responsible and not to be a sub-contractor.

34·3 ·1 If in the opinion of the Architect compliance with the provisions of clause 34·1 or with an instruction issued under clause 34·2 has involved the Contractor in direct loss and/or expense for which he would not be reimbursed by a payment made under any other provision of this Contract then the Architect himself shall ascertain or shall instruct the Quantity Surveyor to ascertain the amount of such loss and/or expense.

34·3 ·2 If and to the extent that it is necessary for the ascertainment of such loss and/or expense the Architect shall state in writing to the Contractor what extension of time, if any, has been made under clause 25 in respect of the Relevant Event referred to in clause 25·4·5·1 so far as that clause refers to clause 34.

34·3 ·3 Any amount from time to time so ascertained shall be added to the Contract Sum.

Part 2: Nominated Sub-Contractors and Nominated Suppliers

Nominated Sub-Contractors

35   GENERAL

Definition of a
Nominated Sub-
Contractor

35·1   Where

35·1   ·1   in the Contract Bills; or

35·1   ·2   in any instruction of the Architect under clause 13·3 on the expenditure of a provisional sum included in the Contract Bills; or

35·1   ·3   in any instruction of the Architect under clause 13·2 requiring a Variation to the extent, but not further or otherwise,

·3   ·1   that it consists of work additional to that shown upon the Contract Drawings and described by or referred to in the Contract Bills and

·3   ·2   that any supply and fixing of materials or goods or any execution of work by a Nominated Sub-Contractor in connection with such additional work is of a similar kind to any supply and fixing of materials or the execution of work for which the Contract Bills provided that the Architect would nominate a sub-contractor; or

35·1   ·4   by agreement (which agreement shall not be unreasonably delayed or withheld) between the Contractor and the Architect on behalf of the Employer

the Architect has, whether by the use of a prime cost sum or by naming a sub-contractor, reserved to himself the final selection and approval of the sub-contractor to the Contractor who shall supply and fix any materials or goods or execute work, the sub-contractor so named or to be selected and approved shall be nominated in accordance with the provisions of clause 35 and a sub-contractor so nominated shall be a Nominated Sub-Contractor for all the purposes of this Contract. The provisions of clause 35·1 shall apply notwithstanding the requirement in rule A51 of the Standard Method of Measurement, 7th Edition, for a PC sum to be included in the Bills of Quantities in respect of Nominated Sub-Contractors; where however such sum is included in the Contract Bills the provisions of the aforesaid rule A51 shall apply in respect thereof.

Contractor's
tender for works
otherwise
reserved for a
Nominated Sub-
Contractor

35·2   ·1   Where the Contractor in the ordinary course of his business directly carries out works included in the Contract Bills and to which clause 35 applies, and where items of such works are set out in the Appendix and the Architect is prepared to receive tenders from the Contractor for such items, then the Contractor shall be permitted to tender for the same or any of them but without prejudice to the Employer's right to reject the lowest or any tender. If the Contractor's tender is accepted, he shall not sub-let the work to a Domestic Sub-Contractor without the consent of the Architect. Provided that where an item for which the Architect intends to nominate a sub-contractor is included in Architect's instructions issued under clause 13·3 it shall be deemed for the purposes of clause 35·2·1 to have been included in the Contract Bills and the item of work to which it relates shall likewise be deemed to have been set out in the Appendix.

35·2   ·2   It shall be a condition of any tender accepted under clause 35·2 that clause 13 shall apply in respect of the items of work included in the tender as if for the reference therein to the Contract Drawings and the Contract Bills there were references to the equivalent documents included in or referred to in the tender submitted under clause 35·2.

35·2   ·3   None of the provisions of clause 35 other than clause 35·2 shall apply to works for which a tender of the Contractor is accepted under clause 35·2.

PROCEDURE FOR NOMINATION OF A SUB-CONTRACTOR

35·3   The nomination of a sub-contractor to which clause 35·1 applies shall be effected in accordance with clauses 35·4 to 35·9 inclusive.

Appendix 1

Documents relating to Nominated Sub-Contractors

35·4 The following documents relating to Nominated Sub-Contractors are issued by the JCT and are referred to in the Conditions and in those documents by the use either of the name or of the identification term:

Name of document	Identification term
The Standard Form of Nominated Sub-Contract Tender 1998 Edition which comprises:	NSC/T
Part 1: The Employer's Invitation to Tender to a Sub-Contractor	– Part 1
Part 2: Tender by a Sub-Contractor	– Part 2
Part 3: Particular Conditions (to be agreed by a Contractor and a Sub-Contractor nominated under clause 35·6)	– Part 3
The Standard Form of Articles of Nominated Sub-Contract Agreement between a Contractor and a Nominated Sub-Contractor, 1998 Edition	Agreement NSC/A
The Standard Conditions of Nominated Sub-Contract, 1998 Edition, incorporated by reference into Agreement NSC/A	Conditions NSC/C
The Standard Form of Employer/Nominated Sub-Contractor Agreement, 1998 Edition	Agreement NSC/W
The Standard Form of Nomination Instruction for a Sub-Contractor	Nomination NSC/N

Contractor's right of reasonable objection

35·5 ·1 No person against whom the Contractor makes a reasonable objection shall be a Nominated Sub-Contractor. The Contractor shall make such reasonable objection in writing at the earliest practicable moment but in any case not later than 7 working days from receipt of the instruction of the Architect under clause 35·6 nominating the sub-contractor.

35·5 ·2 Where such reasonable objection is made the Architect may either issue further instructions to remove the objection so that the Contractor can then comply with clause 35·7 in respect of such nomination instruction or cancel such nomination instruction and issue an instruction either under clause 13·2 omitting the work which was the subject of that nomination instruction or under clause 35·6 nominating another sub-contractor therefor. A copy of any instruction issued under clause 35·5·2 shall be sent by the Architect to the sub-contractor.

Architect's instruction on Nomination NSC/N – documents accompanying the instruction

35·6 The Architect shall issue an instruction to the Contractor on Nomination NSC/N nominating the sub-contractor which shall be accompanied by:

35·6 ·1 NSC/T Part 1 completed by the Architect and NSC/T Part 2 completed and signed by the sub-contractor and signed by or on behalf of the Employer as 'approved' together with a copy of the numbered tender documents listed in and enclosed with NSC/T Part 1 together with any additional documents and/or amendments thereto as have been approved by the Architect;

35·6 ·2 a copy of the completed Agreement NSC/W entered into between the Employer and the sub-contractor;

35·6 ·3 confirmation of any alterations to the information given in NSC/T Part 1

item 7: obligations or restrictions imposed by the Employer
item 8: order of Works: Employer's requirements
item 9: type and location of access; and

35·6 ·4 a copy of the Principal Contractor's Health and Safety Plan.

– copy of instruction to sub-contractor

A copy of the instruction shall be sent by the Architect to the sub-contractor together with a copy of the completed Appendix for the Main Contract.

Appendix 1

Contractor's obligations on receipt of Architect's instruction	**35·7**	The Contractor shall forthwith upon receipt of such instruction:
	35·7 ·1	complete in agreement with the sub-contractor NSC/T Part 3 and have that completed NSC/T Part 3 signed by or on behalf of the Contractor and by or on behalf of the sub-contractor; and
	35·7 ·2	execute Agreement NSC/A with the sub-contractor

and thereupon shall send a copy of the completed Agreement NSC/A and of the agreed and signed NSC/T Part 3 (but **not** the other Annexures to Agreement NSC/A) to the Architect.

Non-compliance with clause 35·7 – Contractor's obligation to notify Architect

35·8 If the Contractor, having used his best endeavours, has not, within 10 working days from receipt of such instruction, complied with clause 35·7, the Contractor shall thereupon by a notice in writing inform the Architect

either

35·8 ·1 of the date by which he expects to have complied with clause 35·7

or

35·8 ·2 that the non-compliance is due to other matters identified in the Contractor's notice. [pp]

Architect's duty on receipt of any notice under clause 35·8

35·9 Within a reasonable time after receipt of a notice under clause 35·8 the Architect shall:

35·9 ·1 where **clause 35·8·1 applies**, after consultation with the Contractor and so far as he considers it reasonable, fix a later date by which the Contractor shall have complied with clause 35·7;

35·9 ·2 where **clause 35·8·2 applies**, inform the Contractor in writing

either that he does not consider that the matters identified in the notice justify non-compliance by the Contractor with such nomination instruction, in which case the Contractor shall comply with clause 35·7 in respect of such nomination instruction

or that he does consider that the matters identified in the notice justify non-compliance by the Contractor with such nomination instruction, in which case the Architect shall either issue further instructions so that the Contractor can then comply with clause 35·7 in respect of such nomination instruction or cancel such nomination instruction and issue an instruction either under clause 13·2 omitting the work which was the subject of the nomination instruction or under clause 35·6 nominating another sub-contractor therefor. A copy of any instruction issued under clause 35·9·2 shall be sent by the Architect to the sub-contractor.

35·10 [Number not used]

35·11 [Number not used]

35·12 [Number not used]

Footnote [pp] The "other matters identified in the Contractor's notice" may include: any discrepancy in or divergence between the numbered tender documents or a discrepancy in or divergence between the numbered tender documents and the documents referred to in clauses 2·3·1 to 2·3·4; and any reasons given to the Contractor by the sub-contractor for not agreeing the items in NSC/T Part 3 or for not being prepared to have NSC/T Part 3 signed by or on his behalf which may relate to: the items in the Main Contract Appendix sent to him by the Architect with a copy of the nomination instruction differing from those in the Main Contract Appendix attached to the Architect's Invitation to Tender (NSC/T Part 1); or to any information given to him in items 7, 8 and 9 of the Architect's Invitation to Tender having been changed as confirmed by the Architect when issuing his nomination instruction (see clause 35·6·3), which changes have to be identified in NSC/T Part 3.

Appendix 1

PAYMENT OF NOMINATED SUB-CONTRACTOR

Architect
– direction as to
interim payment
for Nominated
Sub-Contractor

35·13 ·1 The Architect shall on the issue of each Interim Certificate:

·1 ·1 direct the Contractor as to the amount of each interim or final payment to Nominated Sub-Contractors which is included in the amount stated as due in Interim Certificates and the amount of such interim or final payment shall be computed by the Architect in accordance with the relevant provisions of Conditions NSC/C; and

·1 ·2 forthwith inform each Nominated Sub-Contractor of the amount of any interim or final payment directed in accordance with clause 35·13·1·1.

35·13 ·2 Each payment directed under clause 35·13·1·1 shall be paid by the Contractor by the final date for its payment in accordance with Conditions NSC/C.

Direct payment of
Nominated Sub-
Contractor

35·13 ·3 Before the issue of each Interim Certificate (other than the first Interim Certificate) and of the Final Certificate the Contractor shall provide the Architect with reasonable proof of payment by the Contractor pursuant to clause 35·13·2.

35·13 ·4 If the Contractor is unable to provide the reasonable proof referred to in clause 35·13·3 because of some failure or omission of the Nominated Sub-Contractor to provide any document or other evidence to the Contractor which the Contractor may reasonably require and the Architect is reasonably satisfied that this is the sole reason why reasonable proof is not furnished by the Contractor, the provisions of clause 35·13·5 shall not apply and the provisions of clause 35·13·3 shall be regarded as having been satisfied.

35·13 ·5 ·1 If the Contractor fails to provide reasonable proof under clause 35·13·3, the Architect shall issue a certificate to that effect stating the amount in respect of which the Contractor has failed to provide such proof, and the Architect shall issue a copy of the certificate to the Nominated Sub-Contractor concerned.

·5 ·2 Provided that the Architect has issued the certificate under clause 35·13·5·1, and subject to clause 35·13·5·3, the amount of any future payment otherwise due to the Contractor under this Contract (after deducting any amounts due to the Employer from the Contractor under this Contract) shall be reduced by any amounts due to Nominated Sub-Contractors which the Contractor has failed to discharge (together with the amount of any value added tax which would have been due to the Nominated Sub-Contractors) and the Employer shall himself pay the same to the Nominated Sub-Contractors concerned. Provided that the Employer shall in no circumstances be obliged to pay amounts to Nominated Sub-Contractors in excess of amounts available for reduction as aforesaid.

·5 ·3 The operation of clause 35·13·5·2 shall be subject to the following:

·3 ·1 where the Contractor would otherwise be entitled to payment of an amount stated as due in an Interim Certificate under clause 30, the reduction and payment to the Nominated Sub-Contractors referred to in clause 35·13·5·2 shall be made at the same time as the Employer pays the Contractor any balance due under clause 30 or, if there is no such balance, not later than the expiry of the period of 14 days within which the Contractor would otherwise be entitled to payment;

·3 ·2 where the sum due to the Contractor is the Retention or any part thereof, the reduction and payment to the Nominated Sub-Contractors referred to in clause 35·13·5·2 shall not exceed any part of the Contractor's retention (as defined in clause 30·4·2) which would otherwise be due for payment to the Contractor;

·3 ·3 where the Employer has to pay 2 or more Nominated Sub-Contractors but the amount due or to become due to the Contractor is insufficient to enable the Employer to pay the Nominated Sub-Contractors in full, the Employer shall apply the amount available pro rata to the amounts from time to time remaining undischarged by the Contractor or adopt such other method of apportionment as may appear to the Employer to be fair and reasonable having regard to all the relevant circumstances;

35·13 **·5** *continued*

·3 ·4 clause 35·13·5·2 shall cease to have effect absolutely if at the date when the reduction and payment to the Nominated Sub-Contractors referred to in clause 35·13·5·2 would otherwise be made there is in existence

either a Petition which has been presented to the Court for the winding up of the Contractor

or a resolution properly passed for the winding up of the Contractor other than for the purposes of amalgamation or reconstruction

whichever shall have first occurred. [qq]

Agreement
NSC/W –
pre-nomination
payments to
Nominated Sub-
Contractor by
Employer

35·13 **·6** Where, in accordance with clause 2·2 of Agreement NSC/W, the Employer, before the date of the issue of an instruction nominating a sub-contractor, has paid to him an amount in respect of design work and/or materials or goods and/or fabrication which is/ are included in the subject of the sub-contract sum or tender sum:

·6 ·1 the Employer shall send to the Contractor the written statement of the Nominated Sub-Contractor of the amount to be credited to the Contractor, and

·6 ·2 the Employer may make withholdings or deductions up to the amount of such credit from the amounts stated as due to the Contractor in any of the Interim Certificates which include amounts of interim or final payment to the Nominated Sub-Contractor; provided that the amount so withheld or deducted from that stated as due in any one Interim Certificate shall not exceed the amount of payment to the Nominated Sub-Contractor included therein as directed by the Architect.

EXTENSION OF PERIOD OR PERIODS FOR COMPLETION OF NOMINATED SUB-CONTRACT WORKS

35·14 **·1** The Contractor shall not grant to any Nominated Sub-Contractor any extension of the period or periods within which the sub-contract works (or where the sub-contract works are to be completed in parts any part thereof) are to be completed except in accordance with the relevant provisions of Conditions NSC/C which require the written consent of the Architect to any such grant.

35·14 **·2** The Architect shall operate the relevant provisions of Conditions NSC/C upon receiving any notice, particulars and estimate and a request from the Contractor and any Nominated Sub-Contractor for his written consent to an extension of the period or periods for the completion of the sub-contract works or any part thereof as referred to in clause 2·3 of Conditions NSC/C.

FAILURE TO COMPLETE NOMINATED SUB-CONTRACT WORKS

35·15 **·1** If any Nominated Sub-Contractor fails to complete the sub-contract works (or where the sub-contract works are to be completed in parts any part thereof) within the period specified in the Nominated Sub-Contract or within any extended time granted by the Contractor with the written consent of the Architect, and the Contractor so notifies the Architect with a copy to the Nominated Sub-Contractor, then, provided that the Architect is satisfied that clause 35·14 has been properly applied, the Architect shall so certify in writing to the Contractor. Immediately upon the issue of such a certificate the Architect shall send a duplicate thereof to the Nominated Sub-Contractor.

35·15 **·2** The certificate of the Architect under clause 35·15·1 shall be issued not later than 2 months from the date of notification to the Architect that the Nominated Sub-Contractor has failed to complete the sub-contract works or any part thereof.

Footnote

[qq] Where the Contractor is a person subject to bankruptcy laws and not the law relating to the insolvency of a company, clause 35·13·5·3·4 will require amendment to refer to the events on the happening of which bankruptcy occurs. (See also footnote [a].)

Appendix 1

PRACTICAL COMPLETION OF NOMINATED SUB-CONTRACT WORKS

35·16 When in the opinion of the Architect practical completion of the works executed by a Nominated Sub-Contractor is achieved and the Sub-Contractor has complied sufficiently with clause 5E·5 of Conditions NSC/C he shall forthwith issue a certificate to that effect and practical completion of such works shall be deemed to have taken place on the day named in such certificate, a duplicate copy of which shall be sent by the Architect to the Nominated Sub-Contractor; where clause 18 applies practical completion of works executed by a Nominated Sub-Contractor in a relevant part shall be deemed to have occurred on the relevant date to which clause 18·1 refers and the Architect shall send to the Nominated Sub-Contractor a copy of the written statement which he has issued pursuant to clause 18·1.

EARLY FINAL PAYMENT OF NOMINATED SUB-CONTRACTORS

35·17 Provided clause 5 of Agreement NSC/W remains in force unamended, then at any time after the day named in the certificate issued under clause 35·16 the Architect may, and on the expiry of 12 months from the aforesaid day shall, issue an Interim Certificate the gross valuation for which shall include the amount of the relevant sub-contract sum or ascertained final sub-contract sum as finally adjusted or ascertained under the relevant provisions of Conditions NSC/C; provided always that the Nominated Sub-Contractor:

35·17 ·1 has in the opinion of the Architect and the Contractor remedied any defects, shrinkages or other faults which have appeared and which the Nominated Sub-Contractor is bound to remedy under the Nominated Sub-Contract; and

35·17 ·2 has sent through the Contractor to the Architect or the Quantity Surveyor all documents necessary for the final adjustment of the sub-contract sum or the computation of the ascertained final sub-contract sum referred to in clause 35·17.

Defects in nominated sub-contract works after final payment of Nominated Sub-Contractor – before issue of Final Certificate

35·18 Upon payment by the Contractor by the final date for payment to the Nominated Sub-Contractor ('the original sub-contractor') of the amount certified under clause 35·17 then:

35·18 ·1 ·1 if the original sub-contractor fails to rectify any defect, shrinkage or other fault in the sub-contract works which he is bound to remedy under the Nominated Sub-Contract and which appears before the issue of the Final Certificate under clause 30·8 the Architect shall issue an instruction nominating a person ('the substituted sub-contractor') to carry out such rectification work and all the provisions relating to Nominated Sub-Contractors in clause 35 shall apply to such further nomination;

·1 ·2 the Employer shall take such steps as may be reasonable to recover, under the Agreement NSC/W, from the original sub-contractor a sum equal to the sub-contract price of the substituted sub-contractor. The Contractor shall pay or allow to the Employer any difference between the amount so recovered by the Employer and the sub-contract price of the substituted sub-contractor provided that, before the further nomination has been made, the Contractor has agreed (which agreement shall not be unreasonably delayed or withheld) to the sub-contract price to be charged by the substituted sub-contractor.

35·18 ·2 Nothing in clause 35·18 shall override or modify the provisions of clause 35·21.

Final payment – saving provisions

35·19 Notwithstanding any final payment to a Nominated Sub-Contractor under the provisions of clause 35:

35·19 ·1 until the date of Practical Completion of the Works or the date when the Employer takes possession of the Works, whichever first occurs, the Contractor shall be responsible for loss or damage to the sub-contract works for which a payment to which clause 35·17 refers has been made to the same extent but not further or otherwise than he is responsible for that part of the Works for which a payment as aforesaid has not been made;

35·19 ·2 the provisions of clause 22A or 22B or 22C whichever is applicable shall remain in full force and effect.

Appendix 1

POSITION OF EMPLOYER IN RELATION TO NOMINATED SUB-CONTRACTOR

35·20 Neither the existence nor the exercise of the powers in clause 35 nor anything else
contained in the Conditions shall render the Employer in any way liable to any Nominated
Sub-Contractor except by way and in the terms of the Agreement NSC/W.

CLAUSE 2·1 OF AGREEMENT NSC/W – POSITION OF CONTRACTOR

35·21 The Contractor shall not be responsible to the Employer for:

- ·1 the design of any nominated sub-contract works insofar as such nominated sub-
  contract works have been designed by a Nominated Sub-Contractor;

- ·2 the selection of the kinds of materials and goods for any nominated sub-contract works
  insofar as such kinds of materials and goods have been selected by a Nominated Sub-
  Contractor;

- ·3 the satisfaction of any performance specification or requirement insofar as such
  performance specification or requirement is included or referred to in the description of
  any nominated sub-contract works included in or annexed to the numbered tender
  documents enclosed with any NSC/T Part 1;

- ·4 the provision of any information required to be provided pursuant to Agreement NSC/W
  in reasonable time so that the Architect can comply with the provisions of clauses 5·4·1
  and 5·4·2 in respect thereof.

Nothing in this clause 35·21 shall affect the obligations of the Contractor under this Contract
in regard to the supply of workmanship, materials and goods by a Nominated Sub-
Contractor.

RESTRICTIONS IN CONTRACTS OF SALE ETC. – LIMITATION OF LIABILITY OF NOMINATED SUB-CONTRACTORS

35·22 Where any liability of the Nominated Sub-Contractor to the Contractor is limited under the
provisions of clause 1·7 of Conditions NSC/C, the liability of the Contractor to the Employer
shall be limited to the same extent.

35·23 [Number not used]

CIRCUMSTANCES WHERE RE-NOMINATION NECESSARY

35·24 If in respect of any Nominated Sub-Contract:

35·24 ·1 the Contractor informs the Architect that in the opinion of the Contractor the
Nominated Sub-Contractor has made default in respect of any one or more of the
matters referred to in clauses 7·1·1·1 to 7·1·1·4 of Conditions NSC/C; and the Contractor
has passed to the Architect any observations of the Nominated Sub-Contractor in regard
to the matters on which the Contractor considers the Nominated Sub-Contractor is in
default; and the Architect is reasonably of the opinion that the Nominated Sub-
Contractor has made default; or

35·24 ·2 the Contractor informs the Architect that one of the insolvency events referred to in
clause 7·2·1 of Conditions NSC/C *(Insolvency of Nominated Sub-Contractor)* has
occurred and **either** that under clause 7·2·3 of the aforesaid Conditions the employment
of the Nominated Sub-Contractor has been automatically determined **or** that under
clause 7·2·4 of those Conditions the Contractor has an option, with the written consent
of the Architect, to determine the employment of the Nominated Sub-Contractor; or

35·24 ·3 the Nominated Sub-Contractor determines his employment under clause 7·7 of
Conditions NSC/C; or

Appendix 1

35·24 **·4**   the Contractor has been required by the Employer to determine the employment of the Nominated Sub-Contractor under clause 7·3 of Conditions NSC/C and has so determined that employment; or

35·24 **·5**   work properly executed or materials or goods properly fixed or supplied by the Nominated Sub-Contractor have to be taken down and/or re-executed or re-fixed or re-supplied ('work to be re-executed') as a result of compliance by the Contractor or by any other Nominated Sub-Contractor with any instruction or other exercise of a power of the Architect under clauses 7 or 8·4 or 17·2 or 17·3 and the Nominated Sub-Contractor cannot be required under the Nominated Sub-Contract and does not agree to carry out the work to be re-executed;

then:

35·24 **·6**   Where **clause 35·24·1 applies**:

   ·6 **·1**   the Architect shall issue an instruction to the Contractor to give to the Nominated Sub-Contractor the notice specifying the default or defaults to which clause 7·1·1 of Conditions NSC/C refers; and may in that instruction state that the Contractor must obtain a further instruction of the Architect before determining the employment of the Nominated Sub-Contractor under clause 7·1·2 or 7·1·3 of Conditions NSC/C; and

   ·6 **·2**   the Contractor shall inform the Architect whether, following the giving of that notice for which the Architect has issued an instruction under clause 35·24·6·1, the employment of the Nominated Sub-Contractor has been determined by the Contractor under clause 7·1·2 or 7·1·3 of Conditions NSC/C; or where the further instruction referred to in clause 35·24·6·1 has been given by the Architect the Contractor shall confirm that the employment of the Nominated Sub-Contractor has been determined; then

   ·6 **·3**   if the Contractor informs or confirms to the Architect that the employment of the Nominated Sub-Contractor has been so determined the Architect shall make such further nomination of a sub-contractor in accordance with clause 35 as may be necessary to supply and fix the materials or goods or to execute the work and to make good or re-supply or re-execute as necessary any work executed by or any materials or goods supplied by the Nominated Sub-Contractor whose employment has been determined which were not in accordance with the relevant Nominated Sub-Contract.

35·24 **·7** **·1**   Where **clause 35·24·2 applies** and the Contractor has an option under clause 7·2·4 of Conditions NSC/C *(Insolvency of Nominated Sub-Contractor)* to determine the employment of the Nominated Sub-Contractor, clause 35·24·7·2 shall apply in respect of the written consent of the Architect to any determination of the employment of the Nominated Sub-Contractor.

   ·7 **·2**   Where

     –   the administrator or the administrative receiver of the Nominated Sub-Contractor, or

     –   the Nominated Sub-Contractor after making a composition or arrangement with his creditors or, being a company, after making a voluntary arrangement for a composition of debts or a scheme of arrangement approved in accordance with the Companies Act 1985 or the Insolvency Act 1986 or any amendment or re-enactment thereof as the case may be

   is, to the reasonable satisfaction of the Contractor and the Architect, prepared and able to continue to carry out the relevant Nominated Sub-Contract and to meet the liabilities thereunder, the Architect may withhold his consent. Where continuation on such terms does not apply the Architect shall give his consent to a determination by the Contractor of the employment of the Nominated Sub-Contractor unless the Employer and the Contractor otherwise agree.

   ·7 **·3**   Where the written consent of the Architect to the determination of the employment of the Nominated Sub-Contractor has been given and the Contractor has determined that employment or where, under clause 7·2·3 of the Conditions NSC/C, the employment of the Nominated Sub-Contractor has been automatically determined the following shall apply. The Architect shall make such further nomination of a sub-contractor in accordance with clause 35 as may be necessary to supply and fix the materials or goods or to execute the work and to make good or re-

35·24 ·7 ·3 *continued*

supply or re-execute as necessary any work executed by or any materials or goods supplied by the Nominated Sub-Contractor whose employment has been determined which were not in accordance with the relevant Nominated Sub-Contract.

·7 ·4 Where **clause 35·24·4 applies** the Architect shall make such further nomination of a sub-contractor in accordance with clause 35 as may be necessary to supply and fix the materials or goods or to execute the work and to make good or re-supply or re-execute as necessary any work executed by or any materials or goods supplied by the Nominated Sub-Contractor whose employment has been determined which were not in accordance with the relevant Nominated Sub-Contract.

35·24 ·8 ·1 Where **clause 35·24·3 applies** the Architect shall make such further nomination of a sub-contractor in accordance with clause 35 as may be necessary to supply and fix the materials or goods or to execute the work and to make good or re-supply or re-execute as necessary any work executed by or any materials or goods supplied by the Nominated Sub-Contractor who has determined his employment which were not in accordance with the relevant Nominated Sub-Contract.

·8 ·2 Where **clause 35·24·5 applies** the Architect shall make such further nomination of a sub-contractor in accordance with clause 35 as may be necessary to carry out the work to be re-executed referred to in clause 35·24·5.

35·24 ·9 The amount properly payable to the Nominated Sub-Contractor under the Nominated Sub-Contract resulting from such further nomination under clause 35·24·6·3 or 35·24·7·3 or 35·24·7·4 shall be included in the amount stated as due in Interim Certificates and added to the Contract Sum. Where clauses 35·24·3 and 35·24·8·1 apply any extra amount, payable by the Employer in respect of the sub-contractor nominated under the further nomination over the price of the Nominated Sub-Contractor who has validly determined his employment under his Nominated Sub-Contract, and where clauses 35·24·5 and 35·24·8·2 apply the amount payable by the Employer, resulting from such further nomination may at the time or any time after such amount is certified in respect of the sub-contractor nominated under the further nomination be deducted by the Employer from monies due or to become due to the Contractor under this Contract or may be recoverable from the Contractor by the Employer as a debt.

35·24 ·10 The Architect shall make the further nomination of a sub-contractor as referred to in clauses 35·24·6·3, 35·24·7, 35·24·8·1 and 35·24·8·2 within a reasonable time, having regard to all the circumstances, after the obligation to make such further nomination has arisen.

DETERMINATION OR DETERMINATION OF EMPLOYMENT OF NOMINATED SUB-CONTRACTOR – ARCHITECT'S INSTRUCTIONS

35·25 The Contractor shall not determine any Nominated Sub-Contract by virtue of any right to which he may be or may become entitled without an instruction from the Architect so to do.

35·26 ·1 Where the employment of the Nominated Sub-Contractor is determined under clauses 7·1 to 7·5 of Conditions NSC/C, the Architect shall provide the Contractor with the information and with the direction in an Interim Certificate to enable the Contractor to comply with clause 7·5·2 of Conditions NSC/C: namely the amount of expenses properly incurred by the Employer and the amount of direct loss and/or damage caused to the Employer by the determination of the employment of the Nominated Sub-Contractor; and shall, pursuant to clause 35·13·1, issue an Interim Certificate which certifies the value of any work executed or goods and materials supplied by the Nominated Sub-Contractor to the extent that such value has not been included in previous Interim Certificates.

35·26 ·2 Where the employment of the Nominated Sub-Contractor is determined under clause 7·7 of Conditions NSC/C and clause 7·8 of those Conditions applies, the Architect shall, pursuant to clause 35·13·1, issue an Interim Certificate which certifies the value of any work executed or goods and materials supplied by the Nominated Sub-Contractor to the extent that such value has not been included in previous Interim Certificates.

Appendix 1

Nominated Suppliers

Definition of a
Nominated
Supplier

36·1 ·1 In the Conditions 'Nominated Supplier' means a supplier to the Contractor who is nominated by the Architect in one of the following ways to supply materials or goods which are to be fixed by the Contractor:

·1 ·1 where a prime cost sum is included in the Contract Bills in respect of those materials or goods and the supplier is either named in the Contract Bills or subsequently named by the Architect in an instruction issued under clause 36·2;

·1 ·2 where a provisional sum is included in the Contract Bills and in any instruction by the Architect in regard to the expenditure of such sum the supply of materials or goods is made the subject of a prime cost sum and the supplier is named by the Architect in that instruction or in an instruction issued under clause 36·2;

·1 ·3 where a provisional sum is included in the Contract Bills and in any instruction by the Architect in regard to the expenditure of such a sum materials or goods are specified for which there is a sole source of supply in that there is only one supplier from whom the Contractor can obtain them, in which case the supply of materials or goods shall be made the subject of a prime cost sum in the instructions issued by the Architect in regard to the expenditure of the provisional sum and the sole supplier shall be deemed to have been nominated by the Architect;

·1 ·4 where the Architect requires under clause 13·2, or subsequently sanctions, a Variation and specifies materials or goods for which there is a sole supplier as referred to in clause 36·1·1·3, in which case the supply of the materials or goods shall be made the subject of a prime cost sum in the instruction or written sanction issued by the Architect under clause 13·2 and the sole supplier shall be deemed to have been nominated by the Architect.

36·1 ·2 In the Conditions the expression 'Nominated Supplier' shall not apply to a supplier of materials or goods which are specified in the Contract Bills to be fixed by the Contractor unless such materials or goods are the subject of a prime cost sum in the Contract Bills, notwithstanding that the supplier has been named in the Contract Bills or that there is a sole supplier of such materials or goods as defined in clause 36·1·1·3.

Architect's
instructions

36·2 The Architect shall issue instructions for the purpose of nominating a supplier for any materials or goods in respect of which a prime cost sum is included in the Contract Bills or arises under clause 36·1.

Ascertainment of
costs to be set
against prime cost
sum

36·3 ·1 For the purposes of clause 30·6·2·8 the amounts 'properly chargeable to the Employer in accordance with the nomination instruction of the Architect' shall include the total amount paid or payable in respect of the materials or goods less any discount other than the discount referred to in clause 36·4·4, properly so chargeable to the Employer and shall include where applicable:

·1 ·1 any tax (other than any value added tax which is treated, or is capable of being treated, as input tax (as referred to in the Finance Act 1972) by the Contractor) or duty not otherwise recoverable under this Contract by whomsoever payable which is payable under or by virtue of any Act of Parliament on the import, purchase, sale, appropriation, processing, alteration, adapting for sale or use of the materials or goods to be supplied; and

·1 ·2 the net cost of appropriate packing, carriage and delivery after allowing for any credit for return of any packing to the supplier; and

·1 ·3 the amount of any price adjustment properly paid or payable to, or allowed or allowable by, the supplier less any discount other than a cash discount for payment in full within 30 days of the end of the month during which delivery is made.

36·3 ·2 Where in the opinion of the Architect the Contractor properly incurs expense, which would not be reimbursed under clause 36·3·1 or otherwise under this Contract, in obtaining the materials or goods from the Nominated Supplier such expense shall be added to the Contract Sum.

Appendix 1

36·4   Save where the Architect and the Contractor shall otherwise agree, the Architect shall only nominate as a supplier a person who will enter into a contract of sale with the Contractor which provides, inter alia:

36·4 ·1   that the materials or goods to be supplied shall be of the quality and standard specified provided that where and to the extent that approval of the quality of materials or of the standards of workmanship is a matter for the opinion of the Architect such quality and standards shall be to the reasonable satisfaction of the Architect;

36·4 ·2   that the Nominated Supplier shall make good by replacement or otherwise any defects in the materials or goods supplied which appear up to and including the last day of the Defects Liability Period under this Contract and shall bear any expenses reasonably incurred by the Contractor as a direct consequence of such defects provided that:

      ·2 ·1   where the materials or goods have been used or fixed such defects are not such that reasonable examination by the Contractor ought to have revealed them before using or fixing;

      ·2 ·2   such defects are due solely to defective workmanship or material in the materials or goods supplied and shall not have been caused by improper storage by the Contractor or by misuse or by any act or neglect of either the Contractor, the Architect or the Employer or by any person or persons for whom they may be responsible or by any other person for whom the Nominated Supplier is not responsible;

36·4 ·3   that delivery of the materials or goods supplied shall be commenced, carried out and completed in accordance with a delivery programme to be agreed between the Contractor and the Nominated Supplier including, to the extent agreed, the following grounds on which that programme may be varied:

        force majeure; or

        civil commotion, local combination of workmen, strike or lock-out; or

        any instruction of the Architect under clause 13·2 *(Variations)* or clause 13·3 *(provisional sums)*; or

        failure of the Architect to supply to the Nominated Supplier within due time any necessary information for which he has specifically applied in writing on a date which was neither unreasonably distant from nor unreasonably close to the date on which it was necessary for him to receive the same; or

        exceptionally adverse weather conditions

        or, if no such programme is agreed, delivery shall be commenced, carried out and completed in accordance with the reasonable directions of the Contractor;

36·4 ·4   that the Nominated Supplier shall allow the Contractor a discount for cash of 5 per cent on all payments if the Contractor makes payment in full within 30 days of the end of the month during which delivery is made;

36·4 ·5   that the Nominated Supplier shall not be obliged to make any delivery of materials or goods (except any which may have been paid for in full less only any discount for cash) after the determination (for any reason) of the Contractor's employment under this Contract;

36·4 ·6   that full discharge by the Contractor in respect of payments for materials or goods supplied by the Nominated Supplier shall be effected within 30 days of the end of the month during which delivery is made less only a discount for cash of 5 per cent if so paid;

36·4 ·7   that the ownership of materials or goods shall pass to the Contractor upon delivery by the Nominated Supplier to or to the order of the Contractor, whether or not payment has been made in full;

36·4 ·8   that if any dispute or difference between the Contractor and the Nominated Supplier is referred to arbitration the provisions of clause 41B shall apply;

Appendix 1

36·4 ·9 that no provision in the contract of sale shall override, modify or affect in any way whatsoever the provisions in the contract of sale which are included therein to give effect to clauses 36·4·1 to 36·4·9 inclusive.

Contract of sale –
restriction,
limitation or
exclusion of
liability

36·5 ·1 Subject to clauses 36·5·2 and 36·5·3, where the said contract of sale between the Contractor and the Nominated Supplier in any way restricts, limits or excludes the liability of the Nominated Supplier to the Contractor in respect of materials or goods supplied or to be supplied, and the Architect has specifically approved in writing the said restrictions, limitations or exclusions, the liability of the Contractor to the Employer in respect of the said materials or goods shall be restricted, limited or excluded to the same extent.

36·5 ·2 The Contractor shall not be obliged to enter into a contract with the Nominated Supplier until the Architect has specifically approved in writing the said restrictions, limitations or exclusions.

36·5 ·3 Nothing in clause 36·5 shall be construed as enabling the Architect to nominate a supplier otherwise than in accordance with the provisions stated in clause 36·4.

Part 3: Fluctuations

Choice of
fluctuation
provisions – entry
in Appendix

37 ·1 Fluctuations shall be dealt with in accordance with whichever of the following alternatives
clause 38; or
clause 39 [rr]; or
clause 40 [ss]
is identified in the Appendix. The provisions so identified shall be [tt] deemed to be incorporated with the Conditions as executed by the parties hereto.

37 ·2 Clause 38 shall apply where neither clause 39 nor clause 40 is identified in the Appendix.

37 ·3 Neither clause 38 nor clause 39 nor clause 40 shall apply in respect of the work for which the Architect has issued to the Contractor a confirmed acceptance of a 13A Quotation or in respect of a Variation to such work.

Clause 38: Contribution, levy and tax fluctuations
Clause 39: Labour and materials cost and tax fluctuations
Clause 40: Use of price adjustment formulae

These clauses are published separately in 'Fluctuations: Fluctuation clauses for use with the Private versions'.

Footnotes

[rr] Clause 39 should be used where the parties have agreed to allow the labour and materials cost and tax fluctuations to which clauses 39·1 to ·3 refer. Alternatively, clause 40 should be used where the parties have agreed that fluctuations shall be dealt with by adjustment of the Contract Sum under the Price Adjustment Formulae for Building Contracts.

[ss] Clause 40 is used where the parties have agreed that fluctuations shall be dealt with by adjustment of the Contract Sum under the Price Adjustment Formulae for Building Contracts.

[tt] Notwithstanding the provisions of clause 37·1 on deemed incorporation the parties may nevertheless wish to incorporate the agreed alternative fluctuation provisions in the executed Contract.

Appendix 1

Part 4: Settlement of disputes – adjudication – arbitration – legal proceedings [uu]

41A Adjudication

Application of clause 41A

41A·1 Clause 41A applies where, pursuant to article 5, either Party refers any dispute or difference arising under this Contract to adjudication.

Identity of Adjudicator

41A·2 The Adjudicator to decide the dispute or difference shall be either an individual agreed by the Parties or, on the application of either Party, an individual to be nominated as the Adjudicator by the person named in the Appendix ('the nominator'). Provided that [vv]

41A·2 ·1 no Adjudicator shall be agreed or nominated under clause 41A·2 or clause 41A·3 who will not execute the Standard Agreement for the appointment of an Adjudicator issued by the JCT (the 'JCT Adjudication Agreement' [ww]) with the Parties, [vv] and

41A·2 ·2 where either Party has given notice of his intention to refer a dispute or difference to adjudication then

– any agreement by the Parties on the appointment of an adjudicator must be reached with the object of securing the appointment of, and the referral of the dispute or difference to, the Adjudicator within 7 days of the date of the notice of intention to refer *(see clause 41A·4·1)*;

– any application to the nominator must be made with the object of securing the appointment of, and the referral of the dispute or difference to, the Adjudicator within 7 days of the date of the notice of intention to refer.

Upon agreement by the Parties on the appointment of the Adjudicator or upon receipt by the Parties from the nominator of the name of the nominated Adjudicator the Parties shall thereupon execute with the Adjudicator the JCT Adjudication Agreement.

Death of Adjudicator – inability to adjudicate

41A·3 If the Adjudicator dies or becomes ill or is unavailable for some other cause and is thus unable to adjudicate on a dispute or difference referred to him, the Parties may either agree upon an individual to replace the Adjudicator or either Party may apply to the nominator for the nomination of an adjudicator to adjudicate that dispute or difference; and the Parties shall execute the JCT Adjudication Agreement with the agreed or nominated Adjudicator.

Dispute or difference – notice of intention to refer to adjudication – referral

41A·4 ·1 When pursuant to article 5 a Party requires a dispute or difference to be referred to adjudication then that Party shall give notice to the other Party of his intention to refer the dispute or difference, briefly identified in the notice, to adjudication. If an Adjudicator is agreed or appointed within 7 days of the notice then the Party giving the notice shall refer the dispute or difference to the Adjudicator ('the referral') within 7 days of the notice. If an Adjudicator is not agreed or appointed within 7 days of the notice the referral shall be made immediately on such agreement or appointment. The said Party shall include with that referral particulars of the dispute or difference together with a summary of the contentions on which he relies, a statement of the relief or remedy which is sought and any material he wishes the Adjudicator to consider. The referral and its accompanying documentation shall be copied simultaneously to the other Party.

Footnotes

[uu] It is open to the Employer and the Contractor to resolve disputes by the process of Mediation: see Practice Note 28 'Mediation on a Building Contract or Sub-Contract Dispute'.

[vv] The nominators named in the Appendix have agreed with the JCT that they will comply with the requirements of clause 41A on the nomination of an adjudicator including the requirement in clause 41A·2·2 for the nomination to be made with the object of securing the appointment of, and the referral of the dispute or difference to, the Adjudicator within 7 days of the date of the notice of intention to refer; and will only nominate adjudicators who will enter into the 'JCT Adjudication Agreement'.

[ww] The JCT Adjudication Agreement is available from the retailers of JCT Forms.

A version of this Agreement is also available for use if the Parties have named an Adjudicator in their contract.

385

Appendix 1

41A·4 ·2 The referral by a Party with its accompanying documentation to the Adjudicator and the copies thereof to be provided to the other Party shall be given by actual delivery or by FAX or by special delivery or recorded delivery. If given by FAX then, for record purposes, the referral and its accompanying documentation must forthwith be sent by first class post or given by actual delivery. If sent by special delivery or recorded delivery the referral and its accompanying documentation shall, subject to proof to the contrary, be deemed to have been received 48 hours after the date of posting subject to the exclusion of Sundays and any Public Holiday.

Conduct of the adjudication

41A·5 ·1 The Adjudicator shall immediately upon receipt of the referral and its accompanying documentation confirm the date of that receipt to the Parties.

41A·5 ·2 The Party not making the referral may, by the same means stated in clause 41A·4·2, send to the Adjudicator within 7 days of the date of the referral, with a copy to the other Party, a written statement of the contentions on which he relies and any material he wishes the Adjudicator to consider.

41A·5 ·3 The Adjudicator shall within 28 days of the referral under clause 41A·4·1 and acting as an Adjudicator for the purposes of S.108 of the Housing Grants, Construction and Regeneration Act 1996 and not as an expert or an arbitrator reach his decision and forthwith send that decision in writing to the Parties. Provided that the Party who has made the referral may consent to allowing the Adjudicator to extend the period of 28 days by up to 14 days; and that by agreement between the Parties after the referral has been made a longer period than 28 days may be notified jointly by the Parties to the Adjudicator within which to reach his decision.

41A·5 ·4 The Adjudicator shall not be obliged to give reasons for his decision.

41A·5 ·5 In reaching his decision the Adjudicator shall act impartially and set his own procedure; and at his absolute discretion may take the initiative in ascertaining the facts and the law as he considers necessary in respect of the referral which may include the following:

·5 ·1 using his own knowledge and/or experience;

·5 ·2 opening up, reviewing and revising any certificate, opinion, decision, requirement or notice issued, given or made under the Contract as if no such certificate, opinion, decision, requirement or notice had been issued, given or made;

·5 ·3 requiring from the Parties further information than that contained in the notice of referral and its accompanying documentation or in any written statement provided by the Parties including the results of any tests that have been made or of any opening up;

·5 ·4 requiring the Parties to carry out tests or additional tests or to open up work or further open up work;

·5 ·5 visiting the site of the Works or any workshop where work is being or has been prepared for the Contract;

·5 ·6 obtaining such information as he considers necessary from any employee or representative of the Parties provided that before obtaining information from an employee of a Party he has given prior notice to that Party;

·5 ·7 obtaining from others such information and advice as he considers necessary on technical and on legal matters subject to giving prior notice to the Parties together with a statement or estimate of the cost involved;

·5 ·8 having regard to any term of the Contract relating to the payment of interest, deciding the circumstances in which or the period for which a simple rate of interest shall be paid.

41A·5 ·6 Any failure by either Party to enter into the JCT Adjudication Agreement or to comply with any requirement of the Adjudicator under clause 41A·5·5 or with any provision in or requirement under clause 41A shall not invalidate the decision of the Adjudicator.

41A·5 ·7 The Parties shall meet their own costs of the adjudication except that the Adjudicator may direct as to who should pay the cost of any test or opening up if required pursuant to clause 41A·5·5·4.

Appendix 1

Adjudicator's fee and reasonable expenses – payment

41A·6 ·1 The Adjudicator in his decision shall state how payment of his fee and reasonable expenses is to be apportioned as between the Parties. In default of such statement the Parties shall bear the cost of the Adjudicator's fee and reasonable expenses in equal proportions.

41A·6 ·2 The Parties shall be jointly and severally liable to the Adjudicator for his fee and for all expenses reasonably incurred by the Adjudicator pursuant to the adjudication.

Effect of Adjudicator's decision

41A·7 ·1 The decision of the Adjudicator shall be binding on the Parties until the dispute or difference is finally determined by arbitration or by legal proceedings [xx] or by an agreement in writing between the Parties made after the decision of the Adjudicator has been given.

41A·7 ·2 The Parties shall, without prejudice to their other rights under the Contract, comply with the decision of the Adjudicator; and the Employer and the Contractor shall ensure that the decision of the Adjudicator is given effect.

41A·7 ·3 If either Party does not comply with the decision of the Adjudicator the other Party shall be entitled to take legal proceedings to secure such compliance pending any final determination of the referred dispute or difference pursuant to clause 41A·7·1.

Immunity

41A·8 The Adjudicator shall not be liable for anything done or omitted in the discharge or purported discharge of his functions as Adjudicator unless the act or omission is in bad faith and this protection from liability shall similarly extend to any employee or agent of the Adjudicator.

41B Arbitration

A reference in clause 41B to a Rule or Rules is a reference to the JCT 1998 edition of the Construction Industry Model Arbitration Rules (CIMAR) current at the Base Date.

41B·1 ·1 Where pursuant to article 7A either Party requires a dispute or difference to be referred to arbitration then that Party shall serve on the other Party a notice of arbitration to such effect in accordance with Rule 2.1 which states:

"Arbitral proceedings are begun in respect of a dispute when one party serves on the other a written notice of arbitration identifying the dispute and requiring him to agree to the appointment of an arbitrator";

and an arbitrator shall be an individual agreed by the Parties or appointed by the person named in the Appendix in accordance with Rule 2.3 which states:

"If the parties fail to agree on the name of an arbitrator within 14 days (or any agreed extension) after:
(i) the notice of arbitration is served, or
(ii) a previously appointed arbitrator ceases to hold office for any reason,
either party may apply for the appointment of an arbitrator to the person so empowered."

By Rule 2.5:

"the arbitrator's appointment takes effect upon his agreement to act or his appointment under Rule 2.3, whether or not his terms have been accepted."

41B·1 ·2 Where two or more related arbitral proceedings in respect of the Works fall under separate arbitration agreements, Rules 2.6, 2.7 and 2.8 shall apply thereto.

41B·1 ·3 After an arbitrator has been appointed either Party may give a further notice of arbitration to the other Party and to the Arbitrator referring any other dispute which falls under article 7A to be decided in the arbitral proceedings and Rule 3.3 shall apply thereto.

Footnote

[xx] The arbitration or legal proceedings are not an appeal against the decision of the Adjudicator but are a consideration of the dispute or difference as if no decision had been made by an Adjudicator.

Appendix 1

41B·2 Subject to the provisions of article 7A and clause 30·9 the Arbitrator shall, without prejudice to the generality of his powers, have power to rectify this Contract so that it accurately reflects the true agreement made by the Parties, to direct such measurements and/or valuations as may in his opinion be desirable in order to determine the rights of the Parties and to ascertain and award any sum which ought to have been the subject of or included in any certificate and to open up, review and revise any certificate, opinion, decision, requirement or notice and to determine all matters in dispute which shall be submitted to him in the same manner as if no such certificate, opinion, decision, requirement or notice had been given.

41B·3 Subject to clause 41B·4 the award of such Arbitrator shall be final and binding on the Parties.

41B·4 The Parties hereby agree pursuant to S. 45(2)(a) and S. 69(2)(a) of the Arbitration Act 1996 that either Party may (upon notice to the other Party and to the Arbitrator):

41B·4 ·1 apply to the courts to determine any question of law arising in the course of the reference; and

41B·4 ·2 appeal to the courts on any question of law arising out of an award made in an arbitration under this Arbitration Agreement.

41B·5 The provisions of the Arbitration Act 1996 or any amendment thereof shall apply to any arbitration under this Contract wherever the same, or any part of it, shall be conducted. [yy]

41B·6 The arbitration shall be conducted in accordance with the JCT 1998 edition of the Construction Industry Model Arbitration Rules (CIMAR) current at the Base Date. Provided that if any amendments to the Rules so current have been issued by the JCT after the Base Date the Parties may, by a joint notice in writing to the Arbitrator, state that they wish the arbitration to be conducted in accordance with the Rules as so amended.

41C   Legal proceedings

41C·1 Where article 7B applies any dispute or difference shall be determined by legal proceedings pursuant to article 7B.

Footnote

[yy] It should be noted that the provisions of the Arbitration Act 1996 do not extend to Scotland. Where the site of the Works is situated in Scotland then the forms issued by the Scottish Building Contract Committee which contain Scots proper law, adjudication and arbitration provisions are the appropriate documents. The SBCC issues guidance in this respect.

Appendix 1

Part 5: Performance Specified Work [zz]

<table>
<tr><td>Meaning of
Performance
Specified Work</td><td>42·1</td><td colspan="2">The term 'Performance Specified Work' means work:</td></tr>
<tr><td></td><td>42·1</td><td>·1</td><td>identified in the Appendix, and</td></tr>
<tr><td></td><td>42·1</td><td>·2</td><td>which is to be provided by the Contractor, and</td></tr>
<tr><td></td><td>42·1</td><td>·3</td><td>for which certain requirements have been predetermined and are shown on the Contract Drawings, and</td></tr>
<tr><td></td><td>42·1</td><td>·4</td><td>in respect of which the performance which the Employer requires from such work and which the Contractor, by this Contract and subject to the Conditions, is required to achieve has been stated in the Contract Bills and these Bills have included</td></tr>
</table>

either   information relating thereto sufficient to have enabled the Contractor to price such Performance Specified Work

or   a provisional sum in respect of the Performance Specified Work together with the information relating thereto as referred to in clause 42·7.

<table>
<tr><td>Contractor's
Statement</td><td>42·2</td><td>Before carrying out any Performance Specified Work, the Contractor shall provide the Architect with a document or set of documents, referred to in these Conditions as the 'Contractor's Statement'. Before so providing the Contractor shall have referred the draft of such Statement to the Planning Supervisor and shall have made such amendments, if any, as may have been necessary to take account of the comments of the Planning Supervisor. Subject to the Conditions the Contractor shall carry out the Performance Specified Work in accordance with that Statement.</td></tr>
<tr><td>Contents of
Contractor's
Statement</td><td>42·3</td><td>The Contractor's Statement shall be sufficient in form and detail adequately to explain the Contractor's proposals for the execution of the Performance Specified Work. It shall include any information which is required to be included therein by the Contract Bills or, where there is a provisional sum for the Performance Specified Work, by the instruction of the Architect on the expenditure of that sum; and may include information in drawn or scheduled form and a statement of calculations; and, if applicable, shall be provided in reasonable time so that the Architect can provide the information, drawings and details as he is required to provide pursuant to clauses 5·4·1 and 5·4·2.</td></tr>
<tr><td>Time for
Contractor's
Statement</td><td>42·4</td><td>The Contractor's Statement shall be provided to the Architect:
–   by any date for its provision given in the Contract Bills or
–   by any reasonable date for its provision given in the instruction by the Architect on the expenditure of a provisional sum for Performance Specified Work.
If no such date is given it shall be provided at a reasonable time before the Contractor intends to carry out the Performance Specified Work.</td></tr>
<tr><td>Architect's notice
to amend
Contractor's
Statement</td><td>42·5</td><td>Within 14 days after receipt of the Contractor's Statement the Architect may, if he is of the opinion that such Statement is deficient in form and/or detail adequately to explain the Contractor's proposals for the execution of the Performance Specified Work, by notice in writing require the Contractor to amend such Statement so that it is in the opinion of the Architect not deficient. A copy of the Statement as so amended shall be provided to the Architect. Whether or not an amendment is required by the Architect, the Contractor is responsible in accordance with the Conditions for any deficiency in such Statement and for the Performance Specified Work to which such Statement refers.</td></tr>
<tr><td>Architect's notice
of deficiency in
Contractor's
Statement</td><td>42·6</td><td>If the Architect shall find anything in the Contractor's Statement which appears to the Architect to be a deficiency which would adversely affect the performance required by the Employer from the relevant Performance Specified Work, he shall immediately give notice to the Contractor specifying the deficiency. Whether or not a notice is given by the Architect, the Contractor is responsible in accordance with the Conditions for the Performance Specified Work.</td></tr>
<tr><td>Definition of
provisional sum
for Performance
Specified Work</td><td>42·7</td><td>A provisional sum for Performance Specified Work means a sum provided in the Contract Bills for Performance Specified Work where the following information has been provided in the Contract Bills:</td></tr>
</table>

42·7 ·1 the performance which the Employer requires from such work;

42·7 ·2 the location of such Performance Specified Work in the building;

42·7 ·3 information relating thereto sufficient to have enabled the Contractor to have made due allowance in programming for the execution of such Performance Specified Work and for pricing all preliminary items relevant to such Performance Specified Work.

Instructions of the Architect on other provisional sums

42·8 No instruction of the Architect pursuant to clause 13·3·1 on the expenditure of provisional sums included in the Contract Bills shall require Performance Specified Work except an instruction on the expenditure of a provisional sum included in the Contract Bills for Performance Specified Work.

Preparation of Contract Bills

42·9 The inclusion of Performance Specified Work in the Contract Bills shall not be regarded as a departure from the method of preparation of these Bills referred to in clause 2·2·2·1.

Provisional sum for Performance Specified Work – errors or omissions in Contract Bills

42·10 If in the Contract Bills there is any error or omission in the information which, pursuant to clause 42·7·2 and/or 42·7·3, is to be included in the Contract Bills in respect of a provisional sum for Performance Specified Work such error or omission shall be corrected so that it does provide such information; and any such correction shall be treated as if it were a Variation required by an instruction of the Architect under clause 13·2.

Variations in respect of Performance Specified Work

42·11 Subject to clause 42·12 the Architect may issue instructions under clause 13·2 requiring a Variation to Performance Specified Work.

Agreement for additional Performance Specified Work

42·12 No instruction of the Architect under clause 13·2 may require as a Variation the provision by the Contractor of Performance Specified Work additional to that which has been identified in the Appendix unless the Employer and the Contractor otherwise agree.

Analysis

42·13 Where the Contract Bills do not provide an analysis of the portion of the Contract Sum which relates to any Performance Specified Work the Contractor shall provide such an analysis ('the Analysis') within 14 days of being required to do so by the Architect.

Integration of Performance Specified Work

42·14 The Architect shall, within a reasonable time before the Contractor intends to carry out the Performance Specified Work, give any instructions necessary for the integration of such Performance Specified Work with the design of the Works. The Contractor shall, subject to clause 42·15, comply with any such instruction.

Compliance with Architect's instructions – Contractor's notice of injurious affection

42·15 If the Contractor is of the opinion that compliance with any instruction of the Architect injuriously affects the efficacy of the Performance Specified Work, he shall within 7 days of receipt of the relevant instruction specify by notice in writing to the Architect such injurious affection. Except where the Architect amends the instruction to remove such injurious affection, the instruction shall not have effect without the written consent of the Contractor which consent shall not be unreasonably withheld or delayed.

Delay by Contractor in providing the Contractor's Statement

42·16 Except for any extension of time in respect of the Relevant Event stated in clause 25·4·15 an extension of time shall not be given under clause 25·3 and clauses 26·1 and 28·2·2 shall not have effect where and to the extent that the cause of the progress of the Works having been delayed, affected or suspended is that the Architect has not received the Contractor's Statement by the time referred to in clause 42·4 or any amendment to the Contractor's Statement pursuant to clause 42·5.

Performance Specified Work – Contractor's obligation

42·17 ·1 The Contractor shall exercise reasonable skill and care in the provision of Performance Specified Work provided that:

·1 ·1 clause 42·17 shall not be construed so as to affect the obligations of the Contractor under this Contract in regard to the supply of workmanship, materials and goods; and

·1 ·2 nothing in this Contract shall operate as a guarantee of fitness for purpose of the Performance Specified Work.

42·17 ·2 The Contractor's obligation under clause 42·17·1 shall in no way be modified by any service in respect of any Performance Specified Work which he has obtained from others and, in particular, the Contractor shall be responsible for any such service as if such services had been undertaken by the Contractor himself.

Nomination excluded

42·18 Performance Specified Work pursuant to clause 42 shall not be provided by a Nominated Sub-Contractor under a Nominated Sub-Contract or by a Nominated Supplier under a contract of sale to which clause 36 refers.

Appendix 1

Code of Practice: referred to in clause 8·4·4

1   This is the Code of Practice referred to in clause 8·4·4. The purpose of the Code is to help in the fair and reasonable operation of the requirements of clause 8·4·4.

2   The Architect and the Contractor should endeavour to agree the amount and method of opening up or testing but in any case in issuing his instructions pursuant to clause 8·4·4 the Architect is required to consider the following criteria:

    ·1   the need in the event of non-compliance to demonstrate at no cost to the Employer either that it is unique and not likely to occur in similar elements of the Works or alternatively the extent of any similar non-compliance in the Works already constructed or still to be constructed;

    ·2   the need to discover whether any non-compliance in a primary structural element is a failure of workmanship and/or materials such that rigorous testing of similar elements must take place; or where the non-compliance is in a less significant element whether it is such as is to be statistically expected and can be simply repaired; or whether the non-compliance indicates an inherent weakness such as can only be found by selective testing the extent of which must depend upon the importance of any detail concerned;

    ·3   the significance of the non-compliance having regard to the nature of the work in which it has occurred;

    ·4   the consequence of any similar non-compliance on the safety of the building, its effect on users, adjoining property, the public, and compliance with any Statutory Requirements;

    ·5   the level and standard of supervision and control of the Works by the Contractor;

    ·6   the relevant records of the Contractor and where relevant of any sub-contractor resulting from the supervision and control referred to in paragraph 2·5 above or otherwise;

    ·7   any Codes of Practice or similar advice issued by a responsible body which are applicable to the non-complying work, materials or goods;

    ·8   any failure by the Contractor to carry out, or to secure the carrying out of, any tests specified in the Contract Documents or in an instruction of the Architect;

    ·9   the reason for the non-compliance when this has been established;

    ·10   any technical advice that the Contractor has obtained in respect of the non-complying work, materials or goods;

    ·11   current recognised testing procedures;

    ·12   the practicability of progressive testing in establishing whether any similar non-compliance is reasonably likely;

    ·13   if alternative testing methods are available, the time required for and the consequential costs of such alternative testing methods;

    ·14   any proposals of the Contractor;

    ·15   any other relevant matters.

Appendix

Clause etc.	Subject	
Fourth recital and 31	Statutory tax deduction scheme	Employer at Base Date *is a 'contractor'/is not a 'contractor' for the purposes of the Act and the Regulations
Fifth recital	CDM Regulations	*All the CDM Regulations apply/ Regulations 7 and 13 only of the CDM Regulations apply
Articles 7A and 7B 41B 41C	Dispute or difference – settlement of disputes	*Clause 41B applies
		*Delete if disputes are to be decided by legal proceedings and article 7B is thus to apply
		See the Guidance Note to JCT 80 Amendment 18 on factors to be taken into account by the Parties considering whether disputes are to be decided by arbitration or by legal proceedings
1·3	Base Date	_____
1·3	Date for Completion	_____
1·11	Electronic data interchange	The JCT Supplemental Provisions for EDI *apply/do not apply
		If applicable: the EDI Agreement to which the Supplemental Provisions refer is: *the EDI Association Standard EDI Agreement *the European Model EDI Agreement
15·2	VAT Agreement	Clause 1A of the VAT Agreement *applies/does not apply [x]
17·2	Defects Liability Period (if none other stated is 6 months from the day named in the certificate of Practical Completion of the Works)	_____
19·1·2	Assignment by Employer of benefits after Practical Completion	Clause 19·1·2 *applies/does not apply
21·1·1	Insurance cover for any one occurrence or series of occurrences arising out of one event	£ _____

Footnotes

*Delete as applicable.

[x] Clause 1A can only apply where the Contractor is satisfied at the date the Contract is entered into that his output tax on all supplies to the Employer under the Contract will be at either a positive or a zero rate of tax.

On and from 1 April 1989 the supply in respect of a building designed for a 'relevant charitable purpose' (as defined in the legislation which gives statutory effect to

the VAT changes operative from 1 April 1989) is only zero rated if the person to whom the supply is made has given to the Contractor a certificate in statutory form: see the VAT leaflet 708 revised 1989. Where a contract supply is zero rated by certificate only the person holding the certificate (usually the Contractor) may zero rate his supply.

This footnote repeats footnote [x] for clause 15·2.

Appendix 1

Clause etc.	Subject	
21·2·1	Insurance – liability of Employer	Insurance *may be required/is not required Amount of indemnity for any one occurrence or series of occurrences arising out of one event £ _____ [aaa]
22·1	Insurance of the Works – alternative clauses	*Clause 22A/Clause 22B/Clause 22C applies (See footnote [cc] to clause 22)
*22A, 22B·1, 22C·2	Percentage to cover professional fees	_____
22A·3·1	Annual renewal date of insurance as supplied by Contractor	_____
22D	Insurance for Employer's loss of liquidated damages – clause 25·4·3	Insurance *may be required/is not required
22D·2		Period of time _____
22FC·1	Joint Fire Code	The Joint Fire Code *applies/does not apply If the Joint Fire Code is applicable, state whether the insurer under clause 22A or clause 22B or clause 22C·2 has specified that the Works are a 'Large Project': *YES/NO (where clause 22A applies these entries are made on information supplied by the Contractor)
23·1·1	Date of Possession	_____
23·1·2, 25·4·13, 26·1	Deferment of the Date of Possession	Clause 23·1·2 *applies/does not apply Period of deferment if it is to be less than 6 weeks is _____
24·2	Liquidated and ascertained damages	at the rate of £ _____ per _____
28·2·2	Period of suspension (if none stated is 1 month)	_____
28A·1·1·1 to 28A·1·1·3	Period of suspension (if none stated is 3 months)	_____
28A·1·1·4 to 28A·1·1·6	Period of suspension (if none stated is 1 month)	_____

Footnotes *Delete as applicable.

[aaa] If the indemnity is to be for an aggregate amount and not for any one occurrence or series of occurrences the entry should make this clear.

393

Appendix 1

Clause etc.	Subject	
30·1·1·6	Advance payment	Clause 30·1·1·6 *applies/does not apply If applicable: the advance payment will be **£ _____ / _____ % of the Contract Sum and will be paid to the Contractor on _____ and will be reimbursed to the Employer in the following amount(s) and at the following time(s) _____ _____ _____ An advance payment bond *is/is not required
30·1·3	Period of Interim Certificates (if none stated is 1 month)	_____
30·2·1·1	Gross valuation	A priced Activity Schedule *is/is not attached to this Appendix
30·3·1	Listed items – uniquely identified	*For uniquely identified listed items a bond as referred to in clause 30·3·1 in respect of payment for such items is required for £ _____ *Delete if no bond is required
30·3·2	Listed items – not uniquely identified	*For listed items that are not uniquely identified a bond as referred to in clause 30·3·2 in respect of payment for such items is required for £ _____ *Delete if clause 30·3·2 does not apply
30·4·1·1	Retention Percentage (if less than 5 per cent) [bbb]	_____
35·2	Work reserved for Nominated Sub-Contractors for which the Contractor desires to tender	_____
37	Fluctuations: (if alternative required is not shown clause 38 shall apply)	clause 38 [ccc] clause 39 clause 40

Footnotes   *Delete as applicable.

**Insert either a money amount or a percentage figure and delete the other alternative.

[bbb] The percentage will be 5 per cent unless a lower rate is specified here.

[ccc] Delete alternatives not used.

Appendix 1

Clause etc.	Subject	
38·7 or 39·8	Percentage addition	_____
40·1·1·1	Formula Rules	rule 3: Base Month
		_____ 19 _____
		rules 10 and 30 (i): Part I/Part II [ddd] of Section 2 of the Formula Rules is to apply
41A·2	Adjudication – nominator of Adjudicator (if no nominator is selected the nominator shall be the President or a Vice-President of the Royal Institute of British Architects)	President or a Vice-President or Chairman or a Vice-Chairman: *Royal Institute of British Architects *Royal Institution of Chartered Surveyors *Construction Confederation *National Specialist Contractors Council
		*Delete all but one
41B·1	Arbitration – appointor of Arbitrator (if no appointor is selected the appointor shall be the President or a Vice-President of the Royal Institute of British Architects)	President or a Vice-President: *Royal Institute of British Architects *Royal Institution of Chartered Surveyors *Chartered Institute of Arbitrators
		*Delete all but one
42·1·1	Performance Specified Work	Identify below or on a separate sheet each item of Performance Specified Work to be provided by the Contractor and insert the relevant reference in the Contract Bills [zz]

Footnotes

[ddd] Strike out according to which method of formula adjustment (Part I – Work Category Method or Part II – Work Group Method) has been stated in the documents issued to tenderers.

[zz] See Practice Note 25 'Performance Specified Work' paragraphs 2·6 to 2·8 for a description of work which is **not** to be treated as Performance Specified Work.

*This footnote repeats footnote [zz] for clause 42.

Annex 1 to Appendix: Terms of Bonds

agreed between the British Bankers' Association and the JCT

See clause 30·1·1·6:
"Advance Payment Bond", and

clause 30·3:
"Bond in respect of payment for off-site materials and/or goods"

Advance Payment Bond

1   THE parties to this Bond are:

(1) _____

whose registered office is at _____

_____ ('the Surety'), and

(2) _____

of _____

_____ ('the Employer').

2   The Employer and _____ ('the Contractor')

have agreed to enter into a contract for building works ('the Works') at _____

_____ ('the Contract').

3   The Employer has agreed to pay the Contractor the sum of [_____] as an advance
payment of sums due to the Contractor under the Contract ('the Advance Payment') for
reimbursement by the Surety on the following terms:

(a) When the Surety receives a demand from the Employer in accordance with clause 3(b)
the Surety shall repay the Employer the sum demanded up to the amount of the
Advance Payment.

(b) The Employer shall in making any demand provide to the Surety a completed notice of
demand in the form of the **Schedule** attached hereto which shall be accepted as
conclusive evidence for all purposes under this Bond. The signatures on any such
demand must be authenticated by the Employer's bankers.

(c) The Surety shall within 5 Business Days after receiving the demand pay to the Employer
the sum so demanded. 'Business Day' means the day (other than a Saturday or a
Sunday) on which commercial banks are open for business in London.

4   Payments due under this Bond shall be made notwithstanding any dispute between the
Employer and the Contractor and whether or not the Employer and the Contractor are or
might be under any liability one to the other. Payment by the Surety under this Bond shall be
deemed a valid payment for all purposes of this Bond and shall discharge the Surety from
liability to the extent of such payment.

5   The Surety consents and agrees that the following actions by the Employer may be made and done without notice to or consent of the Surety and without in any way affecting changing or releasing the Surety from its obligations under this Bond and the liability of the Surety hereunder shall not in any way be affected hereby. The actions are:

(a) waiver by the Employer of any of the terms, provisions, conditions, obligations and agreements of the Contractor or any failure to make demand upon or take action against the Contractor;

(b) any modification or changes to the Contract; and/or

(c) the granting of any extensions of time to the Contractor without affecting the terms of clause 7(c) below.

6   The Surety's maximum aggregate liability under this Bond which shall commence on payment of the Advance Payment by the Employer to the Contractor shall be the amount of [_____] which sum shall be reduced by the amount of any reimbursement made by the Contractor to the Employer as advised by the Employer in writing to the Surety.

7   The obligations of the Surety and under this Bond shall cease upon whichever is the earliest of:

(a) the date on which the Advance Payment is reduced to nil as certified in writing to the Surety by the Employer;

(b) the date on which the Advance Payment or any balance thereof is repaid to the Employer by the Contractor (as certified in writing to the Surety by the Employer) or by the Surety; and

(c) [*longstop date to be given*],

and any claims hereunder must be received by the Surety in writing on or before such earliest date.

8   This Bond is not transferable or assignable without the prior written consent of the Surety. Such written consent will not be unreasonably withheld.

9   This Bond shall be governed and construed in accordance with the laws of England and Wales.

IN WITNESS hereof this Bond has been executed as a Deed by the Surety and delivered on the date below:

EXECUTED as a Deed by: _____

    for and on behalf of the Surety: _____

EXECUTED as a Deed by: _____

    for and on behalf of the Employer: _____

Date: _____

Appendix 1

Schedule to Advance Payment Bond
(clause 3(b) of the bond)

Notice of Demand

Date of Notice: _____

Date of Bond: _____

Employer: _____

Surety: _____

The bond has come into effect.

We hereby demand payment of the sum of

£ _____ (amount in words)
which does not exceed the amount of reimbursement for which the Contractor is in default at
the date of this notice.

Address for payment: _____

_____

This Notice is signed by the following persons who are authorised by the Employer to act for
and on his behalf:

Signed by _____

    Name: _____

    Official Position: _____

Signed by _____

    Name: _____

    Official Position: _____

The above signatures to be authenticated by the Employer's bankers

Appendix 1

Bond in respect of payment for off-site materials and/or goods

1   THE parties to this Bond are:

(1) _____

whose registered office is at _____

_____ ('the Surety'), and

(2) _____

of _____

_____ ('the Employer').

2   The Employer and _____ ('the Contractor')

have agreed to enter into a building contract for building works ('the Works')

at _____('the Contract').

3   Subject to the relevant provisions of the Contract as summarised below but with which the Surety shall not at all be concerned:

    (a) the Employer has agreed to include in the amount stated as due in Interim Certificates (as defined in the Contract) for payment by the Employer the value of those materials or goods or items pre-fabricated for inclusion in the Works which have been listed by the Employer ('the listed items'), which list has been included as part of the Contract, before their delivery to or adjacent to the Works; and

    (b) the Contractor has agreed to insure the listed items against loss or damage for their full value under a policy of insurance protecting the interests of the Employer and the Contractor during the period commencing with the transfer of the property in the items to the Contractor until they are delivered to or adjacent to the Works; and

    (c) this Bond shall exclusively relate to the amount paid to the Contractor in respect of the listed items which have not been delivered to or adjacent to the Works.

4   The Employer shall in making any demand provide to the Surety a Notice of Demand in the form of the **Schedule** attached hereto which shall be accepted as conclusive evidence for all purposes under this Bond. The signatures on any such demand must be authenticated by the Employer's bankers.

5   The Surety shall within 5 Business Days after receiving the demand pay to the Employer the sum so demanded. 'Business Day' means the day (other than a Saturday or a Sunday) on which commercial banks are open for business in London.

6   Payments due under this Bond shall be made notwithstanding any dispute between the Employer and the Contractor and whether or not the Employer and the Contractor are or might be under any liability one to the other. Payment by the Surety under this Bond shall be deemed a valid payment for all purposes of this Bond and shall discharge the Surety from liability to the extent of such payment.

Appendix 1

7   The Surety consents and agrees that the following actions by the Employer may be made and done without notice to or consent of the Surety and without in any way affecting changing or releasing the Surety from its obligations under this Bond and the liability of the Surety hereunder shall not in any way be affected hereby. The actions are:

    (a)   waiver by the Employer of any of the terms, provisions, conditions, obligations and agreements of the Contractor or any failure to make demand upon or take action against the Contractor;

    (b)   any modification or changes to the Contract; and/or

    (c)   the granting of an extension of time to the Contractor without affecting the terms of clause 9(b) below.

8   The Surety's maximum liability under this Bond shall be * [_____].

9   The obligations of the Surety and under this Bond shall cease upon whichever is the earlier of

    (a)   the date on which all the listed items have been delivered to or adjacent to the Works as certified in writing to the Surety by the Employer; and

    (b)   [*longstop date to be given*],

and any claims hereunder must be received by the Surety in writing on or before such earlier date.

10   The Bond is not transferable or assignable without the prior written consent of the Surety. Such written consent will not be unreasonably withheld.

11   This Bond shall be governed and construed in accordance with the laws of England and Wales.

*The value stated in the Contract which the Employer
considers will be sufficient to cover him for maximum
payments to the Contractor for the listed items that
will have been made and not delivered to the site at
any one time.

IN WITNESS hereof this Bond has been executed as a Deed by the Surety and delivered on the date below:

EXECUTED as a Deed by: _____

    for and on behalf of the Surety: _____

EXECUTED as a Deed by: _____

    for and on behalf of the Employer: _____

Date: _____

Appendix 1

Schedule to Bond
(clause 4 of the bond)

Notice of Demand

Date of Notice: _____

Date of Bond: _____

Employer: _____

Surety: _____

We hereby demand payment of the sum of _____
being the amount stated as due in respect of listed items included in the amount stated as
due in an Interim Certificate(s) for payment which has been duly made to the Contractor by
the Employer but such listed items have not been delivered to or adjacent to the Works.

Address for payment: _____

_____

This Notice is signed by the following persons who are authorised by the Employer to act for
and on his behalf:

Signed by _____

Name: _____

Official Position: _____

Signed by _____

Name: _____

Official Position: _____

The above signatures to be authenticated by the Employer's bankers

Appendix 1

Supplemental Provisions
(the VAT Agreement)

The following are the supplemental provisions (the VAT Agreement) referred to in clause 15·1 of the Conditions:

Interim payments – addition of VAT

1　The Employer shall pay to the Contractor in the manner hereinafter set out any tax properly chargeable by the Commissioners on the Contractor on the supply to the Employer of any goods and services by the Contractor under this Contract. Supplies of goods and services under this Contract are supplies under a contract providing for periodical payment for such supplies within the meaning of Regulation 26 of the Value Added Tax (General) Regulations 1985 or any amendment or re-enactment thereof.

Alternative provisions to clauses 1·1 to 1·2·2 inclusive

1A·1　Where it is stated in the Appendix pursuant to clause 15·2 of the Conditions that clause 1A of this Agreement applies clauses 1·1 to 1·2·2 inclusive hereof shall not apply unless and until any notice issued under clause 1A·4 hereof becomes effective or unless the Contractor fails to give the written notice required under clause 1A·2. Where clause 1A applies clauses 1 and 1·3 to 8 of this Agreement remain in full force and effect.

1A·2　Not later than 7 days before the date for the issue of the first Interim Certificate the Contractor shall give written notice to the Employer, with a copy to the Architect, of the rate of tax chargeable on the supply of goods and services for which Interim Certificates and the Final Certificate are to be issued. If the rate of tax so notified is varied under statute the Contractor shall, not later than 7 days after the date when such varied rate comes into effect, send to the Employer, with a copy to the Architect, the necessary amendment to the rate given in his written notice and that notice shall then take effect as so amended.

1A·3　For the purpose of complying with the VAT Agreement for the recovery by the Contractor, as stated in clause 15·2 of the Conditions, from the Employer of tax properly chargeable by the Commissioners on the Contractor, an amount calculated at the rate given in the aforesaid written notice (or, where relevant, amended written notice) shall be shown on each Interim Certificate issued by the Architect and, unless the procedure set out in clause 1·3 hereof shall have been completed, on the Final Certificate issued by the Architect. Such amount shall be paid by the Employer to the Contractor or by the Contractor to the Employer as the case may be within the period for payment of certificates set out in clause 30·1·1·1 *(Interim Certificates)* or clause 30·8 *(Final Certificate)* as applicable.

1A·4　Either the Employer or the Contractor may give written notice to the other, with a copy to the Architect, stating that with effect from the date of the notice clause 1A shall no longer apply. From that date the provisions of clauses 1·1 to 1·2·2 inclusive hereof shall apply in place of clause 1A hereof.

Written assessment by Contractor

1·1　Unless clause 1A applies the Contractor shall not later than the date for the issue of each Interim Certificate and, unless the procedure set out in clause 1·3 of this Agreement shall have been completed, for the issue of the Final Certificate give to the Employer a written provisional assessment of the respective values (less any Retention Percentage applicable thereto) of those supplies of goods and services for which the Certificate is being issued and which will be chargeable, at the relevant time of supply under Regulation 26 of the Value Added Tax (General) Regulations 1985 on the Contractor at

1·1　·1　a zero rate of tax (Category (i)) and

1·1　·2　any rate or rates of tax other than zero (Category (ii)).

The Contractor shall also specify the rate or rates of tax which are chargeable on those supplies included in Category (ii), and shall state the grounds on which he considers such supplies are so chargeable.

Employer to calculate amount of tax due – Employer's right of reasonable objection

1·2　·1　Upon receipt of such written provisional assessment the Employer, unless he has reasonable grounds for objection to that assessment, shall calculate the amount of tax due by applying the rate or rates of tax specified by the Contractor to the amount of the assessed value of those supplies included in Category (ii) of such assessment, and remit the calculated amount of such tax, together with the amount of the Certificate issued by the Architect, to the Contractor within the period for payment of certificates set out in clause 30·1·1·1 of the Conditions.

Appendix 1

1·2   ·2   If the Employer has reasonable grounds for objection to the provisional assessment he shall within 3 working days of receipt of that assessment so notify the Contractor in writing setting out those grounds. The Contractor shall within 3 working days of receipt of the written notification of the Employer reply in writing to the Employer either that he withdraws the assessment in which case the Employer is released from his obligation under clause 1·2·1 of this Agreement or that he confirms the assessment. If the Contractor so confirms then the Contractor may treat any amount received from the Employer in respect of the value which the Contractor has stated to be chargeable on him at a rate or rates of tax other than zero as being inclusive of tax and issue an authenticated receipt under clause 1·4 of this Agreement.

Written final
statement – VAT
liability of
Contractor –
recovery from
Employer

1·3   ·1   Where clause 1A is operated clause 1·3 only applies if no amount of tax pursuant to clause 1A·3 has been shown on the Final Certificate issued by the Architect. After the issue of the Certificate of Completion of Making Good Defects under clause 17·4 of the Conditions the Contractor shall as soon as he can finally so ascertain prepare a written final statement of the respective values of all supplies of goods and services for which certificates have been or will be issued which are chargeable on the Contractor at

  ·1 ·1   a zero rate of tax (Category (ii)) and

  ·1 ·2   any rate or rates of tax other than zero (Category (ii))

and shall issue such final statement to the Employer.

The Contractor shall also specify the rate or rates of tax which are chargeable on the value of those supplies included in Category (ii) and shall state the grounds on which he considers such supplies are so chargeable.

The Contractor shall also state the total amount of tax already received by the Contractor for which a receipt or receipts under clause 1·4 of this Agreement have been issued.

1·3   ·2   The statement under clause 1·3·1 of this Agreement may be issued either before or after the issue of the Final Certificate under clause 30·8 of the Conditions.

1·3   ·3   Upon receipt of the written final statement the Employer shall, subject to clause 3 of this Agreement, calculate the final amount of tax due by applying the rate or rates of tax specified by the Contractor to the value of those supplies included in Category (ii) of the statement and deducting therefrom the total amount of tax already received by the Contractor specified in the statement, and shall pay the balance of such tax to the Contractor within 28 days from receipt of the statement.

1·3   ·4   If the Employer finds that the total amount of tax specified in the final statement as already paid by him exceeds the amount of tax calculated under clause 1·3·3 of this Agreement the Employer shall so notify the Contractor who shall refund such excess to the Employer within 28 days of receipt of the notification, together with a receipt under clause 1·4 of this Agreement showing the correction of the amounts for which a receipt or receipts have previously been issued by the Contractor.

Contractor to
issue receipt as
tax invoice

1·4   Upon receipt of any amount paid under certificates of the Architect and any tax properly paid under the provisions of clause 1 or clause 1A of this Agreement the Contractor shall issue to the Employer a receipt of the kind referred to in Regulation 12(4) of the Value Added Tax (General) Regulations 1985 containing the particulars required under Regulation 13(1) of the aforesaid Regulations or any amendment or re-enactment thereof to be contained in a tax invoice.

Value of supply –
liquidated
damages to be
disregarded

2·1   If, when the Employer is obliged to make payment under clause 1·2 or 1·3 of this Agreement, he is empowered under clause 24 of the Conditions to deduct any sum calculated at the rate stated in the Appendix as liquidated and ascertained damages from sums due or to become due to the Contractor under this Contract he shall disregard any such deduction in calculating the tax due on the value of goods and services supplied to which he is obliged to add tax under clause 1·2 or 1·3 of this Agreement.

2·2   The Contractor when ascertaining the respective values of any supplies of goods and services for which certificates have been or will be issued under the Conditions in order to prepare the final statement referred to in clause 1·3 of this Agreement shall disregard when stating such values any deduction by the Employer of any sum calculated at the rate stated in the Appendix as liquidated and ascertained damages under clause 24 of the Conditions.

403

Appendix 1

2·3 Where clause 1A is operated the Employer shall pay the tax to which that clause refers notwithstanding any deduction which the Employer may be empowered to make under clause 24 of the Conditions from the amount certified by the Architect in an Interim Certificate or from any balance certified by the Architect as due to the Contractor under the Final Certificate.

Employers' right to challenge tax claimed by Contractor

3·1 If the Employer disagrees with the final statement issued by the Contractor under clause 1·3 of this Agreement he may but before any payment or refund becomes due under clause 1·3·3 or 1·3·4 of this Agreement request the Contractor to obtain the decision of the Commissioners on the tax properly chargeable on the Contractor for all supplies of goods and services under this Contract and the Contractor shall forthwith request the Commissioners for such decision. If the Employer disagrees with such decision then, provided the Employer indemnifies and at the option of the Contractor secures the Contractor against all costs and other expenses, the Contractor shall in accordance with the instructions of the Employer make all such appeals against the decision of the commissioners as the Employer shall request. The Contractor shall account for any costs awarded in his favour in any appeals to which clause 3 of this Agreement applies.

3·2 Where, before any appeal from the decision of the Commissioners can proceed, the full amount of the tax alleged to be chargeable on the Contractor on the supply of goods and services under the Conditions must be paid or accounted for by the Contractor, the Employer shall pay to the Contractor the full amount of tax needed to comply with any such obligation.

3·3 Within 28 days of the final adjudication of an appeal (or of the date of the decision of the Commissioners if the Employer does not request the Contractor to refer such decision to appeal) the Employer or the Contractor, as the case may be, shall pay or refund to the other in accordance with such final adjudication any tax underpaid or overpaid, as the case may be, under the provisions of this Agreement and the provisions of clause 1·3·4 of this Agreement shall apply in regard to the provision of authenticated receipts.

Discharge of Employer from liability to pay tax to the Contractor

4 Upon receipt by the Contractor from the Employer or by the Employer from the Contractor, as the case may be, of any payment under clause 1·3·3 or 1·3·4 of this Agreement or where clause 1A of this Agreement is operated of any payment of the amount of tax shown upon the Final Certificate issued by the Architect, or upon final adjudication of any appeal made in accordance with the provisions of clause 3 of this Agreement and any resultant payment or refund under clause 3·3 of this Agreement, the Employer shall be discharged from any further liability to pay tax to the Contractor in accordance with the VAT Agreement. Provided always that if after the date of discharge under clause 4 of this Agreement the Commissioners decide to correct the tax due from the Contract on the supply to the Employer of any goods and services by the Contractor under this Contract the amount of any such correction shall be an additional payment by the Employer to the Contractor or by the Contractor to the Employer, as the case may be. The provisions of clause 3 of this Agreement in regard to disagreement with any decision of the Commissioners shall apply to any decision referred to in this proviso.

Awards in dispute procedures

5 If any dispute or difference is referred to adjudication or to arbitration pursuant to article 7A or to legal proceedings then insofar as any payment awarded in such adjudication or arbitration or legal proceedings varies the amount certified for payment for goods or services supplied by the Contractor to the Employer under this Contract or is an amount which ought to have been so certified but was not so certified then the provisions of this Agreement shall so far as relevant and applicable apply to any such payments.

Arbitration provision excluded

6 The provisions of article 7A shall not apply to any matters to be dealt with under clause 3 of this Agreement.

Employer's right where receipt not provided

7 Notwithstanding any provisions to the contrary elsewhere in the Conditions the Employer shall not be obliged to make any further payment to the Contractor under the Conditions if the Contractor is in default in providing the receipt referred to in clause 1·4 of this Agreement. Provided that clause 7 of this Agreement shall only apply where:

7 ·1 the Employer can show that he requires such receipt to validate any claim for credit for tax paid or payable under this Agreement which the Employer is entitled to make to the Commissioners, and

404

Appendix 1

7 ·2 the Employer has

paid tax in accordance with the provisional assessment of the Contractor under clause 1 of this Agreement unless he has sustained a reasonable objection under clause 1·2 of this Agreement; or

paid tax in accordance with clause 1A of this Agreement.

VAT on
determination

8 Where clause 27·4 of the Conditions becomes operative there shall be added to the amount allowable or payable to the Employer in addition to the amounts certified by the Architect any additional tax that the Employer has had to pay by reason of determination under clause 27 of the Conditions as compared with the tax the Employer would have paid if the determination had not occurred.

Appendix 1

Annex 2 to the Conditions: Supplemental Provisions for EDI

(clause 1·11)

The following are the Supplemental Provisions for EDI referred to in clause 1·11 of the Conditions.

1   The Parties no later than when there is a binding contract between the Employer and the Contractor shall have entered into the Electronic Data Interchange Agreement identified in the Appendix ('the EDI Agreement'), which shall apply to the exchange of communications under this Contract subject to the following:

    ·1   except where expressly provided for in these provisions, nothing contained in the EDI Agreement shall override or modify the application or interpretation of this Contract;

    ·2   the types and classes of communication to which the EDI Agreement shall apply ('the Data') and the persons between whom the Data shall be exchanged are as stated in the Contract Documents or as subsequently agreed in writing between the Parties;

    ·3   the Adopted Protocol/EDI Message Standards and the User Manual/Technical Annex* are as stated in the Contract Documents or as subsequently agreed in writing between the Parties;

    ·4   where the Contract Documents require a type or class of communication to which the EDI Agreement applies to be in writing it shall be validly made if exchanged in accordance with the EDI Agreement except that the following shall not be valid unless in writing in accordance with the relevant provisions of this Contract:

    ·4 ·1   any determination of the employment of the Contractor;

    ·4 ·2   any suspension by the Contractor of the performance of his obligations under this Contract to the Employer;

    ·4 ·3   the Final Certificate;

    ·4 ·4   any invoking by either Party of the procedures applicable under this Contract to the resolution of disputes or differences;

    ·4 ·5   any agreement between the Parties amending the Conditions or these provisions.

2   The procedures applicable under this Contract to the resolution of disputes or differences shall apply to any dispute or difference concerning these provisions or the exchange of any Data under the EDI Agreement and any dispute resolution provisions in the EDI Agreement shall not apply to such disputes or differences.

Footnote   * The EDI Association Standard EDI Agrement refers to an Adopted Protocol and User Manual; the European Model EDI Agreement refers to EDI Message Standards and a Technical Annex. Delete whichever is not applicable.

APPENDIX 2

SCOTTISH BUILDING CONTRACT WITH QUANTITIES (AUGUST 1998 REVISION)

SBC267 – 17 September 1998

SBCC

Scottish Building Contract
With Quantities.
(August 1998 Revision)

BUILDING CONTRACT

between

(hereinafter referred to as 'the Employer')

and

(hereinafter referred to as 'the Contractor')

WHEREAS the Employer is desirous of and the Contractor has offered to carry out and complete

---

(hereinafter referred to as 'the Contract Works' as defined in Appendix I hereto) for the sum of

---

(£   )

which offer has been or is hereby accepted by the Employer

'Delete if not provided

And the Contractor has provided the Employer with a priced Activity Schedule[1]

AND WHEREAS the Employer has provided the Contractor with a Schedule ("Information Release Schedule") which states what information the Architect will release and the time of that release;[1]

AND WHEREAS if the Employer requires any bond to be on terms other than those agreed between the Joint Contracts Tribunal and the British Bankers' Association the Contractor has been given copies of these terms;

Appendix 2

THEREFORE the Employer and the Contractor HAVE AGREED and DO HEREBY AGREE as follows:-

1   The Contractor shall carry out the Works (as defined in Appendix I hereto) in accordance with the Drawings numbered

---

---

and the Bills of Quantities all as annexed and signed as relative hereto.

2   The Employer shall pay to the Contractor the Contract Sum or such other sum as shall become payable at the times and in the manner specified in the Conditions.

3   The Works shall be completed in accordance with and the rights and obligations of the Employer and the Contractor shall be regulated by

3.1   The Conditions of the Standard Form of Building Contract Local Authorities[2]/Private Edition With Quantities (1980 Edition) and the supplemental provisions known as the VAT Agreement thereto issued by the Joint Contracts Tribunal.

3.2   The JCT Amendments 1: 1984, 2: 1986, 4: 1987 and 5: 1988, except that the references to Articles 5.2.2 and 5.2.3 and to the Appendix in JCT Amendment 2 shall be deemed to have been deleted; JCT Amendments 6 and 7: 1988, except that the reference to amendment No. 1 of Amendment 6 namely '1. Part 4: Amendments to Clause 41 'Settlement of Disputes - Arbitration' shall be deemed to have been deleted; JCT Amendment 8: 1989, except that the reference to the Appendix shall be deemed to have been deleted; JCT Amendment 9: 1990, except Item No. 1 to the extent that it defines 'Works' and 'Contract Documents' and except the Correction contained in Item No. 3 and any reference to the Appendix shall be deemed to have been deleted; JCT Amendment 10: 1991, except that any reference to the Appendix shall be deemed to have been deleted; JCT Amendment 11: 1992 except that references to the Appendix and amendments thereto shall be deemed to have been deleted together with references to Clauses 35.24.2, 35.24.7, 35.24.9, and 41.3.3; JCT Amendment 12: 1993 except that references to the Appendix and amendments thereto shall be deemed to have been deleted; JCT Amendment 13: 1994 except that references to the Appendix and amendments thereto and to Clauses 27.6.2.1 and 27.6.2.2 shall all be deemed to have been deleted; JCT Amendment 14: 1995 except that Item Nos. 1, 9, and 14 and any references to the Appendix and amendments thereto shall all be deemed to have been deleted; JCT Amendment 15: 1995; JCT Amendment 16: 1996 except that any references to Item No. 1 and to the Appendix and amendments thereto shall all be deemed to have been deleted; JCT Amendment 17: 1997 except that any references to the Appendix and amendments thereto shall all be

[2]Delete as applicable or as required

Appendix 2

deemed to have been deleted; and JCT Amendment 18: 1998 except that any references to the Appendix and amendments thereto shall all be deemed to have been deleted.

3.3 The Scottish Supplement forming Appendix I hereto.

3.4 The Abstract of the said Conditions forming Appendix II hereto.

3.5 SBCC Correction Sheet to JCT Amendment 18: 1998 issued August 1998

all of which are held to be incorporated in and form part of this Contract.

4   The term 'the Architect²/the Contract Administrator' shall mean

_____

_____

and the term 'the Quantity Surveyor' shall mean

_____

_____

_____

and in the event of the Architect²/the Contract Administrator or Quantity Surveyor ceasing to be employed for the purposes of the Contract, the Employer shall nominate within a reasonable time but not later than 21 days after such cessation another person to the vacant appointment (provided that the Architect²/the Contract Administrator or the ²Quantity Surveyor shall not be a person or persons to whom not later than 7 days after such nomination the Contractor shall object for reasons considered to be sufficient by an Arbiter appointed as hereinafter provided)³: Provided further that no person or persons subsequently appointed to be the Architect¹/the Contract Administrator under this Contract shall be entitled to disregard or over-rule any certificate or opinion or decision or approval or instruction given or expressed by the Architect²/the Contract Administrator as the case may be for the time being.

5³ᵃ   The extent of the application of the Construction (Design and Management) Regulations 1994 (the 'CDM Regulations') to the Contract Works is stated in Appendix II;

6³ᵇ   The term 'the Planning Supervisor' in the Conditions shall mean the - Architect¹/the Contract Administrator

or_____

of_____

_____

_____

or in the event of the death of the Planning Supervisor or him ceasing to be the Planning Supervisor such other person as the Employer shall appoint as the Planning Supervisor pursuant to Regulation 6(5) of the CDM Regulations.

²Delete or amend the words in brackets when either or both the Architect/the Contract Administrator or the Quantity Surveyor is an official of a Local Authority

³ᵃSee JCT Practice Note 27 'The application of the Construction (Design and Management) Regulations to Contracts on JCT Standard Forms of Contract' for the statutory obligations which must have been fulfilled before the Contractor can begin carrying out the Contract Works.

³ᵇDelete Clauses 6 and 7 when only Regulations 7 and 13 of the CDM Regulations apply. See Appendix II.

Appendix 2

7[3b]   The term 'the Principal Contractor' in the Conditions shall mean the Contractor or in the event of him ceasing to be the Principal Contractor, such other contractor as the Employer shall appoint as the Principal Contractor pursuant to Regulation 6(5) of the CDM Regulations.

8   If any dispute or difference arises under or by reason of breach of this Contract either Party may refer it to Adjudication in accordance with Clause 41A.

9A   Where the entry in Appendix II stating that "Clause 41B applies" has not been deleted then, subject to Clause 8, if any dispute or difference as to any matter or thing of whatsoever nature arising under this Contract or in connection therewith shall arise between the Parties either during the progress or after the completion or abandonment of the Works or after the determination of the employment of the Contract except under Clause 31 (*statutory tax deduction scheme*) to the extent provided in Clause 31.9, or under Clause 3 of the VAT Agreement it shall be referred to arbitration in accordance with Clause 41B.

9B   Where the entry in Appendix II stating that "Clause 41B applies" has been deleted then, subject to Clause 8, if any dispute or difference as to any matter or thing of whatsoever nature arising under this Contract or in connection therewith shall arise between the Parties either during the progress or after the completion or abandonment of the Works or after the determination of the employment of the Contractor it shall be determined by court proceedings and Clause 41C shall apply to such proceedings.

10   Whatever the nationality, residence or domicile of the Employer, the Contractor, any Sub-Contractor or supplier and wherever the Works are situated the law of Scotland shall be the law applicable to this Contract.

Appendix 2

11   Both parties consent to registration hereof for preservation and execution:

[4]Refer to SBCC
'Note to Users:
Attestation'
for guidance

IN WITNESS WHEREOF[4]

In addition, both parties sign on pages 31 and 35.

APPENDIX I

SCOTTISH SUPPLEMENT

_____

(The following are the amendments and modifications to the Conditions of the Standard Form of Building Contract. The numbers refer to clauses in the Standard Form).

PART 1 - GENERAL

1   **Interpretation, Definitions, etc.**

1.1, 1.2 and 1.8 shall be deleted.

1.3 and 35.4   The meanings given to the undernoted words and phrases shall be deleted and the following substituted therefor:

Appendix	Appendix II to the foregoing Building Contract
Arbitrator	Arbiter
Articles or Articles of Agreement and Recitals	The foregoing Building Contract
Contract Bills	The Bills of Quantities referred to in the Building Contract which have been priced by the Contractor and signed by him and the Employer or on their behalf
Contract Documents	The Contract Drawings, the Contract Bills, the Conditions, this Appendix and the Appendix II to the Building Contract
Contract Drawings	The Drawings referred to in the Building Contract which have been signed by the Employer and the Contractor or on their behalf
Contract Sum	The sum stated in the Building Contract subject to Clause 15.2
Nominated Sub-Contract Documents	
NSC/T	NSC/T/Scot
- Part 1	- Part 1
- Part 2	- Part 2
- Part 3	- Part 3
Agreement NSC/A	Sub-Contract NSC/A/Scot
Conditions NSC/C	Conditions NSC/C
Agreement NSC/W	Agreement NSC/W/Scot
Nomination NSC/N	Nomination NSC/N/Scot

Appendix 2

Numbered Documents	Any Document referred to in a Sub-Contract with a Nominated Sub-Contractor
Nominated Sub-Contract	A Scottish Building Sub-Contract between a Contractor and a Nominated Sub-Contractor (Sub-Contract NSC/A/Scot) with the Conditions of Nominated Sub-Contract (Conditions NSC/C) incorporated by reference therein and the documents annexed thereto
Works	The Contract Works shown and described in the Contract Drawings and in the Contract Bills and including any changes made to these in accordance with this Contract

The following clause shall be added:

1.3.1 Additional Definitions:

Assignment	Assignation
Contract Works	The works briefly described in the foregoing Building Contract and shown and described on the Contract Drawings and in the Contract Bills
Court	The Court of Session, Edinburgh
Court proceedings	A Commercial Action brought under Rule of Court 47
Execution of this Contract (5.2 and 5.3)	Formal adoption and signing of the Building Contract
Execution of a binding Sub-Contract Agreement (19.3)	Creation of a Sub-Contract
Real or personal	Heritable or moveable
Section 117 Local Government Act 1972	Section 68 Local Government (Scotland) Act 1973
Sub-Contract Works (35)	The works of a Nominated Sub-Contractor

5   Contract Documents - other documents - issue of certificates

Clause 5.3.1.2 shall apply.[2]

Clause 5.3.1.2 shall not apply and in Clause 5.3.2 the words '(nor in the master programme for the execution of the Works or any amendment to that programme or revision therein referred to in Clause 5.3.1.2)' shall be deleted.[2]

Appendix 2

14 **Contract Sum**

14.2 line 2 There shall be added after the word 'Conditions' the words 'including without prejudice thereto Clause 30.11.'

16 **Materials and goods unfixed or off-site**

16.1 There shall be added at the end 'and for any materials and/or goods purchased prior to their delivery to the site under the separate Contract referred to in Clause 30.3 hereof.'

16.2 shall be deleted.

N.B. - See Clause 30 - Certificates and Payments below.

¹SBCC publish standard forms of domestic sub-contracts and collateral warranties along with appropriate enabling clauses

19¹ **Assignation and Sub-Contracts**

19.1.2 shall be deleted and the following substituted:

Where Clause 19.1.2 is stated in Appendix II to apply, then in the event of the Employer alienating by the sale or lease or otherwise disposing of his interest in the Works, the Employer may at any time after the issue of the Certificate of Practical Completion assign to the person acquiring his interest in the Works, his right, title and interest to bring proceedings in the name of the Employer (whether in arbitration or court proceedings) to enforce any of the rights of the Employer arising under or by reason of breach of this Contract.

19.4.2 shall be deleted.

Position of Employer in relation to Domestic Sub-Contractor

Neither the existence nor the exercise of the powers in Clause 19 nor anything else contained in the Conditions shall render the Employer in any way liable to any Domestic Sub-Contractor. Nothing in Clause 19 shall be construed so as to affect the obligations of the Contractor under this Contract in regard to the supply of workmanship, materials and goods.

Clause 1 of SBCC Standard Form of Employer/Sub-Contractor Warranty Agreement

Whether or not a Domestic Sub-Contractor is responsible to the Employer in the terms set out in the SBCC Standard Form of Employer/Sub-Contractor Warranty Agreement the Contractor shall not be responsible to the Employer in respect of any Domestic Sub-Contract Works for anything to which such terms relate. Nothing in Clause 19 shall be construed so as to affect the obligations of the Contractor under this Contract in regard to the supply of workmanship, materials and goods and timeous performance.

27 **Determination by Employer**

This clause shall be deleted and the following substituted therefor

27.1 Any notice or further notice to which Clauses 27.2.1, 27.2.2, 27.2.3, and 27.3.1 refer shall be in writing and given by actual delivery, or by registered post or by recorded

Appendix 2

delivery. If sent by registered post or recorded delivery the notice or further notice shall, subject to proof to the contrary, be deemed to have been received 48 hours after the date of posting (excluding Saturday and Sunday and public holidays).

27.2.1 If, before the date of Practical Completion, the Contractor shall make a default in any one or more of the following respects:-

27.2.1.1 without reasonable cause he wholly or substantially suspends the carrying out of the Works; or

27.2.1.2 he fails to proceed regularly and diligently with the Works; or

27.2.1.3 he refuses or neglects to comply with a written notice or instruction from the Architect[2]/the Contract Administrator requiring him to remove any work, materials or goods not in accordance with this Contract and by such refusal or neglect the Works are materially affected; or

27.2.1.4 he fails to comply with the provisions of Clause 19.1.1 or Clause 19.2.2; or

27.2.1.5 he fails pursuant to the Conditions to comply with the requirements of the CDM Regulations.

the Architect[2]/the Contract Administrator may give to the Contractor a notice specifying the default or defaults (the 'specified default or defaults').

27.2.2 If the Contractor continues a specified default for 14 days from receipt of the notice under Clause 27.2.1 then the Employer may on, or within 10 days from, the expiry of that 14 days by a further notice to the Contractor determine the employment of the Contractor under this Contract. Such determination shall take effect on the date of receipt of such further notice.

27.2.3 If the Contractor ends the specified default or defaults, or

the Employer does not give the further notice referred to in clause 27.2.2

and the Contractor repeats a specified default (whether previously repeated or not) then, upon or within a reasonable time after such repetition, the Employer may by notice to the Contractor determine the employment of the Contractor under this Contract. Such determination shall take effect on the date of receipt of such notice.

415

27.2.4 A notice of determination under Clause 27.2.2 or Clause 27.2.3 shall not be given unreasonably or vexatiously.

27.3.1 In the event of a provisional liquidator being appointed to control the affairs of the Contractor, the Employer may determine the employment of the Contractor under this Contract by giving him seven days written notice sent by actual delivery, or by registered post or recorded delivery of such determination.

27.3.2 In the event of the Contractor becoming bankrupt or making a composition or arrangement with his creditors or having a proposal in respect of his Company for a voluntary arrangement for a composition of debts or scheme of arrangement approved in accordance with the Insolvency Act 1986 or having an application made under the Insolvency Act 1986 in respect of his Company to the Court for the appointment of an administrator or being an individual or a Scottish partnership having his estate sequestrated or becoming apparently insolvent (as defined by the Bankruptcy (Scotland) Act 1985) or entering into a trust deed for his creditors or having a winding up order made or (except for the purposes of reconstruction) a resolution for voluntary winding up passed or a receiver or manager of his business or undertaking duly appointed or having an administrative receiver, (as defined in the Insolvency Act 1986) appointed, or possession being taken by or on behalf of the holder of any debenture secured by a floating charge, the employment of the Contractor under this Contract shall be forthwith automatically determined.

27.3.3 In the event of the employment of the Contractor being determined under Clauses 27.3.1 or 27.3.2 hereof the said employment may be reinstated and continued if the Employer and the Contractor, his trustee in bankruptcy, provisional liquidator, liquidator, receiver, manager or administrative receiver as the case may be shall so agree.

27.4 The Employer shall be entitled to determine the employment of the Contractor under this or any other contract, if the Contractor shall have offered or given or agreed to give to any person any gift or consideration of any kind as an inducement or reward for doing or forbearing to do or for having done or forborne to do any action in relation to the obtaining or execution of this or any other contract with the Employer, or for showing or forbearing to show favour or disfavour to any person in relation to this or any other contract with the Employer, or if the like acts shall have been done by any person employed by the Contractor or acting on his behalf (whether with or without the knowledge of the Contractor), or if in relation to this or any other contract with the Employer the Contractor or any person employed by him

Appendix 2

or acting on his behalf shall have committed an offence under the Prevention of Corruption Acts 1889 to 1916, or, where the Employer is a local authority, shall have given any fee or reward the receipt of which is an offence under Section 68 of the Local Government (Scotland) Act 1973 or any amendment or re-enactment thereof.

27.5   In the event of the employment of the Contractor under this Contract being determined under clauses 27.2.2, 27.2.3, 27.3.1, 27.3.2 or 27.4 and so long as it has not been reinstated and continued, the following shall be the respective rights and duties of the Employer and the Contractor:

       27.5.1   the Employer may employ and pay other persons to carry out and complete the Works and he or they may enter upon the Works and use all temporary buildings, plant, tools, equipment, goods and materials intended for, delivered to and placed on or adjacent to the Works, and may purchase all materials and goods necessary for the carrying out and completion of the Works; the Employer may employ and pay other persons to carry out and complete the Works and to make good defects of the kind referred to in Clause 17 and he or they may enter upon the site and the Works and use all temporary buildings, plant, tools, equipment and Site Materials, and may purchase all materials and goods necessary for the carrying out and completion of the Works and for the making good of defects as aforesaid; provided that where the aforesaid temporary buildings, plant, tools, equipment and Site Materials are not owned by the Contractor the consent of the owner thereof to such use is obtained by the Employer;

          27.5.2.1   except where the determination occurs by reason of the bankruptcy of the Contractor or of him having a winding up order made or (other than for the purposes of amalgamation or reconstruction) a resolution for voluntary winding up passed, the Contractor shall if so required by the Employer or by the Architect/the Contract Administrator on behalf of the Employer within 14 days of the date of determination, assign to the Employer without payment the benefit of any agreement for the supply of materials or goods and/or for the execution of any work for the purposes of this Contract to the extent that the same is assignable;

          27.5.2.2   except where Clause 27.3.2 applies, the Employer may pay any supplier or sub-contractor for any materials or goods delivered or works executed for the purposes of this Contract before or after the date of determination insofar as the price thereof has not already been discharged by the Contractor. Payments made under 27.5.2.2 may be deducted from any sum due or to become due to the Contractor or may be recoverable from the Contractor by the Employer as a debt;

27.5.3 the Contractor shall when required in writing by the Architect/the Contract Administrator so to do (but not before) remove from the Works any temporary buildings, plant, tools, equipment, goods and materials belonging to him and the Contractor shall have removed by their owner any temporary buildings, plant, tools, equipment, goods and materials not owned by him. If within a reasonable time after any such requirement has been made the Contractor has not complied therewith, in respect of temporary buildings, plant, tools, equipment, goods and materials belonging to him, then the Employer may (but without being responsible for any loss or damage) remove and sell any such property so far as belonging to the Contractor, holding the proceeds less all costs incurred to the credit of the Contractor.

27.5.4 Subject to Clause 27.5.5.2, the provisions of this Contract which require any further payment or any release or further release of Retention to the Contractor shall not apply; provided that this clause shall not be construed so as to prevent the enforcement by the Contractor of any rights under this Contract in respect of amounts properly due to be discharged by the Employer to the Contractor which the Employer has unreasonably not discharged and which have accrued 28 days or more before the date of determination of the employment of the Contractor.

27.5.5 Upon the completion of the Works and the making good of defects as referred to in Clause 27.5.1 (but subject where relevant, to the exercise of the right under Clause 17.2 and/or clause 17.3 of the Architect²/the Contract Administrator, with the consent of the Employer, not to require defects of the kind referred to in Clause 17 to be made good) then within a reasonable time thereafter an account in respect of the matters referred to in Clause 27.5.5 shall be set out in a statement either prepared by the Employer or in a certificate issued by the Architect/the Contract Administrator.

27.5.5.1 The amount of expenses properly incurred by the Employer including those incurred pursuant to Clause 27.5.1 and of any direct loss and/or damage caused to the Employer as a result of the determination;

27.5.5.2   the amount of any payment made or otherwise discharged in favour of the Contractor;

27.5.5.3   the total amount which would have been payable for the Works in accordance with this Contract.

27.5.6   If the sum of the amounts stated under Clauses 27.5.5.1 and 27.5.5.2 exceeds or is less than the amount stated under Clause 27.5.5.3 the difference shall be a debt payable by the Contractor to the Employer or by the Employer to the Contractor as the case may be.

27.6.1   If the Employer decides after the determination of the employment of the Contractor not to have the Works carried out and completed, he shall so notify the Contractor in writing within 6 months from the date of such determination. Within a reasonable time from the date of such written notification the Employer shall send to the Contractor a statement of account setting out:

27.6.1.1   the total value of work properly executed at the date of determination of the employment of the Contractor, such value to be ascertained in accordance with the Conditions as if the employment of the Contractor had not been determined together with any amounts due to the Contractor under the Conditions not included in such total value;

27.6.1.2   the amount of any expenses properly incurred by the Employer and of any direct loss and/or damage caused to the Employer as a result of the determination.

After taking into account amounts previously paid to or otherwise discharged in favour of the Contractor under this Contract, if the amount stated under Clause 27.6.1.2 exceeds or is less than the amount stated under Clause 27.6.1.1 the difference shall be a debt payable by the Contractor to the Employer or by the Employer to the Contractor as the case may be.

27.6.2   If after the expiry of the 6 month period referred to in Clause 27.6.1 the Employer has not begun to operate the provisions of Clause 27.5.1 and has not given a written notification pursuant to Clause 27.6.1 the Contractor may require by notice in writing to the Employer that he states whether Clauses 27.5.1 to 27.5.6 are to apply and, if not to apply, require that a statement of account pursuant to Clause 27.6.1 be prepared by the Employer for submission to the Contractor.

27.7   The provisions of Clauses 27.2 to 27.6 are without prejudice to any other rights and remedies which the Employer may possess.

28   Determination by Contractor

Clause 28.3.1 (Private Editions only) The whole clause shall be deleted and the following substituted:

'28.3.1 If the Employer becomes bankrupt or makes a composition or arrangement with his creditors or has a proposal in respect of his Company for a voluntary arrangement for a composition of debts or scheme of arrangement approved in accordance with the Insolvency Act 1986 or has an application made under the Insolvency Act 1986 in respect of his Company to the Court for the appointment of an administrator or has his estate sequestrated or becomes apparently insolvent or enters into a trust deed for his creditors or has a winding up order made or (except for the purposes of reconstruction) a resolution for voluntary winding up is passed or a receiver or manager of his business or undertaking is duly appointed or has an administrative receiver, as defined in the Insolvency Act 1986, appointed, or possession is taken by or on behalf of the holder of any debenture secured by a floating charge

then:'

30   Certificates and Payments

30.2.1.3 shall be deleted.

30.3   shall be deleted and the following substituted:

If the Architect[2]/the Contract Administrator is of the opinion that it is expedient to do so the Employer may enter into a separate contract for the purchase from the Contractor or any Sub-Contractor of any materials and/or goods prior to their delivery to the site, which the Contractor is under obligation to supply in terms of this Contract, and upon such contract being entered into the purchase of the said materials and/or goods shall be excluded altogether from this Contract and the Contract Sum shall be adjusted accordingly. Provided that when the Employer enters into a separate contract with any Sub-Contractor;

30.3.1 he shall do so only with the   consent of the Contractor, which   consent   shall   not   be unreasonably withheld, and

30.3.2 payment by the Employer to the Sub-Contractor for any of the said materials and/or goods shall in no way affect any cash discount or other emolument to which the Contractor may be entitled and which shall be paid by the Employer to the Contractor.

30.9.3 Substitute "60" for "28" days.

Appendix 2

30.9.4 shall be deleted and the following substituted:

> Where pursuant to Clause 41A.8.1 either Party wishes to have a dispute or difference on which an Adjudicator has given his decision on a date which is after the date of issue of the Final Certificate finally determined by arbitration either Party may commence arbitration within 28 days of the date on which the Adjudicator gave his decision.

The following clauses shall be added:

30.11 Nothing in clauses 30.6.2 or 30.9.1.2 shall prevent the Employer deducting or adding liquidate and ascertained damages in accordance with Clause 24 hereof from any sum due by him to the Contractor or by the Contractor to the Employer as the case may be under the Final Certificate.

30.12.1 Prior to the issue of the Certificate of Practical Completion in the event of the Architect²/Contract Administrator not issuing any Interim Certificate as provided by Clause 30.1.1, the Contractor shall be entitled to make application to the Employer for payment of any sums the Contractor considers due under the Contract pursuant to Clause 30.2.

30.12.2 The said application of the Contractor shall be made in accordance with the statement prepared by the Quantity Surveyor pursuant to Clause 30.1.2.2 or in the absence of the issue of such statement, the Contractor's application submitted by the Contractor in accordance with Clause 30.1.2.2 shall be submitted to the Employer.

30.12.3 For the purposes of Clause 30.12.1 to 30.12.2, the final date for payment shall be 14 days from the date of issue of the said application by the Contractor under Clause 30.12.1 and Clause 30.1.4 shall apply upon the hypothesis of fact that said application is an Interim Certificate.

30.12.4 Not later than five days after receipt of the said application the Employer shall give a written notice to the Contractor with a copy sent simultaneously to the Architect²/Contract Administrator specifying the amount of the payment proposed to be made in respect of that application, the basis on which the said amount is calculated and to what the amount relates and, subject to Clause 30.1.1.4, shall pay the amount proposed no later than the final date for payment.

30.12.5 If the Employer makes any payment to the Contractor in respect of said application, the Architect²/Contract Administrator shall take such payment into account in the next Certificate which he issues.

Appendix 2

PART 2 - NOMINATED SUB-CONTRACTORS AND NOMINATED SUPPLIERS

35   **Nominated Sub-Contractors - Procedure for nomination of a Sub-Contractor**

35.4   shall be deleted and the following substituted:

The following documents relating to Nominated Sub-Contractors are issued by the Scottish Building Contract Committee and are referred to in the Conditions and in the documents themselves as

The Standard Form of Nominated Sub-Contract Tender for use in Scotland which comprises:	Tender NSC/T/Scot
Part 1: The Architect's/the Contract Administrator's Invitation to Tender to a Sub-Contractor	- Part 1
Part 2: Tender by a Sub-Contractor	- Part 2
Part 3: Particular Conditions to be agreed by a Contractor and a Sub-Contractor nominated under Clause 35.6	- Part 3
The Scottish Building Sub-Contract between a Contractor and a Nominated Sub-Contractor	Sub-Contract NSC/A/Scot
The Standard Conditions of Nominated Sub-Contract incorporated by reference into Sub-Contract NSC/A/Scot	Conditions NSC/C
The Standard Form of Employer/Nominated Sub-Contractor Agreement for use in Scotland	Agreement NSC/W/Scot
The Standard Form of Nomination Instruction for use in Scotland	Nomination NSC/N/Scot

and throughout Part 2 of the Conditions, NSC/T/Scot, NSC/A/Scot, NSC/W/Scot and NSC/N/Scot shall be substituted for NSC/T, NSC/A, NSC/W and NSC/N respectively: NSC/A/Scot shall be read in conjunction with NSC/C.

Appendix 2

35.13.5.3.4 shall be deleted and the following substituted:

> Clause 35.13.5.2 shall not apply if at the date, when the reduction and payment to the Nominated Sub-Contractor referred to in Clause 35.13.5.2 would otherwise be made the Contractor has become bankrupt or made a composition or arrangement with his creditors or had his estate sequestrated or become apparently insolvent or entered into a trust deed for his creditors or had a winding up order made or a resolution for winding up passed (except for the purposes of reconstruction).

35.24.2 shall be deleted and the following substituted:

> the Nominated Sub-Contractor becomes bankrupt or makes a composition or arrangement with his creditors or has a proposal in respect of his Company for a voluntary arrangement for a composition of debts or scheme of arrangement approved in accordance with the Insolvency Act 1986 or has an application made under the Insolvency Act 1986 in respect of his Company to the Court for the appointment of an administrator or has his estate sequestrated or becomes apparently insolvent or enters into a trust deed for his creditors or has a winding up order made or (except for the purposes of reconstruction) has a resolution for voluntary winding up passed or a receiver or manager of his business or undertaking duly appointed or has an administrator receiver or an administrator as defined in the Insolvency Act 1986 appointed, or possession is taken by or on behalf of any holder of any debenture secured by a floating charge; or

The following clause shall be added:

35.27   Determination of employment of Contractor

> The Nominated Sub-Contractor shall recognise an Assignation by the Contractor in favour of the Employer in terms of Clause 27.5.2.1.

36   Nominated Suppliers

36.4.8.1 and 36.4.8.2 shall be deleted and the following substituted:

36.4.8.1 that in any dispute or difference between the Contractor and the Nominated Supplier which is referred to arbitration the Contractor and the Nominated Supplier agree and consent that either the Contractor or the Nominated Supplier may require the Arbiter to state a case under Section 3 of the Administration of Justice (Scotland) Act 1972 on any question of law arising out of a proposed award made in the arbitration, and that the Contractor and the Nominated Supplier agree that the Court of Session should have jurisdiction to determine any questions of law;

36.4.8.2 that if any dispute or difference between the Employer and/or the Contractor and the Nominated Supplier raises predominantly issues which are substantially the same as or are connected with issues raised in a related dispute between the Employer and the Contractor under this Contract then, where [6]Clause 41B.2 applies, such dispute or difference shall be referred to the Arbiter already appointed pursuant to Clause 41B; and the Employer and/or the Contractor and the Nominated Supplier agree

- that such Arbiter shall have the same powers and discretions as are enjoyed by the Court of Session in respect of the joining of one or more defenders or joining co-defenders or third parties and he and the parties shall be entitled to apply the same procedures with appropriate modifications as are available under rules of court for such purposes and he may make all directions and awards including part, interim and final awards as he considers appropriate for these purposes;

- that the agreement and consent referred to in Clause 36.4.8.1 on a stated case under Section 3 of the Administration of Justice (Scotland) Act 1972 to the Court of Session on any question of law shall apply to any question of law arising out of the proposed awards of such Arbiter in respect of all related disputes referred to him or arising in the course of the reference of all related disputes referred to him;

- and that in any case, subject to the agreement referred to in Clause 36.4.8.1, the award of such Arbiter shall be final and binding on the parties.

When the Employer and/or the Contractor or the Nominated Supplier require such dispute or difference to be referred to arbitration, then either the Employer and/or the Contractor or the Nominated Supplier shall give written notice to the other to such effect and such dispute or difference shall be referred to the arbitration and final decision of the already appointed Arbiter. Arbitration proceedings shall be deemed to have been instituted on the date when such notice is given. The written notice shall also be given to the already appointed Arbiter and his appointment as Arbiter between the Employer and/or the Contractor and the Nominated Supplier shall take effect when the Arbiter gives the parties notice in writing that he accepts the appointment. If he does not give such notice of acceptance within 28 days after receipt of notice from the Employer and/or the Contractor or the Nominated Supplier, he shall be deemed to have declined the appointment. Any such appointment shall extend to and include the power to determine whether the issues predominantly raised between the Employer and/or the Contractor and the Nominated Supplier are substantially the same as or are connected with issues in the related dispute on which he has already been appointed Arbiter or if having regard to the limited scope of the convergence between the related dispute and the dispute or difference under this Agreement, it is more appropriate that this dispute or difference be referred to a different Arbiter. Save that either the Employer or the Contractor or the Nominated Supplier may require the dispute or difference arising under the Supply Contract to be referred to a different Arbiter (to be appointed under the Supply Contract) if any of them reasonably considers that the Arbiter appointed to determine the related dispute is not appropriately qualified to determine the dispute or difference under the Supply Contract and it is more appropriate that this dispute or difference is referred to a different Arbiter. Any dispute or difference as to the applicability of Clause 36.4.8.2 shall be referred to the determination of the Arbiter appointed to deal with the related dispute. If the Arbiter already appointed declines to deal with the related dispute or determines that the dispute is sufficiently different and shall be referred to another Arbiter, then, failing agreement between the parties upon another Arbiter within 14 days of said declinature or determination, the matter shall be referred to an Arbiter appointed by the Chairman or Vice-Chairman of the Scottish Building Contract Committee.

36.4.8.3 Unless otherwise agreed, the Arbiter may if he thinks fit award simple interest at such rate as he thinks fit (a) on any sum which is subject to the reference but which is paid before the award for such period commencing not earlier than the date on which the right to payment in respect of any part of the said sum (whether then quantified or not) first arose and ending not later than the date of payment as he thinks fit and (b) on any sum which he awards for such period commencing not earlier than the date on which the right to payment first arose in respect of any part of the said sum (whether then quantified or not) and ending not later than the date of his award as he thinks fit; and he may fix different periods for different parts of said sum all as he thinks fit.

36.4.8.3.1 The foregoing power to award interest shall be equally applicable to sums awarded by way of interim and part awards as to sums awarded as final awards, and shall apply irrespective of the basis in law upon which the said sums are awarded.

36.4.8.3.2 The foregoing power to award interest shall be exercisable notwithstanding that the principal sum requires to be quantified or that the debtor has claims by way of retention or set off.

36.4.8.3.3 The foregoing powers to award interest conferred on the Arbiter are without prejudice to any other power of an Arbiter to award interest.

36.4.8.3.4 A sum directed to be paid by an award shall, unless the award otherwise directs, carry interest as from the date of the award at the same rate as the Court of Session judicial rate applying at the date of the commencement of the arbitration.

425

36.4.8.4 Any party to subsisting arbitration proceedings may apply to the Chairman or Vice-Chairman of the Scottish Building Contract Committee for the office of Arbiter to be declared vacant and the Chairman or Vice-Chairman, as appropriate, may declare the office of Arbiter vacant should any of the following circumstances occur:-

36.4.8.4.1   The Arbiter refuses to act or delays unreasonably to act;

36.4.8.4.2   The Arbiter resigns or withdraws from acting;

36.4.8.4.3   The Arbiter becomes incapacitated by reason of mental or physical infirmity from discharging the duties of Arbiter;

36.4.8.4.4   The Arbiter is disqualified for whatever reason from performing the duties of his office;

36.4.8.4.5   The Arbiter dies.

36.4.8.5 The Chairman or Vice-Chairman of the Scottish Building Contract Committee acting under the provisions of Clause 36.4.8 is hereby empowered and shall be entitled to apply the Facilitating Regulations of the Scottish Building Contract Committee's Arbitration Service.

36.4.8.6 Any Arbiter appointed for the purposes of Clause 36.4.8 shall have the same powers as an Arbiter appointed and acting under the provisions of Clause 41B hereof, and without prejudice to the foregoing generality, Clauses 41B.2, 41B.3, 41B.5 and 41B.6.

The following clause shall be added:

36.6   Determination of Employment of Contractor

The Nominated Supplier shall recognise an Assignation by the Contractor in favour of the Employer in terms of Clause 27.4.2.1.

PART 3 - FLUCTUATIONS

(No amendments or modifications are required to this part).

PART 4 - SETTLEMENT OF DISPUTES - ADJUDICATION - ARBITRATION - COURT PROCEEDINGS

41A and B shall be deleted and the following substituted therefor:

41A   Adjudication

41A.1   Clause 41A applies where, pursuant to Clause 8 of the narrative, either Party refers any dispute or difference arising under or by reason of breach of this Contract to Adjudication.

426

[7]The nominators have agreed with the SBCC that they will comply with the requirements of Clause 41A on the nomination of an Adjudicator including the requirements in Clause 41A.2.1 for the nomination to be made with the object of securing the appointment of, and the referral of the dispute or difference to, the Adjudicator within 7 days of the date of the notice of intention to refer; and will only nominate adjudicators who will enter into the "SBCC Adjudication Agreement".

The SBCC Adjudication Agreement, whose text is set out in the Guidance Notes to this Amendment, is available from the retailers of SBCC Forms.

41A.2[7] The Adjudicator to decide the dispute or difference shall be either a person agreed by the Parties or, on the application of the Party who is seeking the appointment of the Adjudicator and the referral of the dispute or difference to Adjudication the nominator shall be the Chairman, Vice-Chairman, President or Vice-President of either the Royal Incorporation of Architects in Scotland or the Scottish Building Employers Federation or the Royal Institution of Chartered Surveyors in Scotland or the National Specialist Contractors Council and the selection of the nominator shall be made by the said Party at a time not earlier than when any dispute or difference arises.

41A.2.1 where either party has given notice of his intention to refer a dispute to Adjudication then

- any **agreement by the parties** on the appointment of an Adjudicator must be reached with the object of securing the appointment of and the referral of the dispute or difference to the Adjudicator within 7 days of the date of the notice of intention to refer (see Clause 41A.5.1)

- any application to the **nominator** must be made with the object of securing the appointment of and the referral of the dispute or difference to the Adjudicator within 7 days of the date of the notice of intention to refer;

41A.2.2 upon agreement by the parties on the appointment of the Adjudicator or upon receipt by the parties from the nominator of the name of the nominated Adjudicator the parties shall thereupon execute the SBCC Standard Agreement for the appointment of an Adjudicator issued by the Scottish Building Contracts Committee ("the SBCC Adjudication Agreement"). In the event of one party refusing or delaying unreasonably to execute the SBCC Adjudication Agreement an Adjudicator shall be entitled to proceed on the basis thereof provided it has been signed by one party and himself.

41A.3.1 An Adjudicator may resign at any time on giving notice in writing to the parties to the dispute.

41A.3.2 An Adjudicator must resign where the dispute is the same or substantially the same as one which has previously been referred to Adjudication, and a decision has been taken in that Adjudication.

41A.3.3 Where an Adjudicator ceases to act under sub-clause 1 hereof -

41A.3.3.1 the referring party may serve a fresh notice under Clause 41A.5.1 and shall request an Adjudicator to act in accordance with Clause 41A.2; and

Appendix 2

41A.3.3.2 if requested by the new Adjudicator and insofar as it is reasonably practicable, the parties shall supply him with copies of all documents which they had made available to the previous Adjudicator.

41A.3.4 Where an Adjudicator resigns in the circumstances mentioned in Clause 41A.3.1 or .2 or where a dispute varies significantly from the dispute referred to him and for that reason he is not competent to decide it, that Adjudicator's fees and expenses shall be determined and payable in accordance with Clause 41A.7.1 and .2

41A.3.5 If the Adjudicator dies or becomes ill or is unavailable for some other cause and is thus unable to adjudicate on a dispute or difference referred to him, the Parties may either agree upon an individual to replace the Adjudicator or failing agreement, either party may apply to the original nominator for the nomination of an Adjudicator to adjudicate that dispute or difference; and the parties shall execute the SBCC Adjudication Agreement with the agreed or nominated Adjudicator.

41A.4.1 The Adjudicator may, with the consent of all the parties to those disputes, adjudicate at the same time on more than one dispute under the same contract.

41A.4.2 The Adjudicator may, with the consent of all the parties to those disputes, adjudicate at the same time on related disputes under different contracts, whether or not one or more of those parties is a party to those disputes.

41A.4.3 All the parties in sub-clause 1 and 2 respectively may agree to extend the period within which the Adjudicator may reach a decision in relation to all or any of these disputes.

41A.4.4 Where an Adjudicator ceases to act because a dispute is to be adjudicated on by another person in terms of this clause, that Adjudicator's fees and expenses shall be determined and payable in accordance with Clause 41A.7.1 and .2.

41A.5.1 When pursuant to Clause 8 of the narrative of the building contract a party requires a dispute or difference to be referred to Adjudication then that party shall give notice to the other party of his intention to refer the dispute or difference, briefly identified in the notice, to Adjudication. If an Adjudicator is agreed or appointed within 7 days of the notice then the Party giving the notice shall refer the dispute or difference to the Adjudicator ("the referral") within 7 days of the notice but if the Adjudicator is not agreed or appointed within 7 days of the notice the referral shall be made immediately on such agreement or appointment and shall include with that referral particulars of the dispute or difference together with a summary of the contentions on which he relies, a statement of the remedy which is sought and any material he wishes the Adjudicator to consider. The referral and its accompanying documentation shall be copied simultaneously to the other party.

41A.5.2 The referral by a party with its accompanying documentation to the Adjudicator and the copies thereof to be provided to the other party shall be given by actual delivery or by E-mail or by Fax or by registered post or recorded delivery. If given by Fax or E-mail then, for record purposes, the referral and its accompanying documentation must forthwith be sent by first class post or given by actual delivery. If sent by registered post or recorded delivery the referral and its accompanying documentation shall, subject to proof to the contrary, be deemed to have been received 48 hours after the date of posting subject to the exclusion of Sundays and any Public Holiday.

41A.6.1 The Adjudicator shall immediately upon receipt of the referral and its accompanying documentation confirm that receipt to the parties.

41A.6.2 The party not making the referral may, by the same means stated in Clause 41A.5.2, send to the adjudicator with a copy to the other party, a written statement of the contentions on which he relies and any material he wishes the Adjudicator to consider with due despatch having regard to the Adjudicator's duties under Clause 41A.6.3.

41A.6.3 The Adjudicator shall within 28 days of the referral and its accompanying documentation under Clause 41A.5.1 and acting as an adjudicator for the purposes of S.108 of the Housing Grants, Construction and Regeneration Act 1996 reach his decision and forthwith send that decision in writing to the parties. Provided that the party who has made the referral may consent to allowing the Adjudicator to extend the period of 28 days by up to 14 days; and that by agreement between the parties after the referral has been made a longer period than 28 days may be notified jointly by the Parties to the Adjudicator within which to reach his decision.

41A.6.4 If requested by one of the parties to the dispute, not later than 7 days from the date of delivering his decision to both parties, the Adjudicator shall provide reasons for that decision.

41A.6.5 In reaching his decision, the Adjudicator shall act impartially, set his own procedure and at his absolute discretion may take the initiative in ascertaining the facts and the law as he considers necessary in respect of the referral and his powers shall include the following:

41A.6.5.1 using his own knowledge and/or experience;

41A.6.5.2 opening up, reviewing and revising any certificate, opinion, decision, requirement or notice issued, given or made under the Contract as if no such certificate, opinion, decision, requirement or notice had been issued, given or made;

41A.6.5.3 requiring from the parties further information than that contained in the notice of referral and its accompanying documentation or in any written statement provided by the parties including the results of any tests that have been made or of any opening up or shall himself or instruct others to carry out any tests or experiments subject to obtaining any necessary consents from any third parties;

41A.6.5.4 requiring the parties to carry out tests or additional tests or to open up work or further open up work;

41A.6.5.5 visiting the site of the Works or any workshop where work is being or has been prepared for the Contract;

41A.6.5.6 obtaining such information as he considers necessary from any employee or representative of the parties provided that before obtaining information from an employee of a party he has given prior notice to that party;

41A.6.5.7 obtaining from others such information and advice as he considers necessary on technical and on legal matters subject to giving prior notice to the parties together with a statement or estimate of the cost involved.

41A.6.5.8 having regard to any term of the contract relating to the payment of interest deciding the circumstances in which or the period for which a simple rate of interest shall be paid;

41A.6.5.9 deciding the language or languages to be used in the Adjudication and whether a translation of any document is to be provided and, if so, by whom;

41A.6.5.10 awarding damages and interest thereon;

41A.6.5.11 giving directions as to the timetable for the Adjudication, any deadlines, or limits to the length of written documents or the number of documents to be supplied; and

41A.6.5.12 issuing other directions relating to the conduct of the Adjudication.

41A.6.6 Any failure by either party to enter into the SBCC Adjudication Agreement or to comply with any requirement of the Adjudicator under Clause 41A.6.5 or with any provision in or requirement under Clause 41A shall not invalidate the decision of the Adjudicator.

41A.6.7 The parties shall meet their own costs of the Adjudication except that the Adjudicator may direct as to who should pay the cost of any test or opening up if required pursuant to Clause 41A.6.5.5.

41A.6.8 The Adjudicator and any party to the dispute shall not disclose to any other person any information or document

430

Appendix 2

provided to him in connection with the Adjudication which the party supplying it has indicated is to be treated as confidential, except to the extent that it is necessary for the purposes of, or in connection with the Adjudication or any subsequent arbitration or court proceedings.

41A.7.1 The Adjudicator in his decision shall state how payment of his fee and reasonable expenses is to be apportioned as between the parties. In default of such statement the parties shall bear the cost of the Adjudicator's fee and reasonable expenses in equal proportion.

41A.7.2 The parties shall be jointly and severally liable to the Adjudicator for his fee and for all expenses reasonably incurred by the Adjudicator pursuant to the Adjudication.

41A.7.3 The Adjudicator may decide that any of the parties to the dispute is liable to make payment under or by reason of breach of the Contract (whether in Sterling or some other currency) and, subject to Section 111(4) of the Act, when payment is due and the final date of payment.

⁸The arbitration or court proceedings are not an appeal against the decision of the Adjudicator but are a consideration of the dispute or difference as if no decision had been made by an Adjudicator.

41A.8.1 ⁸The decision of the Adjudicator shall be binding on the Parties until the dispute or difference is finally determined by arbitration or by court proceedings or by an agreement in writing between the parties made after the decision of the Adjudicator has been given.

41A.8.2 In the absence of any directions by the Adjudicator to the contrary the parties shall, without prejudice to their other rights under the Contract, comply with the decisions of the adjudicator immediately on delivery of the decision to the parties. Such directions may be issued at any stage of the Adjudication and may include security for the principal sum, expenses and interest and any sum counterclaimed and the disposal of related disputes; and the Employer and the Contractor shall ensure that the decisions of the Adjudicator are given effect.

41A.8.3 If either party does not comply with the decision of the Adjudicator the other Party shall be entitled, to take further proceedings including court proceedings to secure such compliance pending any final determination of the referred dispute or difference pursuant to Clause 41A.8.1.

41A.8.4 Where a party or the Adjudicator wishes to register the decision for execution in the Books of Council and Session, any other party or the parties shall, on being requested to do so, forthwith consent to such registration by subscribing the decision before a witness which failing within 7 days of such request, the same may be subscribed on behalf of the defaulting party by the Deputy Principal Clerk of the Court of Session.

41A.9 The Adjudicator shall not be liable for anything done or omitted in the discharge or purported discharge of his functions as Adjudicator unless the act or omission is in bad faith and this protection from liability shall similarly extend to any employee or agent of the Adjudicator.

Appendix 2

'Clause 41B
shall apply
unless the
entry in
Appendix II
stating that
"clause 41B
applies" has
been deleted.

41B' **Arbitration**

41B.1 In the event of any dispute or difference between the Employer and the Contractor arising during the progress of the Works or after completion or abandonment thereof in regard to any matter or thing whatsoever arising out of this Contract or in connection therewith including:

- any matter in connection with or arising out of the decision of an Adjudicator under Clause 41A in relation to enforcement and provided always that any decision of an Arbiter in relation thereto shall not prejudice any subsequent disposal in any subsequent arbitration or court proceedings under Clause 41A.8.1. (For the avoidance of doubt, the Adjudicator dealing with said matter shall not be precluded from acting as Arbiter in any subsequent arbitration under Clause 41B), or

- any matter or thing left by this Contract to the discretion of the Architect2/the Contract Administrator, or

- the withholding by the Architect2/the Contract Administrator of any certificate to which the Contractor may claim to be entitled, or

- the adjustment of the Contract Sum under Clause 30.6.2; or

- the rights and liabilities of the parties under Clauses 27, 28, 32 or 33, or

- unreasonable withholding of consent or agreement by the Employer or the Architect2/the Contract Administrator on his behalf or by the Contractor (but excluding any such dispute or difference arising under Clause 31 to the extent provided in Clause 31.9 and under Clause 3 of the VAT Agreement), then the said dispute or difference shall be and is hereby referred to the arbitration of such person as the parties may agree to appoint as Arbiter or failing agreement within 14 days after either party has given to the other written notice to concur in the appointment of an Arbiter as may be appointed by the person named in Appendix II whom failing by the Chairman or Vice-Chairman of the Scottish Building Contract Committee. Arbitration proceedings shall be deemed to have been instituted on the date on which the said written notice has been given.

41B.2 If the dispute or difference to be referred to arbitration under this Contract raises predominantly issues which are substantially the same as or are connected with issues raised in a related dispute between:

- the Employer and any Nominated Sub-Contractor under Agreement NSC/W/Scot as applicable, or

- the Contractor and any Nominated Sub-Contractor under Sub-Contract NSC/A/Scot, or

432

Appendix 2

- the Contractor and/or the Employer and any Nominated Supplier whose contract of sale with the Contractor provides for the matters referred to in Clause 36.4.8.2,

and if the related dispute has already been referred for determination to an Arbiter who has already been appointed, the Employer and the Contractor hereby agree

- that the dispute or difference under this Contract shall be referred to the Arbiter appointed to determine the related dispute;

- that such Arbiter shall have the same powers and discretions as are enjoyed by the Court of Session in respect of the joining of one or more defenders or joining co-defenders or third parties and he and the parties shall be entitled to apply the same procedures with appropriate modifications as are available under rules of court for such purposes and he may make all directions and awards including part, interim and final awards as he considers appropriate for these purposes;

- and that the provisions of Section 3 of the Administration of Justice (Scotland) Act 1972 shall apply to any question of law arising out of the awards of such Arbiter in respect of all related disputes referred to him or arising in the course of the reference of all related disputes referred to him.

When the Employer or the Contractor requires such dispute or difference to be referred to arbitration, then either the Employer or the Contractor shall give written notice to the other to such effect and such dispute or difference shall be referred to the arbitration and final decision of the already appointed Arbiter. Arbitration proceedings shall be deemed to have been instituted on the date when such notice is given. The written notice shall also be given to the already appointed Arbiter and his appointment as Arbiter between the Employer and the Contractor shall take effect when the Arbiter gives the parties notice in writing that he accepts the appointment. If he does not give such notice of acceptance within 28 days after receipt of notice from the Employer or the Contractor he shall be deemed to have declined the appointment. Any such appointment shall extend to and include the power to determine whether the issues predominantly raised between the Employer and the Contractor are substantially the same as or are connected with issues in the related dispute on which he has already been appointed Arbiter or if having regard to the limited scope of the convergence between the related dispute and the dispute or difference under this Agreement, it is more appropriate that this dispute or difference be referred to a different Arbiter. Any dispute or difference as to the applicability of Clause 41B.2.2 shall be referred to the determination of the Arbiter appointed to deal with the related dispute. Save that the Employer or the Contractor may require the dispute or difference under this Contract to be referred to a different Arbiter (to be appointed under this Contract) if either of them reasonably considers that the Arbiter appointed to determine the related dispute is not

Appendix 2

appropriately qualified to determine the dispute or difference under this Contract. The reference to an already appointed Arbiter shall include a reference of any question whether the issues raised predominantly are substantially the same or connected with those raised in the related dispute.

41B.2.1 Clause 41B.2 shall apply unless in Appendix II the words 'Clause 41B.2 applies' have been deleted.

41B.2.2 If the Arbiter already appointed referred to in Clause 41B.2 declines to deal with the related dispute or determines that the dispute is sufficiently different and should be referred to another Arbiter, then, failing agreement between the parties upon another Arbiter within 14 days of said declinature or determination, the matter shall be referred to an Arbiter appointed by the Chairman or Vice-Chairman of the Scottish Building Contract Committee.

41B.3 Subject to the provisions of Clauses 4.2, 30.9, 38.4.3, 39.5.3 and 40.5 the Arbiter shall have power to

41B.3.1 direct such measurements and/or valuations as may in his opinion be desirable in order to determine the rights of the parties

41B.3.2 ascertain and award any sum which ought to have been referred to or included in any certificate

41B.3.3 open up, review and revise any certificate, opinion, decision, requirement or notice (except where Clause 8.4 is relevant, a decision of the Architect[2]/the Contract Administrator to issue instructions pursuant to Clause 8.4.1)

41B.3.4 determine all matters in dispute which shall be submitted to him in the same manner as if no such certificate, opinion, decision, requirement or notice had been given

41B.3.5 award compensation or damages and expenses to or against any of the parties to the arbitration.

41B.4 The Law of Scotland shall apply to all arbitrations in terms of this clause and the award of the Arbiter shall be final and binding on the parties subject to the provisions of Section 3 of the Administration of Justice (Scotland) Act 1972. Parties are agreed that Section 3 of the said 1972 Act is excluded in relation to any questions of enforcement of an Adjudicator's award.

41B.5 The Arbiter shall be entitled to appoint a Clerk to assist him in accordance with normal arbitration practice, to issue interim decrees-arbitral in connection with or arising out of the decision of an Adjudicator under Clause 41A, to issue interim, part or final awards as well as proposed findings, to remuneration and reimbursement of his outlays, and to find the parties jointly and severally liable therefor, and to decern; and to dispense with a Deed of Submission.

41B.6 Unless otherwise agreed, the Arbiter may if he thinks fit award simple interest at such rate as he thinks fit (a) on any sum which is subject to the reference but which is paid before the award for such period commencing not earlier than the date on which the right to payment in respect of any part of the said sum (whether then quantified or not) first arose and ending not later than the date of payment as he thinks fit and (b) on any sum which he awards for such period commencing not earlier than the date on which the right to payment first arose in respect of any part of the said sum (whether then quantified or not) and ending not later than the date of his award as he thinks fit; and he may fix different periods for different parts of said sum all as he thinks fit;

41B.6.1 The foregoing power to award interest shall be equally applicable to sums awarded by way of interim and part awards as to sums awarded as final awards, and shall apply irrespective of the basis in law upon which the said sums are awarded.

41B.6.2 The foregoing power to award interest shall be exercisable notwithstanding that the principal sum requires to be quantified or that the debtor has claims by way of retention or set off.

41B.6.3 The foregoing powers to award interest conferred on the Arbiter are without prejudice to any other power of an Arbiter to award interest.

41B.6.4 A sum directed to be paid by an award shall, unless the award otherwise directs, carry interest as from the date of the award at the same rate as the Court of Session judicial rate applying at the date of the commencement of the arbitration.

41B.7 Any party to subsisting arbitration proceedings may apply to the Chairman or Vice-Chairman of the Scottish Building Contract Committee for the office of Arbiter to be declared vacant and the Chairman or Vice-Chairman, as appropriate, may declare the office of Arbiter vacant should any of the following circumstances occur:-

41B.7.1 The Arbiter refuses to act or delays unreasonably to act;

41B.7.2 The Arbiter resigns or withdraws from acting;

41B.7.3 The Arbiter becomes incapacitated by reason of mental or physical infirmity from discharging the duties of Arbiter;

41B.7.4 The Arbiter is disqualified for whatever reason from performing the duties of his office;

41B.7.5 The Arbiter dies.

41B.8 The Chairman or Vice-Chairman of the Scottish Building Contract Committee acting under the provisions of Clause 41B is hereby empowered and shall be entitled to apply the

Appendix 2

Facilitating Regulations of the Scottish Building Contract
Committee's Arbitration Service.

41C   Court Proceedings

41C.1   Clause 41C shall apply if the entry in Appendix II Abstract of
Conditions stating that "Clause 41B applies" has been
deleted.

41C.2   When any dispute or difference is to be determined by court
proceedings, then insofar as the Conditions provide for the
issue of a certificate, or the expression of an opinion or the
giving of a decision, requirement or notice such provision
shall not prevent the Court, in determining the rights and
liabilities of the parties hereto, from making any finding
necessary to establish whether such certificate was correctly
issued or opinion correctly expressed or decision,
requirement or notice correctly given on the facts found by
the Court;   nor shall such provision prevent the Court
establishing what certificate ought to have been issued or
what other opinion should have been expressed or what
other decision, requirement or notice should have been given
as if no certificate, opinion, decision, requirement or notice
had been issued, expressed or given.

Appendix 2

PART 5 - PROPER LAW

(This part has been added for convenience so that it may be included by reference in the Contract Document when the formal Scottish Building Contract is not being executed).

43   Whatever the nationality, residence or domicile of the Employer, the Contractor, any Sub-Contractor or supplier and wherever the Works are situated the law of Scotland shall be the law applicable to this Contract.

_____Employer   _____Contractor

Appendix 2

ABSTRACT OF CONDITIONS

[10]Delete as applicable	CDM Regulations	The Building Contract - Narrative Clause 5	[10]all the CDM Regulations apply/Regulations 7 and 13 only of the CDM Regulations apply
[11]Delete if disputes are to be decided by court proceedings, see SBCC Guidance Notes upon Dispute Resolution in Scotland	Dispute or difference - settlement of disputes	Clause 9	Clause 41B applies[11]
		Clause Number	
	Statutory tax deduction scheme - Income and Corporation Taxes Act 1988	31	Employer at Base Date is a "contractor"[2]/ is not a "contractor" for the purposes of the Act and the Regulations
	Base Date	1.3	_____
[12]Clause 1A can only apply where the Contractor is satisfied at the date the Contract is entered into that this output tax on all supplies to the Employer under The Contract will be at either a positive or a zero rate of tax.	VAT Agreement	15.2	Clause 1A of the VAT Agreement applies[2]/does not apply[12]
	Defects Liability Period (if none other stated is 12 months from the day named in the Certificate of Practical Completion of the Works)	17.2	_____
	Assignation by Employer of benefits after Practical Completion	19.1.2	Clause 19.1.2 applies[2]/does not apply
	Insurance cover for any one occurrence or series of occurrences arising out of one event	21.1.1	£_____
[13]If the indemnity is to be for an aggregate amount and not for any one occurrence or series of occurrences the entry should make this clear.	Insurance - Liability of Employer	21.2.1	Insurance may be[2]/is not required Amount of indemnity for any one occurrence or series of occurrences arising out of one event[13] £_____

438

Appendix 2

		Clause Number	
	Insurance of the Works - Alternative Clause	22.1	Clause 22A¹/22B¹/22C applies

<table>
<tr><td>[14]No percentage should be inserted if those concerned are all Employees of a Local Authority, but the sum assured should cover the cost of professional services</td><td>Percentage to cover Professional fees</td><td>22A²/ 22B.1²/ 22C.2</td><td>_____%[14]</td></tr>
<tr><td></td><td>Annual renewal date of insurance as supplied by the Contractor</td><td>22A.3.1</td><td>_____</td></tr>
</table>

	Insurance for Employer's loss of liquidate and ascertained damages - Clause 25.4.3	22D	Insurance may be²/is not required
		22D.2	Period of time_____

	Joint Fire Code	22FC.1	The Joint Fire Code applies²/does not apply

If the Joint Fire Code is applicable, state whether the insurer under Clause 22A or Clause 22B or Clause 22C.2 has specified that the Works are a 'Large Project': YES²/NO

(where Clause 22A applies these entries are made on information supplied by the Contractor)

	Date of Possession	23.1.1	_____
	Date for Completion	1.3	_____
	Deferment of Date of Possession	23.1.2 25.4.13	Clause 23.1.2 applies²/does not apply
		26.1	Period of deferment if it is to be less than 6 weeks is

_____

	Liquidate and Ascertained Damages	24.2	at the rate of £_____per_____

<table>
<tr><td>[15]If no period stated in respect of Clause 28.2.2, period will be 1 month, in respect of Clauses 28A.1.1.1 to 28A.1.1.3, period will be 3 months and in respect of Clauses 28A.1.1.4 to 28A.1.1.6 period will be 1 month.</td><td>Period of Suspension</td><td>28.2.2</td><td>_____[15]</td></tr>
<tr><td></td><td>Period of Delay</td><td>28A.1.1.1 to 28A.1.1.3</td><td>_____[15]</td></tr>
<tr><td></td><td>Period of Delay</td><td>28A.1.1.4 to 28A.1.1.6</td><td>_____[15]</td></tr>
</table>

Appendix 2

Advance payment	30.1.1.6	Clause 30.1.1.6 applies[2]/does not apply

If applicable:
the advance payment will be

£_____/_____%
of the Contract Sum; and will be reimbursed to the Employer in the following amount(s) and at the following time(s)

_____

_____

_____

_____

An advance payment bond is[2]/is not required.

Period of Interim Certificates (if none stated is one month)	30.1.3	_____
Gross Valuation	30.2.1.1	a priced Activity Schedule is[2]/is not attached to this Appendix
Retention Percentage (if less than five per cent)	30.4.1.1	_____%
Work reserved for Nominated Sub-Contractors for which the Contractor desires to tender	35.2	_____
Fluctuations (if alternative required is not shown Clause 38 shall apply)	37	Clause 38[2]/Clause 39[2]/Clause 40
Percentage addition	38.7 or 39.8	_____%
Formula Rules	40.1.1.1	
Rule 3	Base Month	_____19____
[16]Not to exceed 10%	Rule 3	[16]Non-Adjustable Element ____ % (Local Authorities Edition only)

Appendix 2

Rules 10 and 30(i)   Part 1²/Part II of Section 2 of the Formula Rules is
to apply

Settlement of disputes   41B
- Arbitration - if no
appointor is selected
the appointor shall be
the Chairman or Vice-
Chairman of the
Scottish Building
Contract Committee

   The Chairman or Vice-Chairman of
the Scottish Building Contract
Committee²/The Dean of the Faculty
of Advocates²/The Sheriff of the
Sheriffdom in which the Works are
situated.

Settlement of disputes   41B.2
- Arbitration

   Clause 41B.2 applies (See Clause
41B.2.1)

Performance   42.1.1
Specified Work

   Identify below or on a separate sheet
each item of Performance Specified
Work to be provided by the
Contractor and insert the relevant
reference in the Contract Bills[17]

[17]See Practice
Note 25
'Performance
Specified Work'
paragraphs 2.6 to
2.8 for a description
of work which is
not to be treated as
Performance
Specified Work.

_____Employer   _____Contractor

Appendix 2

Changes in April 1982 Revision:

1. Building Contract

Clause 4.1.4	*include*	Clause 4.1
Clause 4.3	*include*	Clause 38.4.3

2. Appendix 1

Clause 1.4	*add*	definition of specification
Clause 30.11	*delete*	ref. to 30.9.2, *substitute* 30.9.1.2
Clause 35.17	new Clause	
Clause 36.4.8	*add*	ref. to Clause 41
Clause 41.1.1	*delete*	ref. to Clause 3 of Building Contract
Clause 41.1.4	*include*	Clause 4.1
Clause 41.3	*include*	Clause 38.4.3

Changes in November 1984 Revision:

Clause 19.4.2	*delete*	not applicable to Scotland
Clause 35.3	*add*	re-ascertainment of date of revision of documents
Appendix II		Length of Defects Liability Period now 12 months if no other period stated.

Changes in January 1988 Revision:

JCT Amendment 2, issued in November, 1986 incorporated: S.B.C.C. Amendment Sheet No. 1 (January 1987) discontinued and changes introduced by JCT Amendment 4 issued in July, 1987 incorporated:

1. Building Contract

   Architect/the Contract Administrator substituted for the Architect/Supervising Officer

Clause 41	new appointor of Arbiter
Clause 41.1.4 and 41.1.5	additional grounds of opening arbitration before completion
Clause 41.5	amplified powers of Arbiter

2. Appendix I

Clause 19.1.2	Assignation by Employer
Clause 22	New Insurance Arrangements
Clause 27	Changes arising from Insolvency Act 1986
Clause 41	Formerly Clause 4 of Building Contract

3. Appendix II

   Consequential changes to

   Clauses 31, 1.3, 19.1.2, 21, 22, 23, 25, 26, 28 (new Clause 28A), 30 and 41.

4. While JCT Amendment 1 is not applicable for Scottish use, it has been necessary, to maintain sense of the numbering to include the Amendment and delete its effect on Clause 19.

Appendix 2

5.   Incorporates JCT Amendment 5: amending Clause 8.

Changes in July 1990 Revision:

1.   Incorporates JCT Amendment 6: omission of Clause 19A 'Fair Wages'

2.   Incorporates JCT Amendment 7: optional use of SMM7

3.   Incorporates JCT Amendment 8: VAT changes effective 1 April 1989

SBCC Amendment Sheet No. 1 (April 1989) discontinued

Changes in January 1992 Revision:

1.   JCT Amendments 9 (July 1990) and 10 (March 1991) incorporated; optional use of SMM6 ended.

2.   Building Contract

        Narrative - Clause 1   Contract Works and Works distinguished

3.   Appendix I

        Clause 1   Revised Definitions

        Clause 35   Revised procedure for nomination of a Sub-Contractor

        Clause 36   Revised arbitration provisions for Nominated Suppliers

        Clause 41   Arbiter empowered to award interest; new provisions for disposal of related disputes.

4.   Appendix II

        Clause 41.2   Multi-party arbitration provisions.

Changes in September 1995 Revision:

1.   Incorporates JCT Amendment 11 (July 1992): Clause 21.1.1.2, Contractor's Insurance; Clause 27, Determination by Employer; Clause 28, Determination by Contractor; Clause 28A, Determination by Employer or Contractor; Clause 32, Outbreak of hostilities; Clause 33, War damage; Clause 35, Nominated Sub-Contractors.

2.   Incorporates JCT Amendment 12 (July 1993): New Clause 42, Performance Specified Work.

3.   Incorporates JCT Amendment 13 (January 1994): Clause 13.2 re-drafted; New Clause 13A, Variation Instruction.

4.   Incorporates JCT Amendment 14 (March 1995); CDM Regulations.

5.   Incorporates JCT Amendment 15 (July 1995); Effect of Final Certificate

Changes in September 1996 Revision:

1.   Incorporates JCT Amendment 16 (July 1996): Insurance and Indemnity Provisions; sundry other amendments

Appendix 2

Changes in July 1997 Revision:

1.   Incorporates JCT Amendment 17 (May 1997):   Joint Code of Practice on the Protection from Fire of Construction Sites and Buildings Undergoing Renovation.

Changes in September 1997 Revision:

1.   Introduces Clause 19A: Procedure for selection of a Domestic Sub-Contractor and
.   formation of a Scottish Domestic Sub-Contract together with consequential amendments to Clause 19.

Changes in April 1998 Revision:

Incorporates JCT Amendment 18 (April1998)

1.   Building Contract

Narrative	Priced Activity Schedule
Narrative	provision to Contractor of an Information Release Schedule.
Narrative	bond terms

2.   Appendix I

Clause 8	reference to adjudicator
Clause 9A	reference to arbitration
Clause 9B	Court Proceedings
Clause 1.3	Additional definitions.
Clause 5.4	Drawings or details:
	revised clause - Information Release Schedule
Clause13.4.1	Valuation of Variations and provisional sum work and work covered by an Approximate Quantity
Clause 19.4	Additional Clause 19.4.3
Clause 19A	Deleted along with consequential deletions to Clause 19; side-note added.
Clauses 22A, 22B, 22C.2	Reinstatement value - Employer exempt or partially exempt from VAT
Clause 24	Damages for non-completion: re-draft of Clause 24.2.1
Clause 25.4	Relevant Events: re-drafted Clauses 25.4.6 and 25.4.7: new Relevant Event - Clause 25.4.18.
Clause 26	Loss and expense caused by matters affecting regular progress of the Works: addition to Clause 26.1; re-draft of Clause 26.2.1; new matter Clause 26.2.10.

Appendix 2

Clause 28.2	Determination by Contractor: default by Employer: re-draft of Clause 28.2.1.1.
Clause 30.1	Interim Certificates: Re-draft of Clauses 30.1.1.1 to 30.1.1.3 as Clauses 30.1.1.1 to 30.1.1.5; Interest on overdue payments; New Clause 30.1.1.6 - advance payment where Appendix so states; advance payment bond. Clause 30.1.2 re-numbered as 30.1.2.1; new Clause 30.1.2.2 - Contractor's application for payment New Clause 30.1.4 - Contractor's right of suspension of his obligations under the Contract to the Employer.
Clause 30.2	Ascertainment of amounts due in Interim Certificates: Revised Clause 30.2. Revised Clause 30.2.1: use of Activity Schedule.
Clause 30.3	Off-site materials and goods: "the listed items": revised provisions and model bond. Not applicable in Scotland.
Clause 30.8	Issue of Final Certificate: re-drafted clause. New provision for interest if payment of Final Certificate is overdue.
Clause 30.9	Effect of Final Certificate - commencement of arbitration.
Clause 35	Nominated Sub-Contractors: re-draft of Clauses 35.13.2, 35.13.3, 35.18 and 35.21; amendment to Clause 35.13.6.2.
Clause 36	Nominated Suppliers: revised Clause 36.4.8.
Clause 38	Contribution, levy and tax fluctuations: landfill tax: new Clause 38.2.3; consequential amendment to Clause 38.4.1.
Clause 41	New Clause 41A: "Adjudication"; Revised Clause 41, renumbered as Clause 41B "Arbitration", New Clause 41C, "Court Proceedings".
3. Appendix II	Additional entries pursuant to items 1, 12, 13, and 20 VAT Agreement - consequential amendments.

Changes in August 1998 Revision:

1. 30.9.3 substitution of 60 for 28 days.

2. Introduces Clauses 30.12.1 to 30.12.5 in conjunction with the Scottish Domestic Sub-Contract.

3. Corrections in JCT Amendment 18. JCT have decided not to issue a fresh amendment to JCT Amendment 18 but instead to expedite complete re-prints. In order to incorporate the corrections to JCT Amendment 18 Clause 3 of the Building Contract has been altered where it refers to JCT Amendment 18 and a separate correction sheet has been issued by SBCC.

Appendix 2

**Scottish Building Contract
With Quantities.
(August 1998 Revision)**

BUILDING CONTRACT

between_____

_____

_____(Employer)

and_____

_____

_____(Contractor)

with

Scottish Supplement 1980

to

The Conditions of the Standard Form of Building
Contract 1980 Edition With Quantities

SBCC

The constituent bodies of the Scottish Building
Contract Committee are:

Copyright of SBCC
27 Melville Street
Edinburgh EH3 7JF
August 1998
SBC267

Royal Incorporation of Architects in Scotland
Scottish Building Employers Federation
Royal Institution of Chartered Surveyors in Scotland
Convention of Scottish Local Authorities
National Specialist Contractors Council
Scottish Casec
Association of Consulting Engineers (Scottish Group)
Confederation of British Industry
Association of Scottish Chambers of Commerce

446

INDEX

Access to sites
  contractors, 4.145
  delays
    claims for losses, 4.287
    extensions of time, 4.239
  implied terms, 5.03
Activity schedules, 4.356
Adjudication, 3.52, 8.22 *see also* **Schemes for construction contracts**
  between architects and contractors, 4.27
  court powers, 8.26, 8.27
  judicial review, 8.25
  meaning, 8.23, 8.25
  model forms, 2,33
  timetable, 8.23, 8.29
Adjudicators
  decisions
    challenges, 8.28, 8.29
    enforcement, 8.29
    registration, 8.28
  fairness, 8.25
  natural justice, 8.24, 8.29
  powers, 8.24
Administration orders, 4.317, 4.324, 4.326, 4.327
  administrators' powers, 4.329
  contractors
    advantages, 4.331
    automatic termination of contracts, 4.331
  petitions, effect, 4.328
Agency, 1.22, 4.60
  architects and employers, 7.04, 7.06–07
Antiquities, 4.363
Arbiters
  corruption, 4.382
  errors, 4.387
  powers, 4.383(n7)
  stated cases, 4.382
Arbitration, 4.380–393
  advantages, 4.380
  between architects and contractors, 4.27
  clauses, 3.52
    incorporation into sub-contracts, 5.14

Arbitration—*cont.*
  registration, 2.08
  SBC, 4.02
  disadvantages, 4.378
  final certificates, 4.359
  judicial review, 4.384–393
  name-borrowing, 5.14
  notices, ICE conditions, 3.91
  principles, 4.381
  variation of instructions, 4.82
Architects, 1.18
  access to works, 4.75
  agents of employers, 7.04
  approval, 4.05
  breaches of contract, 4.308
  certificates *see* **Certificates**
  claims for direct losses and expenses, ascertaining amounts, 4.285, 4.286
  conditions of engagement, 7.31
  consents
    removal of materials, 4.133
    sub-contracts, 4.171
  contractual relationships, 7.02
  critical path analysis, 4.268
  delays, assessment of losses, 4.287, 4.302
  delegation to sub-contractors, 7.30
  design
    errors, 5.35
    implied warranties, 5.30
    liability, 5.30, 7.25
    responsibilities, 7.30–31
  drawings, 1.23
    reasonable time, 4.32–36
    setting out works, 4.53
  duties
    administration, 7.13–15
    probing, 7.26
    reporting deficient performance, 7.13, 7.24
    revision of designs, 7.27–28
    supervision, 4.60, 4.74, 7.12, 7.23–24
    to contractors, 7.16–22, 7.23
    warning of risks, 4.24, 7.25
  extensions of time, 4.237, 4.241–242, 7.15
    analysis, 4.260

Architects—*cont.*
  final certificates *see* **Final certificates**
  financial advice, 7.31
  implied duties, 4.60
    information, 4.34–35
  instructions, 4.26
    divergence with other documents, 4.24
    late instructions, 4.32–39
    postponement of works, 4.208
    procedure, 4.29
    variations, 4.76
      liquidate damages, 4.229
    verbal instructions, 4.29
  jus quaesitum tertio, 7.03–05
  liabilities, 4.60
  opinions, quality of materials, 4.58
  ostensible authority, 4.27
  powers, exclusion of employees, 4.66
  privity of contract, 7.05
  recommendation of builders, 7.29
  replacements, 4.26
  responsibility, 4.15
  role, 4.59, 4.60, 7.01
    main contracts, 7.08
  variations from specifications, 4.28
    duty to contractors, 7.17
    implied authority, 7.07
Arrestments on the dependence, 4.383
Artistic works, 8.19
  installation and repair, 1.05
Assignations, 4.147–170
  and proprietary interests, 4.158–160,
    4.169
  burdens of contract, 4.151, 4.163
  consent, 4.154, 4.157, 4.310
  constructive trusts, 4.166, 4.167–170
  degrees, 4.151
  delectus personae, 4.149–151, 4.154, 4.163
  distinct from
    delegation, 4.153
    novation, 4.152
    sub-contracting, 4.155–156
  executorial contracts, 4.148
  insolvent contractors, 4.335
  intimation, 4.157
  prohibition, 4.161–166
  rights to sue, 4.148, 4.154, 4.158–160
Association of British Insurers
  performance bonds, 3.51
Association of Consulting Engineers
  (ACE), 2.01
  Scottish Group, 4.01
Association of Scottish Chambers of
  Commerce, 4.01
Attestation, 2.08

Bankruptcy, 4.317
Banwell Report, 4.02
Bills of lading, 1.16
Bills of quantities, 1.23, 2.11
  further payments, 5.39
  use for claims, 4.274
  with contract documents, 4.22
Bonds
  advance payments, 4.351
  Latham Report, 8.06
Breaches of contract
  affirmation or repudiation, 4.89
  design errors, 5.35
  employers, extensions of time, 4.239
  materiality, 1.16, 4.05, 4.87
    deferred possession of sites, 4.209
    variations, 4.88
  remedies, 4.06–12, 4.89, 4.90
  temporary defects, 4.142
British Bankers' Association
  bonds, 4.351
British Property Federation (BPF), 2.01
Building control
  protection of public, 4.45
  statutory framework, 4.44
Building regulations, 5.42
  breaches, 4.46
  design errors, 5.42
Building warrants, 4.45
  building without, 4.191
  non-compliance, 4.45
Byelaws
  breach, 6.13
  enforcement, 6.24

Cable broadcasting, 4.48
Cascade diagrams, 4.263
Cautions, 3.38
  improper cautions, 3.40, 3.47
  nature, 3.48
  performance bonds, 3.37, 3.44
  prescription, 3.44
  proper and improper, 3.39
  strict construction, 3.46
CDM regulations, 1.06, 4.49
  contractors' duties, 4.50–52
  incorporation into JCT contract, 4.188
  liability, 4.187
  main contractors, 4.145
  non-compliance, 4.311
Certificates, 7.09–12 *see also* **Final certificates;**
    Interim certificates
  authority, 7.10
  court powers, 4.378, 8.26
  failure to issue, 7.03, 7.18

Certificates—*cont.*
  finality, 4.17
  negligent, 7.12
  revision, 8.26
  valuation certificates, architects'
    immunity, 7.11
***Certiorari*, 4.392**
Charities
  alteration of buildings, 4.100
Charterparties, 1.16
Chemical processing, 1.05
Civil engineering contracts, 1.17
Claims consultants, 4.257
Claims for direct losses and expenses
  applications, 4.280–287
    lack of specification, 4.285
    timing, 4.283
  causation, 4.295, 4.301
  clauses, 4.274
  disruption costs, 4.288, 4.298–299
  double recovery, 4.297
  evidence, 4.274
  financing charges, 4.278, 4.279
    back-dated claims, 4.284
    notices, 4.286
  formulae, 4.291, 4.296
  from nominated sub-contractors,
    4.373
  global claims, 4.300–304
  matters affecting progress of works,
    4.273–304
  meaning, 4.287
  meaning, 4.274
  prolongation costs, 4.288, 4.289–297
  requirements, 4.277, 4.281
  specification, 4.294, 4.302
  timeous claims, 4.274
  with extensions of time, 4.275
Clerks of works, 1.18
  authority, 4.73
  powers, 4.62
  responsibilities, 4.63
  role, 4.74
Clients
  advice, 8.02
  transfer of rights, 8.16
Collateral warranties, 1.18
  Latham Report, 8.16
  need, 4.170
  SBCC standard forms, 2.33, 4.173
Commercial causes, 4.378
Compensation, 3.57–60
  and retention, 3.57, 3.60
  Compensation Act, 3.57
    application, 3.58

Completion
  certificates of non-completion, 4.231
  damages
    late completion, 4.211–234
    non-completion, 4.221–224
  early completion, implied term, 4.267
  late completion, withholding of payments,
    notices, 4.232
  practical completion, 4.135
    certificates, 4.135, 4.137
    definition, 4.135–138
    part possession by employers, 4.146
Completion dates
  advancing, 4.271
  delays, 4.207–209
  information, 4.41
Computer software
  analysis of delays, 4.250, 4.261
  critical path analysis, 4.263
Confederation of British Industry (CBI), 4.01
Confusion
  employers and contractors, 1.19
Consensus ad idem, 1.24
  achievement, 3.13–18
  building contracts, 2.09
  design errors, 5.35
  variations of contracts, 4.92
Construction Confederation, 2.01, 4.79
  copyright, domestic sub-contracts, 2.04,
    4.174
Construction contracts
  assignation *see* **Assignations**
  common law, 1.09–27
  consensus ad idem, 1.24, 2.09
    achievement, 3.13–18
  definition, 1.04, 8.18
  deviations, 4.05–12
  exclusion orders, 8.18
  formation *see* **Formation of contract**
  illegality, breach of building regulations,
    5.42
  material terms, 1.15–16
  nature of contract, 4.107
  parties, 1.18–23
  price and value, 1.25
    schedules of rates, 1.27, 2.12
  relations between contract documents,
    3.24–33
  standard forms *see* **Standard forms**
  statutory regulation, 1.03–08
  terms *see* **Contract terms**
  types, 1.17
  whether entire contracts, 4.04–12, 8.31
    passing of title, 4.109
    tests, 4.11

Construction Industry Council
  guide to clients, 8.03
Construction operations
  definition, 1.05, 8.19
Construction sites
  health and safety, 4.187
  legal occupiers, 4.43
Constructive trusts, 4.166
  assignation of contracts, 4.167–170
  retention sums, 4.335, 4.343
Consultancy services, 8.03
  role, 4.59
Consumer contracts, 4.71
  breaches, materiality, 4.69
  meaning of consumers, 1.03(n11),
    1.03(n13)
  unfair terms, 1.03
Contra proferentem **principle**
  insurance contracts, 4.184
  liquidate damages clauses, 4.233
Contract
  assignation *see* **Assignations**
  breach *see* **Breaches of contract**
  concurrent liabilities in delict, 5.10–13
  definition, 1.01
  delegation, 4.152–153
  determination *see* **Rescission of contracts**
  effect of liquidation orders, 4.318
  English law, 1.16
  errors, 5.35
  formation *see* **Formation of contract**
  impossibilities, 5.36, 5.40
  novation, 4.152
  reduction, 4.92
  self-proving contracts, 2.08
  standard forms, 1.16
  uncertainty, 5.41
Contract bills, 2.16
  custody, 4.31
  divergence with other documents, 4.24
  overriding contract terms, 3.24–33
  standard of materials, 4.57
Contract documents, 4.22
  discrepancies, 4.24, 4.287
Contract sums, 4.97
  adjustments, 4.25
  deductions, defects, 4.140
  VAT, 4.99–102
Contract terms
  direct payment provisions, 3.76–80, 4.335
  incorporation into sub-contracts, 3.19–
    23, 3.24, 5.14
  payment certificates, 3.52–60
  performance and payment, 3.34–51
  priority clauses, 3.33

Contract terms—*cont.*
  relations between contract documents,
    3.24–33
  retention, 3.69–75
Contractors, 1.09, 1.18
  administration orders, 4.331
  and architects, *jus quaesitum tertio,* 7.03–05
  defaults, 4.306–336
    assignation and sub-contracting
      without consent, 4.310
    insolvency, 4.316–336
    SBC, 2.05
    non-compliance with CDM regulations,
      4.311
    non-compliance with instructions,
      4.309
  delays, 4.240
  direct losses *see* **Claims for direct
    losses and expenses**
  duty of care, 6.24
  extension of time, 4.32–40
  financing charges, 4.278, 4.279
  insolvency, assignations, 4.335
  liabilities
    conclusiveness of inspections, 4.63
    for nominated sub-contractors,
      4.367, 5.41
  liquidation, 3.35
  notices, statutory requirements, 4.42–44
  objections to variations, 4.77, 4.82
  obligations, 1.23
    best endeavours, 4.269, 4.270, 4.275,
      4.277
      to prevent delays, 4.270, 4.275,
        4.277
    CDM regulations, 4.50–52
    implied obligations, to sub-
      contractors, 4.37, 5.02
    JCT contract, 4.19–24
    limits, 4.60
    regular and diligent procedure, 4.266,
      4.277, 4.306, 4.307–308, 7.14
  parties to building contracts, 1.19
  performance specified work, 4.394–98
  prequalification, 8.11
  rescission of contracts, 4.337–338
  right of access to sites, 4.145
  specialist contractors, 8.05
  suspension of works, 4.287, 4.306
    employers defaulting, 4.337
    withholding of payment, 4.354
  unskilled labour, 1.11
  variations of works
    loss of profits, 4.272
    objections, 4.76

Contributory negligence, 4.257
  clerks of works, 4.74
**Convention of Scottish Local Authorities
  (COSLA),** 4.01
Copyright
  contract drawings and bills, 4.31
  domestic sub-contracts, 2.04, 4.173
  JCT contracts, 2.04
  SBC, 4.01
Corporate recovery, 4.324, 4.327
Corruption
  arbiters, 4.382
  termination of contracts, 4.334
Critical path analysis, 4.261, 4.262–272
  architects, 4.268
  basic possibilities, 4.262
  buildability, 4.262
  float, 4.265, 4.267
  retrospective delay analysis, 4.264
Cullen Report, 4.378

Damage to property
  delict, 6.13
  determination of liability, 4.191
  insurance, 4.179, 4.190–192
    contractors' negligence, 4.195,
      4.197–203
    definition of property, 4.196
Damages
  breaches of contract, 4.89, 4.90
  VAT, 4.102
  constructive trusts, assignation of
    contracts, 4.167–170
  late completion, 4.211–234
    reasonable foreseeability of loss,
      4.213
    remoteness, 4.213
  misrepresentations, 4.97
  non-completion, 4.221–224
  termination of contracts
    by contractors, 4.338
    by employers, 4.336
Damnum fatale, 4.178
Death *see* **Personal injuries**
Decrees arbitral
  enforcement, 2.08
  reduction, 4.382
Defects
  Defective Premises Act, 6.09
  delict *see* **Delict**
  design, duty to warn, 5.34–45
  foundations, 6.08, 6.10, 6.13, 6.17, 6.18
  latent defects *see* **latent defects**
  liability periods
    commencement, 4.139

Defects—*cont.*
  definition, 4.135
  part possession by employers, 4.146
  nominated sub-contractors, 4.372
  notices, 4.144
  post-completion liability, 8.16
  remedying, 1.16(n45)
  title to sue, prohibition of assignation,
    4.161–166
  whether breaches of contract, 4.142
Definitions
  JCT clause 1, 4.13–18
Delays *see also* **Extensions of time**
  causation, 4.244, 4.245–257
    contractors, 4.240
      regular and diligent procedure,
        4.266
    dominant causes, 4.246
    employers, 4.235, 4.239, 4.250
    employers and contractors, 4.251–257
    faults, 4.256–257
    no-fault events, 4.251
    remoteness of damage, 4.244
    retrospective delay analysis, 4.258–
      261, 4.264
    variations, 4.258
  claims for losses, 4.302
  contractors, 4.281, 4.287
  computer analysis, 4.250, 4.261
  contractors' obligations, best endeavours,
    4.270, 4.275
  critical path analysis, 4.261, 4.262–272
  implied terms, 5.03
  mitigation, 4.270, 4.271
  notices, 4.38, 4.235, 4.242, 4.243
  possession of sites, 4.207–209
Delectus personae, 4.149–151, 4.154
  assignations, 4.163
Delegation, 4.152
  consent, 4.153
Delict, 1.09
  and criminal liability, 4.189
  architects' duties, 4.60
    to contractors, 7.16
  architects' fraud, 7.03
  concurrent liabilities in contract, 5.10–13
  construction cases, 6.08–28
  culpa, 4.191
  defective buildings, 4.177, 6.01–28
    assignations of contracts, 4.162
    complex structure theory, 6.17, 6.19,
      6.20, 6.21
    duty of care, 6.24
  defective products, 6.17
  defective refurbishments, 6.26

Delict—*cont.*
  development of law, 6.02
  meaning, 6.01
  proximity, 6.03–06, 6.22, 6.26
    architects to contractors, 7.16
    definition, 6.23
  requirements, 6.01
  tests, 6.06–08
Delivery
  passing of title
    materials, 4.114
    sale of goods, 4.119
    supply of Goods and Services Act,
      4.127
Design, 2.11
  changes, claims for losses, 4.299
  faults, 4.178
    insurance policy exclusions, 4.184,
      4.190
  impossibility, 5.36, 5.40, 7.27
  Latham Report, 8.04
  liability, 5.24–33
    architects, 5.30, 7.25
    nominated suppliers, 4.374
  meaning, 5.27
  performance specified work, 4.397
  responsibilities
    architects, 7.30–31
    blurring, 1.19
  revisions, architects, 7.27–28
Design and build contracts, 1.20
Deviations from contracts, 4.05–12
Directors
  powers, liquidation, 4.318
  suspension, administration orders,
    4.328
Discrimination
  nationality, 3.05
  public procurement, 3.07
Dispute resolution, 1.09, 4.378–393
  SBCC guidance notes, 2.33
Documentary credits, 3.50
Documents *see* **Contract documents**
Domestic sub-contractors, 4.171, 4.172
  duty of care to employers, 4.202
Domestic sub-contracts, 2.30, 4.173
  copyright, 2.04, 4.173
Drawings
  custody, 4.31
  divergence with other documents, 4.24
  imprecision, 4.23
  provision
    additional drawings, 4.258
    implied terms, 5.03
    reasonable time, 4.32, 4.36, 4.38–39

Duty of care, 5.10–13, 6.01
  construction works, 4.189
  interested parties in building contracts,
    1.18
  local authorities, defective buildings,
    6.09, 6.18, 6.19
  pre-contract information, 5.38
  warning of design defects, 5.34–45

E-mail, 8.21
Economic loss, 5.07, 6.11, 6.12
  architects' duty to avoid, 7.19
  delict, 6.16, 6.18, 6.21, 6.22
  recoverability, 6.24, 6.27
Egan Report, 8.35
Electronic media
  execution of documents, 2.08(n14)
Employers, 1.18
  assignations of contracts, title to sue,
    4.148, 4.164
  defaults
    failure to make payments, 4.337,
      4.354
    insolvency, 4.337, 4.338
    obstruction with certificates, 4.338
    rescission of contracts, 4.337
  extensions of time
    breaches of contract, 4.239
    faults, 4.250
  implied duties, 4.34–35
    information, 4.34–35
  liabilities, to nominated sub-contractors,
    4.368
  obligations, 1.22
  parties to building contracts, 1.19
  possession of sites, 4.145–146
  rescission of contracts, 4.305–336
Enemy actions, 4.362
  extensions of time, 4.247
Engineers, 1.18
  certificates, failure to issue, 7.18
  deficient performance, 7.13
  duty of care to contractors, 7.18, 7.20,
    7.21
Enrichment, 4.05, 4.06
Environmental law, 4.43
Errors
  arbiters, 4.387
  contract sums, 4.97
  contracts, 5.35
  design errors, 5.35–45
  in JCT contract, 4.13
  judicial review, 4.389
  mutual error, 4.92
  unilateral errors, 5.37

Estimators, 3.01
EU law, 1.09
  public procurement, 3.05
Exclusion orders, 8.18
Execution of documents, 2.06
  electronically, 2.08(n14)
  self-proving contracts, 2.08
Executory sales, 1.13, 4.107
Expenses *see also* **Claims for direct losses and expenses**
Expert determination, 8.27
Extensions of time, 4.235–272 *see also* **Delays**
  architects' procedure, 4.237, 4.241–242, 7.15
  certificates of non-completion, 4.231
  late instructions, 4.32, 4.38
    sub-contractors, 4.39
  liquidated damages, loss, insurance, 4.204
  nominated sub-contractors, 4.373
  notices, 4.38, 4.235, 4.242
  relevant events, 4.48, 4.52, 4.237, 4.239
  suspension of works, 4.354
  retrospective extensions, 4.243
  with claims for direct losses and expenses, 4.275
  work by statutory undertakers, 4.48
Extrinsic evidence, 1.07
  contract terms, 2.10

Fax
  service of notices, 4.348(n57)
Fees, 8.09
Final certificates, 4.15
  arbitration, 4.359
  conclusiveness, 4.60, 4.61
  effect, 4.61, 4.177
  evidence, 4.59
  finality, 4.18
  issue, 4.358
Finance charges
  claims for direct losses and expenses, 4.278, 4.279
Fire
  insurance, 4.194
  Joint Fire Code, 4.206
Fitness for purpose, 4.21
  design liability, 5.28, 5.31, 5.33
  implied terms, 1.02, 4.69
  materials, 4.57
    warranties, 5.19
Fixtures
  common law, 4.103
  definition, 4.103

Floating charges, 4.324
  retention of title clauses, 4.130
Fluctuations, 4.375–377
  clauses
    alternatives, 4.377
    freezing, 4.376
  SBC, 2.24
FOCUS, 2.02
Force majeure, 4.178
  extensions of time, 4.239
Formation of contract, 3.01–12
  exchange of letters, 2.09–10, 3.14
  letters of intent, 3.13, 3.15–18, 8.21
  public procurement, 3.05–12
  sub-contracts, incorporation of main contracts, 3.19–23
  tenders, 3.01–04
Fossils, 4.363
Foundations
  defects, 6.08, 6.10, 6.13, 6.17, 6.18
Fraud
  architects, 7.03
  performance bonds, 3.42
Freedom of establishment, 3.05
Freedom of movement of goods, 3.05
Freedom to provide services, 3.05
Frustration of contract, 4.372
  variations, 4.82–86, 4.96, 4.258
Funders, 1.18

Gas works, 4.48
Guarantors, 1.18

Health and safety, 4.20 *see also* **CDM regulations**
  construction sites, 4.187–188
HGCRA, 1.04, 8.17–35
  adjudication *see* **Adjudication**
  application, 8.20–21
  commencement, 8.01
  definitions, 8.18–19
  exclusion orders, 8.18
  pay-when paid clauses, 8.34
  payment, 8.30–34
    stage payments, 4.12, 8.30
  suspension of performance, 8.33
Hire purchase agreements
  insolvency, 4.131

ICE
  contracts, 1.17, 8.08
  performance bonds, 3.51
Impignoration, 4.107, 4.113
Implied terms
  building contracts, 1.02

Implied terms—*cont.*
design
defects, duty to warn, 5.34–45
fitness for purpose, 5.25–33
early completion, 4.267
information to sub-contractors, 5.02
materials, 1.02, 4.67–70
provision of drawings, 5.03
sub-contracts, 5.02, 5.03
Supply of Goods and Services Act, 1.10
passing of title, 4.127
satisfactory quality of materials, 5.23
Indemnities, 3.44
bonds for advance payments, 4.351
contractors to employers, 4.186
definition, 3.38
prescription, 3.44
Information release schedules, 4.41
non-compliance, 4.287
Insolvency *see also* **Administration orders; Liquidation; Sequestrations**
contractors, 4.316–336
automatic termination of contracts, 4.321, 4.332
direct payments to sub-contractors, 3.76–79, 4.335
privity of contract, 5.05
SBC, 2.05
employers, 4.337
JCT contract, 4.322
pay-when-paid clauses, 8.34
performance bonds, 3.35, 3.45, 3.46, 4.320
retention clauses, 3.69, 3.71
SBCC Practice Guide, 2.33
trust funds, 3.74
Institutional Writers, 1.10
Insurance, 3.44, 4.176–206
CAR policies, 4.180–181
definition, 4.205
exclusion of repair of defective work, 4.181, 4.182–184
new buildings, 4.194
contractors' liability, end, 4.139
contracts, 1.16
prescription, 3.44
uberrimae fidei, 4.185
damage to property, 4.179, 4.190–192
contractors' negligence, 4.195, 4.197–203
definition of property, 4.196
exclusions, 4.190
definition, 3.38
insolvency, 4.320

Insurance—*cont.*
joint names policies, 4.190, 4.195, 4.205
new buildings, 4.194
latent defects, 4.176, 8.16, 8.17
liability periods, 4.177
loss of liquidated damages, 4.204
material non-disclosure, 4.185
model clauses, 4.206
partial possession of sites, 4.146, 4.210
performance specified work, 4.396
project insurance, 4.64
risks, 4.178, 4.194
subrogation, 4.195, 4.202
Insurers, 1.18
Intellectual property, 1.09, 4.72
Interest
awards, decrees arbitral, 4.383
claims for direct losses and expenses, 4.283
debts, recoverability, 4.284
late payment, 4.284, 4.342
VAT, 4.102
unpaid certificates, 4.278, 4.279
Interests in land
definition, 2.06
execution of contracts, 2.06
Interim certificates
deductions, advance payments, 4.355
final dates for payment, 4.349
importance, 3.52
issue, 4.349, 4.353, 4.360
nominated sub-contractors, 4.358
renomination, 4.370
obstruction by employers, 4.338
passing of title, 4.133
retention, 3.61–75, 4.357
revision, court powers, 8.28
scope, 7.12
specification, 4.342, 4.349
status, 4.349, 4.356
valuation, 4.352
gross valuation, 4.356
withholding payment, 4.306
Interim payments
advance payments, 4.351
matters affecting progress of works, 4.273–304
passing of title, 4.123
scheme for construction contracts, 4.345–350
Interpretation
contracts, 1.01
JCT clause 1, 4.13–18
precedence of written terms, 3.24

JCT, 2.01
  membership, 2.01
  practice notes, 2.03
  structure, 4.02
JCT contract, 1.17, 2.11–34
  antiquities, 4.363
  architects
    access to works, 4.75
    instructions, 4.26–30
  assignations, 4.147–170
  claims for direct losses and expenses,
    4.273–304
  contract documents, 4.31–41
  contract sums, 4.25, 4.97–98
  Contractor's Designed Portion, 4.394
  contractors' obligations, 4.19–24
  criticism, 4.01(n1), 4.02
  damages, late completion, 4.211–234
  defects liability, 4.135–144
  direct engagement of workers, 4.340
  dispute resolution, 4.378–393
  extension of time, 4.235–272
  fluctuations, 4.375–377
  history, 2.02
  insolvency, 4.322
  insurance, 4.176–206
  Intermediate Form of Contract 1984,
    2.34
  interpretation, 4.13–18
  JCT 80, 2.02
  Latham Report, 8.08
  nominated sub-contractors, 4.364–373
  nominated suppliers, 4.374
  passing of title, 4.103–134
  patent rights, 4.72
  payment, 4.341–360
  performance specified work, 4.394–
    398
  persons in charge, 4.73–74
  possession of sites, 4.207–210
    partial possession by employers,
    4.145–146, 4.210
  rescission of contracts
    by contractors, 4.337–338
    by employers, 4.305–336
    specified events, 4.339
  royalties, 4.72
  setting out the works, 4.53–55
  statutory obligations, 4.42–52
  sub-contracting, 4.171–176
  tax deductions, 4.361
  variations, 4.76–96
  VAT, 4.99–102
  With Quantities, 4.08
  workmanship and materials, 4.56–71

Joint ventures, 4.293
Judicial review
  adjudication, 8.25
  arbitration, 4.384–393
Jus quaesitum tertio, 3.78, 4.170, 5.07–45
  architects and contractors, 7.03–05
  creation, 5.07–09

Labour shortage, 4.65
Landfill tax, 4.375
Late payment
  commercial debts, 4.342
  interest, 4.284, 4.342
  VAT, 4.102
Latent defects
  and architects' final certificates, 4.60
  breaches of contracts, 4.141
  delictual liability, 6.09, 6.15
  discoverability, 3.83, 3.86, 4.60
  insurance, 4.176, 8.16, 8.17
  warranties, 5.24
    implied terms, 5.20
Latham Report, 8.01, 8.02–16
  adoption in JCT contract, 2.01, 4.14
  advance payments, 4.351
  bonds, 8.06
  certificates, 4.342
  checklists, 8.04
  clients, 8.02
  collateral warranties, 8.16
  consultants' role, 4.59
  contents, 8.02–16
  contractors, 8.11
  design procurement, 8.04
  dispute resolution, 4.378
  fees, 8.09
  JCT contract, 8.08
  JCT structure, 4.02
  latent defects insurance, 4.176
  liability periods, 3.81
  nominated sub-contractors, 4.365
  paid-when-paid clauses, 5.15, 8.06
  partnering, 8.13
  performance bonds, 3.34
  post-completion liability, 8.16
  prescription, 8.16
  pricing of variations, 4.76
  project insurance, 4.64
  project management, 8.10
  retention, 3.69
  specialist contractors, 8.05
  standard forms, 8.06
    recommendations, 8.07
  sub-contractor selection, 8.12
  training, 8.14

Latham Report—*cont.*
　transfer of clients' rights, 8.16
　trust funds, 8.15
Letters of intent, 3.13
　status, 3.15–18, 8.21
Liens, 4.134
　plant and machinery, 4.221
Limitation of actions
　personal injuries, 4.177
Liquidate damages, 1.09
　clauses, interpretation *contra proferentem,*
　　4.233
　Compensation Act, 3.58
　enforceability, 4.214–220
　extension of time, loss, insurance, 4.204
　late completion, 4.211–234
　　caused by employers, 4.235
　　impossibility to complete, 4.230
　nil clauses, 4.226–227
　notices, 4.231
　part possession by employers, 4.146
　penal damages, 4.215
　　less than actual loss, 4.225
　repayments, 4.234
　value added tax, 4.102
Liquidation
　contractors, performance bonds, 3.35, 3.46
　legal effect, 4.318–223
　termination of contracts, 4.320
Liquidators
　continuation of contract, 4.332
　termination of contracts, 4.320, 4.338
Listed buildings, 4.100
Local authorities
　duty of care, defective buildings, 6.09,
　　6.18, 6.19, 6.23
Local Government Association (LGA), 2.01
Location, 1.10, 4.107
Lock-out agreements, 3.18
Losses *see* **Claims for direct losses and**
　expenses
Lump sum contracts, 1.25, 2.12, 4.30
　fluctuations, 4.375
　quantification of losses, 4.274

Materials, 1.09
　contracts to supply, *delectus personae,*
　　4.150
　delays, extensions of time, 4.239
　delivery, 1.05
　HGCRA, 8.31
　not as described, damages, 4.54
　off-site, 4.114–126
　　advance payments, 4.351
　passing of title *see* **Passing of title**

Materials—*cont.*
　performance specified work, 4.395
　power to reject, 4.62
　quality, 4.67
　　chain of liability, 5.22
　　warranties, privity of contract, 5.19–23
　selection by nominated sub-contractors,
　　liabilities, 4.367
　site materials
　　definition, 4.125
　　retention, 4.112–113
　　right to use, 4.112–113, 4.115, 4.125
　standards, 4.16, 4.57
　　architects' opinions, 4.58
　　limits, 4.65
　supply, statutory framework, 4.67–71
　unfixed, 4.103, 4.115
　warranties, 5.25
McEwan-Younger Report, 4.02
Measurement
　standard methods, 2.13
　　approximate quantities, 2.19
　　SMM 7, 2.14–15
　　　departures, 4.97
Mediation, 2.33
Misrepresentations
　contract sums, 4.97
　negligent, 4.97
　variations of instructions, 4.84, 4.85
Mitigation of loss, 4.143

National Joint Consultative Committee
　(NJCC), 3.35
National Specialists Contractors' Council
　(NSCC), 2.01, 4.01
Nationality discrimination, 3.05
Natural justice
　adjudication, 8.24
　rescission of contracts, 4.315
Negligence
　certificates, 7.12
　contractors, 4.178
　design, insurance, 4.184
　fault, 4.256–257
Negotiations
　agreements to negotiate, 3.13
New Engineering Contract (NEC), 8.05, 8.08
　trust deed, 3.74
Noise, 4.43
Nominated sub-contractors, 4.172, 4.364–373
　delict, 6.27–28
　design liability, 5.29
　extensions of time, 4.239, 4.373
　liabilities, 4.174
　nomination

Nominated sub-contractors—*cont.*
  difficulties, 4.367
  forms, 4.366
  non-completion of works, 4.369
  privity of contract, 5.04
  renomination, 4.370–372
  SBCC contract, 2.28
  tenders, 4.366
  warranties, 4.366
Non-supersession clauses, 3.24
Novation, 4.152
Nuisance
  culpa, 4.193
  insurance, 4.179
  neighbouring property, 4.191, 4.193
  noise, 4.43

Occupiers
  construction sites, 4.43
  liability, contractors and employers, 4.145
Oil and gas extraction, 1.05
Overheads
  prolongation costs, 4.291–297

Painting, 1.05
Parties to building contracts, 1.18–23
Partnerships, 4.316
Passing of title
  common law, 1.12, 4.108–110
    moveables, 4.104
  implied terms, 4.107
  materials, 1.14, 4.103
    JCT contract, 4.133–134
    off-site, 4.114–126
    on sites, 4.112–113
  moveables, 4.104–111
  partial possession of sites, 4.210
  rescission of contracts, 4.335
  retention clauses, employers unaware of
    clauses, 4.120, 4.121
  Roman law, 1.10
  sale of goods, 4.104–106
    position of suppliers, 4.116–126
Patents, 4.72
Pay-when-paid clauses, 5.15–17, 8.06
  HGCRA, 8.34
Payment, 1.09, 4.341–360 *see also* **Late
    payment**
  advance payments, 4.351
    deduction from interim certificates,
      4.355
  defaults by employers, 4.337
  direct payment provisions, 3.76–80,
    4.335
  privity of contract, 5.05

Payment—*cont.*
  final dates, 4.342, 4.349
  HGCRA, 8.30–34
  interim certificates *see* **Interim
    certificates**
  interim payments *see* **Interim
    payments**
  provisional payments, 4.76
  stage payments, 4.344
  variations, 4.88
Penalties
  and liquidate damages, 4.215–219
  impossible tasks, 4.230
  less than actual loss, 4.225
Performance bonds, 3.34–51
  calling
    requirements, 3.39–40, 3.43, 3.49,
      3.51
    unfair calling, 3.50
  criticism, 3.34, 3.48
  description, 3.35
  English and Scottish judicial attitudes,
    3.36, 3.41, 3.43, 3.47
  fraud, 3.42
  insolvency, 3.35, 3.45, 3.46
  nature, 3.37–44, 3.48
  on demand bonds, 3.41
  similar to letters of credit, 3.37, 3.41
  strict construction, 3.50
  styles, 3.36, 3.51
  whether construction contract, 3.51
Performance specified work, 4.21, 4.47,
    4.394–398
  architects' opinions, 4.58
  insurance, 4.396
  liabilities, 4.396
  meaning, 4.395
Personal injuries
  construction sites, statistics,
    4.186(n87)
  delict, 6.13
  indemnities, 4.186
  insurance, 4.179
  limitation of actions, 4.177
PFI, 8.01
  tendering procedure, 3.12
Planning supervisors, 4.26
Plant and machinery
  installation and demolition, 1.05, 8.19
  passing of title, 4.113
  prolongation costs, 4.290
Pledges, 4.107, 4.134
  and sales, 4.109
  materials and machinery, 4.113
  rescission of contracts, 4.335

Pollution, 4.43
Possession of sites, 4.207–210
  deferment, 4.207, 4.208
  claims for direct losses and expenses,
    4.280
  extensions of time, 4.239, 4.276
  whether material breach of contract,
    4.209
  partial possession, 4.145–146, 4.210
Postal service, 4.348
Practice notes, 2.03
Prescription, 3.82–91
  cautionary obligations, 3.44
  discoverability, 3.83, 3.86, 3.90
  indemnities, 3.44
  insurance contracts, 3.44
  Latham Report, 8.16
  long negative prescription, 3.90
  onus of proof, 3.91
  personal injuries, 4.177
  prescriptive periods, 1.16(n45)
    commencement, 3.44
  stages of construction, 4.12
  relevant acknowledgements, 3.82,
    3.88
Prices, 1.25–27
  adjustment formulae, 4.377
  contract sums, 4.97
  fluctuations *see* **Fluctuations**
  JCT contracts, 2.12–16
  methods, 1.25
    remeasurement, 1.26
    schedules of rates, 1.27, 2.12
  non application, 4.92
  statements for variation, 2.16
Prime Cost Sums
  SBCC contracts, 2.27
  valuation of variations, 4.79
Privity of contract, 5.01–06
  absence, 3.78, 3.80
  architects and employers, 7.05
  co-ordination of works, 5.18
  design liability, 5.24–33
  direct payment provisions, 5.05
  mitigation, 5.06
  nominated sub-contractors, 5.04
  passing of title clauses, 4.111
  warranties as to quality of materials,
    5.19–23
Product liability, 6.03
Productivity incentives, 4.376
Professional negligence
  architects, 7.12, 7.14, 7.29
    certification unseen, 7.30
    duties to contractors, 7.16–17

Profits
  losses
    causation, 4.295
    variations of works, 4.272
    percentages, 4.292, 4.294, 4.297
Project management
  critical path analysis, 4.268
  Latham Report, 8.10
  managers, 1.18
  responsibility, 4.61(n4)
Promises, 1.01
  enforceability, 3.03
Public bodies
  definition, 3.10
  procurement, 3.10
Public procurement, 3.05–12
  criteria, 3.07
  public bodies, 3.10
  public works, 3.09
  tendering procedure, 3.12
    infringement, 3.06, 3.07
    damages, 3.07, 3.08
    restricted procedure, *delectus personae,*
      4.150
    threshold, 3.11
Public works tenders, 3.09

Quantity surveyors, 1.18
  access to sites, 4.80
  analysis of delays, 4.261
  deficient performance, 7.13
  role, 4.55
  valuation
    interim certificates, 4.352
    variations, 4.80
Quantum meruit **claims,** 4.04
  breaches of contract, 4.87, 4.89, 4.90,
    4.92
Quasi-contract, 3.02

Receivers
  legal proceedings, 4.330
Receivership, 4.317, 4.325
  contractors, automatic termination of
    contracts, 4.331, 4.333
Recompense, 4.05
  requirements, 3.04
Recovery of documents, 4.383
Rectification of documents, 1.08
  errors, contract sums, 4.97
Reduction
  contracts, 4.92
  decrees arbitral, 4.382
Reinstatement, 4.53
Remeasurement, 1.26

Remoteness of damage
  extensions of time, 4.244
  late completion, 4.213
  negligence, 4.257
Requirements of writing
  interests in land, 2.06
  promises, 1.01(n2)
  self-proving contracts, 2.08
  trusts, sole trustees of own property, 2.07
Rescission of contracts
  administrators, 4.331
  by contractors, 4.337–338
    damages, 4.338
    failure to pay, 4.337
    insolvency, 4.338
    notices, 4.338
    obstruction of certificates, 4.337
  by employers, 4.305–336
    assignation and sub-contracting without consent, 4.310
    contractor insolvency, 4.316–336
    damages, 4.336
    failure to proceed diligently, 4.307–308
    non-compliance with CDM regulations, 4.311
    non-compliance with instructions, 4.309
    notices, 4.306, 4.312–313, 4.315
    suspension of work, 4.306
    time limits, 4.312–314
  employers' corruption, 4.334
  liquidators, 4.332
  receivers, 4.331, 4.333
  specified events, 4.339
Restitution, 1.09
Retention, 2.07, 3.56
  against instalments, 3.61
  and compensation, 3.57, 3.60
  and payment certificates, 3.52, 3.61–68, 4.357
  and set-off, 3.69
  bonds, 8.16
  clauses, 3.69
    judicial interpretation, 3.70–75
  materials on sites, 4.112
  meaning, 3.59
Retention of title
  clauses, 3.75, 4.120, 4.121, 4.123
    and rights in security, 4.129, 4.130
    rescission of contracts, 4.335
  contractors in administration, 4.331
  Supply of Goods and Services Act, 4.127–134

Roman law, 1.10
Royal Incorporation of Architects in Scotland (RIAS), 4.01
  consultancy service, 8.03
Royal Institute of British Architects (RIBA), 2.01
Royal Institution of Chartered Surveyors in Scotland (RICSS), 4.01
Royal Institution of Chartered Surveyors (RICS), 2.01
Royalties, 4.72

Safety, 4.20
Sale of goods
  applicability of Act to building contracts, 4.107, 4.114
  considerations, 4.119
  delivery, 4.119
  materials, suppliers, 4.116–120
  passing of title, 4.104–106, 4.121, 4.126
  quality of materials, 5.20, 5.22
Samples
  materials
    fitness for purpose, 4.69
    quality, 4.69
Satisfactory quality
  implied terms, 1.02
  materials, 4.67–70
  meaning, 4.67
Scheduled monuments, 4.100
Schemes for construction contracts, 4.341, 4.344, 8.25–26
  final dates, 4.350
  interim payments, 4.345–350
    final dates, 4.349
    notices, 4.346, 4.349
    service, 4.348
    withholding of payments, 4.347
Scott Schedules, 4.303
Scottish Building Contract Committee (SBCC), 2.01, 2.05
  collateral warranties, 2.33
  guidance on dispute resolution, 2.33
  insolvency practice guide, 2.33
  legal input, 4.02
  membership, 4.01
  practice notes, mediation, 2.33
  structure, 4.02
Scottish Building Contract (SBC), 2.05
  amendments, 4.03
  Contractor's Designed Portion, 2.21
  Contracts of Purchase, 2.32
  copyright, 4.01
  Domestic Sub-Contracts, 2.30
  fluctuations and formula rules, 2.24

Scottish Building Contract (SBC)—*cont.*
Nominated Sub-contractors, 2.28
Nominated Suppliers, 2.31
Prime Cost Contract, 2.27
private or local authority, 2.23
reading with JCT conditions, 4.03
Scottish Minor Works, 2.29
Sectional Completion Edition, 2.20
sub-contracts, 4.173
With Approximate Quantities, 2.19
With Contractor's Design, 2.22
With Quantities, 2.17
August 1998 revision, 4.14
Without Quantities, 2.18
Scottish Building Employers' Federation,
4.01
Scottish CASEC, 4.01
Scottish Management Contracts, 2.26
phased completion edition, 2.26
Scottish Measured Term Contract,
2.25
Scottish Minor Works Contract, 2.29
Sequestrations, 4.317
Set-off, 3.52–60
abuse, 3.67
after receivership, 4.330
and instalments, 3.61–68
and retention, 3.69
assignees, 4.163
contractors in administration, 4.331
exclusion, 3.65
HGCRA, 8.32
insurance, unpaid premiums, 4.320
meaning, 3.56
unfair terms, 1.03(n11), 3.65
Setting out works, 4.53–55
Settlement, 4.191, 6.21
Sewerage works, 4.48
Site agents, 4.73
Site clearance, 1.05
Skilled labour, 1.11
shortage, 4.65
Small businesses, 4.342
Specific implement, 4.90
Standard forms, 1.16
JCT *see* **JCT contracts**
Latham Report, 8.06
recommendations, 8.07
opinion surveys, 8.06
Stated cases, 4.382
Statutory obligations
and delict, 6.24
breach, 4.178
changes, extensions of time, 4.239
notices by contractors, 4.42–44

Statutory undertakers
works, extensions of time, 4.48, 4.239
Strikes, 4.246, 4.248
Sub-contractors, 1.18, 1.21
direct payment, 3.76–80, 4.335
domestic sub-contractors *see* **Domestic
sub-contractors**
extensions of time, 4.39, 4.239
knowledge of main contract conditions,
5.14
negligence, damage to property, 4.199–
203
nominated sub-contractors *see* **Nominated
sub-contractors**
passing of title, 4.110–111
selection, 8.12
Sub-contracts, 4.171–175
consent, 4.310
distinct from assignations, 4.155–156
implied terms, 5.02, 5.03
incorporation of main contracts, 3.19–
23, 4.172, 5.14
liabilities, 4.174
SBC, 4.173
stepdown provisions, 3.19–23, 4.172,
5.14
Subrogation, 4.195, 4.202
Suppliers, 1.18
delectus personae, 4.150
domestic suppliers, 4.374
nominated suppliers, 2.31, 4.374
extensions of time, 4.239
position under Sale of Goods Act,
4.116–120
to sub-contractors, 5.21
Supply of goods and services, 1.02
1982 Act
applicability to building contracts,
4.107
retention of title, 4.127–134
assignations, insolvent contractors,
4.335
implied terms, 1.10, 4.67–70
satisfactory quality, 5.23
materials, statutory framework, 4.67–71
Suspension of works, 4.287, 4.306
employers' defaults, 4.337
withholding payment, 4.354
HGCRA, 8.33
notices, 8.33
Suspensive conditions, 3.18

Tax deductions, 4.361
Technical standards, 4.44
Telecommunication works, 4.48

Tenders, 2.10, 3.01–04
  costs, 3.02, 3.03
  damages, 3.03–04
  domestic sub-contracts, 4.173
  invitations, 2.28
  nominated sub-contractors, 4.366
  nominated suppliers, 2.31, 4.374
    SBCC, 5.21
Terrorism
  extensions of time, 4.239, 4.246
Time limits
  completion, 4.207–209
  extension *see* **Extension of time**
  rescission of contracts, 4.312–314
  time of the essence, 4.314
Title
  implied terms, 1.02
  transfer *see* **Passing of title**
Title to sue
  assignations, 4.148, 4.154
    prohibition, 4.161–166
  jus quaesitum tertio see **Jus quaesitum**
    tertio
  transfers of property, 4.158–160
Training, 8.14
Trusts *see also* **Constructive trusts**
  funds, 8.15, 8.17
    insolvency, 3.74
  retention money, 3.69–75
  sole trustees of own property, 3.75
    requirements of writing, 2.07
  validity, 3.74, 3.75

Uberrimae fidei
  contract, 5.41
  insurance contracts, 4.185
Uncertainty of contracts, 5.41
UNCITRAL Model Law
  arbitration, 4.383(n7), 4.386
  electronic commerce, 2.08(n14)
Unfair contract terms, 1.03, 4.107
  exclusion of set-off, 3.65
  variation of contracts, 1.24

Valuation, 1.09
  approximate quantities, 4.76
  certificates, 7.11
  HGCRA, 8.31
  interim certificates, 4.352
    gross valuation, 4.356
  interim payments, 4.25
  variations, 4.78, 4.82
    prime cost sums, 4.79
    quantity surveyors, 4.80

Value added tax, 4.99–102
  alterations, 4.100
  liquidate damages, 4.102
  periodic payments, 4.102
  protected buildings, 4.100
  repair and maintenance, 4.100
Variations
  breaches of contract, 4.88, 4.89, 4.91
  claims for losses, 4.287
    identification, 4.304
  claims for payment, 4.88
  contractors
    loss of profits, 4.272
    objections, 4.77
  damages, 4.90–94
  earlier completion dates, 4.271
  effect on delay, 4.258
  errors, 4.84
  extensions of time, 4.239
  extent, 4.82
  fair rates, 4.93
  frustration of contracts, 4.82–86, 4.96,
    4.258
  meaning, 4.77
  misrepresentations, 4.84, 4.85
  objections by contractors, 4.76, 4.82
  pleadings, 4.95
  pricing, 4.76
  statements, 2.16
  valuation, 4.78, 4.82
    prime cost sums, 4.79
Voluntary arrangements, 4.317
  approval, 4.326

War, 4.247, 4.362
Warranties
  assignation of contracts, 4.165
  breaches, 1.16
  nominated sub-contractors, 4.366
  nominated suppliers, 5.21
Waste management, 4.43
Water works, 4.48
Weather
  contractors' risk, 4.209
  extensions of time, 4.239, 4.247, 4.248
Workmanship, 4.21
  areas of responsibility, 4.62, 4.66
  bad workmanship, insurance policy
    exclusions, 4.181, 4.182–184
  performance specified work, 4.395
  standards, 4.57
    limits, 4.65
  testing, 4.66
  warranties, 5.25